EVOLUTION OF CHORDATE STRUCTURE

An Introduction to Comparative Anatomy

EVOLUTION

OF

CHORDATE

STRUCTURE

An Introduction to Comparative Anatomy

by

HOBART M. SMITH

University of Illinois

Illustrated by Alice Boatright

HOLT, RINEHART AND WINSTON, INC.

New York · Chicago · San Francisco
Toronto · London

Preface

MY INTENTIONS in preparing this book were (1) to lay the bare essentials of a groundwork for understanding the basic structure of primitive chordates; (2) to trace the most obvious or important trends (and whenever possible their functional significance) in the evolution of this basic structure in various vertebrate lines; and thus (3) to convey an appreciation of how the more advanced groups of vertebrates, especially mammals, came to possess the particular combination of characters that makes those groups unique. The emphasis is upon evolution, upon continuity of structure, but where complexity of an organ system has rendered it necessary to omit parts of these objectives, the evolutionary story has been sacrificed in the interest of descriptive anatomy of at least the most essential group, the mammals. Clearly a knowledge of basic structure must precede appreciation of evolutionary trends, and basic structure is thus regarded as of prime importance.

The most forbidding aspect of comparative anatomy is the complexity of variation occurring in different vertebrates. This factor is largely circumvented here by placing emphasis upon selected evolutionary sequences or trends that are in turn made tangible by use of living or fossil types as examples of various stages along those trends.

It would be impossible to emphasize all the important variations that exist among vertebrates and that exemplify stages in other lines of evolution. And it would be undesirable to attempt to draw attention specifically to each class of vertebrates and the variations occurring therein. It has been my objective, rather, to focus attention upon selected structures and to follow these in certain ramifications of their evolution; living vertebrates are useful simply as examples of stages along those lines of evolution.

Since stress is placed upon evolutionary trends as a means to enlighten the study of vertebrate structure, as many accessory descriptive details as possible are omitted from the text. Their place, insofar as possible, is in the laboratory. The text, if it is to serve its proper function, is primarily to

v

convey ideas and concepts. Feather structure, scale structure, the details of the skulls and muscular systems of various exemplary types, and many other complex descriptive materials are thus omitted or briefly treated in the text; completely adequate coverage of most or all of these topics can and should be made in the laboratory, where the direct observation necessary for effective memorization of such information is possible. Certainly not all or even a majority of details can necessarily be handled in the laboratory; but the detail that does remain for the text is largely conceptual rather than descriptive.

Texts in comparative anatomy tend to be too comprehensive, not only because details more appropriate to laboratory manuals are included, but also because they embrace some introductory material that should have been covered in elementary zoology courses, or material that properly belongs to other fields of zoology such as histology, embryology, and physiology. Admittedly there is a great need for integration of zoological fields whose conventional boundaries are wholly artificial, but I do not see that the comparative anatomist should assume the duty of offering an integrated perspective of all zoology. His duty to integration is performed through the constant focus of attention upon the functional significance of structural evolution and upon the complexity of change that involves cellular as well as gross structure, and thus cellular as well as gross function. No aspect of zoology is independent of any other aspect, but the study of zoology is so organized in almost every American university that an appreciation of the whole may be more hindered than aided by its premature consideration at stages where the fundamental concepts and facts in no one of the several conventional fields themselves are yet clearly appreciated. Every course should broaden the student's perspective as it adds to his experience and thus to his mental equipment, and indeed comparative anatomy with its very foundation resting upon evolution can contribute most importantly to that perspective. Nevertheless the strictest conventional confines of the field of comparative anatomy are broad enough for the introductory course without their embracing segments of allied fields.

It is a source of regret that space does not permit presentation of animals as the living, breathing, functioning entities they are in life. Certainly this is one approach to comparative anatomy. But a fairly thorough exploration of such an approach leaves one with a rather disconnected view of vertebrates. It is the "typological" comparative anatomy of earlier decades, wherein the structure and variation seen in living vertebrates are studied as end results, with little attention to the essential principles of continuity of structural change from common ancestral types. The typological approach views animals as seen basically at one time level; the systemic approach adopted here is four dimensional, with time and its correlates the critically important attribute. Ideally a "synthetic" approach is the best, but there are few if any courses blessed with sufficient time for an adequate review of vertebrate natural history as well as vertebrate evolution. Rather than attempt to compromise, to the severe detriment of both, it has seemed wiser to adhere to that approach—the systemic one—which carries naturally with it the most fundamentally important evolutionary concepts of the whole field of vertebrate zoology—concepts that nowhere can be more appropriately presented than in comparative anatomy.

An emphasis on the systemic approach to comparative anatomy requires a choice of materials somewhat different from that characteristic of a more typological approach. The review of vertebrate classification and natural history is lengthy in most textbooks in comparative anatomy; the account given here is relatively brief and limited to a review of essential details of classification and certain evolutionary aspects thereof. A review of vertebrate natural history is more appropriate to other courses and could be included in comparative anatomy only at a sacrifice of concepts that cannot be expected elsewhere. Certain other topics often included have been deliberately omitted for the sake of emphasizing sequences that show noteworthy evolutionary trends.

In tracing evolutionary sequences the convenient mechanism of "steps" or "stages" has frequently been employed. This, admittedly, can be a dangerous procedure, for where continuity of change exists, as it does in all organic evolution, there are no sharp lines between stages. Furthermore the "stages" we see may simply be an accident of preservation that has enabled us to appreciate one evolutionary level but not the many others that must have existed. And, finally, unquestionably in many cases the same facts in the same sequence could be arranged in a different series of "stages." Nevertheless the "stage" approach has been adopted as a calculated risk, in the belief that the advantages of tangibility and objectivity, of ease in understanding and retention, outweigh the disadvantage of loss of dynamics with its attendant and depressing lack of objectivity. In particular is the exchange desirable if, as I trust is the case, it is clearly understood by both student and instructor that the objectivity is largely a matter of convenience; that all "stages" and "steps" are to be regarded merely as conveniently conspicuous high points in continua lacking abrupt breaks; and that with good reason other points of emphasis could in many cases be selected along these continua. It is not to be expected that the student clearly recall the names here applied to all "steps," or the exact "problems" or exact "solutions" or "alterations" pertaining to an exact "stage." In certain cases he should know these facts, because they are unequivocal, but in every case he should know the general nature and pathway or pattern of change. The deliberate indication of landmarks along evolutionary highways and byways is a useful convenience.

The proper balance of emphasis between structure and function in any treatment of comparative anatomy is viewed differently by each instructor. Some have regarded the presentation here as totally devoid of functional emphasis, whereas others have found it liberal in this respect. The desirability of correlation of structure with function, particularly in linkage of structural *change* with functional *change,* is obvious. It is in the latter area, not so much in correlation of static structure with static function, that the responsibility of comparative anatomy lies; yet to a certain degree both types of correlation need to be made. I have gone as far as I thought advisable with each type and have been especially wary (whether so evident or not to the reader) of further exploitation of changing structure and function, despite the fascination of conjecture that they hold. It has been occasionally disconcerting to observe the variety of functional relations it is possible to conceive with many structural changes, the futility of the search for proof even for the most promising possibilities, and the magnitude of possible error in such speculation. Nevertheless a search for some functional correlation for structural change is certainly a stimulating exercise and one of the most rewarding experiences in the study of comparative anatomy. For that reason I have gone as far as I think reason can justify in attempting to explain structural change in terms of function. The reader should accept or reject all such speculation for exactly what it is—an educated guess of greater or lesser probability of accuracy. Most functional correlations noted have been culled from the literature; a few are novel.

The abundance of terms utilized in this book may appear forbidding at first contact, and the utility of introduction of some new ones (for example, protopostcava, protohepatic vein, protoposterior cardinal vein) may be questioned. The reasons are (1) that a concept is more readily recognized objectively if a name is available for it; (2) that it is confusing to lump different concepts under one name (for example, protopostcava and neo-postcava); (3) that knowledge of the name for a concept is a quick and fairly accurate indication of awareness of the concept itself; and (4) that learning the name for a concept is an aid to learning and recollection of the concept itself. An accurate, full, and precise terminology for the concepts pertinent to any science is an important adjunct of that discipline—the essential tool for any advanced study and discourse. Provision of such tools is the duty of any teacher of a discipline. If in specific areas the supply of terms seems too abundant, the excess can readily be omitted; the vocabulary list at the end of each chapter facilitates the selection. All terms are defined as they are used in the text and the index refers the reader to this definition. Thus, the index also acts as the source for a glossary of terms.

For the most part the accounts are relatively terse. Almost all sections could be expanded by making the progression more gradual. Adoption throughout of the expanded account would, however, have lengthened the book excessively. For two-semester courses the instructor may profitably expand the accounts himself, but for the single-semester course a compression of materials is unavoidable if a reasonably thorough survey is to be completed.

In pedagogy there are two sorts of learning: *recognition* learning and *recall* learning. For the average good mind, normal reading procedures are efficient primarily in *recognition* learning; proper answers can be selected for many given questions from a pool of mixed true and false choices. It is the rare mind that acquires much *recall* learning in normal reading procedures. For most of us an efficient and thorough recollection requires repetition of the recall effort, simulating the examination situation. The student will with rare exception find it useful if not actually a necessity as a studying technique to make up his own questions for review. Questions are included in this book as a teaching and learning device—an aid and encouragement to students in taking the bold step in what will be to many a new departure in the technique of study. They have been deliberately designed to be repetitious of information in the chapter concerned, rather than thought-provoking. The latter should arise in abundance in accordance with each students' initiative and with each instructor's inclination for exploration for correlation.

H.M.S.

Urbana, Illinois
January, 1960

ACKNOWLEDGMENTS

The author wishes to thank the authors and publishers of the following books for permission to use their material as either a primary or a secondary source for many of the illustrations, all redrawn, appearing in this text. The figure numbers refer to the illustrations in this text.

Adams and Eddy's *Comparative Anatomy*. John Wiley and Sons, Inc. (Figs. 3.9–3.11, 5.18, 6.6, 6.20, 7.15–7.20, 8.14, 11.9, 11.27, 11.30, 11.34, 14.28, 15.24, 15.26, 15.30).
Bailey's *Textbook of Histology*. The Williams and Wilkins Co. (Figs. 5.39, 6.2, 9.1, 9.21, 11.3, 16.1, 16.8, 16.23, 16.24).
Barbour's *Reptiles and Amphibia*. Houghton Mifflin Co. (Fig. 7.21).
Booth's *Laboratory Anatomy of the Cat*. Wm. C. Brown Publishers (Fig. 6.21).
Bremer's *Textbook of Histology*. Blakiston's, McGraw-Hill Book Co. (Figs. 6.3, 11.30).
Cunningham's *Human Anatomy*. Oxford University Press. (Figs. 6.2 G, 6.21).
Eaton's *Comparative Anatomy of Vertebrates*. Harper & Bros. (Fig. 7.13).
Eddy's *Atlas of Outline Drawings for Chordate Anatomy*. John Wiley and Sons, Inc. (Figs. 5.15, 5.21, 6.16).
Eddy, Oliver and Turner's *Atlas of Outline Drawings for Vertebrate Anatomy*. John Wiley and Sons, Inc. (Figs. 6.6, 6.10).
Flower and Lydekker's *Introduction to the Study of Mammals*. A. & C. Black, Ltd. (Fig. 11.9).
Gadow's *Amphibia and Reptiles*. Wheldon and Wesley, Ltd. (Fig. 7.21).
Goodrich's *Cyclostomes and Fishes*. A. & C. Black, Ltd. (Fig. 15.7).
Goodrich's *Studies on the Structure and Development of Vertebrates*. Macmillan & Co., Ltd. (Figs. 5.4, 6.2, 6.9, 6.19, 7.13, 8.6, 11.31, 15.8, 15.9).
Grasse's *Traite de Zoologie*, Vol. 11. Masson et Cie. (Figs. 2.3–2.9, 2.12, 2.13, 2.19, 2.20, 2.23–2.26, 2.27, 2.28, 2.29, 2.30).
Gray, Kimber and Stackpole's *Textbook of Anatomy and Physiology*. Macmillan Co. (Figs. 6.3, 16.10–16.11).
Gray's *Human Anatomy*. Lea and Febiger. (Fig. 11.5).
Gregory's *Evolution Emerging*. Macmillan Co. (Figs. 3.9, 5.16, 8.11).
Herdmann's section in the *Cambridge Natural History*, Vol. 7. Wheldon and Wesley, Ltd. (Figs. 2.10, 2.11, 2.22).
Herrick's *Introduction to Neurology*. W. B. Saunders Co. (Figs. 15.1–15.4).
Hilzheimer's *Handbuch der Biologie*. Ferdinand Enke. (Figs. 5.27, 5.43, 11.17, 11.34, 13.20).
Hoffman's section of Bronn's *Classen und Ordnung des Thierreichs*. Akademische Verlagsgesellschaft. (Fig. 11.8).

Hyman's *Comparative Vertebrate Anatomy.* University of Chicago Press (Figs. 5.14 A-C, 6.10 G, 9.16).

Kendall's *Microscopic Anatomy of Vertebrates.* Lea and Febiger. (Fig. 6.3).

Kent's *Comparative Anatomy of Vertebrates.* Blakiston's, McGraw-Hill Book Co. (Figs. 3.11, 5.43).

Kent's *Practical Anatomy of the Dogfish, Necturus and Cat.* Wm. C. Brown Publishers. (Fig. 6.6).

Kingsley's *Comparative Anatomy of Vertebrates.* Blakiston's, McGraw-Hill Book Co. (Figs. 4.7, 6.2, 6.21, 11.34–11.35, 15.10).

Kingsley's *Vertebrate Skeleton.* Blakiston's, McGraw-Hill Book Co. (Figs. 7.1, 11.8).

Lohmann's section of the *Handbuch der Zoologie,* Vol. 5 (3). Walter de Gruyter & Co. (Fig. 2.21).

Maximow and Bloom's *Textbook of Histology.* W. B. Saunders Co. (Figs. 5.2, 5.8, 5.9, 5.39, 15.2, 16.3).

Morgan's *The American Beaver and His Works.* J. B. Lippincott Co. (Fig. 5.29).

Neal and Rand's *Chordate Anatomy.* Blakiston's, McGraw-Hill Book Co. (Figs. 4.4, 4.8, 5.13, 5.41, 11.17, 15.11, 15.12).

Netter's *The Ciba Collection of Medical Illustrations.* Ciba Pharmaceutical Products, Inc. (Figs. 5.40, 6.7, 15.4, 15.5, 15.31, 16.12, 16.15–16.17, 16.19, 16.22, 16.29, 16.30).

Newman's *Phylum Chordata.* Macmillan Co. (Figs. 2.1, 3.6, 3.8, 3.10, 5.43).

Noble's *Biology of the Amphibia.* Dover Publications. (Figs. 6.21, 11.17).

Nonidez and Windle's *Textbook of Histology.* McGraw-Hill Book Co. (Fig. 6.3).

Papez' *Comparative Neurology.* Thomas Y. Crowell Co. (Fig. 16.10).

Parker and Haswell's *Textbook of Zoology,* Vol. 2. Macmillan & Co., Ltd. (Figs. 4.3, 6.21, 11.9).

Prosser's *Comparative Physiology.* W. B. Saunders Co. (Fig. 13.10).

Quain's *Elements of Anatomy.* Longmans, Green and Co. (Figs. 9.2–9.5, 9.23).

Quiring's *Functional Anatomy of the Vertebrates.* McGraw-Hill Book Co. (Figs. 13.5, 14.29).

Rand's *The Chordates.* Blakiston's, McGraw-Hill Book Co. (Figs. 3.7, 5.13, 7.25).

Reynold's *Vertebrate Skeleton.* Cambridge University Press. (Fig. 11.9).

Romer's *Man and the Vertebrates.* University of Chicago Press. (Fig. 15.25).

Romer's *Vertebrate Body and Shorter Version of the Second Edition of the Vertebrate Body.* W. B. Saunders Co. (Figs. 3.2, 3.4–3.6, 3.8, 4.2, 4.5, 5.12, 5.13, 5.36, 6.10, 6.21, 7.20, 8.12, 9.17, 9.22, 11.4, 11.8, 11.12, 11.16, 13.9, 15.15, 15.25, 15.28, 15.29, 15.32, 15.33, 16.13, 16.31–16.33).

Romer's *Vertebrate Paleontology.* University of Chicago Press. (Figs. 3.1, 3.3, 5.22, 6.10 BDE, 7.19 D, 7.20 DE, 8.16 ACD).

Schimkewitsch's *Lehrbuch der Vergleichende Anatomie der Wirbelthiere.* E. Schweizerbart'sche Verlagsbuchhandlung. (Figs. 6.10, 11.22, 11.24, 11.32).

Senning's *Outline Drawings for Comparative Anatomy.* McGraw-Hill Book Co. (Figs. 6.9, 7.20, 8.16, 11.21).

Smith's *Handbook of Lizards.* Comstock Publishing Co. (Figs. 5.19, 5.34).

Thomson's *Biology of Birds.* Macmillan Co. (Fig. 11.31).

Walls' *The Vertebrate Eye.* Cranbrook Institute of Science. (Figs. 15.16–15.17, 15.19, 15.22).

Walter and Sayles' *Biology of the Vertebrates.* Macmillan Co. (Figs. 6.21, 7.24, 7.26).

Walter's *Biology of the Vertebrates.* Macmillan Co. (Figs. 5.28, 5.35, 5.37, 5.41–5.43, 7.21, 11.17, 13.6, 15.18, 16.21).

Weichert's *Anatomy of Chordates.* McGraw-Hill Book Co. (Figs. 3.11, 5.5, 6.10, 11.23, 13.6, 13.21, 13.22, 15.27).

Werner's section of the *Handbuch der Zoologie,* Vol. 6 (2). Walter de Gruyter & Co. (Figs. 5.6, 5.7).

Wiedersheim's *Einführung in die Vergleichende Anatomie der Wirbelthiere.* Gustav Fischer Verlagsbuchhandlung. (Figs. 11.17, 11.29).

Wilder's *History of the Human Body.* Henry Holt and Co. (Figs. 5.30, 6.21, 9.24, 9.25, 11.36, 13.23, 14.28, 16.27).

Williston's *Osteology of the Reptiles.* Harvard University Press. (Fig. 8.8).

Young's *Life of Vertebrates.* Oxford University Press. (Figs. 5.1, 5.3, 7.21, 11.9, 11.32).

Zittel's *Grundzuge der Paleontologie,* Vol. 2. R. Oldenbourg. (Fig. 11.9).

Contents

1

INTRODUCTION

COMPARATIVE GROSS CHORDATE ANATOMY, which is what most courses called "comparative anatomy" actually are, may be likened to the elephant in the parable of the blind men, each of whom obtained a distinctively unique idea of the nature of the subject. In the same manner comparative anatomy is many things in the many different eyes that examine it and attempt to convey to others a fitting word picture for it. It may seem primarily a study of function: how differences in role of homologous organs in different animals are reflected in differences of structure, and how similarity in function is reflected in similarity of form in basically different organs. Equally validly it may be presented as a collection of anatomical variations, each precisely correlated with a certain taxonomic grouping. Or an analysis of the taxonomic groupings themselves may command the center of attention. So varied are the approaches that no two courses in comparative anatomy are likely to be closely similar.

For our own part, we cannot explore this elephant with even moderate thoroughness from all angles or even from any one angle in the limited time available. We shall perforce examine it but briefly in each of its several aspects, and through that experience attempt to grasp the common denominator of all the seemingly distinctive aspects. The "whole" that renders comparative anatomy greater than the sum of its parts is the pattern and meaning of evolution. However approached, comparative anatomy is in the end *a study of the changes wrought in the chordate body with the passage of time, and an analysis of the significance of those changes.*

1

Some Basic Evolutionary Terms and Concepts

Phylogeny. The development of a single individual, from fertilized egg to death, is an *ontogeny;* the embryogeny of an organism is that part of the ontogeny occurring before the organism becomes free-living, that is, in the embryonic stage. The history of life is a vast succession of ontogenies of organisms, all connected by the origination of each ontogeny from one or two others. This continuum of ontogenies is *phylogeny.* Usually a phylogeny must be deciphered on the basis of evidence from only one stage, the adult stage, since other developmental stages usually are not known; this has led to the frequent and illogical assumption that phylogeny *is* the succession of adult stages only. In practice, phylogeny can best be envisioned simply as the *course of evolution*—the "family history," as it were. Usually phylogeny is expressed by means of the changes in structure and function that accompany it. The phylogenetic origin of a structure is in effect, then, its evolutionary origin, as opposed, for example, to its embryonic or ontogenetic origin.

Homology and Analogy. Common ancestry of a part of any two or more different species of animals is *homology* (Fig. 1.1). More pre-

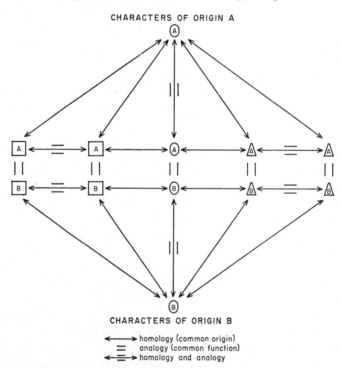

FIG. 1.1 Pictorial representation of the distinction between analogy and homology. Figures of identical shape have essentially similar functions but each individual figure regardless of shape is of at least recognizably different structure.

cisely this is *phylogenetic homology,* whereas similarity in origin of serially duplicated different parts in a single animal is *serial homology.* Unless otherwise specified "homology" implies phylogenetic homology. *Analogy* is similarity of function in two or more parts of one or more animals. Homologous structures may have identical functions or not; thus the tails of horses and cows are homologous and also of identical function (analogous); on the contrary although the tails of beaver and horses are homologous, they are not of the same function (not analogous). Analogous structures likewise may be either homologous or not.

Determination of homology is not often absolute. To be so every generation in the ancestral lines of the two species or individuals compared should be known. This is seldom possible in any except the most obvious cases, in which no question of homology would arise anyway. Similarity in embryonic development, in innervation, in general appearance in fossil series, or in any number of other ways, is usually the basis for assumption of homology. All methods of analysis, save observation of all generations, are beset with pitfalls which require great circumspection in drawing conclusions. In spite of such care some erroneous concepts of homology have become entrenched and with difficulty uprooted. Nevertheless the concept of homology is absolutely fundamental in comparative anatomy, although the actual facts of homology in many cases are unknown.

As homology is basic to phylogeny, so analogy is basic to *ecomorphology,* the study of (a) the *convergent* effect upon basically different structures of adaptation to a common or similar environment, and of (b) the *divergent* effects upon basically similar (homologous) structures of adaptation to different environments. The degree to which existence within like habitats imposes like form and function upon basically different structures is astonishing. Ecomorphology is the "new" functional comparative anatomy, currently receiving more attention than the more classical phylogenetic approach.

The Meaning of Evolution. Throughout this book use of the term "evolution" is, unless otherwise specified, meant to imply *organic evolution* —the evolution of living organisms. It must be understood, however, that evolution in its broadest sense is merely the unfolding of a changing continuity. In this broad sense evolution occurs in all inanimate as well as animate fields—in the chemical elements, in literature and other products of our civilization, and in the behavior of individuals, nations, and man. Each of these many sorts of evolution is governed by its own distinctive laws and limitations; the laws and limitations of organic evolution are not necessarily those of other sorts of evolution, even in part. Organic evolution and the laws and limitations pertaining thereto are unique; similarities to other sorts of evolution do exist but they should be recognized as coincidental and at best analogies, never homologies. To confuse an analogy with a homology is always an error and it can be a most grievous one.

Organic evolution is here regarded as an unshakable fact. Evidence for it is now completely overwhelming. Asking whether one believes in it is similar to, and as disarming as, asking whether one believes in Toledo. It is nevertheless true that at one time, not so many years ago, serious doubts of the existence of the phenomenon of organic evolution were held by many unbiased critics. Bitter debates were commonplace. In remote eddies of modern civilization even yet the word "evolution" arouses antagonism. By another name the phenomenon might never have seemed so objectionable. When it is realized that, after all, organic evolution only means change—*inheritable change in lines of successive generations*—suspicions and doubts are more readily seen to be without basis.

Evolution is a creative, a dynamic process, the essence of which is the invasion of every available sort of habitat (niche). It is a sort of self-perpetuating phenomenon, for occupation of a habitat by different organisms creates new conditions that may in turn afford a place for other kinds of organisms. Creation of niches, as well as occupation of them, is an important aspect of evolution.

Civilized man has seen many evolutionary changes occur in the very short space of time during which he has existed: the passenger pigeon and the Carolina parakeet have reached their end, as have innumerable species before them; the American buffalo, the ivory-billed woodpecker, the whooping crane, and a host of other species have likewise been virtually exterminated. He has seen vast differentiation of various stocks of domestic animals and of plants; and man himself has become more completely integrated, his races so ill-defined that they no longer can be distinguished consistently. Religious objections to the concept of anatomical evolution no longer exist; evolution is a truth, in the best sense of the word (the opinion agreed to by all who investigate a given reality, itself never attainable).

Rudimentary and Vestigial. Vestigial structures are those which are reduced in size and usually in function in one animal as compared with some ancestor. Rudimentary structures (Fig. 1.2) are those that are poorly developed for a given function in (a) one animal as compared with some descendant (*phylogenetic rudiments*) or (b) in an early developmental stage as compared with a later one (*ontogenetic rudiments*). Thus the tiny spurs at the vent of pythons are vestigial limbs, since snakes are derived from strong-limbed ancestors. On the other hand, the complex cochlear structures of the ear of mammals are seen presaged by rudimentary cochlear organs in reptiles and amphibians.

Populations. Evolution is a process that should be thought of as operating largely at the populational level. The genetic changes essential to evolution must occur in individuals, but the success of individual changes hinges upon the proportionate number of individuals in which they ultimately are found. The changes that are important in evolution must become established in the species, or population, as a whole. Individual changes are important only as providing the materials from which those useful in survival of the species as a whole are drawn. Thus a study of evolution is a study of population genetics, and precise concepts of types of populations are essential in further consideration of evolutionary processes.

A *population* may perhaps best be defined, in the present context, as the sum total of individuals sharing in a common gene pool. *Panmictic units* or *demes* are the smallest populations, wherein the occurrence of any one pairing for reproduction is just as probable as any other; all members of such a population have equal chances of mating with any other of the opposite sex. The cricket frogs of one small pond might be regarded as one

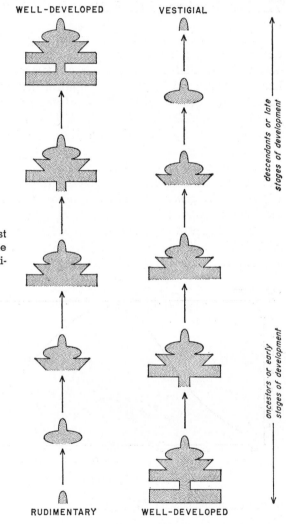

FIG. 1.2 Pictorial contrast of implications of the terms vestigial and rudimentary.

panmictic unit. Barriers of varying magnitude of distance and topography separate panmictic units and groups thereof from each other; any given group can be called a population providing there is a certain degree of free interbreeding between the members thereof. The largest population is a *species,* which may consist of any number of populational subdivisions at various levels down to the smallest panmictic units; even the most closely related species, unlike other populations, do not interbreed with each other under natural conditions, and thus they do not share in a common gene pool.

Micropopulations are panmictic units or small groups thereof; *macro-populations* are species or large populational subdivisions thereof.

The Mechanism of Evolution

Synthetic Hypothesis. The modern concept of the mechanism of evolution is called the *synthetic* hypothesis because it is a synthesis of field observation and laboratory research, of the naturalist's and the geneticist's knowledge, of experimental and empirical theory; in other words, it is a genetically sound explanation of the phenomena observed in nature.

In its simplest form the synthetic hypothesis may be summarized as *a usually gradual and usually multiple alteration in range of variation in characters of structure, function, or habit, through successive generations of living organisms.* The three prime ingredients of evolution are, thus, (1) *ranges of variation,* and (2) *alteration* in those ranges through (3) *successive generations of living organisms.* A brief résumé follows of the factors involved in the first two of these ingredients of evolution.

RANGE OF VARIATION. Characters are seldom if ever absolutely fixed in *all individuals* of a population. Each character varies at least a little; it is said to possess a *range of variation* (Fig. 1.3). For example, not all speci-

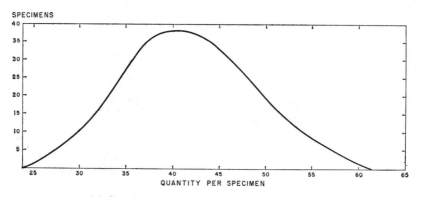

FIG. 1.3 Graphic representation of a range of variation.

mens of a single species of snake have the same number of trunk vertebrae; in fact the number varies in one species of garter snake from 137 to 153, in another from 149 to 171. All characters of all organisms vary in certain ways, and the extent of that variation is the range of variation.

Why do characters vary? Why are they not fixed? The answers are to be found in the incomprehensibly complex variations of the environment itself. However complex, environmental variations exert their effects through production of genetic inconstancy (see Fig. 1.6B), and those effects are limited solely by the degree of flexibility of developmental capacity of any one given genetic arrangement (or *genome*) as seen in one individual and in others exactly like it in composition. We can thus say that, basically, range of variation is a product of two factors: (a) *genetic inconstancy,* and (b) *flexibility of developmental capacity* of any given genetic system under different environmental conditions (see Fig. 1.6C). Alteration in either factor will be expected to produce an alteration in the range of variation.

Flexibility of Developmental Capacity. That organisms of identically the same genetic composition will be different if they develop under different conditions has been known for centuries. Certain salamanders developing wholly in the dark (as in a cave) will lack functional eyes, whereas others of the same batch of eggs will have functional eyes if raised under normal conditions. Certain fish developing in cold water will have more vertebrae than those developing in warm water. Certain small crustaceans have a round snout if raised in fresh water, a sharply pointed snout if grown in salt water. Color tone (not pattern, as a rule) likewise is subject to influence by the temperature of development, dark tones resulting from exposure to cold, lighter tones from warmth. Bare-footed persons have much thicker soles on the feet than persons habitually wearing shoes. Any differences in temperature, humidity, food, light, gravity, or habit may alter the phenotypic expression (effect upon the organism) of identical genetic systems (*genotypes*) in different individuals.

Genetic Inconstancy. Relatively few individuals of any species, especially of the vertebrates, have the identical genetic composition of any other example of the same species. This is genetic inconstancy. Identical genetic duplication is more common among invertebrates. Most, if not all, differences in genetic composition are, of course, ultimately those of environmental origin, since even the cellular protoplasm surrounding the chromosomes is a part of the *genetic* environment. Genetic variation arises from *mutations, chromosomal aberrations,* and *varied gene combinations.*

A mutation is a change in a gene, the ultimate unit of heredity that controls certain developmental sequences and that, as a complex molecule or group of molecules, occupies a given position on the *chromosome* which serves as the carrier for the genes. Mutations occur individually, not *en masse,* and thus some individuals will carry one mutant for a given gene, another individual will carry another. The various mutants that exist for a given gene are the *alleles.* Mutations, with the production of new alleles, occur constantly at a slow rate in all chromosomes of all cells, but the only ones of importance in heredity are those occurring in the reproductive cells. Many mutations are deleterious in effect, and the animals carrying them may die before reproducing. Those of benefit increase the success of their bearers and tend to be retained in the species. Any variation in the cellular environment is likely to produce a mutation. Exposure to excessive amounts of cosmic rays, x-rays, and other forms of radioactivity greatly accelerates the rate of mutation.

Chromosomal aberrations result from anomalous behavior of the chromosomes in *meiosis* (reduction division of cells, wherein the normal complement of chromosomes, usually paired, is halved). A piece of one chromosome of a homologous pair is transposed to or unequally exchanged with the other at almost any point along its length. Such anomalous combinations may be passed on for generations if not deleterious.

Varied gene combinations result in part from chromosomal aberrations, and in part from the endless recombinations resulting from crossing over at meiosis and from the interbreeding of individuals with different genetic compositions. In fact most evolutionary changes have been produced, it is thought, by recombination—by the accidental production of particular combinations of genes superior to others. For example, on an unrealistically gross level, a mutation for long legs might be quite useless unless accompanied by others for a long neck, more powerful heart, more powerful limb muscles, and a shorter body. When a combination of superior survival value chances to occur, it will be passed along to a greater number of successive offspring than will competitive combinations, and in time the species will consist largely if not wholly of that particular combination. But the reassortment of alleles continues apace, providing for a continual selection favoring the most advantageous combinations.

CHARACTERISTICS OF ALTERATIONS. Alterations in ranges of variation (that is, phenotypic alterations) result from any change in genetic composition of the individuals of *a species as a whole*. Any change in the degree of flexibility of developmental capacity is likely to be of genetic origin. All phenotypic alterations of one group of organisms from another group possess four *characteristics,* regardless of origin: (1) *complexity,* (2) *form,* (3) *speed,* and (4) *mode.*

The characteristic of *complexity* pertains to the number of genes controlling a given phenotypic deviation of one group of organisms as compared with another. Most alterations appear to be *polygenic,* involving several genes or sets of genes, since scarcely any character can be altered without affecting others. Any one change may be expected to require adjustment by changes in other, related features. Rarely are alterations *monogenic,* involving a single gene.

The characteristic of *form* pertains to the sort of change occurring in the range of variation. In (a) *canalization* the range of variation narrows (Fig. 1.4), so that a formerly variable character becomes relatively fixed about a usually new mode (average); and in (b) *shift* there is a change in the average within the former limits or any sort of change in the limits themselves (Fig. 1.5), with or without a change in mode, exclusive of the type known as canalization. Thus in an ancestral snake population with 137 to 153 trunk vertebrae a change to a range of 142 to 148, or 137 to 145, or 145 to 153, would be a *canalization;* a change to a range from 135 to 153, or 140 to 156, or a change of mode from 145 to 143 or 147 without narrowing of limits, would be a *shift.*

Speed pertains to the exact rapidity of change of an interbreeding

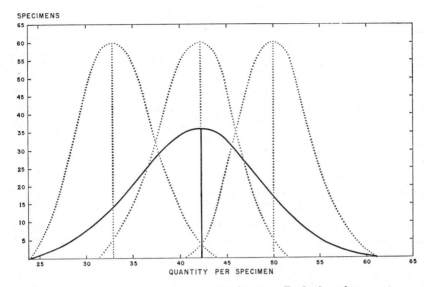

FIG. 1.4 Graphic representation of canalization. Each dotted curve is a result of canalization from the primitive range of variation (solid line).

population. It is influenced by (a) *population size,* small populations changing much faster than large, well-knit ones; (b) *extent of isolation,* populations in complete isolation changing faster from a parent population than those in partial or no isolation; (c) *variability,* some populations being remarkably variable, others not; and (d) *magnitude of selective pressure,* new situations sometimes developing very suddenly and rapidly weeding out individuals lacking the most adaptive gene combinations.

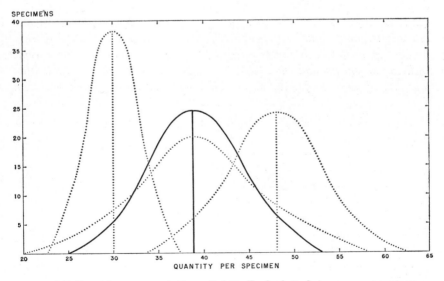

FIG. 1.5 Graphic representation of shift. Each dotted curve represents a shift from the primitive range of variation (solid line).

Three or four *modes* of alteration are recognized: (a) by a purely *random drift* (nonselective change in characters, especially in isolated populations); possibly (it is generally believed not) by (b) a *unidirectional drift* wherein ranges of variation are consistently altered along certain lines by intrinsic molecular forces, even in neutral or disadvantageous directions irrespective of selective pressures, either negative or positive; by (c) *natural selection,* a product of the interaction of environment and organism, wherein individuals possessing the most advantageous genetic composition attain numerical superiority over others; and (d) by *chance selection,* whereby randomly selected individuals representing only a part of the genetic composition of the former population are set apart from the rest of the population (as when a small group of individuals reaches an isolated island by storm or is separated from others by an impassable geographic feature, or survives without natural selection from some almost total catastrophe).

Environmental induction of characters is accepted as occurring within this framework of evolutionary mechanics, but only through the operation of natural selection.

All of these factors of evolution are of known importance and mechanism, at least in broad outline, except for unidirectional drift. It is thought more likely that characters evolving in a single direction (and appearing to exemplify unidirectional drift) do so because they are either directly or indirectly linked with other characters evolving under direct influence of positive selective pressures.

Thus, in accordance with the preceding discussion, the mechanism of evolution may be summarized as follows: *a usually gradual polygenic shift or canalization by means of random drift, perhaps unidirectional drift, by chance selection, and by natural selection in ranges of variation (in structural, functional, and habitual characters) maintained by genetic alterations (mutations, chromosomal aberrations, recombinations) and by developmental flexibility: a process pertaining to successive generations of living organisms and whose speed is influenced primarily by population size and by degree of genetic flexibility, selective pressure, and isolation (geographic, physiologic, psychic).* This statement may appear lengthy, but the process is complex and a more succinct statement of equal accuracy is yet to be formulated.

KINDS OF ORGANIC EVOLUTION. Three kinds of change are evident in organic evolution. In one type, one ancestral form becomes differentiated into two or more forms; this is *schistic evolution* or splitting. In another type, one ancestral form continues gradually to change as a whole and eventually becomes a distinguishably different form; this is *phyletic evolution.* Finally, one ancestral form may, instead of evolving gradually, suddenly evolve very rapidly and develop new adaptations to new situations, jumping from one adaptive zone into another; this is *quantum evolution* (it has no connection with the quantum units of physics).

LEVELS OF SURVIVAL VALUE. The products of evolution have a survival value that can be allocated to three levels. At the lowest level is *random drift;* the changes occurring therein do not necessarily or often lead to competitive superiority. Intermediate is *special adaptation,* by which the bearers are better fitted to specific environmental situations, making them competitively superior to other animals in the same environ ment. At the highest level is *general adaptation,* by which the bearers are better fitted for numerous environmental situations, making them competitively superior to other animals in a variety of environmental situations.

Inheritance of Acquired Characters. One of the most confusing concepts of the recent past, popular in evolutionary thought, has long been known by the very inept name of "inheritance of acquired characters." The idea for which the name has been used is the direct effect of the environment upon the genes themselves, causing them to mutate in such a way that their phenotypic expression is adaptive to the particular environmental situation that initiated the mutations (Fig. 1.6A). Occurrence of such an environmental influence on genetic change is patently absurd. Oddly, the literal meaning of the name for this concept is perfectly acceptable in the modern concept of evolution; in this sense the name is misleading. Genetic characters certainly are "acquired," and certainly are inheritable (Fig. 1.6B). Furthermore, even if "acquired" is interpreted as meaning origination by environmental induction, it must be admitted that presumably many characters are, in the end, environmentally induced; mutations are presumably responses to environmental variations, for gross chemical changes do not vary appreciably in a medium constant in all respects. Finally, even the establishment of characters is environmentally controlled by way of natural selection (Fig. 1.6D).

It may thus be concluded that the concept usually associated with the phrase "inheritance of acquired characters" more aptly might be termed *"direct environmental induction of selectively adaptive mutations."* This hypothesis is not at all acceptable, although it is important to reiterate that environmental induction of mutations and other genetic changes that are *randomly* both adaptive and nonadaptive is admitted (Fig. 1.6B).

Some Evolutionary Principles and Precepts

1. CONTINUITY OF STRUCTURE. There is literally nothing new under the sun in animal structure. *All structures, no matter how unique they may appear in isolated evolutionary stages, have evolved from other structures by means of gradual alterations.* The mammalian brain, even the cerebral cortex of which man is so proud, is far from unique except in degree of development of various parts. *Thus the distinction by different names between structures of common ancestry is perforce arbitrary.* Since all structures evolve gradually from others, obviously the distinction of one stage from another preceding or following it is arbitrary. It is nevertheless con-

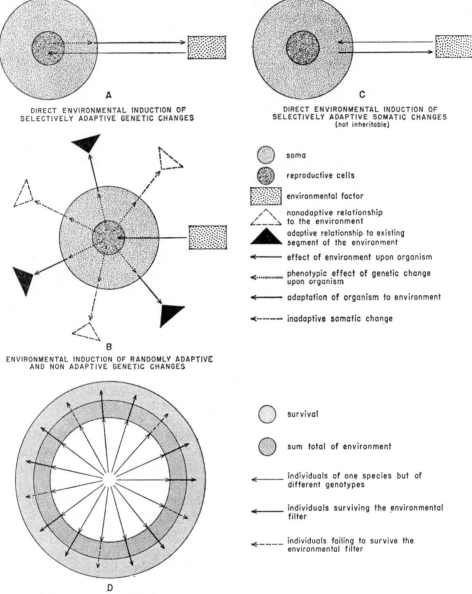

FIG. 1.6 Pictorial representation of modes of environmental influence upon development, inheritance, and evolution. A, an environmental influence that does *not* occur; B-D, environmental influences that *do* occur.

venient to distinguish and recognize by distinctive names the different stages in structural evolution. Limbs and fins are certainly widely different as we ordinarily think of them, yet they blend imperceptibly with each other in their phylogeny. All the evolutionary stages are never known;

there are many more unknown than known. The general pattern of change is nevertheless often clearly evident. It is where seemingly large anatomical or functional gaps occur that the differences meet the eye and are utilized to distinguish one stage from another. The stages are highly useful as a means of grasping the trend, but they should always be recognized as artificial.

2. USE AND DISUSE. When the primary function for which a structure is adapted is lost, the structure itself is usually either lost or adapted for another use. Useless structures are usually a hazard and are lost insofar as possible. When a structure adapted for one function becomes adapted for some other function, it may be assumed that it was originally of multiple function, having a primary and one or more secondary functions, and that the secondary functions became of greater survival value than the original primary function; some secondary function then becomes the primary function, and the former primary function becomes secondary and, perhaps, is ultimately lost.

3. COEXISTENCE AND DIRECT ANCESTRY. *Coexistence precludes direct ancestry,* in the special sense here intended. *Living species of one major group are not ancestral to living species of other major groups,* as, for example, amphibians in relation to reptiles. In most major animal groups some members have managed to survive under proper conditions up to the present time, but in so doing they have not remained static in form. Relatively minor but often confusing alterations are continually added, so that a connected series of living species demonstrating any lengthy evolutionary chain is impossible. Man, for example, is thus not derived from apes, as the two are contemporary types; their common ancestor is an extinct type, neither man nor ape. All organs are thought actually to have some useful function, even though unknown at present. It might be no more than an essential step in the development of some other organ of known function.

4. OPPORTUNISM. *Evolution is opportunistic.* The major trends in evolution, and most of the minor trends, are to the advantage of the groups involved. Organisms tend to evolve in accordance with whatever variations their members happen to possess that confer survival superiority. In any given situation of environmental stress, as in extreme cases when the existence of a species is in jeopardy, the actual survival of the species hinges upon the existence of gene combinations that will permit the individuals carrying those combinations to perpetuate their genetic line. If the proper genetic combinations do not exist or do not arise that will allow some group of individuals to survive and to reproduce an equal or greater number of individuals in the face of new environmental pressures, the species then becomes extinct. Evolution is opportunistic in the sense that it makes use of whatever happens to exist at the time. Undoubtedly the timing of environmental pressures is an important factor in evolution; were a given stress to occur at one time rather than another, the response might be quite different. Certainly this is true: that many different means of meeting common problems have evolved even in closely related groups.

The variety of solutions attempted is astonishing, but certainly is not exhaustive. That animal structure could have been improved by design is a virtual certainty.

There is no evolutionary anticipation of the future. Either the change in structure or the change in way of life may initiate a trend, or both may change simultaneously, but there is no anticipation of possible future need. Structures are modified in accordance with genetic capacity and the demands (selective pressures) of the moment. Only by sheer coincidence are structures available or preadapted for different functions as time and evolution march on. If there is a directive force governing evolution, it seems invariably to operate in this fashion, not by design for anticipated needs.

If evolution is opportunistic in its direction, it should sometimes be degenerative, and sometimes progressive: in some cases it should lead from the simple to the complex, and in others from the complex to the simple. That is exactly what occurs (see principle number 2).

5. COMPETITION. *Evolution is competitive.* The replacement of one structure by another, or the modification of any given structure, occurs in evolution chiefly because the change makes its possessor, in the long run, reproductively superior to animals competing with it, in the sense of producing more offspring in turn capable of maintaining or increasing the lead gained. Without competition in the sense of differences in survival potential, evolution virtually ceases. Competition produces differences in abundance of given types of individuals, through elimination of family lines (1) carrying undesirable gene combinations, and (2) lacking gene combinations rendered necessary by newly manifest environmental pressures. Undesirable gene combinations rarely if ever permeate the entire population of a species. They are instead generally eliminated in the family lines in which they appear. Thus it may be said that the elimination process at the individual or micropopulational level of competition is due *primarily* (not wholly) to the *existence* in the eliminated groups of *undesirable* gene combinations. Conversely the presence or absence of a given desirable gene combination that is rendered necessary by new environmental pressures commonly affects the entire species. If present in any population of the species, it soon permeates the whole, but if absent, the species becomes extinct. Thus it may be said that the elimination process at the macropopulational level of competition is due *primarily* (not wholly) to the *absence* in the eliminated groups of *desirable* gene combinations.

6. ADAPTATION. *Evolution is largely adaptive.* The changes occurring in animals that confer survival superiority to populations in which they occur are adaptive in effect. Adaptation can lead into many channels, producing bizarre and astonishing types as well as commonplace forms. Curiously enough, however, adaptive trends are sometimes linked with detrimental trends, the latter effecting the demise of the species.

Adaptation is ordinarily thought of as concerning free-living stages— as *extrinsic adaptation* to what may be thought of as the *extrinsic environ-*

ment. Probably most of it is, but embryonic adaptations have also played an important role in evolution; the two types have occurred simultaneously. Many such embryonic changes (*intrinsic* or *clandestine adaptation* to what may be thought of as the *intrinsic environment*) produce no change whatever in the adult structure; they are of importance primarily in adaptive simplification of developmental processes.

7. INCONSTANCY OF ENVIRONMENT. It is a general rule that few if any environmental situations are very constant. They change with climatic cycles, with variation in relative abundance of coexistent species, with introduction of new sources of food, new enemies, new competitors, or new collaborators. *Were the environment absolutely constant, evolution would largely, if not entirely, cease.* Regardless of the possible desirability of constancy, it does not exist. It is most closely approached in the oceans, in the great tropical and subtropical forests, and in the lower reaches of the major river systems. As anticipated, *the most conservative animals known*—the most slowly evolving—*inhabit environmentally quasi-constant areas.* Examples include diatoms, the horseshoe crab, Peripatus, and the recently publicized fish (Latimeria) representing an ancient group thought to have been extinct some 75 million years.

Because of the inconstancy of environment, a steady trend toward finer adjustment of a species to a limited environmental situation often leads to extinction. *Progressive perfection of adaptation typically leads to extinction* where there is a sudden radical change in the environment or a loss of plasticity, or both.

In reality a population is never (or but rarely) at peace with its environment, despite the fact that evolution continually moves toward that goal. The evolutionary struggle is analogous to man's constant psychological struggle to attain a peace of mind—a sorry thing to achieve, as there is a question whether the mind at peace remains a mind.

8. THE RATE OF EVOLUTION. Speed of evolution is not necessarily constant in any one group nor is it generally the same in different groups at any time. A group may exist for millions of years changing but little, and then change rapidly over a relatively short span of time.

9. SIZE OF SELECTION PRESSURE. *Magnitude of selection pressure is an important control of rate of evolution.* Selection pressure is simply the influence of environment upon the probability of success or failure of any given genetic line or population; a low probability of failure (or high probability of success) is expressed as low selection pressure, and high selection pressure exists if the environment is so rigorous as to render the probability of survival relatively low. In general, the more precarious the situation, the more quickly adaptive values become apparent and the more rapidly does evolutionary change occur. Wholesale elimination of unfit members produces relatively sudden changes in the genetic composition and therefore in the structure of the residual population, leaving it better adapted to the new conditions than was the former large population.

10. VARIETY OF SELECTION PRESSURE. *Variety of selective pressures*

controls levels of survival value. The three levels of survival value are correlated closely with the magnitude and especially with the variety of selective pressures to which populations are subjected. It is significant that each of the successive major advancements in vertebrate evolution, products of *general adaptation,* marked by the appearance successively of fishes, amphibians, reptiles, birds, and mammals, arose in tropical regions where the variety of competitive species and the reproductive potential of all are the greatest known. Tests of superiority under a wide variety of competition are most rapidly performed where the widest variety of competitive types exist, and that is in the tropics. No matter how strange or rigorous the inanimate or noncompetitive environment may be, the evolutionary products of such environments are not as thoroughly refined by competition, and are thus not as well prepared for widespread success, as the products of highly competitive associations. The evolutionary achievements of the highest level of survival value—*general adaptation*—are thus a product solely of the most highly competitive associations. Achievement of a lower level of survival value obviously may stem from any association, highly competitive or not.

The significance of this principle in the conduct of man is of great importance.

11. UNIVERSALITY OF EVOLUTION. All living organisms of the past, present, and future are at the time of their existence subject to common evolutionary laws. *Man has evolved through evolutionary processes common to all other animals.* Paleontological evidence, though scanty, leaves no doubt that man has evolved gradually from a long sequence of other animals; and that if all parts of the evolutionary chain were present, it would be impossible to draw a logical distinction between man and nonman. *Man is now as in the past subject to universal evolutionary laws.* Regardless of any choice man may ever exercise, he will always be subject to evolutionary forces he can at best anticipate, temper, or utilize in such a manner as to bring about his perpetuation and improvement.

12. MUTABILITY OF SPECIES. Evolutionary knowledge reveals that, no matter what man does, no matter how he conducts himself, despite any effort man may exert to control his destiny, the species we know as man is doomed as surely as the earth itself is doomed. Few species exist more than a few million years. One million is the estimated average span of existence of a species. There is no more reason to expect we shall exceed the average than to think we shall fail to reach it—in fact there is perhaps less reason.

The continued existence of the species man as we know it is not, however, our real concern. Species, as recognizably different populations, successively and imperceptibly replace each other with the passage of time. The exact amount of change requisite in a populational succession through time (*population line*) to regard the representatives at any two times as belonging to different species is arbitrary and essentially immaterial. The important thing is that the succession does occur. Every population line in existence today has been in existence since the beginnings of life; its ancestors form a continuum back a billion years or so. There has been a succession—many successions—of arbitrarily differentiated species throughout the history of life; some lines have ceased to exist, and the others remain with us today.

The concern of man in reality, then, is not whether his species shall survive, but whether his *population line* will persist. It could, if among the successful lines, continue in existence presumably another billion years, at which time its representative species could and undoubtedly would be far different from that of the present day.

Teleology and Evolution

The sequences of events in the normal life of man are in many ways the product of a plan and purpose, either of the person directly involved or of some other person associated in some manner with him. Some utility, of one sort or another, commonly motivates a person to initiate each such event or sequence of events.

In like manner the sequences of evolutionary events have often been interpreted as the product of a manlike plan, purpose, and utility. Such an interpretation is *teleological*. It is a habit of thought, exemplified by reference to given structures or adaptations as having appeared simply because they were needed or wanted. Evolution has not occurred because organisms have wanted it, nor has it necessarily occurred the way they might have wanted even if they were capable of thinking of such matters; even man has been largely incapable of choosing and effecting his mode of evolution. There has been no deliberate choice whatsoever on the part of any evolving organisms of direction, speed, or any other aspect of evolution. Injection of any implication of manlike choice into statement or thought of organic evolution, other than man's, is utterly fallacious and should be strictly avoided.

Organisms have evolved given characteristics because (a) they possessed the genetic capacity to produce those characteristics, and (b) because those characteristics possessed a high survival value under the selective pressures existing at the particular time and place the change was occurring. It is well to refer to "survival values" and "selective pressures" rather than "use" or "need."

As for the existence of a superhuman plan or purpose, this is another matter. Most, if not all, the best, open-minded students of evolution would agree with Simpson (see bibliography): "Adaptation is real, and it is achieved by a progressive and directed process. This process is natural, and it is wholly mechanistic in its operation. This natural process achieves the aspect of purpose without the intervention of a purposer, and it has produced a vast plan, without the concurrent action of a planner. It may be that the initiation of the process and the physical laws under which it functions had a Purposer and that this mechanistic way of achieving a plan is the instrument of a Planner—of this still deeper problem the scientist, as scientist, cannot speak."

QUESTIONS

1. State the modern hypothesis of evolution, and list the factors involved in each ingredient.

2. What would be the implication relative to constancy in environment if, in theory, a given species were to exist absolutely unchanged over a span of a million years?

3. Explain the relation of homology and phylogeny; of analogy and ecomorphology.

4. State and explain the characteristics of phenotypic alteration, and how each varies or is influenced by other factors.

5. Name and distinguish the three kinds of evolution.

6. Name and distinguish the three levels of survival value.

7. Name eleven evolutionary principles or precepts.

8. Explain each of the following evolutionary precepts and principles: continuity of structure; use and disuse; arbitrariness of structural distinctions; that coexistence precludes direct ancestry; evolutionary opportunism and fortuity; indispensability of competition; adaptiveness of change; environmental inconstancy; progressively coordinated environment-organismic relations; inconstancy of evolutionary rates; indispensability of selective pressures; correlation of magnitude of selective pressure and rate of evolution; correlation of variety of selective pressure and level of survival value; mutability of species; universality of evolution.

9. Distinguish the effects of competition at the individual or micropopulational level and at the macropopulational level.

10. In organic evolution an extinct species may belong to a living population line. How is this explained?

11. Explain the meaning and significance of "direct environmental induction of selectively adaptive mutations."

12. In what three ways does the environment influence development, inheritance, and evolution?

13. What are the two groups of factors that produce a range of variation?

14. Genetic inconstancy is produced by what three phenomena?

15. Define the following:

allele	extrinsic adaptation	macropopulation
analogy	gene	meiosis
canalization	general adaptation	micropopulation
chromosomal abbera-	genome	monogenic
tion	genotype	morphological
clandestine adaptation	homology	morphology
deme	hypertrophy	mutation
ecomorphology	inheritance of acquired	mutation pressure
embryogeny	characters	natural selection
evolution	intrinsic adaptation	ontogeny

organic evolution
panmictic unit
phenotype
phyletic evolution
phylogenetic homology
phylogeny
polygenic
population
population line

quantum evolution
random drift
range of variation
recombination
rudimentary
schistic evolution
selection pressure
serial homology

shift
special adaptation
species
synthetic hypothesis of
   evolution
teleology
unidirectional drift
vestigial

2

PREVERTEBRATES

CHORDATE CHARACTERISTICS. Chordates are defined as animals possessing at some ontogenetic stage a solid *notochord* and a *dorsal tubular neural cord*. No other animals possess these structures at any stage, although rudiments are evident in a few nonchordates. These two characteristics are the only ones both *unique* to, and *invariably present* in, the phylum Chordata.

One other characteristic is invariably present in chordates, and is also found in a few related nonchordates: One or more pairs of *pharyngeal clefts or slits* are present at some ontogenetic stage. Primitively pharyngeal clefts were simply vertical, slitlike openings in the lateral wall of the pharynx, used primarily as a filter from which microorganisms serving for food were strained. It is easy to call these *gill slits,* but that term is inappropriate when applied to the pharyngeal slits of all vertebrates collectively; *gills* by definition are, in chordates, structures of the pharynx used for aquatic respiration. Likewise gill slits are defined as openings into a gilled pharynx. In most terrestrial vertebrates and in most primitive chordates, however, the pharynx is not used at all for aquatic respiration; gills are not present, and the pharyngeal slits that *are* always present, at least embryonically, are therefore not gill slits.

Unfortunately only one of these three primary features of chordates (the dorsal tubular nerve cord) is demonstrable in adults of all vertebrates. The notochord is a conspicuous embryonic structure, often losing its identity in adults and becoming incorporated into a vertebral column. In land vertebrates, only a few of the pharyngeal clefts usually appear, briefly, in embryonic stages, leaving in adults but a few vestiges scarcely recognizable

20

as homologs of pharyngeal slits. Even the distinctive central lumen of the neural tube is so greatly reduced in actual, as well as relative, size that it could readily be overlooked in many vertebrates.

Other Chordate Characteristics. Numerous other features are shared with a variety of nonchordates. They include (1) segmentation of parts or all of the body at some stage of life; (2) triploblastic germ layers; (3) location of the blastopore at the anal end of the body; (4) presence of a mesoderm-lined celom; (5) a postanal tail at some stage; (6) bilateral symmetry; (7) cephalization (specialization of a head); and (8) a true endoskeleton.

The Chordate Subphyla. Three subphyla are usually recognized in the most recent taxonomic monographs: the *Cephalochordata,* or lancelets; the *Urochordata,* or sea squirts; and the *Vertebrata,* or vertebrates. The invertebrate chordates are commonly referred to collectively as the *Proto-chordata.* All are exclusively of marine habitat.

Prevertebrates. The prevertebrates are, literally, the direct ancestors of vertebrates. In reality, however, the actual ancestors of vertebrates, or the taxonomic groups to which they belong, are not authoritatively known; numerous groups are reasonable possibilities and among these, certain ones have at one time or another been thought to be especially strong probabili-

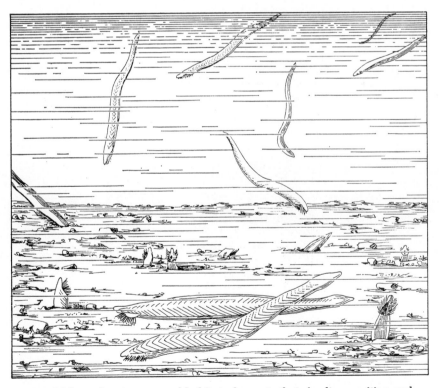

FIG. 2.1 Lancelets in a normal habitat, shown in their feeding position and swimming about. (From Newman.)

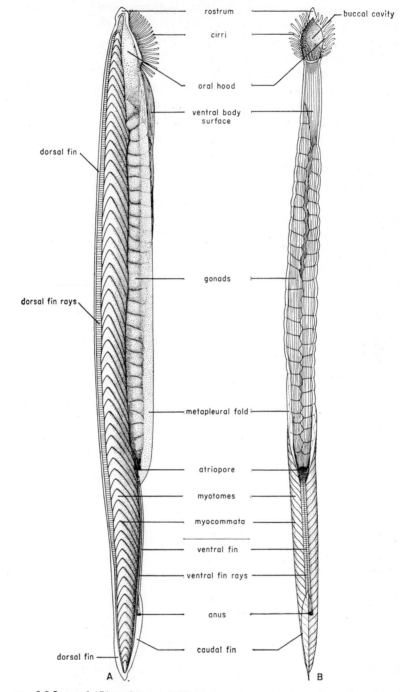

FIG. 2.2 Lateral (A) and ventral (B) views of an adult lancelet, and lateral (C) (*facing page*) view of a cleared young lancelet.

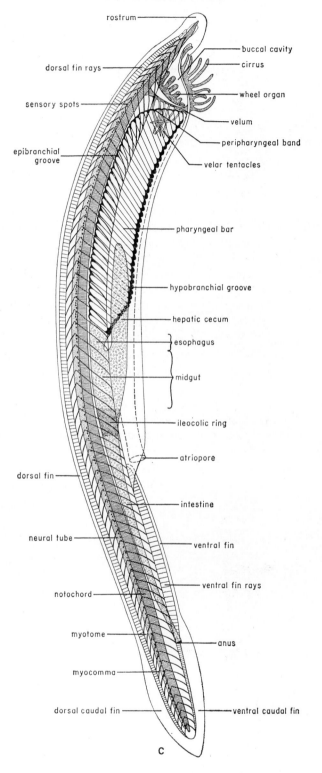

rostrum

buccal cavity

dorsal fin rays

cirrus

wheel organ

sensory spots

velum

peripharyngeal band

epibranchial groove

velar tentacles

pharyngeal bar

hypobranchial groove

hepatic cecum

esophagus

midgut

ileocolic ring

atriopore

dorsal fin

intestine

neural tube

ventral fin

notochord

ventral fin rays

myotome

anus

myocomma

dorsal caudal fin

ventral caudal fin

C

ties. Any groups that may reasonably be construed as closely related to the direct ancestors of vertebrates are properly regarded as prevertebrates; in this sense all the protochordate subphyla are prevertebrates, and so are a number of the nonchordate invertebrate phyla.

Protochordates

The Cephalochordates. Only two genera, *Branchiostoma* and *Asymmetron,* with about 28 species included, belong to the subphylum Cephalochordata. The first genus was long known incorrectly by the generic name *Amphioxus,* which is now often retained as a "common" name, although the genus cannot technically be known by that name. Individuals of the subphylum as a whole are better known as *lancelets.*

The lancelets are laterally compressed, elongate, actively swimming animals about 1½ inches long. They are most active at night, but even then most of the time is passed with the body half buried in an upright position in the ocean floor, the oral end projecting free and a vortex of water directed into the mouth (Fig. 2.1). Upon disturbance the animals burst from their position, swim a short distance, and dive back into the sandy bottom where they eventually force their way back into the feeding position. In some areas they are sufficiently abundant to be used as food, despite their small size.

The anterior end is rather sharply pointed (Fig. 2.2), with a *rostrum* below which is suspended on either side a sheetlike *oral hood* whose two lateral parts are only narrowly connected midventrally toward the rear. The *buccal cavity* enclosed by the oral hood is bounded posteriorly by a transverse *velum,* a membrane blocking the anterior end of the large pharynx which, in turn, is perhaps a third as long as the body. In the mid-

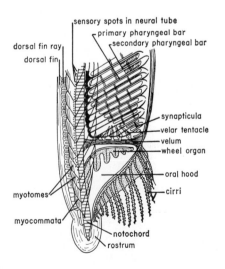

FIG. 2.3 The oral hood region of amphioxus, in lateral view. (From Dawydoff.)

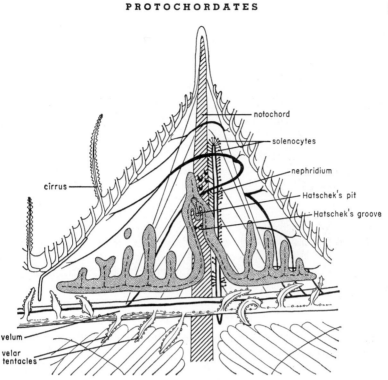

FIG. 2.4 Hatschek's pit and groove, as seen in ventral view of the dorsal wall of the oral hood and rostrum of an immature amphioxus. (From Dawydoff.)

dle of the velum is the narrow *mouth* opening, guarded by numerous long *velar tentacles.*

To the free edges of the oral hood are attached numerous *cirri* (Fig. 2.3), each supported by a central skeletal bar. Six or eight broad, elongate patches of ciliated epithelium on the walls of the buccal cavity extend forward from the velum; this is the *wheel organ.* A groove runs down the middle of each patch, terminating at a shallow pit near the anterior end of the ciliated area. Specific names, *Hatschek's groove* and *pit* (Fig. 2.4), are applied to the particular groove and pit in the median dorsal patch of ciliated epithelium; since these have a special embryonic (and phylogenetic) significance they are discussed in the chapter on the digestive system (p. 264).

In feeding, the sides of the oral hood are widely flared, and the cirri are said usually to be turned inward making a funnel that excludes sand particles. The cilia of the wheel organ beat rapidly in a rhythmical sequence simulating a rotating wheel and thus create a vortex of water directed through the mouth into the pharynx, where other cilia force the current out the atriopore farther back in the body.

The pharynx wall is pierced by about 180 pairs of obliquely slanted, narrow, tall, *pharyngeal slits,* through which the water passes into the *atrium,* a cavity completely surrounding the pharynx (except at its dorsal

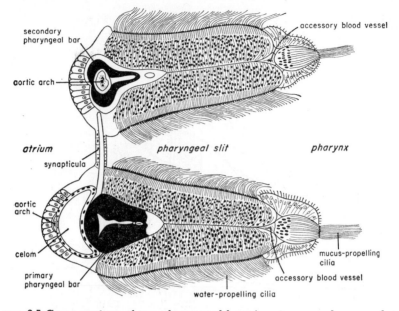

secondary
pharyngeal bar

accessory blood vessel

aortic arch

atrium

synapticula

pharyngeal slit

pharynx

aortic
arch

celom

primary
pharyngeal bar

mucus-propelling
cilia

accessory blood vessel

water-propelling cilia

FIG. 2.5 Cross sections of two pharyngeal bars (a primary and a secondary) in amphioxus. (From Dawydoff.)

border). The atrium has but one other opening, an *atriopore,* situated on the midventral line a short distance back of midbody. The sides of the pharyngeal bars between the slits are profusely provided with cilia which keep the water current moving through the body; and the internal edges of the bars possess a narrow band of cilia serving to propel a mucoid belt in which the microorganisms that serve as the animals' food are caught (Fig. 2.5). A broad, concave, midventral band of tissue, the *endostyle,* on the midventral wall of the pharynx produces the mucuslike fluid propelled along the pharyngeal bars. Reaching the dorsal line of the pharynx, the many belts of mucus coming up each side of the pharynx along the pharyngeal bars unite together as one and pass posteriorly into the esophagus along a deep groove called the *epibranchial groove,* lying in an *epibranchial band.* Because of gross similarity to the epibranchial band, the endostyle is often called the *hypobranchial band,* with its *hypobranchial groove.*

A narrow *esophagus* at the rear of the pharynx leads into a wide *midgut,* from the anterior part of which, ventral to the esophagus, a spacious *hepatic cecum* extends forward a short distance on the right side of the pharynx. The food is directed into this cavity by a crescent-shaped lateral patch of cilia on the midgut wall. Emerging from the hepatic cecum, the food passes on through the *midgut* and into the *hind gut;* on the walls of the anterior half of the hind gut is an extensive ciliated area (Fig. 2.6) that churns the food before passing it onward toward the anus. The anus is situated to the left of the midventral line a short distance from the posterior end of the body.

On the ventrolateral surface on either side of the body between the atriopore and the oral hood is a loose epithelial flap—the *metapleural folds;* these lack skeletal support. Between the atriopore and the anus is a median ridge, the ventral fin, stiffened by two rows of thin, quadrangular skeletal supports called *fin rays.* Posterior to the anus is another median ridge, the *caudal fin,* stiffened by a single row of fin rays. The caudal fin extends to the tail tip, and thence forward along the median dorsal line to a point opposite the anus; thus *ventral* and *dorsal* caudal fins can be recognized. A low median *dorsal fin,* also with a row of internal fin rays, extends forward to the head region.

The *celom* is vestigial in the pharyngeal region, where the atrium has, as it were, pushed it into nooks and crannies here and there. A series of segmented spaces persists on either side of the dorsal wall of the pharynx. Each is connected on each side with a fine celomic tube extending along the adjacent pharyngeal bar and terminating in a longitudinal space on the midventral surface of the pharynx. Other spaces persist in the

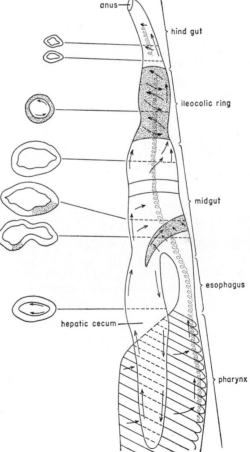

FIG. 2.6 Ciliary currents in the postpharyngeal gut of amphioxus. (From Dawy-doff.)

metapleural folds. Posterior to the pharynx, the celom surrounds the alimentary tract in typical fashion, the atrium being reduced to a relatively small size anterior to the atriopore and being absent posterior to that point.

The muscular system is essentially vertebratelike, consisting chiefly of longitudinal fibers grouped into up-ended V-shaped segmental *myotomes* covering the sides of the body and tail. A ventral zone of *transverse muscle* is located below the atrium. A comparable zone is absent in vertebrates.

The *notochord* is complete and very well developed, extending from rostrum to the tip of the tail.

The central nervous system consists of a hollow dorsal *nerve cord* that extends the length of the body, terminating anteriorly in a brainlike structure of two vesicles. *Spinal nerves,* with separate dorsal and ventral roots, are segmentally attached to the spinal cord. *Sensory pigment spots* are present along the central nervous system, but there are no specialized cranial optic, olfactory, or auditory organs such as vertebrates possess.

The excretory system consists of a segmental series of *nephridia* (Fig. 2.7) located on each side of the pharynx and derived from and projecting into the dorsal celomic spaces as branched, blind tubes. The nephridia open into the atrium, into which excretory wastes are propelled by groups of flagellated cells (*solenocytes*) at the innermost blind ends of the tubes (Fig. 2.8). Actual extraction of wastes seems to be accomplished by the transfer of materials from a blood sinus that surrounds each nephridium;

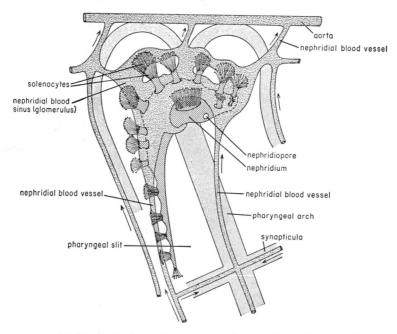

FIG. 2.7 Nephridial structure in amphioxus. (From Dawydoff.)

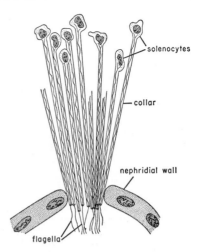

FIG. 2.8 Structure of the nephridial solenocytes of amphioxus. (From Dawydoff.)

the solenocytes appear to serve chiefly, if not exclusively, to propel fluids through the nephridia. A great deal of argument has centered about the homology of these nephridia. They are much like those of some annelids, but rather markedly different from the excretory tubules ("celomoducts") primitively draining the celom in vertebrates. Thus the elaborate cephalo-chordate excretory apparatus is commonly regarded as having no homology whatsoever with the vertebrate organs. As similar as the lancelets and vertebrates are in other aspects, this apparent discrepancy has proved very puzzling. More recent views discount the similarity of annelid and Am-phioxus excretory systems, which can scarcely be other than parallelisms in view of the very remote relationship of these two groups. Furthermore, the differences in vertebrate and cephalochordate excretory organs seem much less significant in view of (1) their basic similarity in origin from the celomic wall, and (2) the specialized conditions imposed by the atrium. It is to be remembered that the modern cephalochordates have had just as long a time to evolve as vertebrates, and it is only astonishing that the differences between them are no greater than they are. Vertebrates, having no atrium, have evolved with a celom that long served both excretory and reproductive functions; in cephalochordates the gonads utilize the atrium, and that the primitive excretory ducts should have evolved along com-pletely different lines is to be expected. That the vertebrate kidney tubules and the cephalochordate nephridia are homologous seems highly probable, if not a certainty, granting that each lacks most of the finer elaborations of the other.

The circulatory system is diagrammatically vertebratelike, with a *ventral* and a *dorsal aorta, aortic arches* about the pharynx, a system of *cardinal veins,* and a *hepatic portal vein* (Fig. 2.9).

The Urochordates. Three classes of the phylum Urochordata are com-monly recognized: the class *Ascidiacea* of some 2000 species, the class

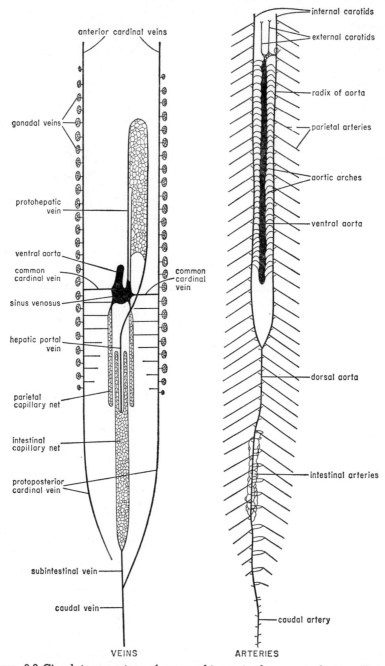

FIG. 2.9 Circulatory system of an amphioxus in dorsoventral view. Note the presence of a hepatic portal system essentially the same as that of vertebrates. A renal portal system, characteristic of vertebrates, is absent since vertebratelike kidneys are absent. Amphioxus has another portal system, however—the intestinal portal system—not present in any vertebrate now in existence. (From Dawvdoff.)

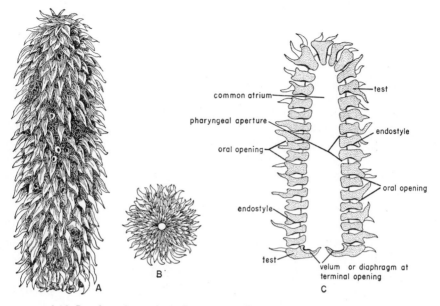

FIG. 2.10 A colonial ascidian, Pyrosoma. A, lateral view; B, end view; C, sagittal section. (From Herdman.)

FIG. 2.11 Various types of ascidian urochordates in adult stages. (From Herdman.)

Thaliacea of about 100 species, and the class *Appendicularia* of some 75 species. The name Tunicata is often used for the whole subphylum.

THE ASCIDIANS. As might be expected in a group as large as this, considerable variation occurs in outward appearance (Figs. 2.10 through 2.13). Some genera have long stalks, others are attached directly to a substrate. Some are solitary, others colonial to a varying degree. Some colonies share their covering (tunic) and the individual members are thus protectively integrated with each other. Despite this variation the basic structure of all ascidians is rather constant. The morphology of *Molgula* may be considered in a general way exemplary of the class.

The body is ovoid, with two more or less prominent projections opposite the attached base. The more centrally located projection surrounds the *incurrent* or *oral siphon* or *mouth* (Figs. 2.14, 2.15), through which a more or less constant current of water enters the body; the more lateral projection surrounds the *excurrent* or *atrial siphon* or *atriopore*, out of which the water current flows. The body is covered by a fibrous *test* or *tunic*, composed chiefly of *tunicin*, a substance closely similar to cellulose. This is secreted by scattered cells lying within the tunic but originating

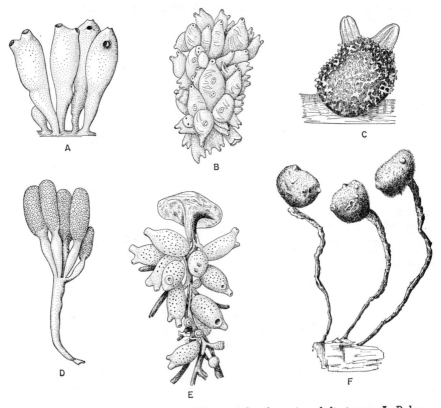

FIG. 2.12 Various types of ascidian urochordates in adult stages. A, Polycitor; B, Dendroa; C, Microcosmus; D, Sycozoa colony; E, Stolonica colony; F, Pyura. (From Dawydoff.)

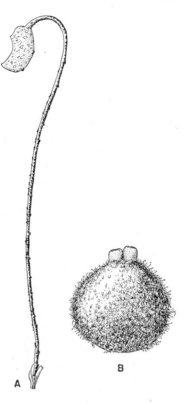

FIG. 2.13 Two ascidian urochordates, adult stages. A, Bolteniopsis; B, Eugyra. (From Dawydoff.)

from the mesoderm of a gelatinous inner layer, the *mantle*. The outer surface of the mantle is lined with a single layer of ectodermal cells, whereas the relatively thick central area is composed of a mesoderm in the form of cells scattered in a jellylike matrix they secrete. All the internal organs are imbedded in the mantle. An enormous *pharynx,* pierced by thousands of slits (Fig 2.16) arranged in "panes" between vertical pharyngeal bars, occupies nearly all the volume of the body. At one side the pharynx is continuous with a short, narrow tube, the *esophagus,* which leads past a set of *hepatic ceca* directly into an enlarged *stomach.* The stomach lies transversely on the left side of the pharynx and leads into an *intestine* which loops backward over the stomach. It then turns upward and opposite the atriopore empties through the *anus* into an ectoderm-lined, pocketlike invagination, the *atrium.* As a matter of fact, the atrial invagination is very extensive, surrounding almost the entire pharynx (excluding only a narrow belt ventral to the oral siphon) and separating it from all other viscera (Figs. 2.17, 2.18). There is thus a *visceral* layer of mantle separated almost completely from the *parietal* layer (against the tunic) by a very thin, ectoderm-lined atrial cavity. The esophagus is the only organ traversing the atrium, which has the superficial appearance of a true celom. It is not a true celom, however, which is a cavity within the mesoderm; a celom is lined with mesoderm. The atrium exists, as a matter

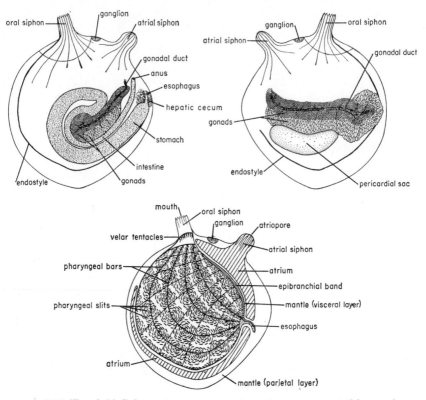

FIG. 2.14 (*Top left*) Schematic representation of structures visible on the left side of Molgula, tunic removed.

FIG. 2.15 (*Top right*) Schematic representation of structures visible on the right side of Molgula, tunic removed.

FIG. 2.16 (*Bottom*) Schematized drawing of sagittal section of Molgula, medial view of right half of body.

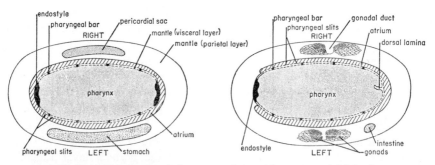

FIG. 2.17 (*Left*) Schematized drawing of frontal section of Molgula at a level just below esophagus.

FIG. 2.18 (*Right*) Schematized drawing of frontal section of Molgula, at a level just above esophagus.

of fact, at the expense of the celom, only small vestiges of which remain in the urochordates.

The atrium serves as a passageway for water passing through slits in the pharynx wall to reach the exterior. The pharynx is primarily a food-capturing device, filtering microorganisms from the water forced through it by means of cilia. The food is carried along the vertical pharyngeal bars in numerous cilia-propelled belts of mucus; this mucus originates at a broad, concave, midventral pharyngeal band, the *endostyle,* that extends from near the esophagus to the oral siphon. Extending along the middorsal line of the inner wall of the pharynx from the oral siphon into the esophagus is a pendant, narrow ridge, the *epibranchial band* (dorsal lamina of authors) which like an overhead track carries the single mucus belt produced by a fusion of the several belts coming from the pharyngeal bars. The food is thus conveyed indirectly into the esophagus from the filtering walls of the pharynx.

Two sets of gonads are present, one set on either side of the body (Figs. 2.14, 2.15). Each set consists of a pair of gonads, each with its own duct leading independently into the atrial cavity opposite the atriopore. Both testes and ovaries are present in a single individual, but the germ cells mature at different times, so that self-fertilization does not occur. Fertilization takes place in the atrial cavity, and the zygotes are soon swept out into the adjacent environment where they develop into free-swimming larvae of a peculiar, tadpolelike shape.

A nerve net surrounds most of the body which is capable of only a general contraction resulting in squirting water from both siphons, hence the name "sea squirts." A solid *ganglion* situated in the dorsal wall between the siphons is the sole feature of a "central" nervous system. On its ventral surface is a crescentic *neural gland* of uncertain function.

An *excretory sac* receiving products from a group of excretory cells on one side empties into the atrium near the atriopore.

The circulatory system consists of a *heart* in a sausage-shaped *pericardial sac* (Fig. 2.15). The heart beat is in one direction for a time, forcing blood into a branched series of pharyngeal spaces, and then in the opposite direction, forcing blood into a branched series of visceral spaces. The molecular structure of the hemoglobin of the blood is unique in the presence of vanadium instead of iron.

There is no vestige of a notochord in the adult, but the tadpole larva possesses a well-developed notochord in the tail (Fig. 2.19). Furthermore the larva possesses a hollow tubular nerve cord in the tail. This nerve cord extends forward to a hollow *brain* vesicle, containing a *statocyst,* lying just back of the mouth. The notochord disappears and the central nervous system, in transformation to the adult, is reduced to a solid ganglion. In the larva the anterior end of the body is occupied by an *adhesive gland,* by means of which the animal eventually becomes attached to some object. The mouth is on the dorsal surface just back of the adhesive gland and leads into a small *pharynx,* pierced by one or two pairs of slits,

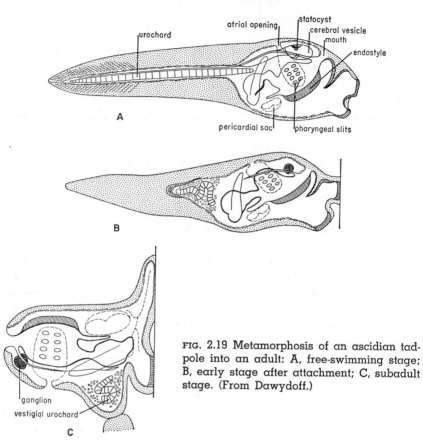

FIG. 2.19 Metamorphosis of an ascidian tadpole into an adult: A, free-swimming stage; B, early stage after attachment; C, subadult stage. (From Dawydoff.)

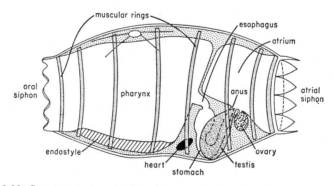

FIG. 2.20 Structure of a thaliacean urochordate, schematized. (From Dawydoff.)

thence into a short *stomach-intestine* opening onto the posterior dorsal surface at the *anus*. A middorsal ectodermal invagination between anus and mouth is the *atrium*, consisting simply of a forked bag straddling the pharynx. As the animal becomes sessile, the area between mouth and adhesive gland grows disproportionately and rapidly, resulting in a rotation of the mouth to a position opposite the attachment. The tail likewise rotates ventrally toward the base, but rapidly decreases in size and eventually disappears completely. The atrium grows inward, greatly enlarging to assume the adult size and engulfing the anus in the process.

The animals are capable of reproduction by *budding* as well as by sexual devices. Budded progeny may remain attached to their parents, forming colonies of varied shape.

THE THALIACEA. The members of this class are much like the ascidians (Fig. 2.20) except (1) the opaque tunic is absent, the body wall being almost perfectly transparent; (2) the body is barrel-shaped and with a straight axis, the mouth anterior, and the anus and atriopore posterior; (3) the body wall in most species is encircled by six to ten muscular bands by means of which the body is periodically compressed, squirting water out the rear and propelling the body forward; and (4) reproduction is more frequently accomplished by asexual means. Astonishing variations occur in different species in mode of life history. Sexual reproduction does occur, and the animals are monecious as in the ascidians. The sexually produced larva is much like that of other urochordates.

THE APPENDICULARIA. These are small, free-swimming creatures having only one pair of pharyngeal slits, an elongate tail, and an internal structure much like that of the tadpoles of other urochordates (Figs. 2.21, 2.22). Their most conspicuous peculiarity is the secretion, chiefly by the tail, of a rather expansive, thaliacealike tunic, through which a narrow water duct passes. The organism is situated beside the water duct. On occasion the animal leaves the test, swims about freely for a time, and then secretes another encasement. In the encased state, of course, the animal's movements are completely passive.

The members of this class are generally interpreted as derivatives

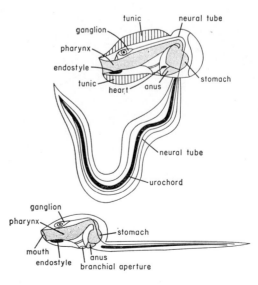

FIG. 2.21 Structure of an appendicularian urochordate, schematized. (From Lohmann.)

from either the Thaliacea or Ascidiacea. Having evolved chiefly by progressive delay in transformation from the larval stage, the eventual result is the retention of the larval form throughout life, although the gonads mature without delay. This is an example of neoteny (a trend toward reproduction in a progressively more larval state).

Prechordates

Phyla Related to Chordates. Two phyla seem especially closely related to chordates, primarily because of the occurrence in one of them, the

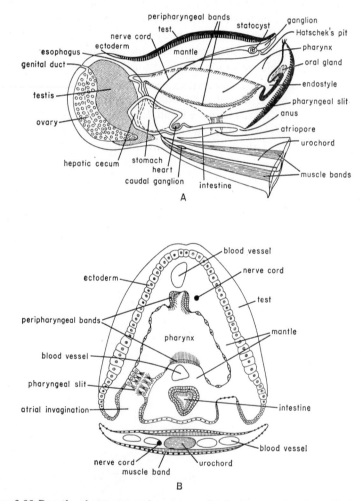

FIG. 2.22 Details of structure of an appendicularian urochordate. A, sagittal section, tail not shown in its entirety; B, cross section at level of atriopore. (From Herdman.)

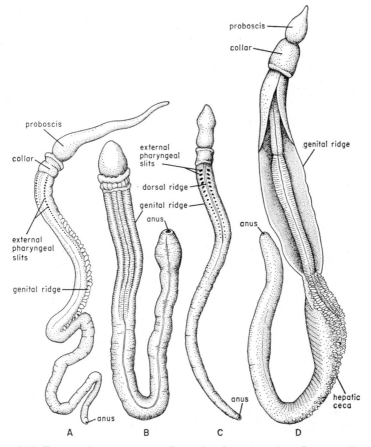

FIG. 2.23 Types of enteropneust hemichordates, in dorsal view. (From Dawydoff.)

Hemichordata, of pharyngeal slits, known otherwise only in chordates. The other phylum, the *Brachiata* or *Pogonophora,* is apparently a direct derivative of the Hemichordata. Many texts include one or both groups in the phylum Chordata.

The Hemichordates. Two classes of the phylum Hemichordata are recognized: the *Enteropneusta* of some 12 genera and 60 species, and the *Pterobranchia* of 3 genera and 20 species. The Enteropneusta are the best known, the genera *Balanoglossus* and *Saccoglossus* most frequently being used as examples of the subphylum. All members of the Enteropneusta are rather similar in appearance (Fig. 2.23).

THE ENTEROPNEUSTA. In *Balanoglossus* the body is elongate and wormlike, with three regions clearly differentiated: a large anterior *proboscis* attached by a narrow stalk to a short *collar,* followed by the very elongate trunk. The proboscis is an expansible organ serving solely as an aid in burrowing; it is inflated by intake of water through a basal *water pore,* through which the fluid is ejected in deflation.

No so-called "vital" organs occur in the proboscis (except very near its base, at the collar), which is composed chiefly of an areolate muscularized stroma surrounding a space (celomic) into which water may readily filter (Fig. 2.24).

The collar is also an expansible structure, with its own separate water pores; but unlike the proboscis, it houses a variety of vital organs. In burrowing, the collar functions with the proboscis, the two alternating in expanding and deflating. The collar, when expanded, holds the body firmly in position while the proboscis is extended and subsequently expanded; then the collar deflates and the whole body is pulled forward as much as possible; the collar again anchors the body, thus permitting the proboscis to be pushed forward to a new position. This manner of locomotion is similar to that of earthworms.

The proboscis is attached at the dorsal inner margin of the collar, which ventrally encircles a large *mouth;* the mouth leads into a *buccal cavity* occupying the interior of the collar ring. The buccal cavity is continuous with the *pharynx-esophagus* portion of the alimentary tract, which is, in turn, continuous with the *stomach intestine.* The stomach intestine extends the full length of the remainder of the trunk, ending at the terminal *anus.* Contrary to all chordates at least at some stage in their life history, there is no postanal tail. The trunk itself, not shown in its entirety in Fig. 2.23, is proportionately longer than in chordates.

The pharynx esophagus is constructed in a unique manner. The gut, for a short distance posterior to the buccal cavity, is constricted along its length so as to form two narrowly connected tubes, one above the other. The dorsal tube, the *pharynx,* is continuous by a narrow ventral slit throughout its length with the ventral tube, the *esophagus* (Fig. 2.25). The pharynx-esophagus region may be very short, only five or six times the length of the collar, or half the length (or more) of the trunk. Muck, sand,

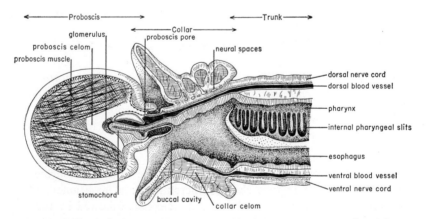

FIG. 2.24 Sagittal section of anterior end of an enteropneust hemichordate. (From Dawydoff.)

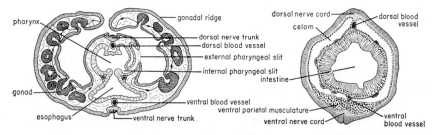

FIG. 2.25 (*Left*) Cross section of an enteropneust hemichordate at level of pharynx and esophagus. (From Dawydoff.)

FIG. 2.26 (*Right*) Cross section of an enteropneust hemichordate at level of intestine. (From Dawydoff.)

and water entering at the mouth (the worms are said literally to "eat" their way through the ocean floor) are sorted in the pharynx esophagus, the water passing into the pharynx, the heavier particles into the esophagus. The solid matter passes posteriorly into the stomach. The water passes through a large number (up to 700 pairs) of tiny, curious, U-shaped, *internal pharyngeal slits;* thence it goes into pharyngeal pouches of which there is one per slit; and then it passes to the exterior through single *external pharyngeal slits* (or pharyngeal pores), which can be seen along the dorsolateral surface of a middorsal ridge above the pharynx. The most important pharyngeal function undoubtedly is not respiration (it is therefore not a "gill" structure), but simply extraction of food from water. Respiration does take place in the pharynx, but it also occurs generally over the surface of the body; the pharyngeal respiratory function is therefore not essential, whereas the alimentary function is.

The stomach intestine is a straight tube with no modification (Fig. 2.26) except for a group of diverticula, called *hepatic ceca,* that occur in an area perhaps a third of the distance from the pharynx esophagus to the anus.*

The circulatory system (Fig. 2.27) consists primarily of a dorsal and a ventral longitudinal vessel; the two are connected with each other by a ringlike vessel in the collar. A series of sinuses, which may or may not be contractile, communicate with the collar. The direction of blood flow is forward in the dorsal vessel, backward in the ventral vessel. The basic plan is somewhat like that of the annelid.

The *celom* is well developed, being subdivided into a single proboscis cavity, which possesses an opening to the exterior (the water pore); a pair

---

* Many authors use the term "esophagus" for the postpharyngeal gut anterior to the hepatic pouches, and the term "intestine" for only the part following the pouches. The part called "esophagus" in this text is commonly termed the "alimentary pharynx," above which lies the "respiratory pharynx." Such terminology seems anomalous. The "esophagus" of most other authors is more properly comparable to a midgut or stomach of other chordates.

of collar cavities, each with its opening to the exterior; and a pair of elongate cavities in the trunk, neither opening to the exterior.

The reproductive system consists of a segmental series of *gonads* along much of the length of either side of the body; these form a pair of very conspicuous continuous flaps or ridges. They open to the exterior segmentally by minute pores. The sexes are separate (*diecious*), and fertilization takes place free of the body, in the surrounding water.

The skeletal system consists chiefly of a series of bars strengthening the pharynx, and a support (the *stomocord*) in the proboscis thought to represent the notochord although the two are not the same. The stomochord is a thick-walled evagination extruding forward into the base of the proboscis from the dorsal wall of the buccal cavity. It is regarded as a homolog of the notochord, despite its small size, because its cells are vacuolated just as in typical notochord tissue (which is stiffened chiefly by the turgidity of its component cells), and because it forms embryonically as a hollow

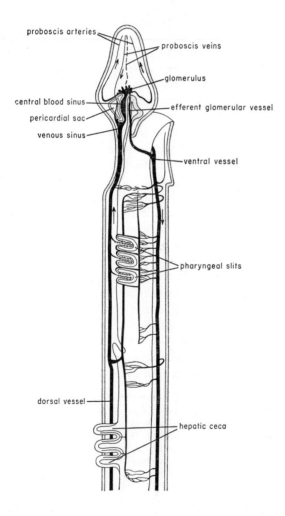

FIG. 2.27 Circulatory system of an enteropneust hemichordate. (From Dawydoff.)

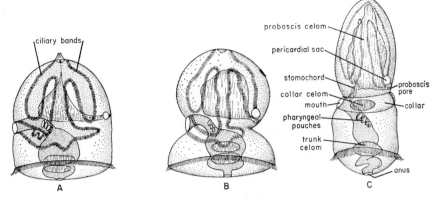

FIG. 2.28 Successive early stages, A-C, in transformation of a tornaria into an adult enteropneust. (From Dawydoff.)

diverticulum from the gut just as in protochordates. The notochord forms in vertebrates as a solid structure of mesodermal origin, or even independent of all the three primary germ layers; there seems to be no question, however, that in earliest chordates the notochord was a hollow evagination from the gut.

The nervous system consists of a nerve net which is thickened to form a cordlike structure along the midventral and middorsal lines. The anterior end of the dorsal cord is hollow, and scattered spaces occur along the length of the dorsal cord.

The developmental stages involve a free-swimming, ciliated, bell-shaped larva (*"tornaria,"* Fig. 2.28), which bears a most remarkable similarity to the "auricularia" larva of the echinoderm sea cucumbers.

THE PTEROBRANCHIA. These are small, sessile, colonial (Fig. 2.29) animals with a proboscis, collar, and short trunk, the latter attached to the substrate by a lateral stalk. The alimentary tract is U shaped, the anus situated not far from the mouth. To the collar are attached ciliated tentacles by which food is captured (Fig. 2.30); there is a considerable similarity between this structure and the "lophophore" feeding device of the phyla Phoronida, Brachiopoda, Bryozoa, and others. A single pair of pharyngeal clefts exists in two genera, where they serve as a washing device to remove microorganisms caught by the tentacles; no pharyngeal slits whatsoever occur in the other genus. The rudimentary notochord (stomocord) is essentially the same as in the Enteropneusta, but there is no cavity within the central nervous system. Reproduction by both budding (from the stalk) and sexual means occurs. The larva is somewhat similar to that of the Echinodermata and the Enteropneusta, but more like those of the lophophore phyla. The celom and circulatory system are much as in other members of the subphylum.

The Brachiates. This is a poorly known phylum of 18 species living in tubes secreted on the ocean floor at the incredible depths of 3 to 5 miles.

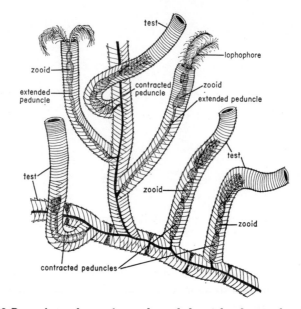

FIG. 2.29 Part of a colony of pterobranch hemichordates, showing individuals in various stages of emergence from the test. (From Dawydoff.)

Few examples have been collected and their anatomy has never been adequately studied. They appear to have no pharyngeal slits, but the internal anatomy is sketchily known. No mouth, anus, and alimentary tract have been seen, although they no doubt exist. The trunk is occupied solely by the reproductive organs and their accessories. The adhesive glands are unique, and are so distributed as to give a false impression of segmentation in certain areas of the body. The general organization is hemichordate in character (Fig. 2.31), bearing a considerable resemblance to that of the Enteropneusta. The tentacular lophophore also resembles that of

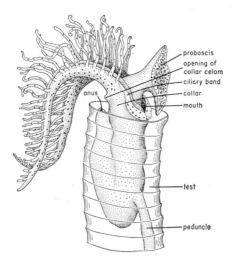

FIG. 2.30 Rhabdopleura, a genus of pterobranch hemichordates. (From Dawydoff.)

the Phoronida and is unique in providing not only for capture of micro-organismic food but also for its digestion; if this is true, the brachiates are among the very few complex metazoans (for example, scorpions) having external digestion. They are seemingly unique in their external absorption of digestive products, for even the scorpion swallows the externally digested food which is absorbed by the digestive tract.

Phylogeny of the Chordate Subphyla

Origin of Chordates. Animals now living are unfortunately so modified and so far removed from significantly remote common ancestral structure that no conclusive picture has, up to the present time, been gleaned from them of the pattern of evolution of the protochordates and verte-brates. Some evidence can be found supporting a variety of views, but the weighing of one theory as final is patently unjustified. Were fossils of ancient forms of prechordates more generally preserved, much uncertainty could be eliminated. Soft bodied as they seemingly were, they were rarely fossil-ized, since ordinarily only hard parts, notably bone, are preserved.

The perpetual argument about chordate phylogeny by serious students who continually sift and extract more possible bits of evidence from the structure and habits of living species has, however, resulted in the past 50 years in a marked restriction of the limits of acceptable inference. For one, serological tests have proved a close relationship of echinoderms, chordates, and hemichordates. Biochemical tests have shown a remarkable similarity of the phosphagens, essential for muscle contraction, between these groups. Creatin and arginin are amino acids found in the very

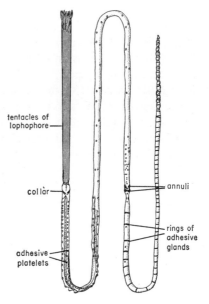

FIG. 2.31 A pogonophoran in ventral view. Regions of the body are (1) the lophophore region, (2) collar, and (3) trunk. The trunk region is subdivided in this particular genus (Lamellisabella) into two regions (preannular and post-annular) of subequal length, separated from each other by a pair of enlarged, adhesive annuli. (From Ivanov.)

tentacles of lophophore

collar

annuli

rings of adhesive glands

adhesive platelets

labile phosphates, the phosphagens, essential for muscle contraction. Phosphocreatin and phosphoarginin are the two forms occurring in animal muscle tissue. Curiously, only creatin is present in the phosphagens of all vertebrates and cephalochordates, and only arginin in all invertebrates except the hemichordates and echinoderms, which have both creatin and arginin. The same phyla (chordates, hemichordates, echinoderms) are also similar in having (1) a bilaterally symmetrical *dipleurula* larva in primitive types; (2) a mesodermal skeleton; (3) a *regulation* egg with no precise pattern of distribution of cellular components in the undivided fertile egg, so that in subsequent division several complete individuals may form from the one egg; (4) *indeterminate* cleavage whereby the first division of the fertilized egg may take place between a number of parts of the egg, and need not occur precisely in one plane and only that plane; (5) the mesoderm formed by evagination from the primitive gut; (6) the *paired* trunk celoms forming in the mesodermal outpouching as an *enterocele,* in primitive types; (7) basically five celomic cavities; (8) gastrulation by invagination; (9) a nervous system formed from a diffuse sheet or nerve net; and (10) location of the blastopore at the posterior end of the body, forming or lying close to the anus. The hemichordates are obviously closely related to chordates through possession of pharyngeal clefts, a stomochord and scattered cavities in the dorsal nerve cord. All of these characters form the basis for separation of one of the three great divisions (subkingdoms) of multicellular animals, the *Deuterostomia,* to which not only the echinoderms and chordates belong, but also the few small phyla of Hemichordata, Brachiata, Bryozoa, Chaetognatha, Brachiopoda, and Phoronida.

A second subkingdom, the *Archeostomia,* is characterized by having (1) little serological similarity to chordates and echinoderms; (2) arginin only in muscle phosphagens; (3) a radially symmetrical *trochophore* larva; (4) an ectodermal skeleton; (5) a *mosaic* egg with a precise pattern of distribution of cellular components so that only one individual can result from subsequent division of the egg; (6) *determinate* cleavage, each division occurring in specific planes; (7) the mesoderm formed by splitting from other tissues; (8) the paired trunk celoms forming as a *schizocele,* as the mesoderm splits to form a central cavity on each side; (9) a varied arrangement and number of celoms; (10) *invasive* gastrulation by an internal rearrangement, the gastrular cavity secondarily opening to the exterior; (11) a nervous system consisting of ganglionated cords; and (12) location of the blastopore at the anterior end of the body, forming or lying close to the mouth. The most significant of all the differences between the Archeostomia and Deuterostomia involves orientation of the blastopore, which lies near or forms the mouth in the former, the anus in the latter. The Archeostomia includes all the phyla with separate mouth and anus, except for those in the Deuterostomia: Acanthocephala, Annelida, Arthropoda, Aschelminthes, Echiuroidea, Endoprocta, Mollusca, Nemathelminthes, and Sipunculoidea.

A third subkingdom is the Proctostomia, in which a single opening of the alimentary tract serves as both the mouth and anus. The Cnidaria (coelenterates), Ctenophora, Platyhelminthes, and Porifera belong to this group. The Protozoa and Mesozoa may be regarded as constituting a separate subkingdom, the *Astomia*. The Proctostomia and Archeostomia are collectively referred to as the *Proterostomia*.

The conclusion that the echinoderms and chordates had a common ancestry is inescapable. But what was the common ancestor like? Little agreement on this point has as yet been attained. It does seem likely, however, that the deuterostomian line of evolution began at an extremely remote time, with animals having a more or less spherical body and a blind gut like coelenterates, with no anus. Certainly no sudden or even gradual (were such a thing possible) shift in antero-posterior orientation of an animal already with anus, mouth, and cephalic end would occur to produce the deuterostomian condition from an established archeostomian one. As soon as an animal so evolves that it possesses an elongate body, with one end directed forward to seek food and test its environment, the evolutionary door may be considered closed to a reversal of axis orientation.

In departing from a coelenteratelike stage, apparently neither archeostome nor deuterostome ancestors had established an anterior or posterior end. When the gut became a continuous tube, in each line of evolution, the axial orientation, with concomitant cephalization and elongation of body, was free to evolve in either direction. Solely upon that axial orientation, presumably, was the functional fate of the former mouth anus (embryonic blastopore) determined. In the Deuterostomia the orientation evolved so that the blastopore derivative was directed posteriorly, thus retaining only anal functions, as at the same time the new opening at the opposite end of the alimentary tract served as the mouth. Exactly the reverse occurred in the Archeostome line of evolution. There is no indication that either of these two groups was derived from the other; there is every reason to believe that they are of common origin, from some proctostome group (see Fig. 2.32).

The Pterobranchia are thus regarded as the most primitive of all living direct prevertebrates because of (1) their simple structure (few pharyngeal slits, no elaborate systems); (2) their similarity to most other deuterostomians (save the echinoderms and most chordates) in having sessile habits and a lophophorelike accessory feeding organ; (3) possession of at least two of the most fundamental unique chordate characteristics, or of a homolog thereof (pharyngeal slits, notochord); and (4) possession of a body form from which chordate animals may most easily have been differentiated.

Curiously enough, fixation of common ancestry of archeostomes and deuterostomes does not establish whether the common ancestor (1) was a sessile animal, developing at first a U-shaped body axis which subsequently straightened as the animals became free swimming, or (2) was, from the first, a free-swimming animal. Either would be a reasonable possibility. Very likely both are true, as either or both of the deuterostome and archeostome groups may have evolved from two or more proctostome groups (this is *polyphyly*).

Whatever the ancestral form of archeostomes, so many protochordates and chordatelike invertebrates (like the Phoronida, Bryozoa, Pterobranchia, Ascidia) are sessile and with a U-shaped body axis that modern investigators are leaning more and more to the view that from such forms at least the chordates evolved. The presence of the deuterostomian orientation even in *radially* symmetrical animals like the echinoderms can best be explained as a by-product of at least a brief history as a sessile animal with a U-shaped body axis. That they evolved from free-swimming, radially symmetrical animals remains a possibility. Further investigation of the problem will, however, be necessary before a definite conclusion is reached.

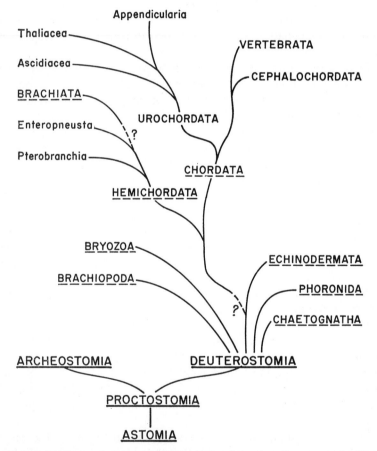

FIG. 2.32 Phylogeny of the animal subkingdoms (continuous underline), deuterostome phyla (dashed underline), chordate subphyla (capitals, not underlined), and the protochordate classes.

At any rate, present evidence makes wholly untenable all of the ingenious theories receiving much attention in the past that chordates have evolved from annelids, arthropods, or arachnids.

Origin of the Vertebrates. Doubtful as is the ancestry of the phylum Chordata, the origin of the most successful and largest subphylum (vertebrates) is little better established. Both considerations bog down on whether the end products are somewhat neotenous, free-swimming derivatives of formerly sessile animals, or have continuously evolved as active, free-swimming animals. The answer in neither case is clear.

A possible phylogeny of vertebrates, and of the classes of protochordates, is shown in Figure 2.32. The biggest puzzle is the curious specializations of Amphioxus that do not occur in vertebrates and cannot well be primitive. The atrium and solenocyte excretory organs are particularly disturbing. One theory envisions the cephalochordates as degenerate vertebrates from which the urochordates evolved: almost the reverse of the pattern shown in Figure 2.32. Regardless of direction, the similarities of vertebrates and cephalochordates are too numerous to be passed off as parallelisms; the relationship is universally accepted as very close. Especially significant are the complete notochord, neural tube, complete myotomic segmentation, hepatic portal system, pharyngeal blood-vessel arrangement, cardinal veins, metapleural folds, endostyle, segmental gonads, and the separate dorsal and ventral roots of the spinal nerves of both primitive vertebrates and cephalochordates.

QUESTIONS

1. Distinguish what is meant by "pharyngeal clefts" and "gill clefts."
2. What characteristics of chordates may be said to be both universal and unique? Name one other feature that is very nearly universal and very nearly unique.
3. Name the basic, general characteristics shared by the Chordata with other phyla.
4. On what bases (three good ones, at least) might the hemichordates be included in the phylum Chordata? On what bases (four good ones at least) could they be excluded?
5. Which of the two hemichordate classes would appear to be the most primitive? Why (four good reasons, at least)?
6. How do the two hemichordate classes differ? How are they alike?
7. What is the significance of tornaria in chordate phylogeny?
8. Explain how food is captured and reaches the intestine, and how the water is eliminated, in an ascidian. Compare and contrast with the procedure in the Enteropneusta and Cephalochordata.
9. How do the Hemichordata and the two protochordate subphyla differ in (a) nature of gonads possessed by each individual, (b) method of reproduction, (c) number of living species known, (d) development of the three primary chordate characteristics?

10. Name 15 features of the urochordates, or of any class of urochordates, not duplicated in any other chordate subphylum.

11. How do the three urochordate classes differ? How are they alike?

12. By what reasoning can the annelids, arthropods and arachnids be conclusively eliminated as possible ancestors of chordates?

13. What cephalochordate features may be regarded as vertebratelike? Which ones are specialized?

14. What possible role has neoteny played in the evolution of the chordate subphyla?

15. Draw a phylogenetic tree showing the differentiation and relationships of the subphylum Vertebrata and of all the subphyla and classes of protochordates.

16. Differentiate and draw a phylogenetic tree of the subkingdoms of the animal kingdom.

17. Name the several phyla most closely related to the chordates.

18. Define the following words, and where appropriate state occurrence or list examples:

amphioxus	determinate cleavage	Phoronida
Appendicularia	Deuterostomia	phosphocreatin
Archeostomia	diecious	phosphoarginin
Ascidiacea	dipleurula	Pogonophora
Astomia	Echinodermata	Proctostomia
Asymmetron	endostyle	Proterostomia
atriopore	enterocele	Pterobranchia
atrium	Enteropneusta	regulation egg
auricularia	epibranchial	rostrum
Balanoglossus	gill	Saccoglossus
bilateral symmetry	Hatschek's groove	schizocele
blastopore	Hatschek's pit	sessile
Brachiata	Hemichordata	solenocytes
Brachiopoda	indeterminate cleavage	stomocord
Branchiostoma	lophophore	Thaliacea
Bryozoa	mantle	tornaria
buccal cavity	metapleural folds	triploblastic
celom	monecious	trochophore
Cephalochordata	mosaic egg	tunicin
Chaetognatha	neoteny	Urochordata
Chordata	nephridia	velum
cirri	notochord	Vertebrata
	pharynx	

3

VERTEBRATE
CLASSIFICATION

THE SUBPHYLUM Vertebrata is distinguished from other chordates by a large number of features. The following are among the more prominent: (1) a *vertebral column* (very rudimentary in primitive species): (2) a *cranium;* (3) a true *skin,* consisting of both epidermis and dermis, each several layers of cells in thickness; (4) a ventral *chambered heart;* (5) *erythrocytes* (with a few exceptions); (6) a pair of kidneys derived from *celomoducts;* (7) a largely solid *liver;* (8) a *pancreas* (not always grossly evident); (9) *a pharynx whose function is chiefly respiratory;* (10) egg *cleavage unequal* (secondarily equal in some); (11) a number of identifiable *endocrine organs;* (12) *eyes* (secondarily absent in some); (13) *olfactory organs,* generally paired; (14) one to three *semicircular canals* as parts of the inner ear; (15) a *brain of three primary vesicles,* usually subdivided; and (16) a well-defined *autonomic nervous system.* Some of these features occur in nonchordate phyla, but not in the protochordates.

Perspective of Classification. Perhaps a million species of animals now are known to exist on earth. About 6 percent of these are vertebrates, which have received a disproportionately large share of the attention— perhaps 35 percent—of taxonomists. Yet even a superficial acquaintance with the history of vertebrate classification reveals that stability of nomenclature has never existed and does not now exist even for this, the most thoroughly studied group of all. An evolution has been evident in classification as well as in the animals themselves. Since science so often attains positive establishment of conclusions, acceptance of taxonomy as a science has been questioned.

As science is defined, taxonomy is a science. It is based upon facts, and requires an open, inquiring mind, as does any other science. Two factors work toward the unique instability of conclusions characteristic of taxonomy: (1) the unfavorable ratio of known to unknown facts; and (2) the complete continuity through time of life and forms of life.

Classification is basically a grouping of like and a separating of unlike individuals and groups of individuals in accordance with certain similarities and dissimilarities. But it is more than that. *Biological classification is a grouping of organisms that reflects relationship as well as degrees of difference and similarity.* We know that Aristotle's classification, in which all vertebrates that fly were allocated to one group and all that live in the water to another, is not a *natural* classification, reflecting relationship; it is *artificial*. By his classification whales and fishes were grouped together, as were bats and birds, whereas bats and whales are more closely related to each other than either is to the other groups. Thus in given groups of animals, some characters are plastic while others are more or less fixed. Unfortunately characters that are constant in one group may be flexible in another; they faithfully reflect relationship in one and mask it in the other. Not only is there a virtually limitless number of facts involved in taxonomy, but the significance of each fact varies greatly.

Scientific conclusions constitute a whole spectrum of stability, from mere hypotheses at one extreme to established laws at the other. The greater the proportion of known facts to unknown ones, the more stable can be the conclusion. Unfortunately only a small proportion of the existent facts relevant to the taxonomy of a given group are usually known. As new facts are unearthed at least certain concepts of relationship will inevitably be altered to a greater or lesser degree. It is a necessary evil, if a scientific attitude is maintained, that the schemes of classification should not remain static, although as the ratio of known to unknown grows more favorable, the degree of stability increases. In details and to a progressively lesser degree in successively higher categories above the species the classification of organisms may be expected always to change as new data are accumulated, but less as the ratio of the known to the unknown increases.

One of the most depressing aspects of taxonomy as a science, however, is the fact that even if all relevant data were known, a universally acceptable system of classification, based on present criteria, would not necessarily be a logical sequel. The system of classification we now have is based largely upon existing types and widely scattered fossil representatives. The morphological gaps created by (1) extinction of various types, (2) incompleteness of our knowledge of types that formerly existed and even that now exist, and (3) continued divergence of isolated population lines, all necessitate the coincidence of limits of supraspecific categories with those gaps. Given the incompleteness of the record, this pragmatic mode of classifi-

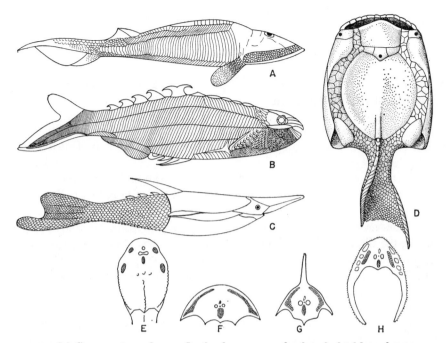

FIG. 3.1 Some ostracoderms. In the lower row the head shields only are shown. Genera and orders: A, Hemicyclaspis, Osteostraci; B, Birkenia, Anaspida; C, Anglaspis, Heterostraci; D, Drepanaspis, Heterostraci (dorsal view); E, Cephalaspis; F, Benneviaspis; G, Boreaspis; H, Sclerodus (E-H all of order Anaspida). (From Romer.)

cation is the only sensibly practical solution to the problem of pigeonholing organism populations that now are different, but that in the sliding scale of time blend perfectly with each other. Were all pertinent data suddenly to become available, the shift from the criterion of "gapsize" to some other criterion not as yet determined would probably be chaotic. This probability has given rise to the erroneous thought that accumulation of all pertinent data would really be a hindrance rather than an aid to classification. Under our present "gapsize" system it would indeed be a hindrance, but it is certainly to be expected that little by little, as data become available, a gradual shift to other criteria will occur. Certainly had all data pertinent to taxonomy been available at the outset, we would undoubtedly long since have devised some arbitrary criterion suitable for and resulting in a classification of organisms as permanently satisfactory as the periodic chart of the elements. There is no reason to assume that these criteria cannot and will not be devised in due normal growth of our knowledge and interpretation of the facts pertaining to organic evolution and classification.

The following classification is therefore not given as, and should not be assumed to represent, a finality. It is the product, as it stands today, of the most considered opinions of the best-qualified students in vertebrate taxonomy, adapted to use at the particular level of concern to beginning students of vertebrate anatomy. Many additional categories could be recognized between suborders and subphyla, but those here listed are the ones regarded as of greatest importance in the present context.

Subphylum Vertebrata

Class Agnatha. The most primitive of all known vertebrates. Pharyngeal skeleton not supporting mouth (no true jaws). No paired fins. Two subclasses.

SUBCLASS OSTRACODERMI. Most species with a heavy bony (dermal) armor varying from large plates to small scales (Fig. 3.1). Presumably marine. Fossils only, Ordovician into Devonian.

SUBCLASS CYCLOSTOMATA. The most primitive living vertebrates, but not in the direct line of evolution of land vertebrates. No bony integumentary armor whatsoever. Known only in the Quaternary, but of course existent from a time at least as early as the Devonian to the present.

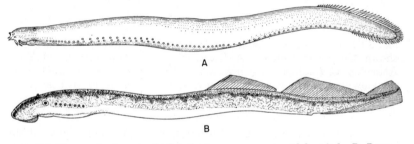

FIG. 3.2 The cyclostomes. A, Bdellostoma, a myxinoid hagfish; B, Petromyzon, a lamprey. (From Romer.)

Order Myxinoidea. Hagfishes (Fig. 3.2A). No buccal funnel. Internal scavengers on fish. Nasohypophyseal duct connected with pharynx. Marine only.

Order Petromyzontia. Lampreys (Fig. 3.2B). A well-developed buccal funnel. Intermittent external parasites on fish, or nonparasitic. Nasohypophyseal duct blind internally. Marine and fresh water.

Class Placodermi. Derivatives of the ostracoderms (Fig. 3.3), with certain members on the direct line of evolution of land vertebrates. An anterior pharyngeal bar (mandibular arch) modified to support mouth (as jaws), but all other bars unmodified, supporting gill structures. Paired *fins* (*ichthyopterygia*) or derivatives thereof (limbs) present in this and all following classes. Presumably marine, except perhaps later members. Fossils only, Silurian into Permian.

Class Chondrichthyes. No endoskeletal bone whatsoever. Derivatives of the placoderms, not on line of evolution of land vertebrates. Jaws present,

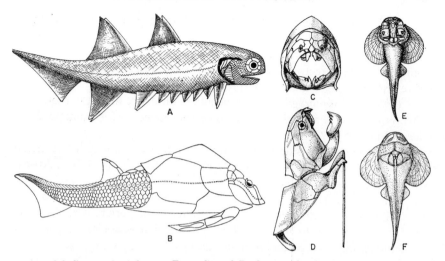

FIG. 3.3 Some placoderms. Figs. C and D show only the cranial and anterior trunk armor. Genera and orders: A, Climatius, Acanthodii; B, Pterichthyodes, Antiarchi; C, D, Dinichthys, Arthrodira; E, F, dorsal and ventral views, respectively, Gemuendina, Stegoselachii. (From Romer.)

and in addition the second (hyoid) pharyngeal bar lacking a gill function, at least on its anterior surface, and modified as a tongue and jaw support (true in this and in all following classes). Marine with a few tropical exceptions. Devonian to present.

SUBCLASS ELASMOBRANCHII. External gill slits not concealed. Sharks, skates, rays (Fig. 3.4A). Unlike rays, skates are spiny bodied and have a blunt tail with dorsal fins.

SUBCLASS HOLOCEPHALI. Gill slits covered by a fleshy operculum. Rat-tailed fishes (Fig. 3.4B).

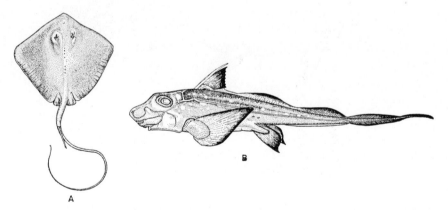

FIG. 3.4 Some chondrichthyans. A, Dasybatus, a ray; B, Chimaera, a rat-tailed fish. (From Romer.)

Class Osteichthyes. Endoskeleton at least partly bony. Primarily freshwater, secondarily marine.

SUBCLASS CHOANICHTHYES. Derivatives of the placoderms, certain members on the direct line of evolution of land vertebrates. Internal nares (rare exceptions). Devonian to present.

Order Crossopterygii. Certain members on direct line of evolution of land vertebrates. A spiracle. Two living marine genera (for example, *Latimeria,* Fig. 3.5A).

Order Dipnoi. A side branch in evolution. No spiracle. Three living fresh-water genera (lungfishes), one each in Australia (Fig. 3.5B), Africa, South America.

SUBCLASS ACTINOPTERI. Derivatives of either the placoderms or ancient Choanichthyes, not on line of evolution of land vertebrates. No internal nares. Devonian to present. Some 30,000 living species—the largest vertebrate group. Three major living groups for simplicity here cited as superorders.

Superorder Chondrostei. Relatively little endoskeletal bone. Fresh-water inhabitants. Sturgeons, paddlefish, and two African genera (Fig. 3.6) of armored fishes (*Polypterus, Calamoichthys*).

Superorder Holostei. Moderate amount of endoskeletal bone. Fresh-water inhabitants. Bowfin (freshwater dogfish, *Amia*), gars (Fig. 3.7).

Superorder Teleostei. Most of endoskeleton bony. Freshwater and marine. All fish other than those listed above. This is by far the largest group of fishes.

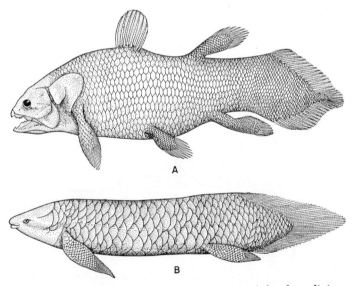

FIG. 3.5 Some choanichthyans. A, Latimeria, one of the three living genera of crossopterygians; B, Epiceratodus, a living dipnoan of Australia. (From Romer.)

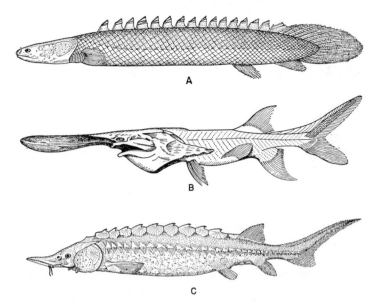

FIG. 3.6 Some chondrosteans. A, Polypterus, an African genus; B, Polyodon, the spoonbill or paddlefish of North America; C, Scaphirhynchus, the sturgeon of North America. (From Romer and Newman.)

Class Amphibia. Derivatives of crossopterygians. Paired fins modified as land *limbs* (*cheiropterygia*) in this and following classes; metamorphosis present in most species (that is, transformation from aquatic to terrestrial stages occurring in free-living animals); no epidermal scales. Devonian to

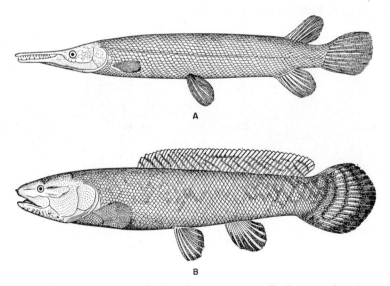

FIG. 3.7 Some holosteans. A, Lepidosteus, a gar; B, Amia, a bowfin or freshwater dogfish. (From Rand.)

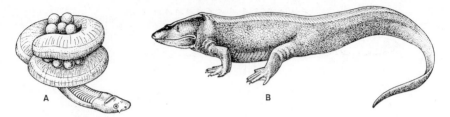

FIG. 3.8 Some amphibians. A, Ichthyophis, a member of the Apoda; B, Diplovertebron, a labyrinthodont. (From Romer and Newman.)

present. Three living orders, many fossil orders. Two subclasses and two superorders are commonly recognized; for the sake of simplicity only one of these groups, ancestrally important, is listed here. All living species with four or fewer fingers.

Order Anura. Frogs, toads. Adults lacking a tail (a vestige, not prominent, in one family). Four limbs, rear pair usually considerably larger than others; ear adapted for reception of airborne sound waves, with few exceptions; vocal cords.

Order Caudata. Salamanders. A prominent tail. One or two pairs of limbs, rear pair usually not much if any larger than anterior pair; incapable of detecting airborne sound waves; no vocal cords.

Order Apoda. Caecilians. Tail very short, anus almost terminal. No limbs. Wormlike, ringed, incapable of detecting airborne sound waves; no vocal cords. (Fig. 3.8A.)

SUPERORDER LABYRINTHODONTIA. From this group, reptiles apparently evolved. Fossils only (Fig. 3.8B).

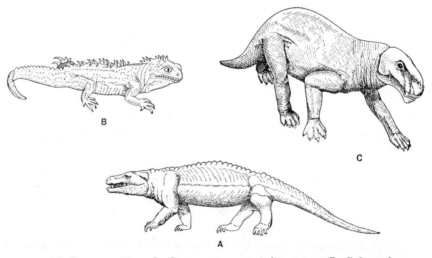

FIG. 3.9 Some reptiles. A, Seymouria, a cotylosaurian; B, Sphenodon; C, a mammallike, therapsid reptile. (From Gregory, Adams, and Eddy.)

Class Reptilia. Derivatives of the Labyrinthodontia. No metamorphosis in this and subsequent classes, recapitulation of ancestral aquatic morphology occurring embryonically. Epidermal scales present. No feathers or hair. Pennsylvanian to present. About 6 subclasses and 16 orders. Four living orders are recognized. For the sake of simplicity we omit all except these four, and three fossil orders of special evolutionary significance.

Order Cotylosauria. Most primitive reptiles (Fig. 3.9A), derived from Labyrinthodontia, ancestral to all other reptilian groups, directly or indirectly. Fossils only.

Order Testudines. Turtles. A shell of carapace and plastron. A single copulatory organ.

Order Rhynchocephalia. A single, lizardlike genus now living: *Sphenodon* (common local name, tuatara; Fig. 3.9B). No copulatory organ.

Order Squamata. Lizards, snakes. Two copulatory organs. *Suborder Sauria,* lizards, with two or four bony arches in temporal region, halves of lower jaw firmly united, usually limbs present, movable eyelids usually present, ear opening usually present. *Suborder Serpentes,* snakes, with no arches in temporal region, halves of lower jaw not firmly united, no limbs, no movable eyelids, no ear opening.

Order Thecodontia. Fossil reptiles that gave rise to the class Aves.

Order Saurischia. Many dinosaurs, as *Brontosaurus, Tyrannosaurus.*

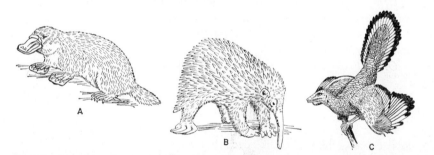

FIG. 3.10 Some mammals and birds. A, Ornithorhynchus, the duckbilled platypus. B, Zachyglossus, the spiny anteater. C, Archaeopteryx, an ancient bird. (From Newman, Adams and Eddy.)

Order Ornithischia. The rest of the dinosaurs; examples are *Triceratops, Stegosaurus.*

Order Crocodilia. Crocodiles, alligators, caimans, gavials. A single copulatory organ. No shell on body.

Order Therapsida. Advanced fossil reptiles which gave rise to mammals (Fig. 3.9C).

Class Aves. Birds. Feathers and epidermal scales. Jurassic to present. Some 25 or 30 orders are recognized. For the sake of simplicity we include here only the two subclasses commonly accepted.

SUBCLASS ARCHAEORNITHES. Fossils only. A long tail with feathers attached to either side along its length (Fig. 3.10C).

SUBCLASS NEORNITHES. A short tail from which feathers radiate.

Class Mammalia. Mammals. Mammary glands and hair present, as well as some epidermal scales in some species. Jurassic to present. Several subclasses, infraclasses and fossil orders are recognized. For the sake of simplicity we omit all except the common living orders and their essential higher categories.

SUBCLASS PROTOTHERIA. Egg laying. One order.

Order Monotremata. Duckbilled platypus (Fig. 3.10A), spiny anteater (Fig. 3.10B).

SUBCLASS THERIA. Live bearing. Four infraclasses, two fossil only.

INFRACLASS METATHERIA. Young born at extremely immature stage, completing development attached to nipples of mammary glands, in an abdominal pouch (marsupium); placenta rudimentary.

Order Marsupialia. Kangaroo, opossum, etc.

INFRACLASS EUTHERIA. Born relatively late; a well-developed placenta. No marsupial development and young born at a more mature stage than in preceding orders, but requiring mammary sustenance.

Order Insectivora. Primitive dentition, uterus, brain, skull. Moles, shrews, etc.

Order Chiroptera. A pair of wings between elongate fingers and body; bats.

Order Primates. Primitive or generalized in many respects, advanced in brain structure. Monkeys, apes, man, etc.

Order Carnivora. Dentition specialized for flesh eating. Cats, weasels, bears, dogs, wolverines, seals, etc.

Order Proboscidea. Incisors elongated as tusks. Elephants, mastodons, etc.

Order Perissodactyla. Odd-toed, hoofed mammals: horses, tapirs, rhinoceroses, etc.

Order Artiodactyla. Even-toed, hoofed mammals: pigs, hippopotamuses, camels, llamas, cattle, deer, etc.

Order Sirenia. Sea cows or manatees (Fig. 3.11A) with oarlike forelimbs, a caudal flipper.

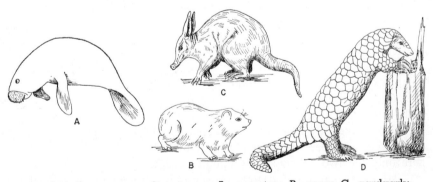

FIG. 3.11 Some mammalian types. A, manatee; B, cony; C, aardvark; D, scaly anteater. (From Kent, Weichert, Adams, and Eddy.)

Order Hyracoidea. Conies (Fig. 3.11B) with rodentlike body and hooflike claws.

Order Edentata. Toothless, or nearly so. Armadillos, sloths, furry anteaters.

Order Cetacea. Fishlike, a horizontal tail fin. Whales, porpoises, etc.

Order Tubulidentata. Burrowing anteater or aardvark (Fig. 3.11C) of Africa.

Order Pholidota. Scaly anteater (Fig. 3.11D), with large epidermal plates presumably evolved from matted hair.

Order Rodentia. One pair of gnawing incisors above and one pair below. Rats, gophers, beavers, squirrels, porcupines, ground hogs, etc.

Order Lagomorpha. Like rodents, but with a small incisor tooth back of each large upper front incisor. Hares, rabbits, etc.

Other Terms Used in Classification

In addition to the preceding "formal" taxonomic groups, we shall find a number of "informal" groupings to be of great convenience. In fact, most of the terms listed hereafter are recognized formally in more detailed classifications.

Amniotes and Anamniotes. The amniotes are the reptiles, birds, and mammals, so called because they possess an amnion, an extra-embryonic membrane essential to development of an egg outside of water. The anamniotes (all other classes) lack the amnion.

Agnathans and Gnathostomes. The cyclosomes and ostracoderms are agnathous, lacking "true" jaws. All other vertebrates are gnathostomous, having "true" jaws of pharyngeal arch origin.

Ectotherms and Endotherms. The mammals and birds are endotherms; all other classes are ectotherms. These terms refer to a body temperature that characteristically reflects external environmental temperatures more faithfully in the ectotherms, less faithfully (heightened more extensively by internal metabolic processes) in the endotherms. These terms have precisely the same *scope* as the formerly popular "poikilotherm" or "cold blooded" (in place of ectotherm), and "homoiotherm" (-homotherm) or "warm blooded" (in place of endotherm), but are more accurate in actual *meaning*. Poikilothermous means of variable temperature, but many fishes and some salamanders are incapable of withstanding deviations of more than a very few degrees from that to which they have become adapted. Furthermore, homoiotherms (of even temperature) are scarcely of constant temperature; mammals that hibernate experience a very marked seasonal fluctuation in body temperature. Equally inaccurate is the term "cold blooded" in reference to, for example, desert reptiles, which at times certainly get as warm as or warmer than the "warm-blooded" mammals or birds. Likewise some mammals become rather cold blooded in the stage of hibernation, although their temperature never drops as low as that of the environment.

Mammalian hibernation is obviously controlled or regulated by metabolism. On the contrary, in ectotherms in the inactive stage of overwintering as well as in all other stages the body temperature is almost exactly that of the environment, and is therefore not controlled or regulated by metabolism. In fact, some physiologists define hibernation solely as the inactive overwintering state characteristic of some mammals. In reality the term is well established in usage for the inactive overwintering state also of ectotherms. The distinction between the two types of hibernation is often and perhaps best expressed by reference to the mammalian type as *regulated hibernation,* that of ectotherms as *nonregulated hibernation.*

There is virtually no intrinsic control of temperature in living ectotherms. In almost every living ectotherm the body temperature is exactly the same, with two provisions, as that of the environment, assuming of course that all components of the environment—air as well as substrate—be considered; the two provisions are that there is no evaporation, and no direct absorption of the sun's rays (insolation). Evaporation can lower the body temperature below that of the environment, and insolation can raise it above. Excluding these two factors the temperature of the ectotherm body is only in a few types as much as a degree different from that of the environment; the maximum deviation is about 3 degrees. Ectotherms control their temperature primarily by behavior, insofar as possible, retiring to cool places when too warm, and seeking a relatively warm or insolated spot when too cold. Curiously enough, very few vertebrates have ever evolved a resistance to subfreezing temperatures. An ability to "bind" water is essential for such resistance. Only a few fishes have evolved that capacity.

Fishes and Tetrapods. The tetrapod, or four-footed, vertebrates are the amphibians, reptiles, birds, and mammals. Members of all the other classes are collectively referred to as fishes. Technically the fishes may be known as the *Pisces*—the "piscine" (fish) division of the vertebrates.

Ganoid Fishes. The fishes with scales possessing a hard outer layer called ganoin. Living examples include part of the Holostei (gars) and Chondrostei (*Polypterus, Calamoichthys*).

Ichthyopsida. The fishes and amphibians.

Sauropsida. Birds and reptiles.

Synapsids. A subclass of fossil reptiles containing the ancestors of mammals, and their relatives (including the Therapsida).

Ungulates. The hoofed mammals are ungulates. Two orders are included: the Perissodactyla and Artiodactyla. The *subungulates* are the surprisingly related orders Proboscidea, Hyracoidea, and Sirenia.

Special terms are applied to the study of individual classes. *Ichthyology* is the study of fishes; *herpetology* the study of amphibians and reptiles; *ornithology* the study of birds; and *mammalogy* the study of mammals. The word herpetology is often erroneously used in reference to the groups themselves for example, "a herpetological collection"), since there is no well-accepted name for the two classes involved. They can succinctly be referred to in a descriptive way as ectothermal tetrapods, but the most popular collectives in recent use are "herptiles" and "herpetozoa."

Phylogeny

It is difficult to imagine our world as it was a few hundred million years ago, just as the earliest vertebrates appeared on the scene. The earth did possess large animals, but they were big arthropods, some (eurypterids) resembling huge scorpions (about 20 feet in length) which no doubt preyed upon the early vertebrates. The heavy armor of most ostracoderms may, according to one theory, have been evolved in response to the predation of such huge arthropods as the eurypterids.

The earliest reliably identifiable ostracoderm remains are from the Ordovician period (Fig. 3.12), although probably the group was present in the Cambrian. It became extinct in the Devonian period, but during its existence gave rise to two other groups: the cyclostomes and the placoderms. Actually no fossil cyclostomes are known, although in view of the absence of bony parts this is not surprising. Only on the basis of similarity of structure can one conjecture that the cyclostomes are derived from the ostracoderms, but this basis leaves no room for doubt. The placoderms are first known from the Silurian period, became abundant in the Devonian, and disappeared in the Permian. Not until the Devonian did the vertebrates invade the seas.

The Devonian was a period of abrupt flowering of vertebrate classes. The Choanichthyes, Actinopteri, Chondrichthyes, and Amphibia all appeared first in this period, in more or less the order listed. The Choanichthyes and Chondrichthyes evolved, probably independently of each other, from different placoderm groups. The Actinopteri may likewise have evolved from some other placoderm group, or from primitive Choanichthyes; the evidence here is inconclusive but favors a choanichthyan origin. The amphibians, of course, evolved from the primitive Choanichthyes. All four groups became abundant in the Mississippian and Pennsylvanian periods.

In the Pennsylvanian another class, the Reptilia, became recognizably differentiated from the Amphibia. This class expanded into many habitats in the Mesozoic, developing a variety of form not matched before or since by any other terrestrial class. Only a few reptiles persisted beyond the Mesozoic, but in that era the reptiles gave rise to two other classes, the birds and the mammals, that together eventually nearly matched the former variety of reptiles, compensating to a large extent in the Cenozoic for the decline of reptiles. The earliest definite remains of mammals are known from the Jurassic, where the earliest birds also are found. Both classes flowered greatly in the Cenozoic. As a matter of fact one group, the mammals, passed its peak of abundance in that era.

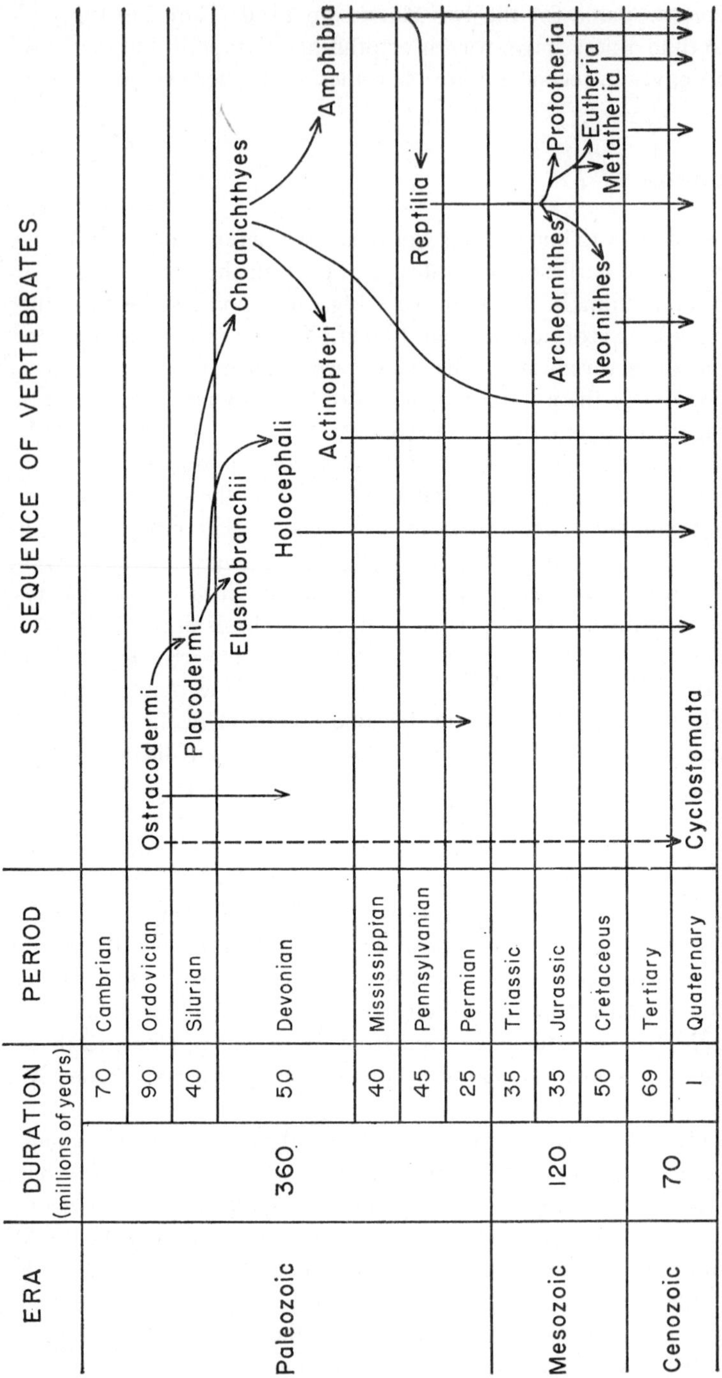

FIG. 3.12 Geological chronology and phylogeny of the vertebrate classes, subclasses and infraclasses.

Thus it is very clear from the geological record that there has been a succession in time of progressively more highly modified, more highly complex vertebrates. Some groups, even though little advanced, have managed to persist relatively unchanged despite competition with refined and improved animals. The sequence leading to placental mammals is: Ostracodermi—Placodermi—Crossopterygii—Labyrinthodontia—Cotylosauria—Therapsida—Eutheria. The monotremes and marsupials seem to be off the line of evolution of the eutherian mammals, being derived from groups of primitive mammals known only as fossils.

The habitat in which vertebrates evolved has been a matter of debate and, as yet, no widespread agreement. Romer has long maintained that vertebrates first evolved as adaptations to a fresh-water environment, and Homer Smith has held this view even longer on the basis of changes in the kidney that occurred coincidentally with evolution of the vertebrates. He interpreted the kidney changes as obvious adaptations for a fresh-water environment of organs formerly adapted to the marine environment. More recently these views, and all evidence now available for and against them, have been carefully weighed by Robertson and White who conclude that the earliest vertebrates actually were of marine origin, that the basic vertebrate kidney structure first appeared in marine animals and was merely preadapted to fresh-water use, and that not until the Devonian did vertebrates invade the fresh-water habitat to an important degree. According to this view the fresh-water invasion by vertebrates actually was initiated by the osteichthyan fishes, which may be construed as adaptations primarily to fresh water. The extraordinary variety of marine bony fishes is, presumably, the result of a secondary invasion of the marine habitat.

Likewise, the habitats in which the various vertebrate classes first evolved have not been widely agreed upon. According to the older views, the endotherm classes evolved as adaptations to cold climate, and therefore in northern continents. Tetrapods as a whole and reptiles in particular were thought to have evolved as adaptations to semiarid conditions. Both views have been seriously questioned in recent years, and perhaps have been laid permanently to rest. Both Darlington and Inger have, independently and from different approaches, come to the conclusion that an unbiased reappraisal of all information now available requires the view that all classes at least *originated* in tropical regions where conditions were most favorable for the maximum number and variety of individuals. The successive major improvements in bodily organization that mark the several vertebrate classes arose in this region because they were tried and tested under the conditions that exerted the greatest *variety* of selective forces—*not,* as previously supposed, under a condition providing great selective pressure of a single kind, such as coldness or aridity. Types evolving in the tropics with a body organization that provided an advantage over others in a wide variety of habitats thus successfully spread over the world, and became the large groups we now accept as classes.

An examination of the niches occupied by the vertebrate classes and subclasses is a revelation of the extraordinary influence of adaptation and competition upon evolution. It may be noted that not a single major vertebrate group coexists on equal terms in the same major habitat with any other major vertebrate group. Repeatedly the offspring of a newly evolved group have become better adapted to the new way of life than the parent stock, and have replaced it. The Archeornithes, Prototheria, Choanichthyes, Ostracodermi, and Placodermi undoubtedly would have flourished indefinitely through time if it were not for the superior competition provided, not so much by unrelated or less closely related stocks, but by their own derivatives. The Archeornithes were no match for the Neornithes, the Prototheria no match for the Theria. The sole reason the Prototheria still exists today is that it was isolated from competition with most of its descendants; unquestionably it will soon disappear as its descendants successfully flourish. The Amphibia have persisted because they occupy a peculiar, borderline niche having little to offer either to confirmed tetrapods (the amniotes) or confirmed fishes; they occupy a limited habitat, and therefore have a tenuous existence without prospect of dominance as long as the high caliber of both terrestrial and aquatic competition exists. Reptiles persist fairly abundantly because they can live in a forbidding climate—the deserts—not particularly inviting to any of their competitors. More northerly reptiles live largely out of competition with mammals. The choanichthyans have scarcely survived to the present, and only from the benefit of isolation; where in direct competition with their offspring, the Actinopteri, they have failed to survive. The Placodermi and Ostracodermi likewise were unable to survive competition from their descendants. The cyclostomes have managed to persist tenuously, largely because of their unique, near-parasitic life, and their secretive elusive form.

Only the elasmobranchs and teleosts appear to be in direct competition, and even there it may be suspected that the role each performs is distinctive in some important way. The elasmobranchs are largely predators and scavengers, or bottom dwellers; they likewise are blessed with a body structure that seems to permit the attainment of a greater size than is true of the teleosts. These may be the redeeming factors. With rare exceptions, however, the chondrichthyans are marine, whereas teleosts are successful in both the marine and fresh-water habitats. Chondrichthyans are incapable of invading the fresh-water habitat partly because they have no air bladder, a necessary adjunct of success in fresh water. Their chief stumbling block would appear to be their complete physiological adjustment to a high osmotic pressure, brought about by a tolerance of all body cells to an excess of urea—an excess that makes the body of these fishes possess essentially the same diffusion value as sea water, thus maintaining the water balance essential to life. The teleosts have instead adapted themselves to the problem of water balance by simple, special modifications of the gills and kidneys; these modifications are more readily subject to change in adaptation than is the modification adopted by the elasmobranchs, which is seemingly irreversible and inflexible, at least against efficient competition such as now exists in other habitats. It is nevertheless a virtual certainty that, if all vertebrates save the chondrichthyans were removed from both land and water, in time these fishes would give rise to descendent groups adapted to the same major habitats as the present vertebrate groups. Beyond question the adaptations would be different in detail, for the same materials for evolution would not be available then that formerly existed, but the end results would be essentially the same.

We can thus summarize the general principles of vertebrate adaptation as follows:

1. None of the major groups (classes and subclasses) of vertebrates are directly competitive, except possibly in marine habitats.

2. A group well adapted to a habitat is difficult for a newcomer to dislodge, because the newcomer is less well adapted to that habitat.

3. A newcomer to a habitat can replace an adapted occupant only by (a) swamping it with markedly greater reproductive powers, or (b) exploiting some vulnerable stage wherein it is much superior to the adapted occupant.

4. No major habitat long remains unoccupied.

5. Almost any group is capable, given time, of producing types adapted to all major habitats.

6. Problems of adaptation need not be solved necessarily in but one way.

7. General physiological adaptations (involving all or most cells) are perhaps more inflexible in evolution than special adaptation of a limited group of cells (as a single organ).

8. Any group meets its most severe competition from its offspring, which tend to be progressively better adapted.

9. All the major groups of vertebrates, except perhaps some of the fishes, originated in the tropics where they were tested more severely than elsewhere by a varied competition.

QUESTIONS

1. Characterize the subphylum Vertebrata.

2. Draw a phylogenetic tree for the classes, subclasses, and infraclasses of vertebrates.

3. List the characteristics important in distinguishing and grouping the classes, subclasses and infraclasses, as, for example, ectothermic, with an amnion, epidermal scales present, mandibular arch branchial in function, second arch wholly branchial in function, paired appendages, etc. For each one indicate to which classes, subclasses, or infraclasses it pertains.

4. Name the subdivisions of each class for which subdivisions are here given. Give an example by common name, and where possible distinguish the subdivisions of each class from each other.

5. How do the terms ectotherm, cold blooded, and poikilothermous differ in meaning? In application? Endotherm, warm blooded, and homoiotherm?

6. What are two theories accounting for the heavy armor of the very early vertebrates?

7. Did the early vertebrates live in a marine or in a fresh-water habitat?

8. Name the geological eras and periods in their proper order and indicate which vertebrate classes were present in each.

9. Name in proper order the seven steps to eutherian mammals, and classify the group cited for each step.

10. State the general principles of vertebrate adaptation.

11. Define the following words, and where possible cite occurrence or list examples.

Actinopteri	eurypterids	Paleozoic
Agnatha	Eutheria	Pennsylvanian
Amia	ganoid	Perissodactyla
amniotes	gnathostome	Permian
Amphibia	herpetology	Petromyzontia
anamniotes	herpetozoa	Pholidota
Anura	herptile	pisces
Apoda	Holocephali	piscine
Archaeornithes	Holostei	Placodermi
artificial classification	homoiotherm	poikilotherm
Artiodactyla	Hyracoidea	Primates
autonomic nervous	ichthyology	Proboscidea
system	Ichthyopsida	Prototheria
Aves	ichthyopterygium	Quaternary
biological classification	incisors	regulated hibernation
Cambrian	Insectivora	Reptilia
Carnivora	insolation	Rhynchocephalia
Caudata	Jurassic	Rodentia
celomoduct	Labyrinthodontia	Sauria
Cenozoic	Lagomorpha	Saurischia
Cetacea	Latimeria	sauropsida
cheiropterygium	Mammalia	semicircular canals
Chiroptera	mammalogy	Serpentes
choanae	Marsupialia	Silurian
Choanichthyes	Mesozoic	Sirenia
Chondrichthyes	Metatheria	Sphenodon
Chondrostei	Mississippian	spiracle
Cotylosauria	Monotremata	Squamata
cranium	Myxinoidea	subungulates
Cretaceous	nasohypophyseal duct	Synapsida
Crocodilia	natural classification	Teleostei
Crossopterygii	Neornithes	Tertiary
Cyclostomata	nonregulated hiberna-	Testudines
Devonian	tion	tetrapods
Dipnoi	operculum	Therapsida
ectotherms	Ordovician	Theria
Edentata	Ornithischia	Triassic
Elasmobranchii	ornithology	tuatara
endocrine organ	Osteichthyes	Tubulidentata
endotherms	Ostracodermi	ungulates

EMBRYOLOGY

EMBRYOLOGY is of importance in three ways to students of comparative anatomy: (1) it provides evidence for concepts of phylogeny; (2) it is essential for understanding the significance of many adult characteristics and variations thereof; and (3) it involves a number of evolutionary trends of great significance in the attainment of adult form of various groups of vertebrates.

Many evolutionary sequences suggested by comparative studies upon both living and extinct adult stages receive confirmatory support from embryology, and in many cases ontogenetic data provide the only bases for conjecture regarding the nature of ancestral adults. On the other hand, embryogeny alone, of extant types of animals, can never provide conclusive proof of phylogenetic sequences, because mode of development may vary without affecting adult structure.

The Evolutionary Principles of Embryology

Perhaps the grandest concept contributed by vertebrate embryology to the understanding of evolutionary phenomena is the principle of *paleogenesis: descendent ontogenies tend to recapitulate ancestral ontogenies.* Paleogenesis was first clearly conceived by Garstang in 1922, but even the ancient Greeks (Aristotle) were aware that some principle of this general nature existed. Many attempts were made before Garstang's time to understand and express accurately the exact nature of this principle, but all were ultimately proved to involve one or more serious misconceptions. The most widely accepted of the ill-fated forerunners of Garstang's principle was Haeckel's (1874) "biogenetic law," a brilliant aphorism ("ontogeny recapitulates phylogeny") known to every student of biology for 75 years. The concept of Haeckel was that the successive *developmental* stages of any animal duplicate the *adult* stages of that animal's ancestors, in the same

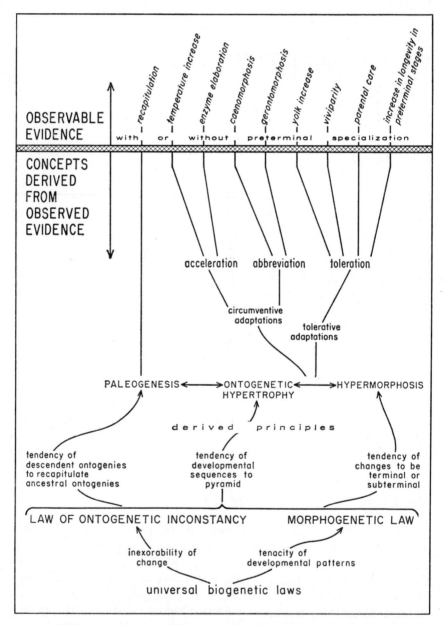

FIG. 4.1 Diagram of relationship of observed evidence to laws, principles, and other phylogenetic concepts contributed by embryology.

succession. Ample evidence now available shows that Haeckel's "law," as stated and generally understood, is simply not literally true, and that literal acceptance has been and continues to be most deceptively misleading. The concept of paleogenesis, on the contrary, recognizes not only the powerful, fundamentally important *tendency* for recapitulation, but that equally potent forces necessarily limit full expression of that tendency, and that recapitulation involves ontogenies and not just the adult stages alone.

Premises. The premises basic to all the evolutionary principles of embryology, including the principle of paleogenesis, are two well-established biogenetic laws: the *morphogenetic law* and the *law of ontogenetic inconstancy* (Fig. 4.1).

According to the morphogenetic law, *developmental sequences tend to be constant, and the earlier the ontogenetic stage the greater the degree of constancy.* Developmental sequences tend to be preserved simply because they are interrelated at all stages with other events going on at the same time. Although we study the embryogeny of given organs or systems separately, those systems cannot develop independently any more than a functional building can be constructed without continual integration of masonry, drainage, lighting, heating, and plumbing construction. Thus it is not so readily possible to change a developmental sequence as it is to add a further step at the end, for a change along the sequence requires adjustment in all related sequences. The earlier the stages are, the greater the number of sequences to which they are related, and therefore the greater their evolutionary stability.

According to the law of ontogenetic inconstancy *evolutionary change in developmental sequences is continuous.* The change is inexorable simply because of the inconstancy of environment. The environment is different in different regions, and is different in any one region at different times (see Chap. 1, p. 15). To "keep up" with their environments animals of necessity change, and their rate of change or evolution is correlated fairly closely with rate of environmental change.

Derived Principles. From these two biogenetic laws three principles may be derived: the principles of *hypermorphosis, ontogenetic hypertrophy,* and *paleogenesis.*

According to the principle of hypermorphosis, *developmental patterns tend to change more by terminal or subterminal addition than by substitution, omission, or preterminal addition.* That is to say, the changes that do occur with evolution in ontogeny tend primarily to be added onto previous ontogenies, rather than occurring in earlier developmental stages. There is a sort of superimposition of changes upon each other at the ends of ontogenies. Changes at late developmental stages tend, of course, to be related to epembryonic (postembryonic) environmental situations; they are therefore essentially *extrinsic adaptations.* The much less numerous but equally important changes at earlier developmental stages tend to be related to embryonic situations; they are therefore essentially *intrinsic adaptations.*

According to the principle of ontogenetic hypertrophy, *developmental sequences tend to become longer or more complex in evolution.* This is a logical sequel to the principle of hypermorphosis. Furthermore, in vertebrates in general the trend toward increase in length of developmental period is fairly clear. A few exceptions appear among living types, certain reptiles and fishes perhaps having gestation periods as long as or even longer than mammals. However, rate of development is faster, in general, in endotherms than in ectotherms; were as many stages involved in the typical ectotherm development as in endotherms the developmental period would undoubtedly be much longer. Certainly the advanced members of vertebrates in general and in each class separately have commonly and extensively exploited various ingenious devices for increase of developmental longevity.

The principle of paleogenesis—that *descendent ontogenies tend to recapitulate ancestral ontogenies*—is a logical sequel to acceptance of the two preceding principles, and may be regarded as the most significant concept of all. Evidence in support of its existence is overwhelming, although its significance has not yet been ranked equally by all students. As at present understood its eventual general acceptance seems assured. The greatest hurdle to acceptance is the expectation that recapitulation be faithful in detail in all cases, whereas in reality no recapitulation is ever complete and in many cases it is almost nonexistent. Vertebrates are conspicuously disposed in their typical developmental pattern to exhibit strong evidence of fixity of developmental sequences, whereas some other types of animals, as well as some plants, do not retain such clear evidence. This disparity does not mean, however, that the general principles of hypermorphosis, ontogenetic hypertrophy, and paleogenesis are invalid or imaginary; it simply means that the *circumventive* adaptations to the morphogenetic law are predominant in some groups of organisms, whereas in other organisms such as vertebrates the *tolerative* adaptations are predominant.

Modes of Developmental Adjustment. The evolutionary characteristics of developmental patterns pose a combination of two serious problems for all evolving organisms: (a) the provision of food and other related adjustments to the lengthening developmental period; and (b) the compression of the sequences into reasonably short periods that do not require such extensive adjustment by way of provision of food.

Faced with these problems, organisms have taken at least four courses in their evolution: (1) *acceleration* of actual rate of passage through developmental sequences; (2) *abbreviation* of the sequences; (3) *toleration* of the increased developmental period, with necessary provisions therefor; and (4) *extinction.* Very likely many cases of extinction may be explained by the failure to work out an adjustment to the developmental problems induced by continual and cumulative change in ontogeny. The other three courses of evolution actually are adjustments or adaptations to these problems. It is safe to say that all vertebrates have adjusted to these problems by all three courses, not exclusively by one alone. However, any one type of adjustment may be more conspicuously evident than the others.

ACCELERATION. The first adjustment, acceleration, has been widely exploited, for we can readily see that embryonic changes are generally far faster than epembryonic ones. Physiological sequences such as are involved in embryonic development seemingly are most readily speeded by (a) *temperature manipulation* and (b) *enzyme elaboration*. Very likely the evolution of endothermy by mammals was primarily an accelerative adaptation initially of embryonic survival value, rather than, as has seemed so obvious, an adaptation primarily to epembryonic environments. It is nevertheless true that many apparent cases of acceleration are probably simulated by subtle abbreviations.

TOLERATION. Increase in length of the developmental life introduces the major problem of supplying food and disposing of waste products for the additional developmental time. Three devices have been adopted by vertebrates as solutions to this problem: * (1) increase in amount of yolk, (2) development of viviparity, and (3) increase in parental care.

The first and simplest solution was to supply more and more yolk with the egg. In birds this device reaches its culmination. Simple and widely occurring though this solution has been in vertebrates, the provision of additional yolk presented still further problems. Segmentation could not proceed in the primitive holoblastic way because of the hindrance of added inert yolk material. The solution was for the yolk to be concentrated at one end, permitting cleavage to proceed less hindered in at least one area. Of course, tremendous changes were imposed in turn by the yolk concentration, not only upon cleavage but also upon subsequent stages, especially the blastula and gastrula.

A second device to provide for the increased demand for an extensive embryonic food supply has been *viviparity* or birth of the young as opposed to the laying of eggs. All vertebrates primitively laid eggs and were thus *oviparous,* but certain species or groups of species in almost every class have chanced upon the device of retaining the eggs in the uterus of the female until they hatch. Some viviparous types have not capitalized upon the possibilities of the situation by supplementing the food supply of the egg (the yolk) by food from the mother, but in these the eggs simply develop entirely in the uterus instead of in some nest outside of the body. Such viviparous vertebrates are *ovoviviparous;* they hold an advantage over oviparous types by enabling them to transport the embryos to situations most conducive to rapid development, such as a warm spot in the sun. Others, in rather numerous groups, did develop a supplementary uterine food supply; these are *euviviparous*. The extent of dependence upon the

---

* Advanced archeostomes, with a rather complex evolutionary history, attain the adult organization by still a different device, little explored by vertebrates: *increase in free-living developmental longevity,* characterized by a succession of free-living stages such as nymphs, larvae, and pupae. This device enables the length of the developmental stage in many cases to exceed that of the adult stage.

maternal supply varies tremendously from one extreme of very slight dependence (as in some fishes, like the dogfish shark) to the other extreme of complete and absolute dependence (as in eutherian mammals). Maternal dependence permits a much greater evolutionary attainment than an egg, allowing a much longer embryonic period, and a faster rate of development at least under certain circumstances.

Third, parental care has markedly increased in birds and mammals as a supplement to either the oviparous or viviparous devices of embryonic care. The less complex ectotherms have adopted parental care only in rare instances, but most birds must provide food for their young for a few weeks after birth, and all mammals provide food (at least *via* the mammary glands, and usually in other ways also) and usually an indispensable education (or conditioning) for their young. As vertebrates continue to evolve, further increase in length of the developmental period may unquestionably be expected; whether the increase will be prenatal or postnatal, or both, is conjectural. It is possible that the trend may be noticeable even within the evolution of man.

ABBREVIATION. In the absence of mutations enabling elaboration of a method that actually would effect a longer developmental life, abbreviation of developmental processes may be expected. When, for example, the pelvis or oviducts cannot be adapted to handle larger eggs, or when no further increase in length of the intrauterine developmental period is possible, the only recourse then is to abbreviation of developmental processes; for the persistent accumulation of extrinsic adaptations is inexorable. In such cases the absence of a genetic capacity to work out a system of developmental abbreviation means, of course, prompt extermination of the species.

Abbreviation of developmental processes may occur by (1) *caenomorphosis* (strictly embryonic, therefore intrinsic, adaptation), whereby shortcuts or alternative routes in preterminal developmental sequences are taken in arriving at adult structures essentially identical with those of ancestral species; and (2) *paedomorphosis,* whereby late developmental sequences in certain organs or systems are simply omitted and formerly juvenile characteristics thus appear in the terminal (adult) or subterminal (subadult) stages. In the latter method, the animal terminates its development in a more "larval" state in certain respects—respects that do not interfere with reproductive potential; "the character that was embryonic or juvenile in the ancestor becomes adult in the descendant" (Simpson). The neotenic salamanders (like Necturus) are excellent examples. They evolved from ancestors that were gill-less in adult stages; but in doing so they have lopped off more and more of the terminal adult stages, so that they now reproduce in an otherwise larval form.

For purposes of clarification and correlation with concepts acquired from other sources, it may be well to point out that (1) *caenogenesis* is a type of caenomorphosis wherein occurs an addition of extra sequences or substitution of new sequences for old (but not an actual omission of sequences, to which another term is applied); (2) *paedogenesis* is sexual acceleration—a type of paedomorphosis wherein sexual development is accelerated and terminal stages of development in other systems are omitted after reaching sexual maturity; and (3) *neoteny* is somatic retardation—another type of paedomorphosis wherein attainment of sexual maturity is not speeded up but the terminal stages in development of other systems are retarded.

Caenomorphosis is seen in the development of practically every organ of the body. The amniote eye, kidney, lungs, liver, and bladder, each passes through many ontogenetic stages that would be totally useless even in primitive adult stages, skipping conformations that must have existed in the functional adult stages of ancestral animals. Caenomorphosis is normally clandestine, in the sense that the changes taking place affect embryonic processes only and are not evident in adult structure. It is obvious, however, that such clandestine evolution could conceivably become so extensive that ultimately it would break to the surface, as it were, producing a relatively sudden and gross change in adult form. Some of the puzzling discontinuities in animal form exhibited in the fossil record (for example, the establishment of most phyla) may have had their origin from the emergence into postnatal stages of previously clandestine evolutionary changes.

Egg Form and Cleavage

Four trends are conspicuous in the adaptation of egg and early zygote to the conditions imposed by the necessity of providing more food (yolk) in adjustment to a persistently increasing developmental period. They involve (1) increase in egg size, (2) proportional increase of yolk, (3) progressive asymmetry in distribution of yolk, and (4) progressive asymmetry in cleavage.

Size of Egg. Chordate eggs have rather consistently increased in size from more primitive to more advanced forms. Most of the increase is in the amount of yolk, but the volume of cytoplasm itself also has increased greatly. The trend holds rather generally throughout vertebrates except for the mammals, which have very small eggs much like the protochordates. The reason for the mammalian reversal is the development of a highly perfected type of viviparity enabling the embryo to secure its food and eliminate its wastes *via* the maternal circulation instead of relying upon the yolk and extraembryonic membranes.

Proportion of Yolk. There is a steady evolutionary trend (excluding mammals) toward increase in amount of inert yolk in proportion to amount of actively metabolic cytoplasm. The more primitive *meiolecithal* type with a more or less equal proportion of yolk and cytoplasm occurs in the protochordates; the *mesolecithal* type with a moderately large amount of yolk occurs in virtually all amphibians and in primitive fishes; the *polyleci-*

thal type occurs in advanced fishes and amphibians (for example, the East Indian frog Rhacophorus), and in all reptiles and birds; and in the mammals there is a reversion to the earlier type, with the yolk being virtually absent (*alecithal*).

Yolk Distribution. In the protochordates and mammals (with meiolecithal and alecithal eggs, respectively) the yolk is distributed evenly through the egg. Such eggs are *isolecithal*. This is not true of the *telolecithal* eggs of all other vertebrates, in which a "vegetal" pole and an "animal" pole are distinguished. The animal pole is that where the cytoplasm is concentrated; and the vegetal pole is the one toward which the yolk is concentrated.

Cleavage. In the protochordates and mammals (with meiolecithal and alecithal eggs, respectively), the divisions of the fertilized egg result in formation of cells of approximately equal size, splitting the entire cell in the early stages of division. This is called *holoblastic equal* cleavage (Fig. 4.2A-F).

In primitive fishes and amphibians, with mesolecithal eggs, the first few cleavages pass through the entire zygote much as in the preceding type, but the horizontal cleavages are displaced, as though by the inert yolk, toward the animal pole. Thus the cells toward the animal pole are smaller

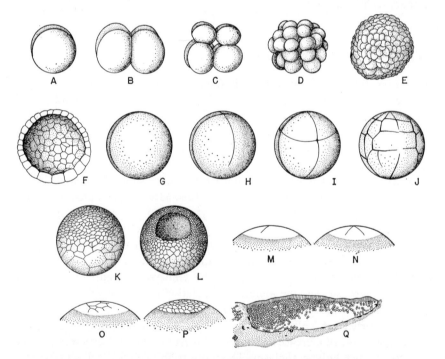

FIG. 4.2 Patterns of cleavage. A-F, holoblastic equal cleavage, or close approximation thereto, as in amphioxus egg. G-L, holoblastic unequal cleavage, as in amphibians. M-Q, meroblastic cleavage, as in sauropsids and some fish. F, L and Q are vertical sections. (From Romer.)

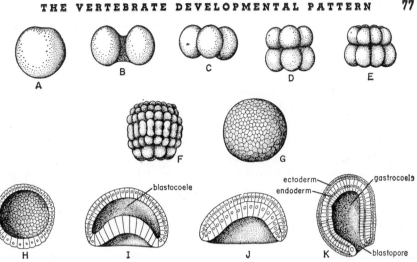

FIG. 4.3 Formation of the blastula and gastrula in the amphioxus. A-G, lateral views of various stages of cleavage from the single cell to the fully-developed blastula. H, vertical section of blastula. I-K, formation of gastrula, as seen in vertical sections. (From Parker and Haswell.)

than those toward the vegetal pole. This is called *holoblastic unequal* cleavage (Fig. 4.2G-L).

In vertebrates with polylecithal eggs, the amount of yolk is so great that the vertical cleavages extend only a negligible distance into the yolk. The divisions are restricted to the *embryonic disc* of the animal pole. Such cleavage is called *meroblastic* (Fig. 4.2M-Q).

The Vertebrate Developmental Pattern

Formation of the Blastula. Successive divisions of the fertilized egg produce a more or less hollow ball of small cells (Fig. 4.3). The cavity in the ball is called the *blastocele*. It is greatly flattened in the polylecithal types.

Formation of the Gastrula. In vertebrates with meiolecithal or mesolecithal eggs, the blastula develops an inpocketing at one point, the invagination eventually obliterating the blastocele (Fig. 4.3). The cavity within the invagination is the *gastrocele* or *archenteron,* and the opening to the exterior is termed, rather inappropriately, the *blastopore*. This marks the posterior end of the embryo. In polylecithal eggs gastrulation is highly distorted by the huge yolk mass, but the process is basically the same in all vertebrates. Even in mammals, which lack a yolk but are derived from polylecithal ancestors, the process although highly modified is demonstrably the same as in reptiles.

Formation of Primary Organs. The alimentary tract, neural tube, and notochord are the first organs to appear embryonically. The alimentary tract is essentially the lining of the gastrocele. In many vertebrates its primary opening, the blastopore, closes early in embryogeny. At a relatively late time the mouth and anus are both formed by an inpocketing of ectoderm (essentially the outer layer of the gastrula) which eventually reaches the gut. The ectoderm-lined buccal invagination is called the *stomodaeum,* the anal invagination the *proctodaeum.* The rather surprising existence of an ectoderm lining at the anterior and posterior ends of the alimentary tract is responsible for the presence in these regions of certain integumentary structures (for example, teeth, palatine rugae, ectodermal glands, taste buds) that would not otherwise be associated with the gut.

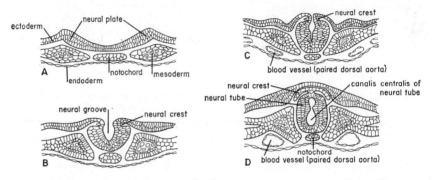

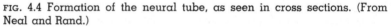

FIG. 4.4 Formation of the neural tube, as seen in cross sections. (From Neal and Rand.)

The true endoderm is incapable of giving rise to these integumentary products.

The neural tube arises by formation of longitudinal ridges in the ectoderm on the upper surface of the egg or embryonic disc (Fig. 4.4). These start rather far toward each side, delimiting a central *neural plate,* and roll inward toward the center line where the *neural crests* of the two ridges (*neural folds*) fuse, thus forming a hollow *neural tube.* The central cavity (*neurocele*) persists throughout life. The anterior end of the tube is expanded as the brain, the remainder forming the spinal cord. Cells designated as "neural-crest cells" remain for a time in aggregations between the outer ectoderm and the neural tube after the latter closes.

The notochord forms in different ways in different chordates. In the protochordates it is derived as a dorsal evagination from the primitive gut, whereas in vertebrates it generally forms as a derivative of the mesoderm (endoderm in the opossum). Its mode of growth in most vertebrates has led some students to regard it as a really independent, fourth germ layer, proliferating forward, between ectoderm and endoderm, from the dorsal lip of the blastopore.

Mesoderm Formation. The mesoderm forms by segregation of cells from the other layers (ectoderm, or endoderm, or both) on either side of the notochord and neural tube (or positions thereof), beginning near the anterior end of the embryo. It is not as distinct a layer of tissue as the ectoderm and the endoderm. The cells are more apt to migrate and to form loose aggregates of separate cells collectively called *mesenchyme*. The cells are imbedded in a jellylike protein matrix. Many are essentially secretory and others become specialized and sometimes subdivided in adults. When finally differentiated, they are often named according to their secretory function or the cells they subsequently form. Thus fibroblasts produce the fibers of connective tissue, myoblasts become contractile fibers of muscle, chondroblasts secrete the matrix of hyaline cartilage, osteoblasts form bone, lipoblasts produce fat-storing cells, hemocytoblasts produce blood cells, and still others become mast cells, macrophages, endothelial cells, lymphoblasts, etc.

The Yolk Sac. In meiolecithal and mesolecithal eggs the gut surrounds the yolk, which to be sure may produce, under mesolecithal conditions, a swollen abdominal region which shrinks to normal as development proceeds (Fig. 4.5A-C). Under telolecithal conditions, however, the yolk cannot conveniently be surrounded directly by the gut. Instead the connection of gut and yolk is constricted to form a narrow, short stalk, through which blood vessels run to carry the yolk to the embryo (Fig. 4.5D). The sac that surrounds the yolk is an *"extraembryonic membrane,"* called specifically the *yolk sac*. In primitive vertebrates (fishes and amphibians) the yolk sac, where present, is regarded as *trilaminate,* consisting of ectoderm, mesoderm, and endoderm (Fig. 4.5E). The ectoderm and the layer of mesoderm associated with it forms the *somatopleure,* and the endoderm with its layer of mesoderm forms the *splanchnopleure*. The mesoderm-lined space between somatopleure and splanchnopleure is the celom. In reptiles, birds, and mammals the yolk sac is regarded as *bilaminate,* consisting solely of splanchnopleure (endoderm and mesoderm, Fig. 4.8); the ectoderm in these groups forms part of another extraembryonic membrane.

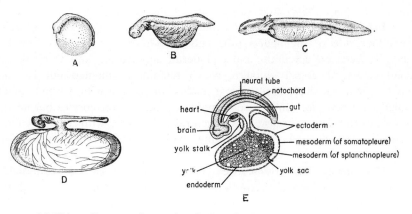

FIG. 4.5 The yolk sacs of mesolecithal and telolecithal anamniotes. A-C, lateral views of successive stages of a salamander. D, lateral view of an early developmental stage of a shark, showing distinct yolk stalk and yolk sac. E, sagittal section of a telolecithal embryo, showing trilaminate yolk sac. (A-D from Romer.)

A yolk sac of some sort is present in all telolecithal vertebrates, and is commonly vestigial (and never contains yolk) in mammals. It might be regarded as rudimentary, at least to a degree, in certain mesolecithal vertebrates (for example, many amphibians), in which no yolk stalk exists but the gut is greatly swollen by enclosure of the yolk.

Ectoderm Derivatives. A rather large proportion of the ectoderm is involved in the extensive neural plate and neural folds previously described. This is the *neurectoderm.* The brain (as well as embryonic brain derivatives such as the retina and posterior lobe of the hypophysis) and spinal cord are the most conspicuous derivatives of the neurectoderm, but from the neural-crest cells—remaining between the outer ectoderm and the spinal cord—a remarkable variety of structures is formed. They include the ganglia of the sympathetic chain and the spinal nerves; the neurilemma (sheath cells) of the peripheral nerves; chromatophores, which wander rather generally over the body, concentrating especially under the epithelium; the medulla of the adrenal glands; and most surprisingly, at least in many forms, the pharyngeal skeleton and those parts of the skull and respiratory apparatus (ear ossicles, larynx) derived from the pharyngeal skeleton.

From the nonneural ectoderm are derived the epidermis and a vast number of epidermal products: the linings of the mouth, nasal cavity, skin glands, and part of the cloaca and its derivatives; the lens of the eye; the enamel of teeth; and the anterior lobe of the pituitary gland.

Endoderm Derivatives. This layer forms the linings of numerous internal cavities: the linings of the entire alimentary tract, except the mouth and part of the cloaca; the linings of the lungs, bladder, gill chambers, liver, middle ear cavity, and Eustachian tube; and the linings of the embryonic yolk sac and allantois. The secretory cells of the thyroid and pancreas, as well as of the other glands of the gut, are of endodermal origin. The supporting cells of these same organs are of mesodermal origin.

Mesoderm Derivatives. Forming as segmental aggregations of cells on either side of the neural tube and notochord, the mesoderm grows laterally between ectoderm and endoderm, subdividing into three major components: a dorsal *epimere,* which remains segmented but has no cavity (or a transitory *myocele*); a median *mesomere* with a small cavity called a *nephrocele,* which is segmented in primitive vertebrates but not in more advanced vertebrates; and a ventral *hypomere,* with a large cavity termed the *splanchnocele,* forming without trace of segmentation (Fig. 4.6).

Hypomeric Derivatives. The hypomere may be regarded as subdividing into three major parts: the branchiomeres, the splanchnocele, and the splanchnolemma. The splanchnocele does not extend throughout the length of the hypomere, at least in vertebrates. It is absent anteriorly in the pharyngeal region (Fig. 4.6D). It may have been continuous throughout the hypomere in ancestral protochordates, but the existence of an

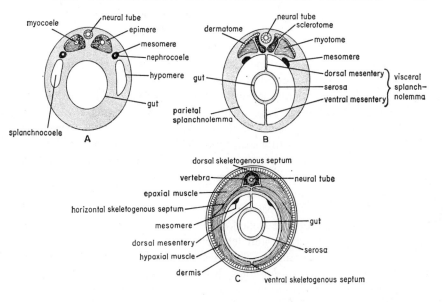

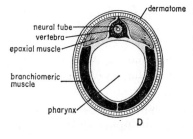

FIG. 4.6 Mesodermal development in vertebrates. A, early stage, showing division of mesoderm into epimere, mesomere, and hypomere. B, a later stage, showing expansion of hypomere to form the splanchnocele and splanchnolemma, and early differentiation of epimere into dermatome, sclerotome, and myotome. C, adult conformation in postpharyngeal trunk region, with dermis derived from dermatome, vertebrae from sclerotome, and epaxial and hypaxial muscles from myotome; the ventral mesentery is largely degenerate. D, adult conformation in pharyngeal region, showing absence of hypaxial muscles and celom; the splanchnolemma is represented by the branchiomeric muscles.

atrium (essentially eliminating the celom) in the living protochordates that are most like vertebrates suggests that the hypomere was solid in the pharyngeal region of all chordates, living and extinct. The solid, pharyngeal part gives rise in vertebrates to muscles—the branchiomeric muscles. The presence of pharyngeal slits results in a serial arrangement of the hypomere in this region. This is not true segmentation, which involves the epimere, but is *branchiomerism*. The muscles to which the branchiomeres give rise are voluntary, skeletal muscles, not distinguishable except by embryonic origin from other skeletal muscle. Primitively branchiomeric muscles operated the gill skeleton; a few other functions were acquired in tetrapods.

The splanchnocele is primitively a single cavity on either side. The dorsal and ventral mesenteries separate the two cavities from each other.

In all living vertebrates, however, at least the ventral mesentery is incomplete, resulting in fusion of the right and left splanchnoceles. Furthermore, in all vertebrates the *celom* is, unless otherwise stated, understood as the splanchnocele, despite the fact that other celoms (nephrocele and myocele) exist in the vertebrate body.

The splanchnolemma may be regarded as consisting basically of two divisions: a *parietal* layer, lying against the body wall, and a *visceral* layer, not in contact with the body wall. The latter gives rise to three parts: (1) the cardiac and smooth visceral muscles; (2) the *serosa,* a thin epithelium lying against any body organ projecting into the celom; and (3) the *dorsal* and *ventral mesenteries.* The serosa, which covers such organs as the heart, lungs, liver, stomach, and other viscera, is ordinarily completely indistinguishable by gross inspection, being intimately bound with the organ. The mesenteries are double walled, since they are formed by fusion of the medial walls of both right and left celoms.

Mesomeric Derivatives. The mesomere is segmented in fishes and amphibians, but is not in amniotes. It develops with a cavity, the nephrocele, primitively in continuity with the splanchnocele. The continuity is lost in adult amniotes, but is retained to a greater or lesser degree in adult anamniotes. The only organs that develop from the mesomere are the kidneys, gonads, and their ducts. The *nephrotomal plate* is that part giving rise to the kidneys.

Epimeric Derivatives. The dorsal division of the mesoderm, the epimere, is segmented in all vertebrates. Its segmental components are *somites.* Each somite subdivides into three main parts: the *dermatome, sclerotome,* and *myotome.* The dermatomes of the different somites produce cells that spread uniformly beneath the epidermis, losing all evidence of segmentation, and that together form the dermis of the skin. The sclerotomes subdivide and recombine in special ways in different vertebrates, but eventually give rise to the vertebral column. The myotomes give rise to all nonbranchiomeric voluntary muscles of the body. They enlarge ventrally, extending between the hypomere and dermis, those on one side meeting the myotomes of the opposite side on the midventral line at the *ventral skeletogenous septum* (*linea alba* in abdominal region). The linea alba consists only of connective tissue separating the myotomes, and the muscles formed by them, of one side from those of the other. Growth occurs dorsally as well as ventrally, terminating at the *dorsal skeletogenous septum* above the vertebral column. Very few myotomic muscles cross either the middorsal or midventral line. A horizontal plate of connective tissue, the *horizontal skeletogenous septum,* eventually develops across the myotomes and connects the vertebral column with the median lateral line of the body. This septum separates a dorsal *epaxial* muscle mass from a ventral *hypaxial* mass. Primitively each myotome is separated from adjacent myotomes by essentially transverse vertical plates of connective tissue, the *myosepta* of the embryo, or *myocommata* of the adult.

The Amniote Cleidoic Egg

Complete adaptation to a terrestrial life involves, among other things, modification of the eggs and embryos to an existence in a nonaquatic environment. Some evidence shows that these modifications may well have been among the earliest of the terrestrial adaptations to appear, although they might at first thought seem logically to be the last to become fixed.

The water in which the eggs of all fishes are (and were) laid provides two functions the air cannot serve: prevention of desiccation, and removal of soluble metabolic wastes. Eggs laid on land must be so constructed as to prevent loss of the precious water supply, to rid the body of metabolic wastes, and also at the same time to permit respiration to go on. Perfection of evolution of such a highly adapted egg (a *cleidoic* egg), the rudimentary form of which first appeared in reptiles, was not accomplished at once: most amphibians of today still lay their eggs in water, most reptiles lay eggs in moist places where the environment itself is an important factor in prevention of water loss, and only in birds is the cleidoic adaptation so perfected that embryogeny is relatively independent of the environment. Only a fairly constant and high temperature need be provided extraneously in the most efficient types, and this is ordinarily accomplished by brooding by the female. Four outstanding features characterize the cleidoic egg: (a) a shell, (b) albumen, (c) four extraembryonic membranes, and (d) uric acid excretion.

The Shell. First seen in reptiles, the shell is generally soft, with little calcium, and is rather pervious to water. In birds considerable calcium is added to the shell, resulting in a structure relatively impervious to water. Independent of the tetrapod line of evolution, some fishes (notably cyclostomes, chondrichthyes) have evolved protective egg shells. They are not calcified.

Albumen. A second feature is egg "white," a watery gelatin surrounding the yolk. Its basic function is presumably to store water for use during embryonic development (secondarily it may provide a growth factor). It is virtually completely absorbed by the time the egg hatches. In reptiles, with a rather pervious shell, relatively little white occurs. It is in birds that a complete dependence upon water enclosed within the egg is evolved; a relatively large quantity of egg white is thus a necessity in the avian egg.

Extraembryonic Membranes. A third feature is the presence of four extraembryonic membranes instead of the more primitive single membrane (yolk sac). All three additional membranes first appear, as extraembryonic membranes, in the class Reptilia; they are present in all living representatives of that class and its two derivative classes, Aves and Mammalia. These classes are thus collectively referred to as the *amniotes,* as opposed to all other vertebrates, which are referred to as *anamniotes.*

Two of these membranes form by upward growth of an ovoid ridge immediately surrounding the embryo (Fig. 4.7). The ridge at first forms

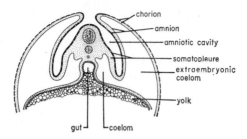

FIG. 4.7 Formation of the amniote extraembryonic membranes, as seen in cross section of the embryo. (From Kingsley.)

like the edge of a saucer, then grows upward, and then finally centripetally over the embryo, its edges eventually fusing to form an inner sac (*amnion,* composed of ectoderm and mesoderm) completely enclosing the embryo, and an outer sac (*chorion,* composed also of ectoderm and mesoderm) enclosing the entire embryo and, if present, the yolk sac. The amnion is attached to the embryo by the *umbilical cord* at the locus of, and containing, the yolk stalk. The basic function of the amnion is to contain a watery fluid —the *amnionic fluid*—in which the embryo is immersed throughout development. Thus an aquatic environment is maintained, in a special sense, for the developing embryos even of the most terrestrial tetrapods. The chorion serves primitively simply as a protective membrane.

The third extraembryonic membrane, the *allantois* (composed of endoderm and mesoderm) forms as a ventral outpouching from the gut near the rear end of the embryo (Fig. 4.8). It extends forward, into the umbilical cord, and then spreads out into a considerable area between the amnion and chorion. Its functions are (1) respiration, (2) absorption of albumen and water, and (3) excretion. The latter function is passive in cleidoic animals, in which the allantois is excretory only in the sense that it serves as a storage organ for excretory wastes. The membrane lies close to the inner surface of the shell and is highly vascularized. Air does permeate the shell, although water may be largely excluded, and thus the allantois is

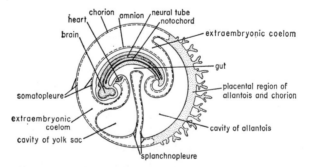

FIG. 4.8 Arrangement of extraembryonic membranes in a mammal with a chorioallantoic placenta, as seen in sagittal section. (From Neal and Rand.)

in a position to serve as a respiratory organ. In most mammals it forms an important part of the placenta, serving as both a respiratory and excretory membrane.

Uric Acid Excretion. A fourth feature essential to the success of the cleidoic egg is the evolution of a technique of nontoxic excretion. All anamniotes and mammals excrete metabolic wastes in soluble forms (urea, ammonia) that are toxic in moderate concentrations. This is no handicap to anamniotes because their embryos typically develop in a water medium where wastes can be eliminated without restriction; or to mammals because the mother can extract metabolic wastes for the embryos. In advanced reptiles and in birds, however, the problem of waste elimination is serious because the embryos develop within a restricted space surrounded by a more or less impervious wall. Accumulation of metabolic wastes in soluble form in a cleidoic egg would be fatal to the embryo. Thus in these groups the kidneys have evolved a capacity to transform metabolic wastes to a nontoxic and but slightly soluble substance, uric acid, which can be deposited in the extraembryonic membranes (allantois) without harm to the embryo. The conservation of water effected by resorption of fluids in deposition of uric acid has also been of great value, to both embryos and adults of modern reptiles and birds, as a preadaptation for existence under exceptionally arid conditions.

Origin of the Cleidoic Egg

Perhaps the best essay on the origin of the cleidoic egg characteristic of amniotes appeared in an essay by Romer in 1957 (see bibliography). Part of that essay is reproduced herewith as an outstanding example of repertorial skill in the field of vertebrate evolution.

"One of the most important steps in the evolution of vertebrates was the 'invention' of the amniote egg, which, with associated developmental processes, is characteristic of the higher vertebrate classes. Its appearance marks the beginnings of the history of the reptiles and the potentialities of evolution of the great groups that are dominant today, the birds and mammals. The evolution of the amniote type of development was a necessary antecedent to the true conquest of the land.

"Amphibian versus Reptilian Reproduction. As it is seen today on the breakfast table, the amniote egg is a familiar, commonplace, and hence seemingly prosaic object. It is, however, marvelously well adapted for the reproduction of terrestrial animal types and permits a developmental history of quite a different sort from that found in lower vertebrates. Among fishes, the eggs are laid in the water, and the resulting young remain there as persistently gill-breathing water-dwellers.

"The amphibians (of which the frogs, toads, newts, and salamanders are the common modern types) developed limbs, and thus the ability to walk abroad upon the land, many millions of years ago, in Paleozoic times.

But even today, the most familiar North Temperate Zone representatives of that group have hardly changed a whit in their reproductive processes. No matter how far common frogs, toads, or newts may have wandered during the year, every spring sees them returning to ponds and streams. There they lay unprotected clusters or strings of eggs similar to those of their fish ancestors. There is little nourishing yolk in this typical amphibian egg, and consequently the tiny creature which hatches from it must, from an early stage, be highly adapted to an active, food-seeking life as a water-dwelling, gill-breathing, essentially fishlike larva. After a considerable period of feeding and growth, there takes place a radical change in structure and mode of life—a change which is most strikingly seen in the rapid metamorphosis of tadpole into frog or toad. Gills atrophy; lungs expand, and air takes the place of water as an oxygen source; the tail fin is reduced; legs develop, and the amphibian is freed to walk out onto the land.

"This necessity of leading a 'double life' is a serious handicap to the development of the individual; it must, at successive stages, be structurally and functionally fitted for two very different modes of life and, in consequence, falls far short of perfection in adaptation for either. And even if the end product is a terrestrial, or potentially terrestrial, adult, the release from the water is never complete, for every spring the typical amphibian must return to its natal element to deposit eggs and initiate the next life cycle. Such an amphibian is bound to the water; its release is never complete.

"Quite in contrast is the mode of reproduction seen in typical reptiles (and in birds and the most primitive mammals as well). The amniote egg can be laid on land; neither young nor adult need ever enter the water. The young amphibian must be prepared to make its own living while still of very small size; the amniote egg is richly supplied with nutritious yolk, which enables the young to attain considerable growth before birth. If they were exposed to air, the delicate tissues of a developing embryo would be subject to fatal desiccation; early in its development the amniote embryo is surrounded by a continuous membrane, the amnion (to which this developmental type owes its name).

"Within the liquid-filled amniotic sac, the developing embryo is in a miniature replica of its ancestral pond. Protection against mechanical injury is afforded by the shell. Extending out from the body of the embryo is a sac—the allantois—which expands beneath the shell and serves two further vital functions. The growing embryo, in which metabolic processes are proceeding at a rapid rate, must breathe. The shell is porous; the allantois beneath it forms an embryonic lung, receiving oxygen from the air and giving off carbon dioxide waste. A result of the rapid metabolism of the growing embryo is the accumulation of nitrogenous waste—an embryonic urine which must be stored, until hatching, within the compass of the egg. The cavity of the allantois also serves this purpose, acting as a temporary bladder.

"As a result of this complex but efficient series of amniote adaptations, the animal is completely freed from an aquatic life. No longer is the adult compelled to return to the water for reproductive purposes. The young, within the protection of its shell and membranes, is freed from the necessity of undergoing a fish-like larval life; nourished by the abundant yolk, it can hatch directly as a vigorous little replica of its parent, fully and directly equipped for terrestrial existence.

"Once this new amniote pattern of development had evolved, in Upper Paleozoic days, there began the great radiation of reptiles that is characteristic of the Mesozoic 'Age of Reptiles,' during which period the relatively unprogressive amphibians were reduced to their present insignificance. And from this reptilian radiation there presently emerged the still more progressive lines which gave rise to the birds and mammals. As far as can be told from the fossil record, the adult structure of the very earliest reptiles showed little if any advance over that of their amphibian relatives and contemporaries. It was solely owing to the amniote mode of development that the evolution of higher vertebrates was made possible.

"**Aquatic Nature of the Oldest Amniotes.** How, when, and at what stage did this crucial reproductive improvement appear? The story once seemed clear to me, in a form in which I told it to many a student audience. Well before the close of the Carboniferous period, the fossil record shows us, there had appeared advanced amphibian types with well-developed limbs and other features indicating that, as adults, they could be, and were, mainly terrestrial forms rather than water-dwellers. A sole obstacle lay in the path of their conquest of the land—their mode of development, through which they were chained to the water (a lovely and dramatic phrase!). At long last there came the final stage in their release—the development of the terrestrial amniote egg. Their bonds were broken, and, as true terrestrial forms, the early reptiles swept on to a conquest of the earth!

"This is a fine story. However, I now suspect that it is far from the truth. It assumes that the *adult* first became a land-dweller and that terrestrial reproduction was a later development. It now seems to me more probable that the reverse was the case—that the *egg* came ashore first and that the adult tardily followed.

"**Why the Amniote Egg?** If we accept this as a reasonable conclusion from the paleontological evidence, we are, nevertheless, faced with a major puzzle. In the light of the earlier point of view, one could readily account for the success of the amniote type of development as being strongly favored by selective processes in animals which were otherwise terrestrial in habits. But what strong advantage could there be in terrestrial embryonic development in the case of forms which were still aquatic or, at the most, amphibious in adult life?

"To attempt a solution, let us review reproduction in modern amphibians. I have cited the reproductive habits of familiar North Temperate frogs, toads, and newts. But if we examine the developmental histories of the modern orders as a whole—and particularly the varied tropical anurans —we gain quite another picture. The fishlike mode of development I have described is, to be sure, primitive, but so many modern amphibians have departed from it that it can hardly be regarded as typical of the group as a whole.

"In a large proportion of modern forms, the eggs are not laid in the water in ancestral fashion. In fact, these amphibians may go to any extreme to avoid this. The eggs may be laid on the bank near the water, under logs or stones or in a cavity in the earth, in a hollow stump, or in a 'nest' of leaves in a tree. They may be carried about on land, placed in pockets on the back of one or the other parent, kept (curiously) in the vocal pouch of the male, or, in the case of the 'obstetrical toad,' wrapped clumsily around the father's legs.

"The 'typical' amphibian egg, like that of the fish ancestors, is small in size, with only a modest amount of yolk, and, except for the presence of a surrounding jelly, there is no development of membranes or other protective devices for the embryo. This is quite in contrast to the amniote egg; but, in one modern amphibian or another, we find a variety of modifications which parallel those of amniotes in most respects. In some instances the amount of yolk is greatly increased, the developing embryo is perched above a distended yolk sac, much as in an amniote, and the necessity of larval feeding is done away with. There is no expansion of an allantoic 'bladder' to function as a lung, but comparable air-breathing organs may be formed by expansion of a highly vascular tail or by the development of broad, thin sheets of superficial tissue extending out from the gill region. There is no development of a complete amnion as a protection against desiccation, but in some forms there is a nearly complete covering of the embryo by somewhat comparable sheets of tissue. In fact, the only amniote structure that is not paralleled is the shell—a relatively minor part of the whole complex.

"In sum, many modern amphibians have developed, to varied degrees and in varied fashion, adaptations which, like those of amniotes, tend to reduce or eliminate the water-dwelling larval stage. What is the significance of this series of adaptations? Not any 'urge' toward a purely terrestrial existence, for the amphibians which show these trends toward direct development are as varied in adult habits as are amphibians as a whole.

"There appear to be two major advantages. (i) Eggs and young in a pond form a tempting food supply, an amphibian 'caviar,' open to attack by a variety of hungry animals, ranging from insects to other vertebrates; furthermore, the larvae are in heavy competition for food with other small water-dwellers. If eggs are laid in less obvious places, the chance of survival is greatly increased; if guarded or carried by a parent, they are under protection. (ii) In some regions there are annual dry seasons, when the ponds and pools in which 'normal' amphibians would lay their eggs tend to dry up. Reduction or elimination of the water stage increases the chances of survival of the young, which might be destroyed if they were living as tadpoles in a drying pond.

"May not the amniote type of development have been similarly evolved to gain some immediate advantage rather than as any sort of 'preadaptation' for land life? For modern amphibians, protection of the eggs from enemies is by far the more important of the two major advantages that are gained by changes in reproductive methods (although, in certain instances, adaptations which shorten larval life appear to be related to protection against potential drought conditions). For the Paleozoic reptile ancestors, the reverse was probably the case. Potential egg devourers were then presumably less abundant, but danger of desiccation was far greater.

"Today there are only limited regions of the tropics in which the annual weather cycle is one of seasons of heavy rains alternating with droughts. But as Barrell first pointed out, large areas of the earth in late Paleozoic days appear to have been subject to marked seasonal drought (the presence of numerous red-bed deposits in the Upper Paleozoic appears to be correlated in great measure with drought phenomena). Under such conditions, the life of the amphibious vertebrates of the day was a hazardous one. Particularly hazardous was the developmental process. If the old-fashioned methods were retained, and the young must, perforce, spend a long period of time as gill-breathing larvae, they were in grave danger of being overtaken by the oncoming of the rainless season and of being killed in their drying natal ponds. Any reproductive improvement which would reduce or eliminate this danger had a strong survival value. It is probable that various essays in this direction were made. The one truly successful one was that which led to the development of the amniote egg and the resultant origin of the reptiles, which, from that time on, became increasingly successful over their less progressive amphibian relatives. Today, a variety of amphibians are struggling (so to speak) to attain some type of development comparable to that which the reptile ancestors achieved eons ago, but their efforts are too little and too late.

"Deductions from the study of climatic history are thus consonant with the facts of the fossil record. The fine story of the reptile ancestor as an animal which had become fully terrestrial in adult life and needed only, as a final step, to improve its reproductive habits in order to conquer the earth is, apparently, pure myth. It was the egg which came ashore first; the adult followed later.

"We may picture the ancestral reptile type as merely one among a variety of amphibious dwellers in the streams of late Paleozoic days. All were basically water-dwellers. All, alike, found their living in the water, with fishes and invertebrates as the food supply, for there was, at first, little animal life on land to tempt them. In most respects the early reptile had no advantage over its amphibian contemporaries. Only in its new type of development was the reptile better off. This advantage, however, did not at first imply the necessity of any trend toward increased adult life on land. And it was only slowly, toward the close of the Paleozoic Era, that many (but not all) of the reptiles took advantage of the new opportunities which amniote development offered them and became terrestrial types, initiating the major evolutionary reptilian radiation in the Mesozoic—the Age of Reptiles. This potentiality of conquest of the earth by the reptiles was not the result of 'design.' Rather, it was the result of a happy accident —the further utilization of potentialities that had been attained as an adaptation of immediate value to their amphibious ancestors."

Placental Evolution

Euviviparity has, as stated previously, evolved independently in a number of vertebrates. Maternal support of the young is accomplished generally by a *placenta*—an organ serving functional needs of the embryo and consisting in part of embryonic membranes and in part of maternal (uterine) membranes. Where present it is rudimentary in all vertebrates except some mammals.

The embryonic contribution to the placenta may consist in different vertebrates of any one of the four extraembryonic membranes except the amnion, which never contributes to the placenta. Thus *yolk sac, allantoic* and *chorionic placentas* are recognized on the basis of the membrane contributing to the placenta. In anamniotes only a yolk sac placenta, of course, can occur, and it must be a *trilaminar yolk sac placenta* since the yolk sac is trilaminar (consisting of ectoderm, mesoderm, endoderm) in all amniotes in which it occurs. This is the most primitive type of placenta in vertebrates.

In amniotes various combinations of extraembryonic membranes contribute to the placenta in different species. In all, however, the chorion is necessarily involved since that membrane surrounds the entire embryo (including the yolk sac). Those types including also the yolk sac are termed *choriovitelline placentas,* whereas those including the chorion and allantois (Fig. 4.8) are termed *chorioallantoic placentas.* In more general terms, the choriovitelline placentas can be referred to as either "yolk sac" or "chorionic" placentas, and likewise the chorioallantoic types can be referred to as either "allantoic" or "chorionic."

Allantoic placentas occur only in a few advanced reptiles and in most mammals; it is the most advanced of the types that are treated here. Choriovitelline types represent intermediate stages between the primitive trilaminar yolk sac placenta and the advanced chorioallantoic type, and two are clearly distinguishable: a *prochoriovitelline* type occurring in reptiles, and a *metachoriovitelline* type occurring in most marsupials and to a transitory degree in eutherian mammals. These differ in presence or absence of yolk (absent in mammals) and in time of implantation (relatively late in reptiles, very early in mammals) in the uterine wall.

QUESTIONS

1. By what logical steps can it be shown that inconstancy of environment and stability of developmental sequences have led to meroblastic cleavage? Itemize answer.

2. Name and explain the evolutionary principles of embryology and the biogenetic laws on which they are based.

3. In what four ways may organisms react to the inherent tendency of developmental periods to become progressively longer?

4. In what four ways have animals solved the nutritional problem of progressively longer developmental periods?

5. Name and differentiate the two methods of abbreviation of developmental processes; of acceleration.

6. State four evolutionary trends in egg form and cleavage, naming and differentiating stages in each trend where recognized.

7. Name the four extraembryonic membranes and the germ layers forming each.

8. Name the distinctive features of the cleidoic egg. What is the role of each of these features? In what class is the cleidoic egg most nearly perfect? What is the single prime deficiency in the most perfect cleidoic eggs that usually prevents development without parental assistance?

9. Name the derivatives in adult animals of the neurectoderm; of the nonneural ectoderm; of the endoderm.

10. Name the subdivisions of the mesoderm, and the lesser divisions (if any) and derivatives of each.

11. How may intrinsic adaptation or clandestine evolution possibly explain discontinuities in the fossil record?

12. Contrast amniote and anamniote placentas, naming and distinguishing all types occurring in each group.

13. How would a yolk sac placenta of a reptile differ from that of a fish in identity and structure of its embryonic membranes?

14. Define the following words, and where appropriate state occurrence or cite examples.

alecithal	chorioallantoic placenta	extraembryonic membrane
allantoic placenta	chorion	
allantois	chorionic placenta	fibroblast
ammonia	choriovitelline placenta	gastrocele
amnion	clandestine	gastrula
archenteron	cleidoic egg	Haeckel's biogenetic law
bilaminar yolk sac	dermatome	
biogenesis	egg albumen	hemocytoblast
blastocele	embryogeny	holoblastic cleavage
blastopore	embryology	hypaxial
blastula	embryonic disc	hypermorphosis
branchiomere	epaxial	hypomere
caenogenesis	epembryonic	isolecithal
caenomorphosis	epimere	law of ontogenetic inconstancy
celom	euviviparous	
chondroblast		

linea alba
lipoblast
meiolecithal
meroblastic cleavage
mesenchyme
mesolecithal
mesomere
metachoriovitelline
  placenta
morphogenetic law
myoblast
myocele
myocomma
myoseptum
myotome
neoteny
nephrocele
nephrotomal plate
nephrotome
neural crest
neural fold

neural plate
neural tube
neurectoderm
neurocele
ontogenetic hypertro-
  phy
ontogeny
osteoblast
ovoviviparous
paedogenesis
paedomorphosis
parietal
placenta
polylecithal
postnatal
prenatal
proctodaeum
prochoriovitelline pla-
  centa
sclerotome
serosa

skeletogenous   septum,
  dorsal, horizontal
  and ventral
somatic
somatopleure
somite
splanchnic
splanchnocele
splanchnolemma
splanchnopleure
stomodaeum
telolecithal
trilaminar yolk sac
umbilical cord
urea
uric acid
visceral
viviparous
yolk sac
yolk sac placenta
yolk stalk

5

INTEGUMENTARY
SYSTEM

As a DIRECT MEETING GROUND of an enormous variety of environmental forces, each acting upon an even more enormous variety of animals, the integument is not surprisingly a highly varied system, possessing many specialized organs or structures of restricted occurrence. General evolutionary trends are obscured by the numerous specializations seen in small groups of vertebrates. It is upon these general trends, however, that we shall focus our attention, with only a cursory glance at the fascinating but relatively ephemeral, isolated specializations.

Basic Types of Integument

The integumentary system may be regarded as consisting of (a) the integument itself, and (b) the integumentary derivatives. The integument constitutes the general outer covering of the body, of one or two layers, lying external to the loose connective tissue that overlies muscles and other superficial structures. The integumentary derivatives are specialized structures or organs formed embryonically from one or both layers of the integument; they may be soft (that is, glands), or hard, and the hard structures may consist either of bone or of keratin, or both.

Two basically different types of integument occur in chordates. One, the *invertebrate type*—obviously the most primitive and probably of oc-

currence in vertebrate ancestors—occurs in living protochordates (modified in the urochordates). In this type (Fig. 5.1) the integument consists
solely of a single layer of epidermis, underlaid by a *basement membrane* or
cutis consisting of a thin layer of loose connective tissue or of a noncellular
secretion from the epidermis. There is no dermis, and no prominent epidermal derivatives.

The *vertebrate type* of integument is skin (Fig. 5.2). It occurs in all
living vertebrates, and differs from the invertebrate integument in consisting of several to many layers representing both epidermal and dermal
tissues.

How the dermis first appeared is of course unknown. Probably the
connective tissue lining the epidermis internally became modified chiefly if
not wholly as bone in the ancestors of vertebrates, as suggested by the
earliest known vertebrate fossils (ostracoderms) with their heavy bony
armor.

The selective forces that may have been responsible for development
of such armor in early vertebrates have been a source of much speculation.
Since the earliest vertebrates are thought to have departed from ancestral
precedent by invasion of fresh water rather than the sea, the bony armor
may have served a function of preventing absorption of water—a real and

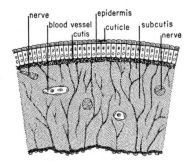

FIG. 5.1 Section of skin of Branchiostoma.
(From Young.)

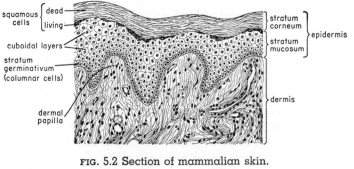

FIG. 5.2 Section of mammalian skin.
(From Maximow and Bloom.)

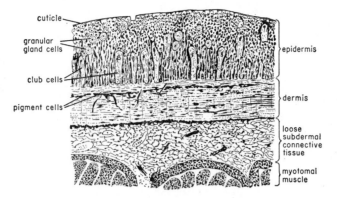

FIG. 5.3 Section of skin of a cyclostome.
(From Young.)

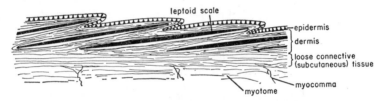

FIG. 5.4 Section of skin of a teleost fish.
(From Goodrich.)

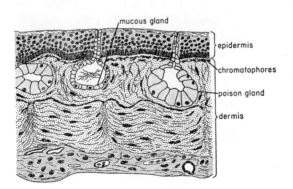

FIG. 5.5 Section of skin of a frog.
(From Weichert.)

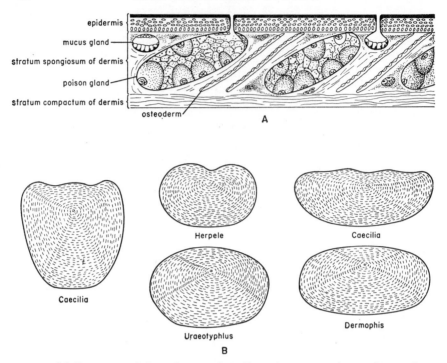

FIG. 5.6 A, section of skin of a caecilian. B, surface view of osteoderms of different genera of caecilians. (From Werner.)

vital problem for animals lacking an efficient kidney. With later perfection of a renal control of water content and development of a more impervious epidermis, the bone disappeared. A second theory is based upon the existence at that time of large invertebrate predators such as eurypterids. As these predators disappeared from the scene and as vertebrates later invaded habitats (such as the ocean) unoccupied by other similar animals, the cumbersome armor was gradually lost.

In either case the loss of bone in later vertebrates was accomplished by the simple expedient of retaining the tissues unossified as in the embryonic stages. Modification of the embryonic mesenchyme into the compact connective tissue characteristic of at least part if not all of the dermis of all living vertebrates was a minor hurdle, The close relation of bone and connective tissue is firmly established on a histological basis; in fact, bone is often regarded as a type of connective tissue.

Reduction of the bone and dermis generally has progressed to such a degree that in cyclostomes the dermis is little if any thicker than the epidermis (Fig. 5.3); in teleosts the dermis is nearly as thin (Fig. 5.4), but does retain in most species thin vestiges of the formerly extensive bony armor; and in modern amphibians (Fig. 5.5) only one primitive group (caecilians, Fig. 5.6) retains even slight vestiges of the heavy armor that

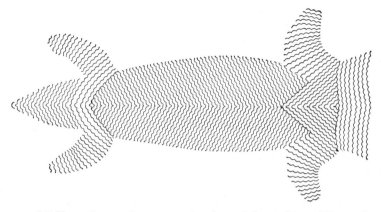

FIG. 5.7 Ventral osteoderms in a fossil amphibian. (From Werner.)

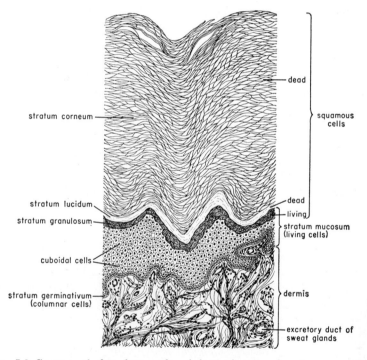

FIG. 5.8 Section of skin from sole of foot of man, showing excessive thickness of stratum corneum. (From Maximow and Bloom.)

even fossil amphibians are known to have possessed (Fig. 5.7). Only in the ganoid fish does some respectable remnant of the ancestral armor exist among living vertebrates.

The epidermis apparently evolved relatively slowly as the dermal changes were taking place in the fishes. It did develop a stratified arrangement typical of the vertebrate skin, but retained approximately the same moderate thickness throughout.

Thus the vertebrate integument has, in the course of evolution of the anamniotes, for the most part been characterized by (1) a decrease in thickness, and (2) a decrease in degree of ossification. These trends are advantageous in permitting greater mobility, and in amphibians in permitting greater reliance upon the skin as a respiratory organ; and they were made possible by modifications of the epidermal seal (see following discussion).

A reversal of evolutionary trend is seen, however, in amniotes, in which the skin has become progressively thicker, especially in the dermal layers. Two selective forces have been primarily involved: (1) prevention of loss of water, and (2) retention of heat. Mechanical protection has been a minor factor. Only those amniotes provided with skin accessories such as feathers, or a thick coat of hair, are free from the necessity of possessing a thick skin. The reversal has even been carried to the extreme of development of a new dermal bony armor (turtles, armadillos).

In any animal the thickness of the skin varies greatly in different parts of the body, in accordance with the function it serves. The skin on the soles of feet (Fig. 5.8) and hands is extremely thick, chiefly because of the retention of keratinized epidermis; that over the surface of the eye is extremely thin (Fig. 5.9). To a certain degree, thickness is an individual and not wholly a racial matter: humans accustomed to walking barefooted have astonishingly thick soles, whereas those accustomed to wearing shoes possess relatively thin skin and can tolerate little of the irregularities that their barefooted brethren take without thought.

Having dealt briefly with the integument itself, let us consider the derivatives of each integumentary layer.

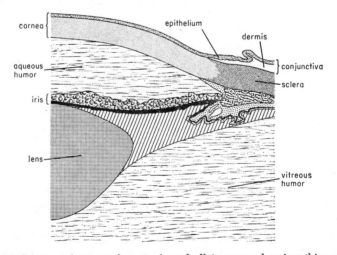

FIG. 5.9 Section of exposed part of eyeball in man, showing thinness of skin. (From Maximow and Bloom.)

Dermal Derivatives

Three general groups of structures may be regarded as essentially dermal, both in embryogeny and in phylogeny: (a) the primary armor and derivatives thereof, (b) secondary dermal armor, and (c) miscellaneous armor derivatives. A fourth group is comprised of (d) the chromatic structures of the dermis; these differ from the other dermal structures here discussed by almost certainly having evolved separately from the dermis.

Primary Dermal Armor and Its Evolution. Ostracoderms, the earliest known vertebrates, possessed a bony armor of large plates presumably underlying the epidermis and developing embryonically from mesenchyme representing the thin loose layer between epidermis and somatic muscle of their protochordate ancestors. In adult ostracoderms presumably no dermis, as we now know it, existed; probably only a minimum of loose connective tissue remained between the bony "skin" and muscle. The dermis itself, as well as numerous kinds of bony elements, is thought to have been derived phylogenetically from the primary dermal armor. The primary derivatives or groups of derivatives from the ostracoderm armor are shown in Figure 5.10, and the details in Figure 5.11.

In the cyclostome derivatives of the ostracoderms precisely the same trend that most other vertebrates demonstrate is duplicated: the primary dermal armor is reduced. In this group, however, the reduction has proceeded farther (Fig. 5.3) than in any other group of vertebrates, no hard vestiges whatsoever remaining in the form of teeth, scales, or anything else of the kind. Only the dermis remains in testimony of the presence of a dermal armor in cyclostome ancestors.

In those placoderms in the tetrapod line of evolution, the primitive armor of large plates became on the contrary smaller fragments permitting greater mobility of the body. Ostracoderms must have possessed relatively little mobility, in part because of the heavy armor; they apparently were highly sedentary bottom-dwellers. feeding by pharyngeal filtration. In placoderms, however, with the newly devised jaws permitting a more aggressive type of food catching, a premium was unavoidably placed upon mobility. The population lines of those placoderms that happened to develop this trait best, by subdivision of the plates (Fig. 5.12), persisted: some of their descendents gradually transformed into fishes such as now inhabit the earth. In other placoderm lines the large plates were retained and modified in various ways, but these lines were not successful in coping with the changing environment and soon disappeared.

The scales developed in the advanced placoderms were, it is generally believed, *denticulate cosmoid scales;* the single difference between these and the cosmoid scales of later fishes was that they possessed very hard, tiny spines (*dermal denticles*) on their external surfaces. As in cosmoid scales, three recognizably different layers were present, and the dermal denticles added still another, making a total of four bony or bonelike layers in the placoderm cosmoid scale.

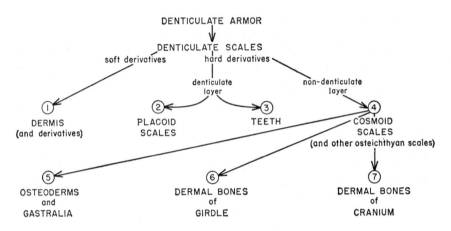

FIG. 5.10 Primary derivatives or groups of derivatives from the ostraco-derm denticulate armor.

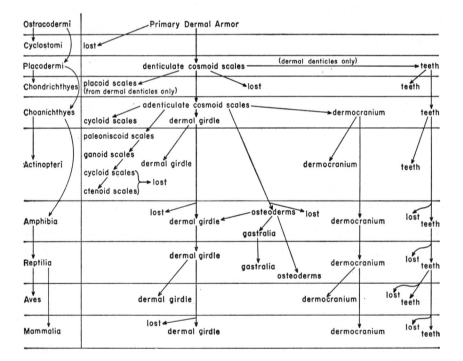

FIG. 5.11 Evolutionary chart of the hard derivatives of the primary der-mal armor.

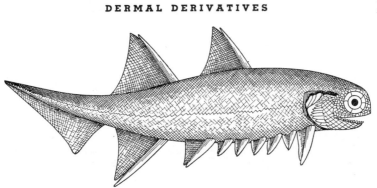

FIG. 5.12 A placoderm with small scales. (From Romer.)

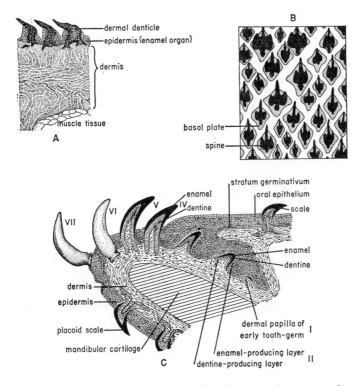

FIG. 5.13 Shark skin, with placoid scales. A, vertical section, showing the *spine* of the placoid scales projecting through the epidermis, and the *basal plate* imbedded in the dermis; B, surface view. C, transition into teeth, at edge of jaw. Roman numerals indicate the sequence of tooth succession, the replacement series ending at VI and VII (shown entire, not in section) that are about to be shed. (From Romer, Neal and Rand, and Rand, respectively.)

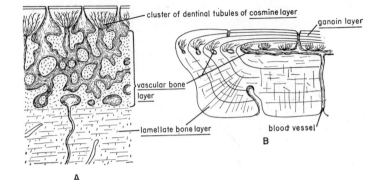

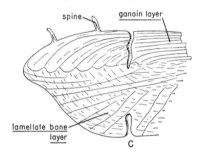

FIG. 5.14 Cross sections of cosmoid (A), paleoniscoid (B), and ganoid (C) scales. Note the three layers in A and B, two in C. (From Hyman.)

About the jaws the denticulate cosmoid scales were for the most part reduced in the pretetrapod placoderms, but the dermal denticles were, on the contrary, enlarged and served as *teeth*. The placoderm teeth, being of dermal denticle origin, are thus homologous with the teeth of all later vertebrates.

Two main lines of evolution appear to have followed the placoderms. In one line, leading toward the modern Chondrichthyes, the three basal layers of the denticulate cosmoid scales were lost simply by failure of mineral deposition, the tissues normally forming scales being retained as connective tissues, specialized as the dermis. The fourth or outermost layer, comprising the dermal denticles, was, on the contrary, retained and somewhat elaborated, becoming the *placoid scales* of modern elasmobranchs (Fig. 5.13). The teeth, of course, were retained, and in most sharks show their homology with dermal denticles by a remarkably convincing (1) gradation of teeth and placoid scales about the mouth (particularly embryonically), and (2) similarity of form and structure of their placoid scales and teeth.

In the second and more propitious line of evolution, toward the Choanichthyes, the reverse trend occurred, with the loss of dermal denticles and retention of the three-layered bony *cosmoid scales* (Fig. 5.14). Those cosmoid scales lying on the head assumed a regularity of position, shape, and size presaging their ultimately complete integration with the skull; thus in the Choanichthyes that part of the cranium derived from dermal tissues (*dermocranium*) is seen for the first time (Fig. 5.15). The dermocranium is derived from cosmoid scales. Likewise, those cosmoid scales lying in close apposition with the pectoral girdle assumed a greater importance and regularity, becoming ultimately the components of the dermal girdle and consisting primitively of about a dozen or more bones (Fig. 5.16). The dermal girdle is represented in all species of virtually every descendent class, but there is a general trend toward reduction in number of components throughout. The extreme is reached in some mammals (ungulates) and amphibians (salamanders) which retain no dermal girdle whatsoever. No dermal scales are integrated with the pelvic girdle in any vertebrate.

In some Choanichthyes, for instance the modern Dipnoi, the cosmoid scales have become greatly reduced, being thinned to a single layer of bone as *leptoid scales*. In all Choanichthyes, of course, a certain part of the embryonic tissues representing the formerly completely ossified primary armor remains unossified, being transformed into dermis.

FIG. 5.15 Scales on skull of bowfin (Amia), dorsal view, showing approximation to dermocranial elements of tetrapods. (From Eddy.)

FIG. 5.16 Pectoral girdle and fins of a fish, showing position of bones relative to each other and to other parts of the skeleton. (From Gregory.)

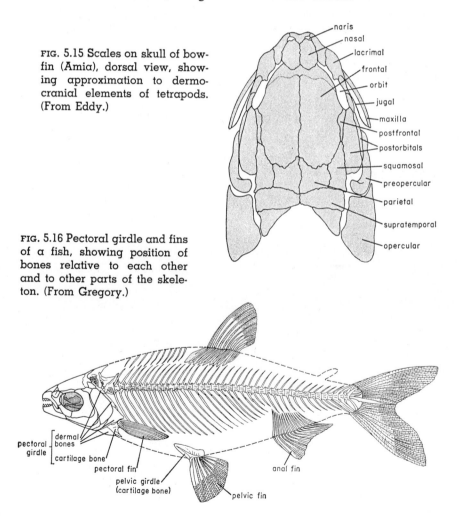

In the Actinopteri the teeth, dermocranium, and dermal girdle elements, all originating from the primary dermal armor, were retained, but the body scales evolved independently along new lines, as summarized in Figure 5.17. The cosmoid scales are replaced by *paleoniscoid scales* (Fig. 5.14), which differ primarily in transformation of the outer layer of each scale into a very hard substance, *ganoin*. Paleoniscoid scales persist in certain modern Chondrostei (Polypterus, Calamoichthys) but have been replaced in other living Actinopteri by still thinner types of scales. Directly derived from the primitive paleoniscoid scales are *ganoid scales* (Fig. 5.14); persistent in modern gars and sturgeons, these are distinguished by the retention of only one bony layer in addition to the ganoin.

Most Actinopteri, however, possess a still thinner *leptoid* type of scale derived from the ganoid type by loss of the ganoin layer. Two kinds of leptoid scales are commonly recognized: *cycloid* and *ctenoid scales* (Fig. 5.18). These two differ from each other in a relatively minor way, involving only the presence or absence of microscopically tiny tines (*cteni*) on the free, posterior edge; fundamentally the two are the same type. It will be observed that leptoid scales have evolved independently in at least two lines (Dipnoi, Teleostei), but only in one line (Teleostei) did the ctenoid variant appear.

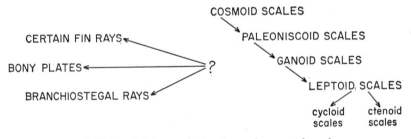

FIG. 5.17 Osteichthyan derivatives of cosmoid scales.

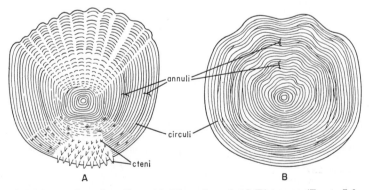

FIG. 5.18 Leptoid scales: Ctenoid (A) and cycloid (B) types. (From Adams and Eddy.)

FIG. 5.19 Osteoderms of a gila monster, seen in radiograph as whitish nodules widely distributed over skin and head. (Courtesy Comstock Publ. Co. From Smith.)

In some Actinopteri (for example, catfish) the ultimate extreme of complete loss of dermal scales has occurred, paralleling the usual condition in modern tetrapods.

Certain other derivatives from osteichthyan scales include the bran-- chiostegal rays (rodlike bones supporting the ventral pharyngeal wall), bony plates (as in the sturgeon), and certain fin rays (rodlike supports, often jointed, each joint homologous with the body scales of the fish).

Hard parts originating from the piscine dermal armor and persisting generally throughout the tetrapod line of evolution from the Choa- nichthyes are (1) at least parts of the dermocranium (in all classes), (2) the teeth (lacking in modern turtles, birds, a few mammals), (3) the dermal girdle (lacking in modern salamanders, ungulates), and (4) body scales (with their derivatives). The evolutionary history of the first three is discussed elsewhere, and attention may be directed here to the body scales. It must be realized that a somewhat arbitrary distinction is made between the piscine bony scales and their homologs in tetrapods. Tetrapod dermal scales are, in unmodified form, called *osteoderms* (Fig. 5.19). They are thick in some vertebrates (such as crocodilians), thin in others (such as skinks among the lizards), but in either case are regarded as consisting of but one type of bonelike material, whereas all dermal scales of fishes, ex- cept the leptoid scales, consist of at least two types of bonelike material organized in separate layers. The fundamental distinction between osteoderms and dermal scales of fishes remains, however, the arbitrary one that the bony dermal scales of tetrapods are osteoderms, those of fishes something else.

Osteoderms were commonly present in primitive extinct amphibians, but the trend throughout tetrapods was toward loss of them as the epidermal scales became functionally superior. They are gone completely in all modern amphibians except most species of caecilians, which retain vestiges concealed in the skin on certain parts of the body. Many extinct reptiles possessed them, but in relatively few living groups (some crocodilians and

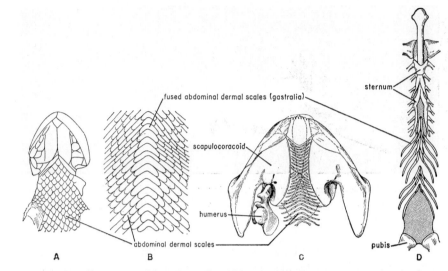

FIG. 5.20 Transition from dermal scales to gastralia, as seen in ventral view of thoracic region. A, a fossil choanichthyan; B, an early fossil amphibian; C, a later fossil amphibian; D, alligator. (From Gregory, Eddy.)

lizards) have they persisted. In both of the most advanced classes (Aves, Mammalia) osteoderms are completely missing both in living and in extinct species.

Before osteoderms disappeared they gave rise, however, to two other structures. In primitive amphibians one large osteoderm (or several fused together) became incorporated into the pectoral girdle, becoming associated (as the *interclavicle*) with the other dermal bones already acquired by the girdle in fishes. The evolutionary history of this element is discussed in

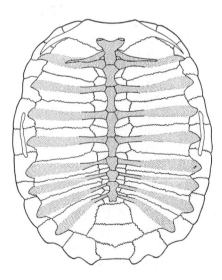

FIG. 5.21 Secondary dermal armor on carapace of a modern turtle, ventral view. Primary endoskeleton (ribs and vertebrae) shown in stipple; all remaining elements are dermal bones. (From Eddy.)

Chapter 7. A second derivative also appeared in the ancient amphibians through the fusion together of whole rows of osteoderms to form a series of rodlike (and riblike) structures called *gastralia* in the ventrolateral abdominal wall (Fig. 5.20). Gastralia were not destined to much more success than osteoderms themselves, however, for in extinct vertebrates they are confined to certain amphibians and reptiles, and in living vertebrates they have persisted only among the crocodilians, Sphenodon, and some lizards.

Secondary Dermal Armor. Although the general trend in vertebrates has been toward elimination of bone formation in the layers representing the dermis, the process is reversible. This is thought to be the case in turtles (Fig. 5.21), the most ancient examples of which were virtually or entirely without shell. In later types new centers of ossification, not homologous with the old, arose and enlarged in the dermis, forming a shell much as we now see it in modern forms. It is possible that some crocodilian and lizard osteoderms are secondary developments although they appear to be of primary dermal origin.

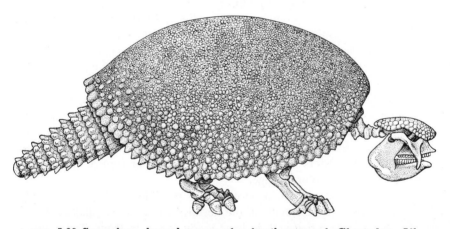

FIG. 5.22 Secondary dermal armor of a fossil mammal, Glyptodon. All the parts shown of the carapace, tail, and cap on skull, shown as nodular structures, consist of dermal bone. (From Romer.)

In the armadillos of existing mammals and in the glyptodonts (Fig. 5.22) of fossil mammals, there has unquestionably been a similar, independent (nonhomologous) formation of bone in the dermis, although in these groups it does not involve the venter.

In some of these cases, certainly, and in others possibly, the new formation is not directly homologous with the primary bony armor, despite a remarkable superficial similarity.

Miscellany. Through fusion and enlargement a number of dermal oddities have been produced in different classes. Protective growths developed independently in several tetrapod classes from elements of the primary dermal armor. The bony outgrowths forming the core of a variety of horns in living mammals are examples. Numerous fossil reptiles and some fossil mammals possessed a varied assortment of other types of bony horns. Fusion of formerly separate scales occurs among some fishes, producing large bony plates and spines. The body plates of sturgeons and the dermal fin spines of teleost fishes are examples.

Chromatic Structures. All vertebrates possess special color cells, *chromatophores,* derived apparently from the early embryonic nervous system. During embryogeny most of these cells move into the positions they are to hold throughout postembryonic life. Most are stellate cells with long, slender processes, and they contain color granules that may either concentrate in a small central mass or become dispersed throughout the cell even into all the slender processes. Some are situated along blood vessels, some in the celomic walls, some in the liver and other organs of the body; exactly what the function is that these chromatophores may have is unknown.

In ectotherm vertebrates most chromatophores are located in the upper levels of the dermis (Fig. 5.23). The most abundant are *melanophores,* a type containing melanin, a black or dark brown pigment; this is the type distributed elsewhere in the body. In the dermis also occur *lipophores,* containing oil droplets usually of yellow (*xanthophores*) or reddish (*erythrophores*) hues, *guanophores* (or *leucophores*) containing a noniridescent white substance, and *iridocytes,* containing light-diffractive crystals producing a variety of iridescent effects. Interaction of these four kinds of chromatophores and the tissues in which they lie makes possible a kaleidoscopic *metachrosis* (color change) in some especially talented vertebrates such as flounders and chameleons. Most other ectotherms are more or less metachrotic, although snakes, because of their evolution from subterranean ancestors that lost most color and color control, are capable of relatively little color change.

Extensive metachrosis in ectotherms is possible chiefly because of the location of the color elements in the dermis, where the circulatory system and nervous system can and do have ready access to them. The chroma-

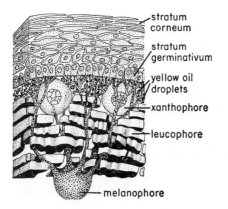

stratum corneum

stratum germinativum

yellow oil droplets

xanthophore

leucophore

melanophore

FIG. 5.23 Section of skin of a lizard (Anolis), showing chromatic structures. (From Von Geldern.)

CHORDATE GROUPS	INTEGUMENTARY SEAL				ECDYSIS
	DERMAL	EPIDERMAL			
		mucoid coat	cuticle	keratin	
Protochordates	none	present	present	none	none
Ancestral Vertebrates	heavy bony armor	present	present	none	slow, continual
Fishes	light scales	present	lost	granules	slow, continual
Amphibians	lost	present	lost	thin layer	periodic
Reptiles	lost	lost	lost	thick layer	periodic
Birds	lost	lost	lost	thick layer	continual, feathers' periodic
Mammals	lost	lost	lost	thick layer	continual, feathers' periodic

FIG. 5.24 Chart of evolution in certain features pertaining to the integumentary seal.

tophores are controlled chiefly, if not exclusively, by hormones (adrenalin, acetylcholine, or similar compounds), which reach them via dermal capillaries or are produced by the terminal branches of involuntary nerve fibers.

Because of the development of the superficial skin coats of hair and feathers in mammals and birds, the extensive metachrotic potential of the dermis is not exploited in these groups. Here the color and pattern devolve upon the epidermis as discussed hereafter.

Epidermal Derivatives

The epidermis, serving as the ultimate surface of contact and communication between two highly variable systems (environmental and somatic), has had a complex evolutionary history. Most specializations, developed in many separate lines of evolution, have not permitted the sort of flexibility needed for the main streams of evolution through the several vertebrate classes, and thus are of short history. These we shall mention but briefly. Largely obscured by the multiplicity of specializations are a number of major trends, however, concerning the following: (a) the epidermal seal; (b) epidermal scales; (c) claws; (d) chromatic structures; and (e) glands. Other items of lesser phylogenetic importance we shall group together as (f) miscellany.

The Epidermal Seal. The integument in all animals includes some sort of protective layer that acts as a "seal," preventing free passage of water and its solutes (Fig. 5.24). The integumentary seal is effected either by the epidermis (the "epidermal seal") or the dermis (the "dermal seal"). The dermal seal was of prime importance in primitive vertebrates, the bony armor apparently serving this purpose. As we have already seen, however, there has been a gradual trend away from the bony armor of the skin, and it is evident that even in the only living vertebrates (the fishes) with the best developed remnant of that armor, it no longer serves importantly as an integumentary seal except in a very few species. In all living tetrapods and in most fishes and protochordates, the epidermis is the most important component in the integumentary seal.

Three devices have served to provide an epidermal seal in chordates: the *cuticle, mucoid coat,* and *keratin.* The cuticle (Fig. 5.1) is a continuous nonliving layer secreted by and situated on the outer surface of the epidermis. It is present only in protochordates, embryonic fishes, and larval amphibians. In all cases it is supplemented by a mucoid coat secreted by numerous epidermal glands. The mucoid coat itself is highly impervious, when wet, to the passage of water and its solutes, but it is useless in this respect when dry. Thus vertebrates possessing a mucoid seal must remain in water or at least in a moist environment. Fishes and amphibians possess a mucoid seal, and in early developmental stages also possess a cuticle.

It may be presumed that in the earliest vertebrates—the ostracoderms—the mucoid seal had not evolved, or at least had not been adequately perfected, else the bony dermis would not have appeared on the scene. Presumably the perfection of the mucoid coat initiated the transformation of the bony dermis to soft tissues characteristic of the dermis in vertebrates living today.

With invasion of the land habitat, however, the mucoid coat could no longer suffice, at least for the extremes of terrestrial adaptation, for it cannot function as a seal when dry. The vertebrate skin was already preadapted to meet this problem, however, by the continual replacement of the epidermal cells; this feature led to the development and perfection of a highly efficient layer of keratin that replaced the mucoid coat as the primary device effecting an epidermal seal in tetrapods.

To trace the evolution of keratin let us go back to the prevertebrate protochordates. These animals possess an epidermis of but a single layer of cells; this layer is capable of regeneration upon injury, but the cells in it do not continually divide. In fact, the presence of a cuticle effectively precludes continual division and consequent sloughing off of epidermal cells, simply because it would be impossible to maintain the cuticular covering intact at all times and places.

In all living vertebrates the epidermis consists of numerous layers of cells. The deepest layer is columnar in form (Fig. 5.23), and is called the *stratum germinativum,* since in that layer, and that layer only, cell division is constantly taking place to give rise to the cells that form the more superficial layers. Cell division may occur either slowly or rapidly in this layer, and either continuously or periodically. Cells derived from the basal layer are first pushed peripherally to become a part of the several layers of *cuboidal* cells, characterized by their more or less cubed appearance (Fig. 5.23). In time the cuboidal cells are pushed still farther peripherally to become a part of the several layers of *squamous* cells (Fig. 5.23) characterized by their flat, scalelike shape (*L. squama,* scale). Later on the outer squamous cells die and are sloughed from the skin either continuously or at intervals. There is no sharp line of demarcation between the squamous, cuboidal, and columnar cells, but the three zones are clearly evident.

The epidermis is not invaded by blood vessels. Its metabolic needs are met solely by diffusion. Therefore, the outermost epidermal cells are less efficiently supplied than the deeper ones, and their tendency to die and be sloughed away is, of course, correlated with the decrease in efficiency of diffusion with increase in distance from the dermis. As the squamous cells begin to degenerate, their cytoplasm is gradually transformed into granules of *keratin*—a hard, horny, substance. In fishes the keratin is not abundant in the peripheral cells, which are moulted before extensive deposits of keratin can form. Furthermore, in fishes there is a very slow, continual replacement of the epidermal cells, which are sloughed separately or in small groups as the layer of mucus is worn away. The mucous layer is, despite wear, continually maintained by secretion from epidermal glands. The substance keratin *is* present in fishes, and in certain areas of the body it contributes to specialized structures such as certain rays and spines; yet it does not form a continuous layer, and its occurrence in grossly visible quantities in fishes is regarded as exceptional.

In amphibians the keratin has become more regularly present, but even in this group it forms a continuous layer only in the more terrestrial types; in completely aquatic forms the keratin exists mostly as scattered granules in the outermost cells, much as in fishes. In terrestrial types the outer cells remain attached to the underlying ones, even after they are dead and consist of virtually nothing but keratin; in this form they constitute a keratinoid layer, the *stratum corneum* (Fig. 5.2), as opposed to the *stratum mucosum* (Figs. 5.2, 5.23) of living epidermal cells internal to them. The corneum, as a continuous layer, is very thin and only microscopically visible in amphibians, but in many frogs and toads there are small, scattered areas of corneal accumulation that form *warts* useful as protective and supportive devices for tactile sensory organs (see following discussion of prototriches). A few other grossly visible corneal structures occur, such as claws and friction pads on the digits and legs, but, as in fishes, these are regarded as the exception rather than the rule.

It is in reptiles that the stratum corneum first became a grossly visible, continuous layer, with the accumulation of numerous layers of keratinized cells on the surface of the skin. Hypertrophy of the keratinoid layer and loss of the mucoid coat were adaptations to the necessity for an integumentary seal under conditions of lower humidity than other vertebrates had been able to withstand.

All the tetrapod classes, at least primitively, possess a certain periodicity in replacement or *ecdysis* of the stratum corneum; it is not sloughed continually, as in the fishes, except in advanced groups. In both amphibians and reptiles the outer layers are sloughed at intervals of a few days or weeks, as an *exuvia* which may take the form of a single large skinlike structure or as large sections thereof. The familiar cast "skins" of snakes are not in reality the entire skin, but only the outermost layers of the stratum corneum, under which a new stratum corneum has already developed. Many lizards and amphibians pull the exuviae in large sections from the body with the jaws, and eat them at once; snakes crawl from their exuviae and leave them unmolested.

The periodicity of ecdysis characteristic of the tetrapod ectotherms is not retained as a general integumentary phenomenon in mammals and birds, primarily because of the existence in both of these groups of epidermal structures—hair and feathers, respectively—that cannot be shed with the stratum corneum and which interfere with ecdysis of a typical exuvia. Therefore, in both endotherm classes the stratum corneum is continuously worn away little by little; there is no periodicity of moult from the skin. However, both classes retain some evidence of periodicity, since both hair and feathers are characteristically replaced periodically instead of continually.

The periodicity of moulting basically characteristic of tetrapods presumably evolved as a device assuring maintenance of a protective seal at all times, regardless of the stress of wear. Certainly the crawling habits of primitive tetrapods subjected the skin to greater wear than it received from movements in water by fishes. It is of interest that under situations of unusual stress the frequency of moulting is increased. The periodicity is reflected even at the germinative layer of the epidermis, being marked by cycles of rapid division followed by a resting period. Thus a new stratum corneum is formed before the old is shed.

In limited regions of the body several to many replacement layers are built up on the scales in certain lizards to produce thickened coverings or projections. This phenomenon is seen in unspecialized form on the *escutcheon scales* found in certain species over the rear part of abdomen and on the ventral surfaces of the hind legs, all with several layers of outer epidermal cells forming a visibly thick covering on each scale. Specialized *cteni* have evolved from scales such as these by retention of a large number of layers arising like a cone from *femoral pores* in scales along the rear edge of the thigh and from *preanal pores* (Fig. 5.34) in scales in front of the anus. These structures are not glands, as they have almost universally been regarded in the past (see Taylor).

Since amphibians possessed a stratum corneum, their failure to enlarge upon it as an epidermal seal, eliminating the mucoid coat, requires expla-

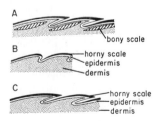

FIG. 5.25 Diagrammatic sections of skin of lizards and snakes, with and without osteoderms. A, lizard with osteoderm; B, lizard without osteoderm; C, snake, without osteoderms.

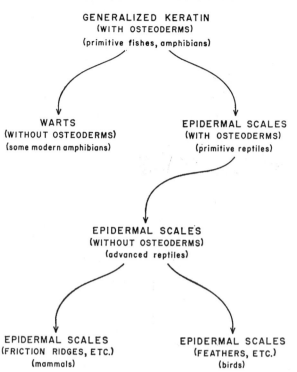

GENERALIZED KERATIN
(WITH OSTEODERMS)
(primitive fishes, amphibians)

WARTS
(WITHOUT OSTEODERMS)
(some modern amphibians)

EPIDERMAL SCALES
(WITH OSTEODERMS)
(primitive reptiles)

EPIDERMAL SCALES
(WITHOUT OSTEODERMS)
(advanced reptiles)

EPIDERMAL SCALES
(FRICTION RIDGES, ETC.)
(mammals)

EPIDERMAL SCALES
(FEATHERS, ETC.)
(birds)

FIG. 5.26 Evolutionary chart of generalized keratinoid structures, showing homology of amphibian warts and epidermal scales.

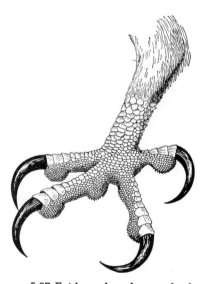

FIG. 5.27 Epidermal scales on the leg of a hawk. (From Hilzheimer.)

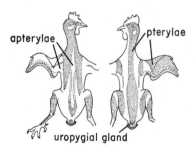

FIG. 5.28 Feather tracts (pterylae) in a rooster. (From Walter.)

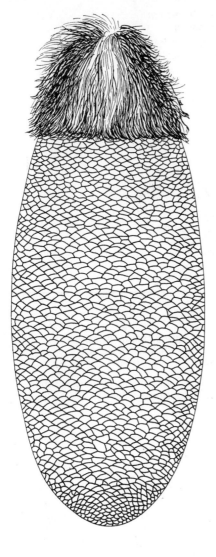

FIG. 5.29 Epidermal scales in mammals: tail of a beaver, dorsal view. (From Morgan.)

nation. The answer presumably lies in their extensive reliance upon the skin for respiration, especially in hibernation, as most amphibians hibernate under water. The skin cannot serve as a respiratory organ (a) if it is dry, or (b) if it has an impervious covering such as a thick stratum corneum.

Epidermal Scales. As keratin evolved in reptiles, a new structure appeared upon the scene—the epidermal scale. Primitively, epidermal scales were simply thickenings of keratin superimposed over the bony osteoderms that generally were present over the body in ancestral reptiles. The epidermal scales necessarily reproduced the form of the dermal osteoderms (Fig. 5.25). Some lizards and crocodilians have retained both on certain parts of the body, but most modern reptiles have lost the osteoderms, the lighter epidermal structures serving as an adequate or superior protective substitute. The scattered warts found in some modern amphibians appear to be homologous with the reptilian epidermal scales, but did not give rise to them (see Fig. 5.26).

Naturally certain effects of the existence of epidermal scales in reptiles have been transmitted to their avian and mammalian descendants. Birds retain some epidermal scales unmodified, as, for example, on the feet and legs (Fig. 5.27), but over parts of the rest of the body (*pterylae,* as opposed to the featherless *apterylae,* Fig. 5.28) they have been strikingly modified as *feathers.* Even in mammals some epidermal scales persist essentially as in the reptiles, as, for example, on the tails of rodents (Fig. 5.29). Others are modified as subarticular pads or friction ridges (Fig. 5.30) on the hands and feet.

The most conspicuous epidermal specialization in mammals (*hair*) is

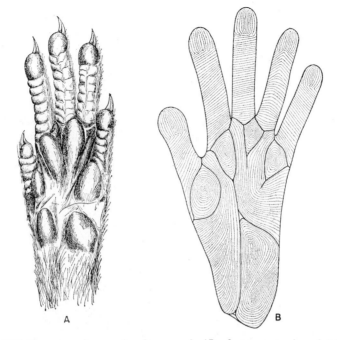

FIG. 5.30 Correspondence of palmar pads (**A**, shrew mouse) and friction ridges (**B**, monkey). (From Wilder.)

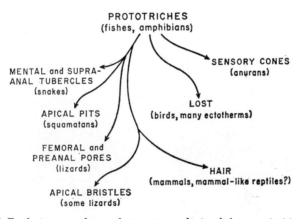

FIG. 5.31 Evolutionary chart of structures derived from primitive tactile pits (prototriches) of ancient vertebrates.

only secondarily associated with scales, contrary to the situation in birds with their feathers derived directly from scales. It is thought that hair, unique to mammals, evolved originally (Fig. 5.31) from tactile sensory pits, called *prototriches* (singular, *protothrix*) of fishes (Fig. 5.32) and primitive amphibians. From these simple sensory organs, scattered on the surface of the skin, more specialized *sensory cones,* often arising from the

FIG. 5.32 A prototrich (unshaded) as seen in section of dogfish skin. (From Elias and Bortner.)

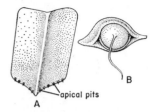

FIG. 5.33 Apical pits and bristles on a lizard scale. A, entire scale; B, a single pit and bristle enlarged from A. (From Scortecci.)

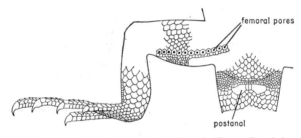

FIG. 5.34 Femoral pores of a lizard. (From Smith.)

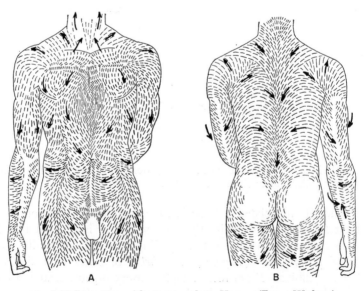

FIG. 5.35 Direction of hair growth in Homo. (From Walter.)

center of a pit, evolved in many modern anurans. Homologous derivatives are the *apical pits* of living snakes and lizards, so called because they are situated one to seven in a row, at or near the posterior, free apex of the epidermal scales. Apical pits are of particular importance in reptiles as a means of circumventing the otherwise virtually tactile-impervious, corneous skin characteristic of that class. In some living species of lizards a tiny hair-like filament (an *apical bristle*) protrudes from the bottom of each pit (Fig. 5.33) and is presumably of tactile function much like the more primitive apical pits and prototriches. Other apical pits have become specialized among reptiles as the tactile *mental tubercles* on the scales of the chin in snakes, and the *supra-anal tubercles* on the scales above the anus in snakes. All of these specialized derivatives are primarily of *hedonic* (sexually stimulating) function.

From progenitors that must have resembled apical bristles, the hair of mammals is thought to have evolved. Presumably of sensory function originally, hair subsequently attained a certain degree of efficiency in repelling water (Fig. 5.35), and in temperature and color control.

Since the reptilian sensory pits were located on the apices of epidermal scales, and these scales are typically arranged in rows with the scales of one row alternating with those of the adjacent rows instead of lying even with them, it follows that the distributional pattern of the apical pits over the body should be, and is, the same as that of the scales. It is of great interest that the primitive distributional pattern of hair is likewise that of the sensory pits (Fig. 5.36). In most parts of the body this primitive pattern has

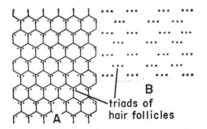

FIG. 5.36 Distributional pattern of hair in the presence of epidermal scales (A) and without scales (B). (From Romer.)

been lost in advanced mammals, but it may still be seen in a few areas, as for example, in the tail of rodents and on the side of the hand in man.

Claws. Claws appeared simultaneously with epidermal scales in reptiles. A very few amphibians have clawlike thickenings on their digit tips.

The basic claw structure in reptiles is found to persist in the claws of birds and mammals. No question of homology arises in this connection, but the fact that the nails and hooves (Fig. 5.37) of certain mammals are likewise homologous with claws, although also unquestionable, is not so readily obvious. All three (claws, hooves, nails) possess a long, hard upper *unguis,* and a relatively soft *subunguis* underneath.

Chromatic Structures. As stated before, the development of a layer of hair or feathers covering the epidermis of birds and mammals rendered use-

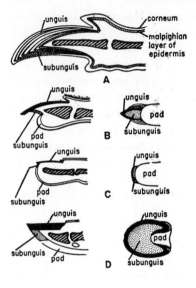

FIG. 5.37 Reptilian claws and some of their derivatives, showing basic similarity of structure. A, Reptilian claw; B, mammalian claw; C, nail of man; D, hoof of horse. (From Walter.)

less the complex chromatic system of ancestral reptiles. Accordingly the only chromatophores ordinarily found in endotherms are subdermal and of no concern with externally visible color. Color in these animals is produced by freely distributed pigment, not housed in specialized chromatophores. Part of the pigment is in the epidermis, part in the hair and feathers. Location of the pigment in the epidermis is essential to permit its invasion into hair and feathers, both epidermal structures. Since the epidermis is free from direct invasion by blood vessels and nerve endings, color is subject to very little hormone or nervous control. Mammals and birds are virtually nonmetachrotic. The only notable color changes of which they are capable are structural and semipermanent, occurring when the coat of hair or feathers is shed.

Epidermal Glands. The protochordate epidermis is provided with numerous, single-celled glands, but lacks multicellular glands. The same type of gland is persistent throughout fishes and in larval amphibians. Often simple multicellular glands do appear as specializations in some fishes; some *poison glands* (as those associated with the pectoral spines of catfish), *water sacs* of sharks, and *pterygopodial glands* of skates and rays are examples. Most integumentary glands in fishes are single celled, however, and not until amphibians appeared did the *simple* (that is, unbranched) multicellular gland become common. Modern adult amphibians possess them.

Assumption of a life by amphibians even partially free of water necessitated a number of alterations in their inheritance of integumentary glands. Not only did the glands become almost, if not entirely, multicellular, but a few of these were still further modified as *compound* (that is, branched) glands in order to perform certain new functions necessitated by the new habitat. Some, like the lacrimal and Harderian glands of the eyelids (like-

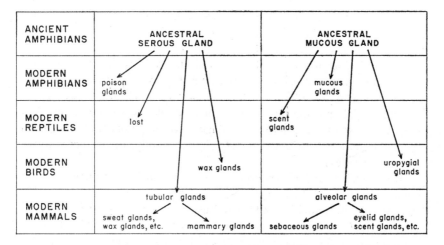

FIG. 5.38 Evolutionary chart of integumentary glands in tetrapod vertebrates.

wise newly developed) and the salivary glands, persist through all except a
few side-line tetrapods; others, like the hatching glands on the snouts of
tadpoles and adhesive glands on the lower surfaces of the digit tips of some
anurans, are limited in occurrence to (presumably) modern amphibians.
Modern amphibians also possess a possibly very significant differentiation
of the general integumentary glands into the ordinary *mucous* gland and
the more specialized, often venomous, *serous* (or "granular") glands. The
latter are particularly abundant in warty skinned species, and one aggregation (the *parotoid gland*) on the skin over the scapula is characteristic of
toads, a group of especially poisonous anurans.

The possible significance (Fig. 5.38) of the existence of two types of
generally occurring integumentary glands in amphibians is that apparently
all of the integumentary glands of mammals—which possess more kinds
and more numerous glands than any other vertebrate—evolved from basically two types: tubular and alveolar. The tubular glands are basically
serous, the alveolar glands basically mucous. The numerous glands of mammals did not simply appear from nowhere, but the virtually complete absence of integumentary glands in living reptiles has been an insurmountable
obstacle to determination of the lineage of the mammalian types. It is safe
to assume that the early reptiles ancestral to mammals possessed an ample
supply of integumentary glands, that they were of at least two types, and
that forerunners of the two general mammalian types existed among them.
The differentiation of the two types, as previously suggested, with good
reason may have been initiated in the amphibians; the serous glands of
modern amphibians may be regarded as homologous with the mammalian
tubular glands, and mucous glands with the mammalian alveolar glands.
Presumably the homologs evident in these two groups were derived not

from each other, but from some unknown, common ancestral type of gland that existed in extinct amphibians. How much either existing homolog may have deviated from this ancestral type is unknown.

The only integumentary glands remaining in modern reptiles are specialized scent glands of several kinds (cloacal, postcloacal, vertebral, inframarginal, angular, etc.). The orbital and salivary glands are, of course, also retained, the latter being modified in some reptiles as venom glands. This remarkable loss of the extensive heritage from amphibians of integumentary glands may be attributed largely, if not wholly, to the necessity for water conservation.

Birds evolved from a group of reptiles in which, presumably, integumentary glands had already been lost, for they have as few as reptiles. Actually, they presumably could make use of more integumentary glands, since their feathers appear to need oil as indeed does mammalian hair, but the paired *uropygial* glands (Fig. 5.28) at the base of the tail, of necessity, serve the purpose, with the help of the beak in dispersing the oil. Some birds

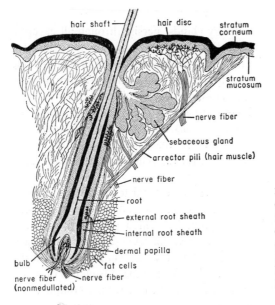

FIG. 5.39 Integumentary organs as seen in cross section of skin: A (*left*), hair and associated sebaceous glands and muscles; B (*below*), sweat glands. (After Bailey, Maximow, and Bloom.)

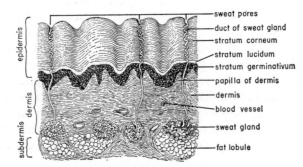

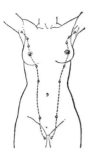

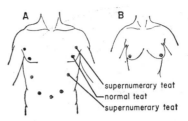

FIG. 5.40 The milk line in man, showing positions in which usually transitory glands form embryonically. (From Netter.)

FIG. 5.41 Anomalous polythelia (A) and polymastia (B) in man. (From Walter, and Neal and Rand.)

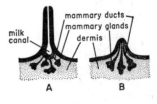

FIG. 5.42 Teats (A) and nipples (B) compared. (From Walter.)

also possess wax glands at the external auditory meatus. Birds presumably could also make use of sweat glands as a means of temperature control, but lacking the necessary materials in their heritage from reptiles, they were not developed. As a result temperature is partly controlled, as in furred mammals, by manipulation of the covering coat; the thin skin is of importance in permitting control of temperature by the feathers, and so also is oral evaporation.

Returning to mammals, the alveolar type of gland, perhaps homologous with the amphibian mucous gland, has become modified chiefly as *sebaceous* (oil) glands (Fig. 5.39), largely associated with hair, but also located at all openings of the body. A number of types of sebaceous glands is recognized, including the Meibomian and Zeis glands of the eyelids. Some alveolar glands have become modified as scent glands, commonly located near the anus. All of these glands are of *holocrine* type, in which the secretion is released by a sloughing of the entire secretory cells into the central gland cavity where the cells degenerate into an amorphous fluid.

The tubular type of gland, perhaps homologous with the amphibian serous gland, had become modified chiefly as *sweat* glands (Fig. 5.39), that are distributed over almost the entire body surface in man but of widely different distribution in other mammals. Other glands, derived either from primitive sweat glands or from a more primitive, undifferentiated tubular gland, include mammary glands, ceruminous (wax) glands of the ear, certain types of scent glands, and a few other less familiar types.

Mammary glands themselves have gone through extensive evolutionary changes. They are thought to have evolved from progenitors like sweat glands, in part because in monotremes they are, in fact, but slightly mod-

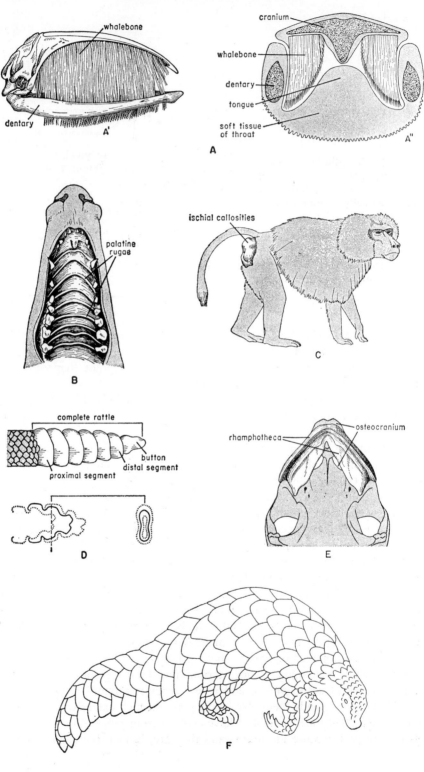

FIG. 5.43 Miscellaneous epidermal structures. (*Opposite page*), A, Whalebone (A′, as seen in lateral view of skull; A″, as seen in cross section of skull); B, palatine rugae of a dog; C, ischial callosities of a monkey; D, rattle of a rattlesnake; E, beak covering (rhamphotheca) in a turtle; F, integumentary armor of a pangolin; (*Right*) G, a photophore of a fish, as seen in cross section of skin. (From Hilzheimer, Kent, Newman, and Walter.)

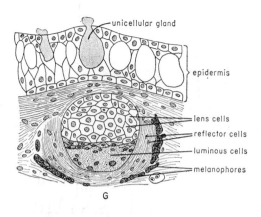

unicellular gland

epidermis

lens cells

reflector cells

luminous cells

melanophores

G

ified from the typical sweat glands, and in part because these as well as all other derivatives of the tubular type are *apocrine* glands, forming their secretion by sloughing only the tips of the secretory cells into the central cavity of the glands. Secondarily, mammary glands have acquired an alveolar structure, but they have evolved from the tubular type. In primitive mammals the mammary glands were arranged along a ventrolateral line (the *milk line*) from chest to groin. At such a stage (as in monotremes) there are no nipples, the mammary secretion merely flowing into depressed areas where the young lap it up. In the more primitive eutherians the glands remain in a single series on either side of the body (for example, in carnivores, pigs), but are provided with nipples. In more advanced mammals the glands are restricted in occurrence to a pectoral area (elephants, primates, sirenians), or to an inguinal area (horses, cows, marsupials, whales). In any vertebrate with a restricted mammary area, occasional anomalous reversions (*atavisms*) to the more primitive condition (Fig. 5.40) may be expected since there is at least a partial recapitulation embryonically of the ancient milk line. The occurrence of supernumerary glands in adults is called *polymastism,* and that of supernumerary nipples lacking glands is *polythelism* (Fig. 5.41). In a very few mammals (monotremes) the adult males possess functional mammary glands (*gynecomastism*), but in others they are rudimentary except as occasional anomalies.

The suctorial projections (nipples) on mammary glands have also evolved along various lines. In *true nipples* the mammary ducts extend to the tip of the projection, whereas in *false nipples* or *teats* the ducts open into a chamber at the base of the projection, whence a central lumen leads to the exterior (Fig. 5.42).

Miscellany. The epidermis has, in different vertebrates, evolved numerous structures apparently quite independent of epidermal scales or the other structures we have discussed thus far. Examples (Fig. 5.43) are photophores (light organs), whalebone (vertical laminae serving as strainers, hanging down from the roof of the mouth in certain whales), palatine

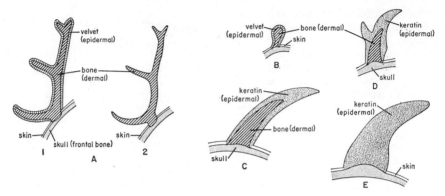

FIG. 5.44 Five types of mammalian horns as seen in section, diagrammatic. A, antler, in velvet (1) and mature (2); B, giraffe; C, bovine; D, pronghorn; E, rhinoceros.

rugae (man, carnivores), ischial and other callosities, warts, rattles (as of rattlesnakes), the bill covering or *rhamphotheca* in birds and turtles, the platelike armor of pangolins, and parts of mammalian horns.

The latter are of special interest. Five types of horns (Fig. 5.44) are commonly recognized in living mammals: antlers, pronghorns, rhinoceros horns, giraffe horns, and bovine or true horns. Antlers (of deer, reindeer) possess a bony dermal core, and, when growing, an epidermal "velvet" which is shed when the horn reaches its full growth; even the core is shed annually. In reindeer both sexes possess antlers; in others only the males possess them. In all, the antlers grow to a large size in mature animals, and are branched.

Giraffe horns are like antlers save that they are short and unbranched, retain the velvet permanently, and are never shed.

Bovine horns are not branched, and possess a permanent bony dermal core and a likewise permanent but hard epidermal covering.

Pronghorns are forked, possess a permanent bony dermal core, but have a hard epidermal covering that is shed annually.

Rhinoceros horns are permanent and entirely epidermal, and appear to represent, phylogenetically, matted hair, for each fiber is separately visible on the base of the horn when removed from its attachment.

Photophores are luminous organs of epidermal origin lying imbedded in outer layers of the dermis. They often include a group of cells acting collectively as a lens, backed by a layer of luminous cells which is in turn backed by a concave layer of reflector cells. They occur in a number of chondrichthyan and osteichthyan fishes, particularly deep-sea varieties. Only two groups of tetrapods are known to possess photophores: a few Old World nestling birds, and a small cave-dwelling lizard occurring in Trinidad. In the lizard the photophores (or "reflection pearls") are small round structures arranged in a series on each side of the back in about the position of the lateral line canal of anamniotes. Many fishes are not self-luminous;

instead the light is produced by bacteria housed in special structures on various parts of the body. The light is given off continuously by the bacteria, but various devices have evolved for concealing the light from view at will.

QUESTIONS

1. State four characteristics of the integumentary system of protochordates.

2. How does skin differ from the protochordate integument? In what animals does it occur?

3. What is thought to have been the evolutionary source of the tetrapod dermis?

4. What adaptive values may integumentary bone first have had?

5. What have been the general trends in evolution of the dermis and dermal bone through anamniotes? How nearly comparable were the trends that were evident in the epidermis?

6. What were the selective advantages of the reversal in evolutionary trend in the dermis in amniotes?

7. Of the major derivatives or groups of derivatives of the ostracoderm armor (a) name four still evident in endotherm vertebrates; (b) seven occurring in vertebrates in general.

8. What was the contribution to evolution of the primary dermal armor by those placoderms ancestral to modern vertebrates?

9. Trace the evolution of cosmoid scales and their derivatives in all classes of vertebrates.

10. In what vertebrates (be specific) do osteoderms still exist? To what different structures have they given rise, and in what groups do they occur?

11. Distinguish secondary dermal armor from primary dermal armor and give examples.

12. Name the types of chromatophores.

13. State how skin color differs in ectotherms and endotherms, and explain the influence of these differences upon metachrosis of pigment.

14. What are the two main types of integumentary seal? What provides the dermal seal, and in what vertebrates are (or was) it important?

15. Name three devices providing an epidermal seal in chordates, and specify the groups of which each is characteristic.

16. Name in proper order and characterize the layers of the vertebrate epidermis.

17. Why would the mucoid coat not be successful in amniotes? Or the keratin seal in amphibians?

18. To what degree does periodicity of ecdysis occur in vertebrates? What survival value exists for each condition?

19. In what class did epidermal scales first appear?

20. Draw a phylogenetic tree of the derivatives of the prototriches, and state in which class or classes each derivative occurs.

21. What was the original function of hair? Secondary functions?

22. How do feathers and hair differ in phylogeny?

23. As what and where do epidermal scales persist as such in birds and mammals? Scale derivatives?

24. Reptiles evolved from amphibians. Amphibian warts are homologous with reptilian scales. Can we correctly deduce that epidermal scales evolved from warts?

25. To what have the claws of reptiles given rise in birds and mammals?

26. Characterize the integumentary glands of fishes. What three advancements over the piscine characteristics are evident in the general integumentary glands of amphibians?

27. Name the kinds of integumentary glands evolved in amphibians. Which persist in amniotes?

28. What are the two basic types of skin glands in mammals and in what group of vertebrates did they presumably first appear?

29. Name the derivatives in mammals of each of two basic types of skin glands.

30. What advantage was it to modern reptiles to have lost most of the integumentary glands? To birds?

31. Name some integumentary glands persistent in reptiles; in birds.

32. What is the primitive distribution of mammary glands?

33. For what reasons are mammary glands regarded as secondarily and not primarily alveolar?

34. Name ten miscellaneous epidermal derivatives.

35. Define the following words, and where appropriate state occurrence or give examples:

alveolar gland
angular gland
antler
apical pits
apocrine
apterylae
atavistic
basement membrane
bovine horn
branchiostegal ray
callosity
ceruminous gland
chromatophore
cosmoid scale
cteni (2 kinds)
ctenoid scale
cuticle
cutis
cycloid scale
denticulate
dermal denticles
dermal girdle
dermis
dermocranium
ecdysis
epidermis
erythrophore

escutcheon scales
exuvia
false nipple
femoral pores
ganoid scale
gastralia
giraffe horn
guanophore
gynecomastism
hedonic
holocrine
inframarginal
integument
iridocyte
keratin
leptoid scale
leucophore
lipophore
Meibomian gland
melanophore
mental tubercles
metachrosis
milk line
mucous gland
osteoderm
paleoniscoid scale
parotoid gland

photophore
placoid scale
polymastism
polythelism
pronghorn
protothrix (proto-
    triches)
pterygopodial gland
pterylae
rhamphotheca
rhinoceros horn
sebaceous gland
serous gland
skin
squamous cell
stratum corneum
stratum germinativum
stratum mucosum
subunguis
teat
true nipple
unguis
uropygial gland
whalebone
xanthophore
Zeis gland

$$\boxed{6}$$

SKELETAL SYSTEM I

Introduction and Postpharyngeal Axial Skeleton

Introduction

THE SKELETAL SYSTEM consists, by definition, of the hard supportive or protective structures of the body. It is comprised of an *endoskeleton* and an *exoskeleton*.

The exoskeleton, not always present in vertebrates, is formed *directly* (that is, in the embryogeny of the individual) from either the dermis or epidermis, or both. The tissues involved are either bone (of the dermis) or keratin (of the epidermis), rarely cartilage. Since the exoskeleton is an integumentary product, discussion of its evolution is confined to the chapter on the integumentary system.

The endoskeleton is that part formed relatively deep within the body from subdermal tissues. It is never derived *directly* (that is, in the embryogeny of the individual animal) from the dermis but instead from embryonic mesenchyme of other sources. It is formed of three different kinds of

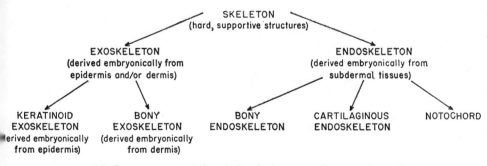

FIG. 6.1 Organization of the skeletal tissues in the vertebrate body.

tissues in different areas: notochord, bone, and cartilage. All vertebrates possess an endoskeleton.

There is no sharp evolutionary line of demarcation between endoskeleton and exoskeleton. The cranial dermal bones of fishes, for example, are an integral part of the cranium itself, but in primitive types are exoskeletal (being derived directly from the dermis), in others endoskeletal. The organization of skeletal tissues is depicted in Figure 6.1.

Skeletal Tissues. There are four kinds of tissues found in the skeleton: notochord, cartilage, bone, and keratinoid tissue. The notochord tissue is unique, and is found only in the notochord itself. It is characterized by possessing large intracellular vacuoles (Fig. 6.2) kept turgid and serving together to exert pressure upon a surrounding sheath of connective tissue. There is no matrix between the cells. The similarity to plant tissue in gross form is rather close. This tissue is found at least embryonically in all vertebrates.

Keratin is a substance of scattered occurrence in fishes, is inconspicuous in amphibians, and is found abundantly only in amniotes. It is produced (Fig. 6.2) by transformation of the cytoplasm of the dead, outer squamous epithelial cells. Tissues containing quantities of keratin are keratinoid tissues.

Cartilage is found in all vertebrates, but almost exclusively in the endoskeleton. It is a tissue with scattered cells (Fig. 6.3) imbedded in a

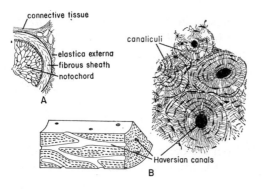

FIG. 6.2 Skeletal tissues. A, notochord tissue; B, bone; C, keratin (labelled stratum corneum). (From Goodrich, Kingsley, Bremer, and Bailey.)

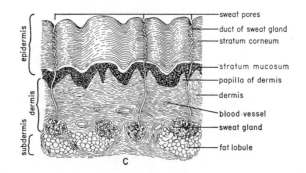

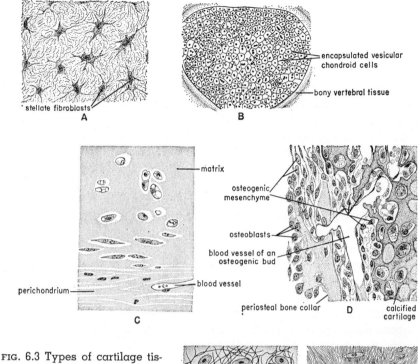

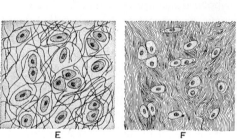

FIG. 6.3 Types of cartilage tissue. A, mucoid cartilage; B, precartilage; C, hyaline cartilage; D, calcified cartilage; E, elastic cartilage; F, fibrous cartilage. (From Kendall, Bremer, Gray, Nonidez and Windle.)

matrix secreted by those cells. No blood vessels penetrate the matrix. All the cells within the tissue must respire by means of diffusion and thus cartilage seldom acquires much thickness. It has evolved through several stages (Fig. 6.4) differing in composition of the matrix. In *mucoid cartilage* the matrix is gelatinous and the *chondrocytes* (cartilage cells) asteroid in shape (for example, in the precerebral cavity housed by the rostrum of the dog-

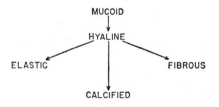

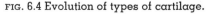

FIG. 6.4 Evolution of types of cartilage.

fish); in *hyaline cartilage* the matrix is clear and hard (for example, the ends of limb bones at joint capsules; much of the dogfish chondrocranium); in *calcified* cartilage a scattered deposition of calcium occurs in the hyaline matrix, producing a very hard, superficially bonelike tissue (for example, parts of the vertebrae of the dogfish, much of the cartilage skeleton of living amphibians and reptiles). In mammals hyaline cartilage in some areas is invaded by inelastic connective tissue fibers, producing a very tough tissue (for example, the intervertebral discs) called *fibrous* cartilage; in other areas it is invaded by elastic connective tissue fibers, producing a flexible tissue (for example, the pinna of the ear) called *elastic* cartilage. The embryonic precursor of cartilage tissue of any sort is called *precartilage;* it lacks a matrix.

Bone resembles cartilage by consisting of cells (Fig. 6.2) scattered in a matrix they secrete, but differs in the nature of the matrix (mostly calcium phosphate and some calcium carbonate deposited around a fibrous protein framework), in possessing direct connections from one cell to another through tiny channels called *canaliculi,* and in possessing a network of blood vessels sufficiently complete to necessitate an intercellular diffusion through at most some six to eight layers of cells.

Ontogenetic Types of Bone. Two ontogenetic or developmental types of bone tissue are recognized. That which is formed directly from mesenchyme or connective tissue is called *membrane* bone, whereas that formed by replacement of cartilage is *replacement* or *cartilage* bone. The structure of these two types of bone tissue cannot consistently be distinguished from each other; they differ only in embryonic origin. Many bones contain tissue of both types. All bones of the skeleton are nevertheless referred to, arbitrarily and not wholly logically, as either cartilage bones or membrane bones on the basis of preponderance of one type or other of bone tissue. Bone is found in the endoskeleton of all vertebrates except the Cyclostomata and Chondrichthyes, and perhaps in some placoderms. It is found (at least in a modified form, as, for example, dentine and other bonelike tissues) in the exoskeleton of all vertebrates except cyclostomes, a few chondrichthyans and teleosts, some reptiles, all birds, most mammals, and most living amphibians. Bone is primarily a postembryonic tissue; its rigidity is of value in a competitive world. Cartilage is the most abundant embryonic skeletal tissue, perhaps because it provides the greater flexibility and lesser weight that developmental dynamics require. Thus cartilage precedes bone where skeletal support is needed ontogenetically, and in certain lines of evolution this essentially embryonic tissue is retained postembryonically in parts of the skeleton (or even in all of it in certain extremes such as the Chondrichthyes and Cyclostomata).

Phylogenetic Types of Bones. There are two phylogenetic types of bones: *dermal* and *nondermal.* Dermal bones are those that form embryonically from dermal mesenchyme, or that are homologous with bones that in ancestral types did form embryonically from the dermal mesenchyme. For example, the large bones on the dorsal surface of the skull in mammals

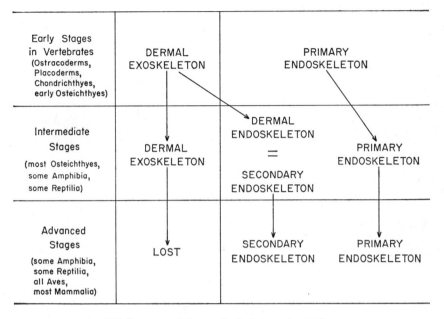

Early Stages in Vertebrates (Ostracoderms, Placoderms, Chondrichthyes, early Osteichthyes)	DERMAL EXOSKELETON	PRIMARY ENDOSKELETON
Intermediate Stages (most Osteichthyes, some Amphibia, some Reptilia)	DERMAL EXOSKELETON	DERMAL ENDOSKELETON = SECONDARY ENDOSKELETON · PRIMARY ENDOSKELETON
Advanced Stages (some Amphibia, some Reptilia, all Aves, most Mammalia)	LOST	SECONDARY ENDOSKELETON · PRIMARY ENDOSKELETON

FIG. 6.5 Sources of the endoskeleton of vertebrates.

(frontals and parietals) now do not form directly from the dermis, but they certainly did in the piscine ancestors of mammals; they are thus properly regarded as dermal bones. Nondermal bones, on the contrary, do not form embryonically from the dermatome nor have they ever been so formed in ancestral types.

Dermal bones are both (1) exoskeletal, including all bones of the skin (for example, osteoderms, the *os palpebra* in the eyelid of crocodilians, the bony plates of turtles and armadillos, etc.) and (2) endoskeletal, including many bones of the skull (the "dermocranium"), some bones of the pectoral girdle (the "dermal girdle"), gastralia, and others. Dermal bones are very rarely preformed in cartilage in ontogeny; they almost invariably form directly from mesenchyme or connective tissue, and thus are comprised of membrane bone tissue. Occasionally dermal bones are referred to as membrane bones, as indeed they generally are, but the terms are not synonymous; all dermal bones are membrane bones, but not all membrane bones are dermal bones. The term "dermal bone" reflects phylogeny, whereas the term "membrane bone" reflects ontogeny. In practice, the terms membrane bone and dermal bone can be used interchangeably in reference to bones of the skull and girdles, since they result in exactly the same groupings, but not in reference to bones of the vertebral column and appendages.

Primary and Secondary Endoskeleton. The endoskeleton of vertebrates has evolved from two sources (Fig. 6.5). Part, the *secondary endoskeleton,* evolved from the exoskeleton, and the rest (the *primary endoskeleton*) was never a part of the exoskeleton. Since bone was the only

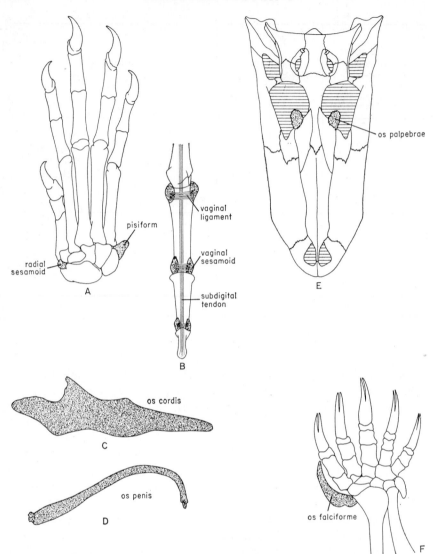

FIG. 6.6 Heterotopic bones, shown in dark stipple. A, cat hand; B, digit of a lizard; C, separate os cordis from ox; D, separate os penis from raccoon; E, alligator skull; F, mole hand. (From Adams, Eddy, Kent, Oliver, and Turner.)

skeletal tissue derived by the endoskeleton from the exoskeleton, the secondary endoskeleton consists entirely of dermal bone, although the two terms are not synonymous since the dermal bones situated in the exoskeleton in any given animal type are not a part of the endoskeleton. The dermal endoskeleton, however, is the same as the secondary endoskeleton.

The remainder of the endoskeleton, without a dermal ancestry, is appropriately termed the primary endoskeleton. It presumably evolved from connective tissue in association with the structures it serves to support or protect. It includes notochordal, membrane bone, cartilage bone, and cartilage tissues. Most parts of the primary endoskeleton have had a long history, but some are of more or less transitory occurrence and contrary to other primary endoskeletal components are of membrane origin. These are termed "*heterotopic bones*" (Fig. 6.6) and include among many others: (1) *sesamoid bones,* forming at points of stress in tendons (for example, patella, pisiform, fabellae); (2) *ossa vaginalia,* forming in ligaments (vaginal ligaments) that guide the tendons on the lower surfaces of the digits in some animals; (3) the *os cordis,* a bone strengthening the interventricular septum in the heart of some large ungulate mammals; (4) possibly the *os penis* or the *os baculum,* a bone forming in the connective tissue of the penis in some mammals (not man) and serving to give rigidity (this may actually be a derivative of the epipubic bones, and thus not be originally of penile origin); (5) the *os rostralis,* a bone in the muzzle of some ungulates; and the (6) *os falciforme,* a bone in the palm of moles, serving as an aid in digging.

Types of Articulation. Bones lying in contact with each other and separated by softer tissues (including cartilage) are *articulated.* They are articulated whether they are movable or not, as long as they retain their separate identity. When the connective tissue or cartilage separating them is transformed into or replaced by bone tissue, the two formerly separate bones becoming fused, they are regarded as *ankylosed.*

Arthroses (joints) or *articulations,* are of two main types: *diarthroses* and *synarthroses.* Diarthroses are primarily distinguished by possessing a *synovial sac* surrounding a joint and containing a *synovial fluid* (Fig. 6.7). The fluid is lymphlike and serves to lubricate the ends of the bone, which are always tipped with cartilage. If the synovial sac is punctured, or if as in old age the cartilage of the joints becomes ossified, increase in stiffness and ultimately ankylosis result.

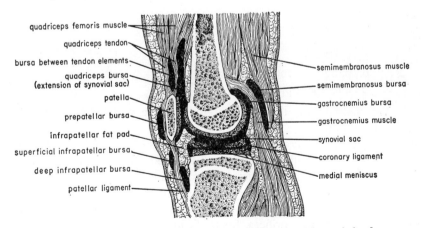

quadriceps femoris muscle
quadriceps tendon
bursa between tendon elements
quadriceps bursa (extension of synovial sac)
patella
prepatellar bursa
infrapatellar fat pad
superficial infrapatellar bursa
deep infrapatellar bursa
patellar ligament

semimembranosus muscle
semimembranosus bursa
gastrocnemius bursa
gastrocnemius muscle
synovial sac
coronary ligament
medial meniscus

FIG. 6.7 A diarthrotic joint (knee) in sagittal section. Most of the bursae are extensions of the synovial sac. The heavily stippled regions, as for example the medial meniscus, are of cartilage. (From Netter.)

Four types of diarthroses are conspicuously distinct: (1) ball-and-socket joints, as at the acetabulum and head of femur; (2) gliding joints, as at the zygapophyses of vertebrae; (3) hinge joints, as at the elbow, between humerus and ulna; and (4) pivot joints, as between the proximal ends of radius and ulna in man. Combinations of these functions occur in some joints, as for example the jaw-cranial articulation in man.

Amphiarthroses comprise a variety of diarthroses in which the synovial structures are poorly developed and allow for relatively little movement. Examples are the joints between the bodies of vertebrae and between parts of the sternum.

Synarthroses have no synovial structures and only on this basis are readily distinguishable from diarthroses. They permit little or no movement. Two types of synarthroses are recognized: *synchondroses,* in which a junction of replacement bones is effected by cartilage; and *syndesmoses,* in which a junction of membrane bones is effected by connective tissue. Most synchondroses are termed *symphyses,* and most syndesmoses are *sutures.* Either type is readily lost by complete fusion of the formerly jointed bones, since the connecting tissue between them is that which is the normal forerunner of bone in ontogeny. Ankylosis is thus a much more common fate of synarthroses than of diarthroses, in which the tissues intervening between bones are not normally forerunners of bone.

Topographic Parts of the Endoskeleton. The endoskeleton, whether primary or secondary, is topographically organized within or around specific parts of the body it serves to support or protect, as follows:

1. Axial
   A. Cranial
   B. Postcranial
      a. visceral skeleton (= pharyngeal skeleton)
      b. vertebral column (including sacrum)
      c. ribs
      d. sternum
2. Appendicular
      a. girdles
      b. paired appendages
      c. unpaired appendages

We shall discuss these several topographic parts separately in the following sections.

Descriptive Conventions. The conventions of terminology relating to the skeleton are not all apparently well founded. Three sorts of characteristics must be dealt with in general terms: cavities, projections, and shapes.

Perhaps the most commonly recognized cavities in the skeletal system are the *foramina* (singular, *foramen*) which are defined literally as "passages, holes, openings, orifices, fissures"; in general, however, the term is applied to a hole that provides for passage of a vessel or nerve. A *canal,* in reference to the skeletal system, is a tubelike passageway that runs some distance through bone or cartilage. A *fissure* is a cleftlike opening between two structures (usually two bones) or parts thereof. A *fenestra* is also defined as "an opening"; and although it might be used interchangeably with any of the preceding, it is commonly implied to be an opening across which a membrane is stretched or that does not serve primarily as a passageway for a specific nerve or vessel. A *fossa* is defined broadly as a "depression, furrow, or sinus," but is commonly used in reference to a large depression or concavity on the surface of a bone or group of bones. *Sinus* and *antrum* are used in reference to a cavity within a bone (or cartilage), particularly in reference to the skull.

In accordance with shape, *long* bones, *short* bones, *flat* bones, and *irregular* bones are recognized. The long bones are the larger bones of the limbs, such as the femur, humerus, radius, ulna, tibia, fibula. Short bones are more or less cuboidal, as the wrist and ankle bones. Flat bones are thin and usually arched, like the scapula and some of the skull bones. Irregular bones are of varied shape, as, for example, the vertebrae. *Ossicles* are tiny bones of irregular shape.

Processes are prolongations or prominences of a part. Certain types are given specific names, although there is a considerable overlap in meaning and application of these several specific names. For example, a *condyle* is a rounded articular eminence. Although a *head* can, in some cases, be described in the same way as a condyle, its general application in the appendicular skeleton is to the proximal end of any long bone. An *apophysis* is "a bony protuberance or outgrowth," but is commonly applied to a relatively slender projection. A *tuberosity,* on the other hand, is a large, usually roughened projection or protuberance, usually serving for attachment of a muscle. The tuberosities on the proximal end of the femur are given the specific name of *trochanters,* whereas those at the ankle are *malleoli,* and those near the distal end of the femur and humerus the *epicondyles.*

QUESTIONS

1. How do the two main divisions of the skeleton of chordates differ in embryonic origin, position in the body, and in tissue composition?

2. What are the four major kinds of skeletal tissues, how do they differ from each other histologically, and with what main division of the skeleton is each associated?

3. Name, differentiate, and give examples of the six kinds of embryonic and adult cartilage; diagram the relationship of adult types to each other in a sort of developmental "tree."

4. What are the ontogenetic types of bone tissue and how do they differ? Phylogenetic types?

5. Bone is lacking from the exoskeleton of what vertebrates? Keratin is present in which?

6. How does the secondary endoskeleton differ from the primary endo-skeleton in evolutionary history? Name the three major components (groups of bones) of the secondary endoskeleton.

7. Name and differentiate the two main divisions of dermal bones.

8. How do the concepts of membrane bone and dermal bone differ? Der-mal bone and secondary endoskeleton? Name some membrane bones that are not dermal bones.

9. Name and give examples of or locate seven heterotopic bones.

10. Name and differentiate the main types of joints and their subdivisions.

11. Explain why ankylosis is a much less common fate of diarthroses than of synarthroses.

12. Name the topographic parts of the endoskeleton, properly grouped.

13. Define the following words, and where appropriate state occurrence or give examples:

amphiarthrosis
ankylosis
antrum
apophysis
appendicular skeleton
arthrosis
articulation
axial skeleton
baculum
calcified cartilage
canal
cartilage
cartilage bone
chondrocyte
condyle
dermal bone
dermal endoskeleton
dermal exoskeleton
diapophysis
diarthrosis

elastic cartilage
endoskeleton
epicondyle
exoskeleton
fenestra
fibrous cartilage
fissure
foramen
fossa
heterotopic bones
hyaline cartilage
joint
malleolus
membrane bone
mucoid cartilage
nondermal bone
os cordis
os falciforme
os penis
os rostralis

os vaginalia
parapophysis
pharyngeal skeleton
precartilage
primary endoskeleton
process
replacement bone
secondary endoskele-
    ton
sesamoid bone
sinus
suture
symphysis
synarthrosis
synchrondrosis
syndesmosis
synovial sac
trochanter
tuberosity
visceral skeleton

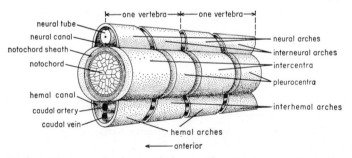

FIG. 6.8 The basic components of the vertebral column, diagrammatic.

Postpharyngeal Axial Skeleton

The evolutionary pattern of the vertebral column is not wholly clear, especially in early stages. Early fossils do not exhibit any evidence whatsoever of a vertebral column, perhaps because of absence of ossification in adults. Chiefly upon the basis of conformation in living primitive vertebrates are the concepts of early phylogeny of vertebrae constructed.

Vertebrae appeared with an original function, apparently, of protecting the spinal cord and the dorsal aorta. With the vertebral components situated immediately above and immediately below the notochord, integration of notochord and vertebrae was a natural sequence. Secondarily the vertebral column became important as an attachment for trunk muscles, and in tetrapods as an arch from which the trunk is suspended.

Adult Vertebral Components

Protection of the neural tube appears to have been initiated in vertebrates with formation of dorsal, ∧-shaped arches over the spinal cord, their bases articulating with the notochordal sheath. Two *dorsal* arches were primitively present for each vertebra: a *neural* arch and an *interneural* arch (Fig. 6.8).

Perhaps second to appear in phylogeny were comparable ∨-shaped arches ventral to the notochord, enclosing the dorsal aorta (caudal artery) and caudal vein, and restricted to the tail region. Two *ventral* arches were present in each vertebra: a *hemal* arch and an *interhemal* arch. No more than rudiments of these arches occur in the trunk region, where the celom interferes with enclosure ventrally of vascular structures. The interneural and interhemal arches are collectively referred to as the *intercalary* arches, the neural and hemal arches as the *basal* arches.

A third stage in phylogeny of the basic components is formation of structures, in or on the notochord, that serve to support and anchor the arches. These structures are the centra, of which, like the arches, there are two per vertebra: an *intercentrum,* associated with the neural arch dorsally and the hemal arch ventrally (not with the interhemal and interneural arches as would by name be most appropriate), and a *pleurocentrum,* associated with the interneural arch dorsally and the interhemal arch ventrally. More doubt exists of the evolutionary pattern of the centra than of the arches; there may have been but a single centrum at first, the subdivision into pleurocentrum and intercentrum occurring later.

Probably all six of the basic components mentioned were originally paired, with separate right and left sections. The parts present in any given vertebrate are generally bilaterally paired at least embryonically, and this condition persists in the adults of a few primitive vertebrates.

The living cyclostomes exemplify attainment of only the first and second stages, since they possess dorsal and ventral arches but no centra. The Chondrostei more or less agree, but the centra clearly appear to have been lost secondarily. Other vertebrates invariably possess centra and arches, but many modifications have been introduced in different groups. The occurrence primitively of double arches and double centra in each segment suggests the concept of the occurrence primitively of what might well be regarded as two vertebrae per segment.

Evolutionary Trends in Vertebral Components in Adults

Some five evolutionary trends affecting the six basic vertebral components are worthy of special attention: (1) loss of intercalary arches; (2) loss of hemal arches; (3) reduction in number of centra; (4) formation and fate of the intervertebral body; and (5) fusion of components.

Loss of Intercalary Arches. The only dorsal arch present in most vertebrates is the neural arch, existing throughout the length of the vertebral column; and the only ventral arch is the hemal arch, present only in the caudal region. The interneural and interhemal arches are lost in all tetrapods, and are present among living vertebrates only in the cyclostomes, chondrichthyans, dipnoans, and Chondrostei (Fig. 6.9).

It is thought that, in primitive vertebrates living before the inter-

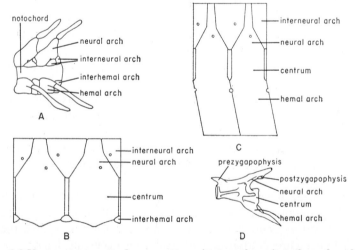

FIG. 6.9 Various stages in degeneration of intercalary (interhemal and interneural) arches exemplified by living vertebrates. A, sturgeon caudal vertebrae; B, dogfish trunk vertebrae; C, dogfish caudal vertebrae; D, salamander caudal vertebra. (From Goodrich and Senning.)

calary arches were lost, both the dorsal and ventral arches as well as the centra had so evolved as to establish close contact with each other, forming a continuous or nearly continuous, bony or cartilaginous neural canal and hemal canal much as in the elasmobranchs of today. Tetrapods and most fishes have, however, lost the continuity of both canals, the spinal cord and blood vessels running through a series of *separate* neural and hemal arches, respectively. The discontinuity was effected primarily by loss of intercalary arches. Contact between vertebrae was maintained by the centra, but additional freedom of movement was gained by providing space between successive dorsal and successive ventral arches.

Loss of Hemal Arches. The hemal arches are virtually constant in occurrence among fishes and amphibians. Vestiges of them (disregarding rib homologies) occur even in the trunk region of some fishes (for example, elasmobranchs, in which they are fused to the centrum as part of the basapophysis). They are well developed in most modern reptiles, but are poorly developed in mammals and birds. Since in amniotes, when present, they commonly lack a hemal spine, they are termed *chevron bones*. The only truly distinctive feature of chevron bones, however, is that they represent paired vestiges of intercentra, one on each side, to which the hemal arches are indistinguishably fused. The caudal hemal arches of amphibians and also fishes are well developed and do not include any centrum component.

Reduction in Number of Centra. The centra are reduced to one (*monospondyly*) or none (*aspondyly*), instead of two per vertebra (*diplospondyly*), in most living vertebrates, exceptions occurring in Amia and some elasmobranchs (Fig. 6.10). This reduction seems to have taken place primarily (1) by fusion of pleurocentra and intercentra (as in most fishes); (2) by incorporation of the intercentrum into the intervertebral bodies (as in all trunk vertebrae except the atlas and axis in all amniotes); (3) by transformation of the intercentrum into parts of the chevron bones (tail region in amniotes); (4) by loss of all true centra and substitution of another (as in living amphibians, see p. 146); and (5) by loss of both centra (Chondrostei). A secondary increase (*polyspondyly*) in number of centra (five or six per vertebra) occurs in the Holocephali and Dipnoi.

Formation and Modification of the Intervertebral Body. The notochord is a large, continuous cord of major importance as a component of the axial skeleton in early chordates. The vertebrae form around the notochord, the centrum actually encircling it, while the dorsal arches rest upon the centra (or notochord in acentrous forms) and the ventral arches are pendant from the same structures (notochord or centra) in the tail. Since the centra are formed of stronger material (bone or cartilage) than the notochord, they tend throughout vertebrates to replace the notochord. In cyclostomes and Chondrostei the notochord is of its primitive large size, and is unconstricted. In all other fishes, in most fossil and all living amphibians except the anurans, and in some fossil reptiles, it remains a continuous cord although it is constricted to a greater or lesser degree in

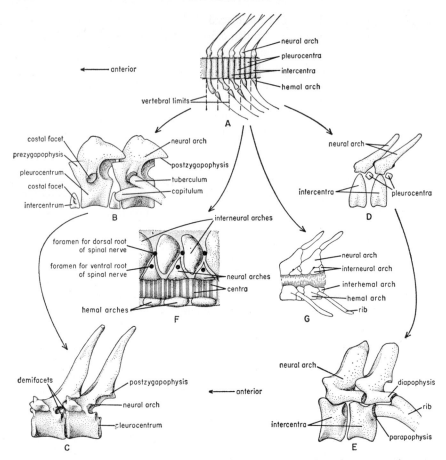

FIG. 6.10 Evolution of vertebrate centra. A, diplospondyly (two centra) in caudal region of Amia; B, trunk vertebrae of Seymouria (a cotylosaur), showing an approach toward the usual amniote condition C of the cat; D, trunk vertebrae of a crossopterygian showing an approach toward the typical amphibian condition E of a fossil type (labyrinthodont); F, Chimaera, showing supernumerary centra; G, sturgeon vertebrae, showing absence of centra. (From Hyman, Weichert, Romer, Schimkewitsch, Eddy, Oliver, and Turner.)

the center of each vertebra. Thus the vertebrae of these groups are perforated by an opening, often minute, through the middle of the centrum, each end of which is hollow and funnellike. Such vertebrae are termed *perforate amphicelous* (Fig. 6.11). In all except primitive tetrapods the constriction is carried still further, limiting the notochord to *intervertebral bodies*. The latter are composed chiefly of connective tissue or cartilage, in which the notochord tissue is indistinguishable by gross inspection. Embryonic vestiges of arches and centra otherwise unrepresented by structures in the adult also contribute to the intervertebral bodies.

The fate of the intervertebral bodies varies in different vertebrates;

in mammals they form essentially flat intervertebral discs between the vertebral centra (which are thus *acelous*); in primitive birds, reptiles, and amphibians they form more or less flattened spheroids between the centra (which are *amphicelous* in shape, but *imperforate*); in some amphibians and reptiles they become fused onto the anterior end of the centrum, thus leaving a concavity at the rear of the centrum (*opisthocelous* condition); and in some amphibians, many reptiles, and in most birds they are fused to the rear ends of the centra, producing a concavity at the front of the centrum (the *procelous* condition).

Secondary modifications of these types occur in various classes. Several complex variants which need not be described here occur in the cervical and caudal vertebrae of turtles. Two other variants are of special interest, however. The most important occurs in some reptiles and in most birds in which the basically procelous centrum is modified as a *heterocelous* type. To visualize this condition, imagine a frontal section (horizontal) through a centrum whose front end in dorsal view appears concave: the rear, convex. Then imagine a sagittal section through the same vertebra, whose front end in this section now appears *convex* in lateral view, the

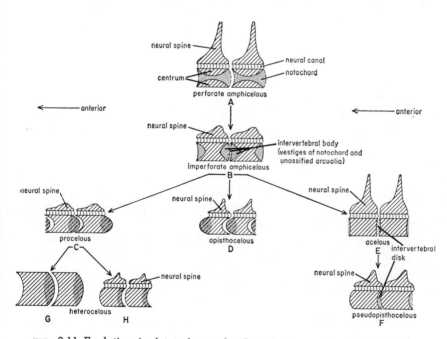

FIG. 6.11 Evolution in fate of notochord and intervertebral body. Note that the intervertebral body is not fused with the centrum in F as in D. All views are of midsagittal sections except G, a midfrontal section through the centrum. Since heterocelous vertebrae have flattened centra the frontal section appears larger than the sagittal section, and because of the rounded front edge the essentially procelous condition so clearly apparent in frontal section (or in dorsoventral view) is distorted in sagittal section to appear opisthocelous.

rear end, *concave*. Comparison with an actual bird vertebra will reveal the basis for such characterization.

A second variant is the *pseudopisthocelic* type occurring in part or all of the vertebral column in the basically acelous ungulate mammals. In this type the anterior ends of the centra become convex, the posterior ends concave. This is not true opisthocely, since the intervertebral discs remain intact and flattened. Other acelous centra in mammals are truly flat or *amphiplatyan*.

Fusion of Components. Primitively all or most of the components of the vertebrae remained separate in adults, not fusing as is true of the vertebrae in adults of virtually all living gnathostomes. Of all components of the vertebrae, the intercentrum and hemal arch most frequently remain separate. In some fishes each intercentrum constitutes a second separate centrum (for example, Amia, in the caudal region). In the caudal region of amniotes the hemal arches (with the intercentra) form the distinctive chevron bones mentioned previously.

Embryonic Components of Vertebrae

Vertebrae arise chiefly if not wholly from the sclerotomes (Fig. 6.12A, D). The sclerotome of each segment on each side typically splits into four components. The two anterior divisions (*arcualia*) on each side are called the *intercalia;* the dorsal arcuale is the *interdorsal,* the ventral the *interventral* (Fig. 6.12B, E). The sclerotomic subdivisions at the rear of each segment are the *basalia;* the dorsal arcuale is the *basidorsal,* the ventral the *basiventral.* Thus primitively the total number of arcualia in any one segment (both sides) is eight.

These eight arcualia typically give rise, directly or indirectly, to certain given components of the vertebrae in adults. The derivatives are as follows: from the interdorsal arcualia, the pleurocentrum and interneural arch; from the interventral, the interhemal arch; from the basidorsals, the neural arch; and from the basiventrals, the intercentrum and hemal arch. In regions of the body where one or more of these adult components do not exist, the arcualia involved remain small and contribute to the intervertebral bodies (Fig. 6.13). Thus procelous, opisthocelous, and heterocelous vertebrae represent, by virtue of the intervertebral bodies co-ossified with them, more arcualia than the traditional adult components would require. The intervertebral body and its origin are disregarded in accounting for the embryonic components of such vertebrae.

Trends in Embryonic Vertebral Modifications

The embryogeny of vertebrae is exceedingly variable, failing to exhibit that constancy seen in many other bodily parts. Just why it should

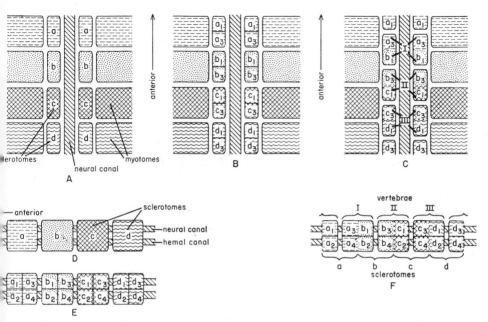

FIG. 6.12 Diagrams of the embryonic staggering process in the trunk vertebrae. A-C, dorsal views; D-F, lateral views. A, D, early stage lacking sclerotomal subdivision. B, E, later stage, the sclerotomes subdivided. C, F, subadult stage, the anterior half of each sclerotome fusing with the posterior half of the preceding sclerotome to form the precursor of an adult vertebra. Subscripts of a-d: 1, interdorsal; 2, interventral; 3, basidorsal; 4, basiventral.

have been subject to so much more variation than most other structures is not readily apparent. Detection of the basic phylogeny from ontogenetic data is completely impractical because of the extensive variation. The most reliable source of data has of necessity been adult structure, which seems to be subject to less variation than the embryonic patterns. Embryonic variation does not, of course, affect homologies, but it does render them difficult to decipher and establish. The course of embryogeny of vertebrae has evolved conspicuously in two respects: (1) staggering of vertebrae and other segmental structures; and (2) formation of the centra.

Staggering. The vertebrae form as segmental structures whose limits correspond primitively with those of other segmental structures such as the myotomes. In living vertebrates except the cyclostomes (in which the vertebrae are rudimentary, their components not in contact with each other) the vertebrae are reorganized so they alternate with the myosepta (Fig. 6.12C, F). The functional advantages are obvious: alternation of vertebrae with myotomes (the myosepta situated opposite to more or less the middle of the vertebra) provides a movable joint between successive myosepta, thus attaining a greater flexibility. This is especially important in primitive animals in which the axial muscle fibers are arranged lengthwise of the body and are no longer than the myotomes. The earlier strictly segmental arrangement meant that the myosepta were attached to the ends of the vertebrae, thus eliminating a movable intervertebral joint between the two levels (successive myosepta) of attachment of any one set of axial muscle fibers. It is very likely, however, that the early formation of anterior and posterior parts in each vertebra was an adaptation to precisely this situation, providing a joint within the length of each myotome. Fusion of the parts to form a succession of solid vertebrae was a natural sequence, and that this should have taken place by uniting the anterior component of one segment with the posterior component of the preceding segment was likewise functionally imperative. It is significant that no vertebrate with solidly formed vertebrae is known to lack, or to have lacked, a staggered arrangement of vertebrae and myotomes.

Formation of Centrum. There are four different modes of embryonic formation of the centrum in any vertebrate. For each mode one of two

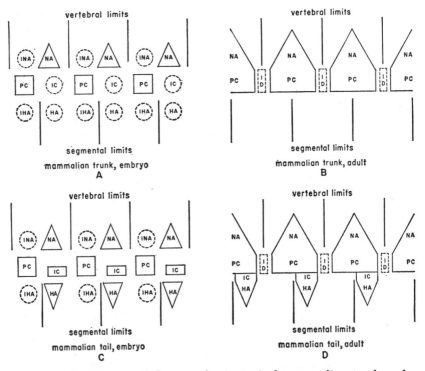

FIG. 6.13 Derivatives of the arcualia in typical mammalian trunk and caudal vertebrae. Parts enclosed with continuous lines are ossified in the adult; those with broken lines are mesenchymatous, cartilaginous, fibrous, or missing. Symbols: IC, intercentrum; ID, intervertebral disc; IHA, interhemal arch; INA, interneural arch; HA, hemal arch; NA, neural arch; PC, pleurocentrum.

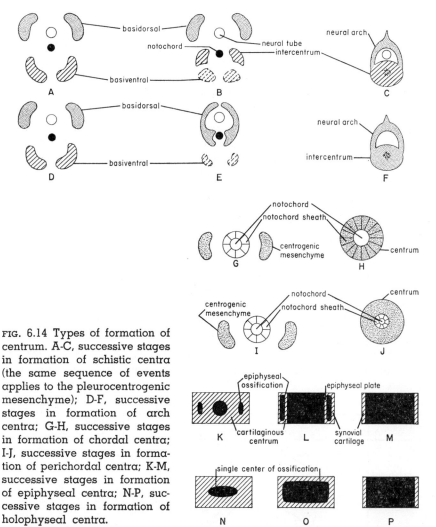

FIG. 6.14 Types of formation of centrum. A-C, successive stages in formation of schistic centra (the same sequence of events applies to the pleurocentrogenic mesenchyme); D-F, successive stages in formation of arch centra; G-H, successive stages in formation of chordal centra; I-J, successive stages in formation of perichordal centra; K-M, successive stages in formation of epiphyseal centra; N-P, successive stages in formation of holophyseal centra.

possibilities has been explored by each vertebrate group. The two alternatives in any single sort of formation are mutually exclusive, but all four features can be considered in almost any single vertebra. The four sets of alternatives are: (1) schistic versus arch centra; (2) chondral centra versus husk centra; (3) chordal versus perichordal centra; and (4) epiphyseal versus holophyseal centra.

1. Typically the mesenchyme giving rise to the centra (either pleurocentrum or intercentrum, or both), separates from the interdorsal and basiventral arcualia, respectively (Fig. 6.14A, C) at an early embryonic stage (if the corresponding adult derivative is to be formed in the given animal and in the given region). The arches and centra thus usually have

a long, separate embryonic history. Centra thus formed are *schistic centra*.

In anurans, however, the centra not only form from the basidorsal arcualia instead of from the basiventrals, but also never separate from the arch component; the neural arches simply grow ventrally around the notochord and shape into the centra (Fig. 6.14D, F). This unusual developmental type of centrum is called an *arch centrum*. Since vestiges of both pleurocentra and intercentra are still present in fossil frogs, we know that the evolution of the arch centrum was completely independent.

2. In the vertebrates generally, all parts of the vertebrae, including the centra, are preformed in cartilage. Centra thus formed may be termed *chondral centra,* whether they are ossified (as replacement bone) as in most vertebrates, or remain as cartilage in adults. A remarkable exception occurs in some fishes, and in all salamanders and caecilians, in which the centra ossify directly from mesenchyme and are therefore composed of membrane bone. Such centra are termed *husk centra,* since they form as a cylinder around the notochord. It is not known whether husk centra are homologous with pleurocentra, intercentra, or neither. It is a curious fact that in none of the modern amphibians can the centrum be homologized in confidence with that of other vertebrates.

3. Still another trend in embryonic development of vertebrae concerns the relationship of the centrogenic primordia and the connective tissue sheath of the notochord. In the *chordal* type (Fig. 6.14G, H), at least a part of the embryonic mesenchyme actually penetrates the notochord

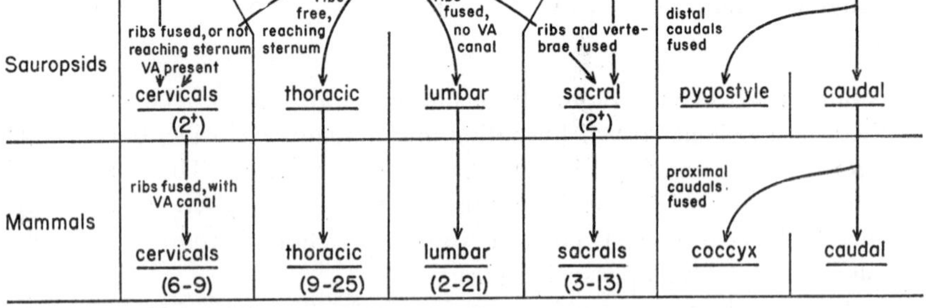

FIG. 6.15 Progressive differentiation of regions of the vertebral column in vertebrates. "Ribs fused" refers to fusion of the vertebra with its two ribs; "VA canal" refers to the vertebrarterial canal; "Ribs and vertebrae fused" refers to fusion not only of each segmental pair of ribs with its corresponding vertebra, but also of successive vertebrae with each other.

sheath, which thus greatly enlarges in forming the centrum. Chordal penetration is conspicuous in the Chondrichthyes (in which chondrification but no ossification follows), Chondrostei (in which neither chondrification nor ossification follows), and Dipnoi. In other vertebrates (except to a minimum degree in most fishes), with a *perichordal* centrum, the centrogenic mesenchyme groups around the notochord, actually constricting it and also retarding its growth at intervals along its length (Fig. 6.14I, J); there is typically no actual penetration of either the notochord or its sheath. It appears likely that primitively the centra were wholly chordal, and that gradually they became completely perichordal as in all modern tetrapods. Many intermediate types occur in living fishes.

4. Finally, mammalian centra are unique in their ossification from three centers in the embryonic cartilage (Fig. 6.14K, M), rather than from the usual single center (Fig. 6.14N-P). Thus the tripartite mammalian centra are not fully co-ossified in immature stages; thin *epiphyses* remain connected by cartilage with the central part until maturity is reached. In reference to this unique attribute mammalian centra are referred to as *epiphyseal,* those of other vertebrates *holophyseal.*

Trends Adaptive to Terrestrial Life

Some of the variations in the vertebral column previously described undoubtedly are in part adaptive to the peculiar conditions of "terrestrial life" as opposed to the primitive "aquatic life" to which vertebrates were initially adapted. Other trends are of significance primarily, not secondarily, as terrestrial adaptations. They involve (1) regionalization of the vertebral column, (2) antitwist mechanisms, (3) suspensory adaptations, and (4) cranial mobility.

Regionalization. Regionalization of the vertebral column begins with differentiation of only two regions (trunk and caudal) in all fishes, and culminates with differentiation of five regions (cervical, thoracic, lumbar, sacral, and caudal) in amniotes (Fig. 6.15). Cervical and sacral vertebrae first appeared in amphibians, which possess but one each. Both are adaptations to terrestrial life. The cervical vertebra served to facilitate movement of the skull on the vertebral column—something that would have been disadvantageous to most fishes because of their freedom of bodily movement and the premium placed upon a rigidity of body axis sufficient for effective cleavage of the water. Amphibians were not, at least at first, capable of moving efficiently on land, and thus an ability to turn the head became of survival importance. Nevertheless the anatomical adjustment for cranial mobility *via* cervical vertebrae was not rapid, for not before the reptilian stage did more than one cervical vertebra become differentiated. The variation in number among amniotes is great, but there is never less than two. The feature that distinguishes cervical vertebrae from the next vertebrae posteriorly is the absence of free ribs, or their reduction in length as compared with more posterior ribs. In mammals all cervical vertebrae lack free ribs; the ribs have clearly become reduced in size and fused to the vertebrae, generally without loss, however, of the *costovertebral* (*vertebrarterial* or *transverse*) foramen. The latter foramen is found incorporated in no vertebrae except the cervicals. In reptiles and birds, however, often a few posterior cervical vertebrae possess free ribs; such vertebrae are distinguished from thoracics by the shortness of the ribs, which fail to reach the sternum whereas the ribs of the thoracic vertebrae typically do this.

Turning to the sacrum, this consists in the first tetrapods (amphibians) of a single vertebra with its ribs to which the pelvic girdle is attached. In fishes no sacral vertebra is present since the fins bear no weight and thus there is no necessity for direct attachment of the girdle to the axial skeleton. With invasion of the terrestrial habitat, however, the weight of the body of necessity is borne upon the limbs. A more solid anchorage of the hind limbs was acquired by direct articulation of their girdle (pelvis) with the axial skeleton. Presence of vertebra between pelvis and sacral ribs was a functional liability, but the evolutionary tendency has been toward thickening of the sacral ribs and their ankylosis with the vertebrae, rather than toward their loss. In reptiles a better anchorage was developed by (1) increase in number of sacral vertebrae (usually two), and by (2) fusion of the sacral vertebrae with each other and with their ribs. Still more vertebrae are incorporated in the sacrum in mammals (three to five in most orders). In birds a remarkable fusion of vertebrae strengthens the vertebral column: the sacral, proximal caudal, all the lumbar, and the posterior thoracic vertebrae collectively form a single structure, the *synsacrum* (Fig. 6.16).

The thoracic and lumbar vertebrae became differentiated in reptiles, although the only consistent difference between them is in articulation with ribs (ribs freely articulating with thoracic vertebrae, absent on lumbar vertebrae). The selective pressures responsible for this differentiation was apparently the concomitant improvement of lung respiration and of locomotion. Locomotion was enhanced by lifting the body from the ground as an emancipation from the creeping and crawling gait of primitive tetrapods. This action presumably placed a premium upon presence of a rigid lateral support from which abdominal structures could be suspended; free ribs would have been a liability in performance of this function through lack of adequate rigidity. More primitive tetrapods, even though they had lungs, had no need for a forced draft mechanism (as made possible by differentiation of a thoracic region) since the lungs were relatively inefficient and respiration was accomplished chiefly through the skin. Both the thoracic and lumbar vertebrae are largely responsible for the powerful trunk movements characteristic of tetrapods, in the same manner that all trunk vertebrae served in fishes. Skeletal attachments for most of the muscles making these movements possible occur on the often exaggerated

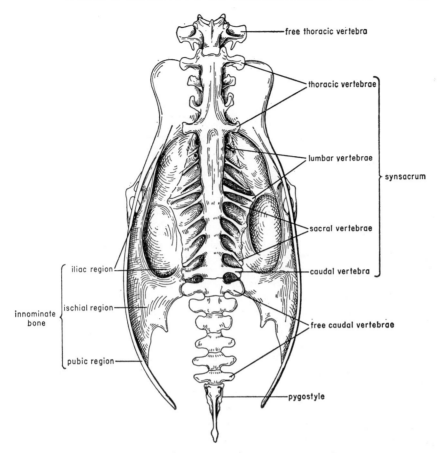

FIG. 6.16 Synsacrum of the pigeon, in ventral view. (From Eddy.)

neural spines and on the ribs or transverse processes. In addition in some vertebrates additional midventral processes (*hypapophyses*) from the centra have evolved and provide attachments for additional muscles (Fig. 6.17A, B).

The caudal vertebrae vary greatly in number in vertebrates; no general trend is evident. Evolutionary lines exhibiting either reduction or increase in number are numerous. Notable minor specializations are the *urostyle* (all caudal vertebrae fused) in anurans, the *pygostyle* (distal caudal vertebrae fused) in birds, and the *coccyx* (proximal caudal vertebrae fused) in man. Skeletal surface to provide for powerful caudal movements is provided primarily by enlarged neural and hemal spines.

Torsional Resistance. Seemingly one of the most important new problems facing tetrapods, and that did not exist to a notable degree among fishes, was the prevention of excessive twisting of the vertebral column. In fishes the whole axial skeleton is supported equally well at all points, whereas in tetrapods it is supported at only one or two points, and ac-

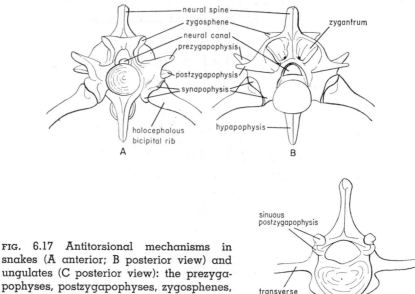

FIG. 6.17 Antitorsional mechanisms in snakes (A anterior; B posterior view) and ungulates (C posterior view): the prezygapophyses, postzygapophyses, zygosphenes, and zygantra of A and B, and the sinuous zygapophyses of C.

cordingly a real and constant hazard exists of excessive twisting occurring at any point along the axis where much weight is or may be concentrated. All tetrapods possess at least one set of structures, the *zygapophyses,* whose primary function is to prevent twist. The zygapophyses are processes bearing smooth articular surfaces on the neural arches. One pair, the *prezygapophyses,* is present on the anterior end of the vertebra; its articular surfaces always face dorsad or dorsomediad. The other pair, the *postzygapophyses,* is present on the posterior end of the vertebra; its articular surfaces always face ventrad or ventrolaterad. In articulated vertebrae the postzygapophyses of one vertebra are directly superimposed over the prezygapophyses of the next posterior vertebra. The zygapophyses are so constructed as to permit bending of the vertebral column in a horizontal or vertical plane as in both situations the articular faces freely glide against each other. They are not designed actually to enable movement, for the swiveling between adjacent vertebrae actually occurs at the centrum. The real function of the zygapophyses seems to be the prevention of twisting movements.

In a few tetrapods subject to unusual twisting stress, *accessory zygapophyses* or *sinuous zygapophyses* have evolved. All snakes and some lizards possess accessory zygapophyses (Fig. 6.17A, B), which consist of articular processes closely resembling the true zygapophyses. An anterior pair (of *zygosphenes*) faces ventrad, a posterior pair (of *zygantra*) upward. The true and accessory zygapophyses lock together in such a manner that, although bending in a vertical or horizontal plane is not impeded, no twisting movement whatever is possible.

In the large ungulate mammals the articular surfaces of the zygapophyses are not flat in all regions of the vertebral column. Instead, especially in the lumbar region, the articular surfaces are curved, actually
attaining an S shape in extreme cases. Such zygapophyses are referred to
as *sinuous* (Fig. 6.17C). They not only provide a perfect antitorsional
mechanism but they also resist the stress of vertical weight loads. Various
other devices aid in preventing torsion. The ball-and-socket joints formed
by the centra in so many vertebrates (with procelous or opisthocelous
vertebrae) are at least in part of antitorsional value. The synsacrum and
fused thoracics of birds certainly have value in the same way, as does also
the articulation in some ungulates of sacrum and transverse processes of
the presacral lumbar vertebrae.

Although antitorsional devices are characteristic of tetrapods, they
are not wholly limited to them. Many teleosts as well as scattered tetrapods
(for example, some mammals) possess nonarticular interlocking processes
called anapophyses. Those of fishes have been termed zygapophyses, but
in error, since there is no homology. Anapophyses do not, in themselves,
provide for movement in any given direction; zygapophyses, of all types,
however, do.

Suspensory Adaptations. In the more primitive, crawling tetrapods
the role of the vertebral column in suspension of the body was not particularly great, and few adaptations to assist in that role appeared. In the
endotherms, however, much of the time the body is supported off the
ground by the legs, rather than allowed to rest directly on the ground or on
other general support, and suspension is thus of great importance in them.
Adaptations correlated with the suspensory role might be expected and did
appear. In birds the general trend was toward fusion of the thoracic and
lumbar vertebrae in the synsacrum or with each other, but this resort was
possible only with loss of most trunk mobility. In mammals most adaptations to vertical weight loads have interfered relatively little with trunk
mobility; such adaptations are enlargement and slanting backward or forward of the neural spines; fusion of ribs and vertebrae to form solid suspensory structures within each segment; and interlocking devices (such as
sinuous zygapophyses) between vertebrae that prevent sagging as well as
twisting.

Cranial Mobility. The survival value of cranial mobility in tetrapods
as contrasted with fishes has already been noted. Increase in number of
cervical vertebrae was one modification contributing to attainment of
cranial mobility. Two other adaptations are specialization of the anterior
two vertebrae in amniotes as the *atlas* and *axis,* and transformation of the
unpaired, nonarticular *occipital process* of the skull in fishes to one or two
articular *occipital condyles* in all tetrapods. Primitive tetrapods possess one
condyle, and in a number of separate advanced lines (modern reptiles,
birds, some fossil amphibians) that number was retained. In others the
number has been increased to two. The occipital process of fishes does not
provide for movement of the skull on the anterior trunk vertebra, whereas

the condyles of tetrapods permit at least a certain amount of movement of the skull on the centrum of the anterior cervical vertebra. Zygapophyses are always absent on the anterior face of the anterior trunk vertebra, since the skull articulates with the centrum of that vertebra.

In amphibians the first cervical vertebra has the same composition as the succeeding trunk vertebrae except for fusion with its ribs. In amniotes, however, the first two vertebrae are quite distinctive from the others in composition. To review the origin of the atlas and axis, let us go back to the embryonic arcualia. After staggering occurs of the pertinent components, the basidorsal (for the neural arch) and intercentrum of the first segment, and the pleurocentrum of the second segment (Fig. 6.18) are seen to comprise the presumptive atlas—that is, the vertebra as one would expect it to be formed if it followed the typical mammalian pattern (Fig. 6.13). The presumptive axis consists of the basidorsal and intercentrum of the second segment and the pleurocentrum of the third segment. Were the atlas and axis to form by fusion of all the presumptive parts except the intercentra (becoming intervertebral disks), they would be of the same composition as other trunk vertebrae. The fusions actually proceed from this point in a unique manner, however. The definitive atlas is produced by fusion of only its presumptive neural arch and intercentrum, forming a ringlike vertebra (a pair of ribs is also fused with it, as in all other cervical vertebrae). The definitive axis is produced by fusion of the pleurocentrum of the presumptive atlas with all parts of the presumptive axis and with the pleurocentrum (*proatlas*) of the first segment; a pair of ribs is also included.

The specialization of the atlas and axis is apparently an answer to the serious problem of *maintaining osseous strength while providing for a considerable degree of cranial mobility*. At least in mammals vertical (nodding) and horizontal (tilting or rocking) movements are largely limited to the skull-atlas joint, whereas twisting (negative, to humans) movements are largely confined to the atlas-axis joint. Performance of all these movements at one joint would require a single, swivellike condyle,

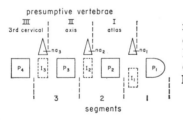

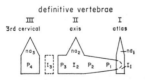

FIG. 6.18 Composition of the amniote atlas and axis. Above, an embryonic stage; below, the adult stage. Symbols: I, intercentrum; na, neural arch; P, pleurocentrum; P_1 proatlas.

which in turn obviously would provide relatively much less osseous strength at this vital point than the amniote device permitting division of labor between two joints. It is obvious that attainment of strength alone was *not* the important factor in specialization of the atlas-axis complex.

Ribs

Phylogenetic Types. Two different modes of origin are evident in vertebrate ribs. The most common origin is through ossification along the myosepta, from connective tissue or cartilage. These are *primary* ribs, belonging to the primary endoskeleton. *Secondary* ribs are derived from the dermis—as a matter of fact, from osteoderms. These are dermal ribs, belonging to the secondary endoskeleton; they are commonly called *gastralia* or *abdominal ribs*. They differ from primary ribs not only by origin but also by occurring along the sides of the ventral body wall (rather than on the dorsal wall, or on the entire body wall, dorsal and ventral); they do not reach the vertebrae (primary ribs do); and they occur only in the lumbar region, between the sternum and pelvis. Otherwise primary and secondary ribs appear much alike.

The function of primary ribs was, originally, to provide a more solid point of attachment for muscles than the myocommata alone could provide. In later vertebrates the ribs serve in some as struts from which parts of the body are suspended, in others as a protective basket, and in some as accessory breathing structures.

Secondary Ribs. Secondary ribs were presumably protective and strengthening devices for the rear ventral body wall, developed in primitive tetrapods that dragged the body on the ground. Already provided with osteoderms, but with only short ribs in the rear trunk region, it was apparently simpler for new ribs to evolve from the osteoderms than for the primary ribs to lengthen in that area of the trunk. The stage was thus set in these animals for complete loss of primary ribs in the abdominal area—in other words, for differentiation of thoracic and lumbar regions.

The remainder of our discussion will concern only primary ribs.

Primary Ribs. POSITION OF ORIGIN. All primary ribs develop in the myosepta, extending outward from the vertebral column to which they are usually attached. Thus primary ribs are truly segmental in arrangement. However, more than one rib may form in each myoseptum (Fig. 6.19). Fishes typically have only one on each side, located at the junction of the myoseptum with the celomic wall; such ribs are referred to as *ventral* or *pleural* or *fish* ribs. They do not occur in tetrapods.

Some fishes have two ribs on either side: the usual ventral rib, and in addition one formed at the junction of the myoseptum and the horizontal skeletogenous septum. The latter are *dorsal* ribs. Other fishes have only dorsal ribs, and still others have not only these but several others along the vertical expanse of the myoseptum.

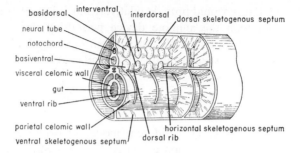

FIG. 6.19 Relation of dorsal and ventral ribs. (From Goodrich.)

COSTOVERTEBRAL ARTICULATION. The dorsal ribs of fishes articulate with undivided processes, the *basapophyses,* on each centrum. The ribs are not forked, but are simply curved structures without special modification. They ordinarily are not capable of much movement, as this ability is not of importance until lungs develop, and thus they usually have no enlargement (head) at the vertebral end to facilitate free articulation; they are *acephalous* (Fig. 6.20A).

In tetrapods only dorsal ribs occur (apparently). Primitively they

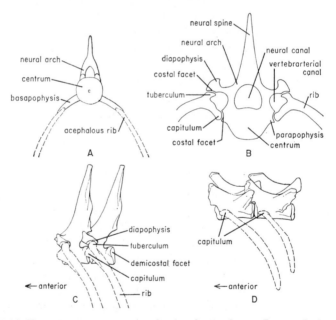

FIG. 6.20 Variations in costovertebral relationships. A, acephalous rib and vertebra with basapophysis, in trunk region of a teleost; B, a generalized tetrapod dichocephalous rib and its vertebral articulations; C, mammalian dichocephalous ribs of intercentral articulation; D, mammalian capitulocephalous ribs and their vertebral articulation. (A and B from Adams and Eddy.)

are *bicipital,* having two heads for articulation with the vertebrae. The anteroventral head (*capitulum*) primitively articulates (Fig. 6.20B) with a process (*parapophysis*) on the intercentrum, the posterodorsal head (*tuberculum*) with a process (*diapophysis*) on the neural arch. With loss of the intercentrum (as in amniotes) the capitulum may shift to articulate with the pleurocentrum (most reptiles, birds), or it may (as in mammals) articulate between centra, in the primitive position. In the latter case *demifacets* on the ends of two adjacent vertebrae typically receive the capitulum (Fig. 6.20C).

The bicipital ribs of primitive tetrapods have been modified in various evolutionary lines as (1) *holocephalous* (Fig. 6.17B), through fusion of the two rib heads and their articulation in effect as one head with a fused vertebral equivalent of the diapophysis and parapophysis (the *synapophysis,* as in snakes, some lizards, and many fossil reptiles); and (2) *monocephalous,* through loss of either the tuberculum (thus becoming *capitulocephalous,* Fig. 6.20D), or the capitulum (thus becoming *tuberculocephalous*). The rear thoracic ribs of many mammals, and most of those of marsupials, are capitulocephalous, but no living examples are known of tuberculocephaly. Truly *dichocephalous* ribs, in which both heads are clearly separate, occur in other tetrapods.

On the basis of modifications of the rib for articulation with the vertebral column, the following rib types can thus be recognized:

acephalous
bicipital
  holocephalous
  dichocephalous
  monocephalous
    capitulocephalous
    tuberculocephalous

COSTOSTERNAL ARTICULATION. Ribs articulate ventrally with the sternum only in amniotes, but certain members (for example, Ophidia, Testudines) even of that group lack a sternum and thus the ribs fail to meet ventrally. Thoracic ribs that do articulate with the sternum are called *true* ribs. Those posterior to these, that articulate with each other or with nothing ventrally, are *false* ribs. The more posterior false ribs that articulate with nothing ventrally are called *floating* ribs (Fig. 6.21).

DIFFERENTIATION OF RIB BODY. In many amniotes the ribs are differentiated into two parts: a dorsal part, the *vertebral rib,* articulating with the vertebral column, and a ventral part, the *sternal rib,* articulating with the sternum (Fig. 6.21). The sternal rib is commonly ossified in birds, but is cartilaginous in mammals. The vertebral rib is always ossified.

THE ROLE OF RIBS IN REGIONALIZATION. Ribs were primitively present throughout the vertebral column—even in the tail region. Pleural ribs, as a matter of fact, represent the hemal arches of the caudal region, which may thus be regarded as modified pleural ribs. Dorsal ribs are limited almost exclusively to the trunk region, although in some amphibians they occasionally are found also at the base of the tail.

The four regions of the trunk vertebral column are differentiated primarily on the basis of the fate of the ribs. In the cervical region the ribs are short, failing to articulate with the sternum, or are fused onto the vertebrae, forming transverse processes called *pleurapophyses* in which ordinarily the vertebrarterial canal remains evident. In the thoracic region the ribs freely articulate with the sternum. In the lumbar region the ribs have become reduced in size and fused onto the vertebrae as *transverse processes,* and in the sacral region also the ribs are fused with the vertebrae. The thoracic region is additionally characterized by the presence in birds and some reptiles of small, separate elements (*uncinate* bones, Fig. 6.21B) connecting one rib with the succeeding rib. These bones are of rib origin and belong to the primary endoskeleton. Their function is to strengthen the rib basket.

Sternum

Function. The sternum is a longitudinal, midventral skeletal structure located near the anterior end of the trunk, posterior to the neck. It first appeared in tetrapods, in which it served a function primitively of protection of the body wall in front of the abdomen where the gastralia perform the same function. Just why there should be a "division of labor" in this fashion is not readily evident. Probably there was and is a necessity for support or protection of vital parts, in the anterior thoracic area, at an earlier embryonic stage than would be possible for dermal structures. It has long been known that cartilage is primarily an embryonic adaptation—a stiff skeletal tissue that allows, however, considerable flexibility and free growth. Abdominal protection is needed only as a large size is attained. Thus the gradual appearance of gastralia postembryonically, in the fashion typical of dermal ossification, serves the purpose admirably, whereas immediate protection at birth or hatching (or before) is of survival value for the thoracic region.

Integration with Other Skeletal Parts. The sternum in its earliest form was independent of all other skeletal components, but it soon acquired connections with enlarged ribs.

Most modern tetrapods retain costal articulation with the sternum. Exceptions include the amphibians (perhaps never having acquired sternocostal articulations in the first place), turtles, snakes, and some lizards.

A secondary association with the pectoral girdle has occurred in many tetrapods, even amphibians. In anurans the sternum appears in two sections, one articulated with the anterior edge of the pectoral girdle, the other with the posterior edge. In reptiles possessing a sternum (excluding turtles, snakes, a few lizards), in birds, and in monotremes, the pectoral

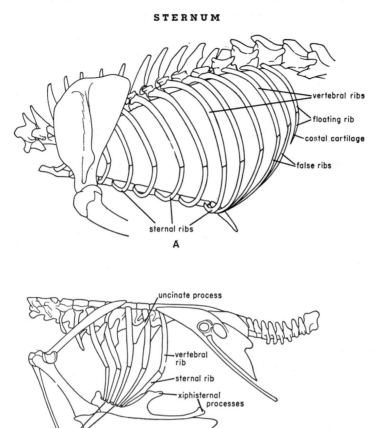

FIG. 6.21 Variation in relation of ribs and sternum. Lateral views of A, mammalian (cat) and B, avian (pigeon) thorax, showing differentiation of parts of rib body (sternal and vertebral ribs), and variation in costo-sternal articulation (floating, false, and "true" ribs). (From Booth, Parker and Haswell.)

girdle is articulated with the sternum by way of the clavicle and inter-clavicle, thus strengthening both the girdle and the rib basket. In most mammals the clavicle alone serves the same purpose, but in some (like carnivores, rodents, lagomorphs, ungulates) there is no skeletal connection whatsoever between the girdle and sternum, the clavicle being very small or absent.

Origin. Apparently the sternum originated independently as chondrifications in the ventral skeletogenous septum and in the adjacent myosepta. Two other theories have received credence at various times in the past, but are now considered untenable: (a) segregation from part of the pectoral girdle (as suggested by anurans, with a well-developed sternum firmly attached to the girdle only, not to the ribs); and (b) expansion of ends of the ribs (as suggested by the embryonic origin of the sternum in mammals).

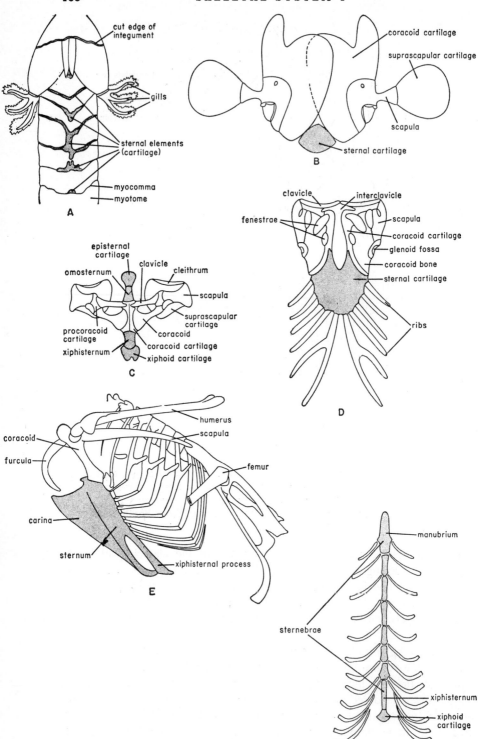

A
cut edge of integument
gills
sternal elements (cartilage)
myocomma
myotome

B
coracoid cartilage
suprascapular cartilage
scapula
sternal cartilage

C
episternal cartilage
omosternum
clavicle
cleithrum
scapula
suprascapular cartilage
procoracoid cartilage
coracoid
coracoid cartilage
xiphisternum
xiphoid cartilage

D
clavicle
interclavicle
fenestrae
scapula
coracoid cartilage
glenoid fossa
coracoid bone
sternal cartilage
ribs

E
humerus
scapula
coracoid
furcula
femur
carina
sternum
xiphisternal process

F
manubrium
sternebrae
xiphisternum
xiphoid cartilage

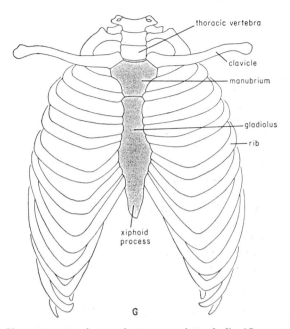

FIG. 6.22 Variations in form of sternum (stippled). (*Opposite page*): A, Necturus, a primitive salamander; B, Ambystoma, a more advanced salamander; C, anuran; D, lizard; E, bird; F, cat; (*above*) G, man. (From Cunningham, Kingsley, Noble, Romer, Wilder, Walter, and Sayles.)

Form. The sternum was probably a segmented structure originally; in view of its theoretical origin it could scarcely have been otherwise. However, only in mammals of existing vertebrates is that segmented condition clearly exhibited in adults. All others show a considerable specialization, all toward fusion of parts or loss (Figs. 6.22, 6.23). In anurans it is split into two sections, one attached to the anterior edge of the pectoral girdle, the other to the rear edge. In reptiles (where present) and birds it is a solid, unsegmented structure more or less completely integrated with the pectoral girdle. Turtles are thought to lack a sternum, although possibly some of the bones of the plastron represent it. Snakes and some snakelike lizards have no vestige whatsoever of the sternum.

FIG. 6.23 Phylogeny in form of the tetrapod sternum.

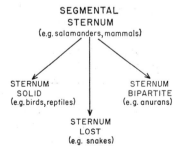

QUESTIONS

1. What was the original function of the vertebral column, and other functions subsequently acquired?

2. Name the six components of a complete vertebra in adults.

3. How is the vertebral structure of cyclostomes and the Chondrostei alike, and how did their means of arrival at the similarity differ?

4. Name five trends in evolution of the components of vertebrae in adults.

5. Name and give examples of five different sorts of reduction in number of centra occurring in vertebrates. Does the reverse trend occur in any vertebrates?

6. By what means do vertebrae become "staggered," and what functional value may it have?

7. Draw an evolutionary tree of the seven types of centra (based upon shape of ends) occurring in tetrapods.

8. What structures or modifications have appeared in vertebrates to resist torsion?

9. Trace the course of regionalization of the vertebral column in vertebrates, beginning with fishes, stating the survival value of each change; state the number of vertebrae in each region at any stage in which the number is fixed.

10. Fusion of what caudal vertebrae has produced what variants (by name) in what vertebrates?

11. Name the components of the embryonic vertebrae and the components of the adult vertebra to which each gives rise in various vertebrates. Specify anterior and posterior position in segment (before staggering) and vertebra. Name the evolutionary components of all vertebrae in *adults* of various classes, and the arcuale from which each has been derived.

12. How does the method of formation of the salamander and apodan centrum differ from that of anurans, and both from that of the ordinary tetrapod?

13. What happens to the arcualia that fail to contribute to the vertebrae?

14. Name and differentiate eight different modes of formation of centrum.

15. How are cervical vertebrae distinguished from those of other regions in amphibians? Reptiles? Mammals?

16. How, in general terms, does the first cervical vertebra of amphibians and amniotes differ?

17. List the components of the definitive atlas and axis.

18. Evolution of the distinctive atlas-axis complex had what survival value? Explain.

19. What three adaptations have contributed to cranial mobility in vertebrates?

20. Name the trends adaptive to terrestrial life occurring in the evolution of the vertebral column.

21. What is the function of the sternum? Why did gastralia not supersede the sternum?

22. What is thought to have been the origin of the sternum?

23. What is the form of the sternum in the various tetrapod classes?

24. In what specific groups of vertebrates is a sternum lacking?

25. Define the following words, and where appropriate state occurrence:

abdominal ribs
accessory zygapophy-
    ses
acentrous
acephalous
acelous
amphicelous
amphiplatyan
anapophysis
arch centra
arcualia
aspondyly
atlas
axis
basal arches
basalia
basapophysis
basidorsal
basiventral
bicipital
capitulocephalous
capitulum
centrum
cervical
cervical vertebra
chevron bones
chondral centra
chordal centra
coccygeal
coccyx
costovertebral foramen
demifacet
diapophysis
dichocephalous
diplospondyly

dorsal arches
dorsal ribs
epiphyseal centra
epiphyses
false rib
fish rib
floating rib
gastralia
hemal arch
heterocelous
holocephalous
holophyseal centra
husk centra
hypapophysis
imperforate amphice-
    lous
intercalary arch
intercalia
intercentrum
interdorsal
interhemal arch
interneural arch
interventral
intervertebral body
intervertebral disc
lumbar vertebra
monocephalous
monospondyly
neural arch
occipital condyle
occipital process
opisthocelous
parapophysis
perforate amphicelous
perichordal centra
pleural ribs

pleurapophysis
pleurocentrum
polyspondyly
postzygapophysis
prezygapophysis
primary ribs
proatlas
procelous
pseudopisthocelous
pygostyle
sacrum
schistic centrum
secondary ribs
sinuous zygapophyses
staggering
sternal rib
sternum
synapophysis
synsacrum
thoracic vertebra
thorax
transverse foramen
transverse process
true rib
tuberculocephalous
tuberculum
uncinate bone
urostyle
ventral arches
ventral ribs
vertebral rib
vertebrarterial canal
zygantrum
zygapophyses
zygosphene

7

SKELETAL SYSTEM II
Visceral and Appendicular Skeleton

Visceral Skeleton

THE SKELETON supporting the pharynx in the protochordates has had an amazingly complex and devious evolutionary history correlated with the equally varied functions the pharynx and its derivatives have adopted through their long history. That part of the alimentary tract actually termed a pharynx, however, becomes more and more limited in vertebrate phylogeny; some skeletal parts that were truly supports for the pharynx in protochordates are utilized for entirely different purposes in vertebrates. Therefore it is more nearly correct to refer collectively to all vertebrate derivatives of the protochordate pharyngeal skeleton in more generalized terms as the *visceral skeleton*—in reference to their association with the alimentary tract—rather than *pharyngeal skeleton,* which is somewhat confusing owing to the more specific and often different application of the term "pharynx" in different vertebrates.

Pregnathostome Arrangement. In the protochordates and agnathous vertebrates, the visceral skeleton consists of a series of curved *pharyngeal bars* or *arches* situated along the medial wall of the pharynx, one bar separating each internal pharyngeal slit from the adjacent slit (Fig. 7.1). The skeletal arches do not surround the pharynx dorsally, but instead leave a broad gap protected only (and adequately) by the dorsal axial skeleton. Ventrally, however, the bars meet at the midline, where they are connected with each other by a series of longitudinal bars.

The number of pairs of visceral skeletal arches existing in this stage was certainly nine or more. Probably there was a reduction in number in the line of evolution toward gnathostomes.

Gnathostome Modifications. The basic number of paired visceral arches in gnathostomes may reasonably be regarded as seven (Fig. 7.1B).

162

FIG. 7.1 A, Pharyngeal bar arrangement in a protochordate comparable with Branchiostoma, diagrammatic; B, visceral skeleton of a lamprey, ventral view; C, frontal section of A; D, frontal section comparable to the stage represented by B, but based upon a hypothetical agnathan ancestral to gnathostomes. (B from Kingsley.)

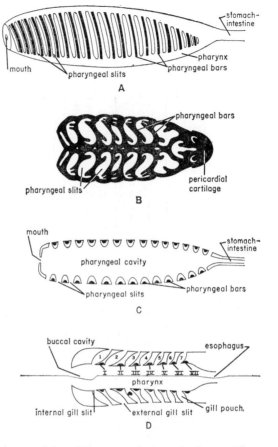

The number is regarded by a few authorities as higher, and by others as lower. The actual number is determinable arbitrarily only, since there has been a fairly steady trend toward reduction in number of visceral arches and since the point at which the gnathostome line is drawn is itself arbitrary. Of great importance, however, is agreement upon the specific number applied to any specific arch, lest homologies be completely obscured by differences in terminology. Thus arch number 1 is invariably regarded as the mandibular arch, and those more posterior are numbered consecutively. Seven is at least generally regarded as the basic number in gnathostomes, since at least that many are evident embryonically in every vertebrate. A few fishes have more postmandibular arches (up to thirteen in living cyclostomes, eight in one shark, seven in another shark), and many sharks have evidence (as *labial cartilages*) of one or more premandibular arches. Nevertheless the extra arches, undoubtedly present in ancestors of gnathostomes, leave no evidence in osteichthyans or tetrapods and are thus conventionally disregarded.

Primitively one visceral pouch lay anterior and another posterior to each arch on each side. However, since the pouch following the last (seventh) arch is missing in virtually all gnathostomes (all except the two sharks previously mentioned, with eight or nine visceral arches), only seven pouches are commonly accounted for in tracing vertebrate evolution. It is important to note that the pouch of a given number always precedes (does not follow) the arch bearing the corresponding number. Unlike the visceral arches, numbered the same by most authorities, the visceral

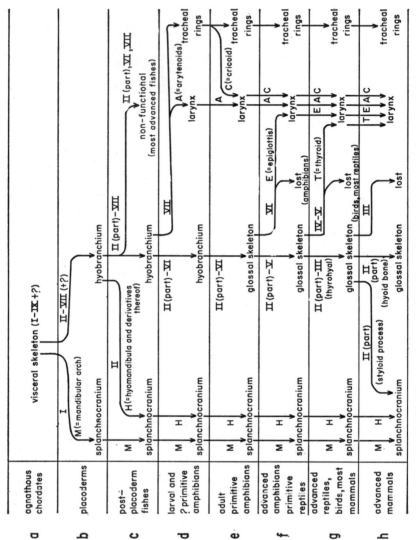

FIG. 7.2 Evolution of visceral skeleton. The eight different stages a-h are depicted in Figs. 7.3–7.10.

pouches are numbered quite differently by different authorities. There is not even agreement in the number applied to any specific pouch. The disparities have arisen from the fact that the pouch of the first arch is not evident as such in any gnathostome, and that the pouch of the second arch is fully functional as a gill pouch in no living gnathostome. These facts are not, however, materially different from those pertaining to the skeletal arches; there has been a fairly steady trend toward decrease in number and toward modification for other uses of both arches and pouches throughout the whole history of vertebrates. Therefore, the most reasonable solution is to proceed from the points of agreement upon number of skeletal arches and upon the fact that the pouch of any given arch lies in front (not back) of that arch. Obviously the most reasonable sequel is to apply the same number to the pouch as to the skeletal arch, and that is uniformly the system adopted here. The student should be prepared, however, in consulting other sources, to find the pouch of either the second (hyoid) or third ("first branchial," of many texts) skeletal arch regarded as the first visceral pouch.

Only in pregnathostomes do all seven visceral pouches possess a branchial (gill) function. In all gnathostomes the first pouch fuses with the mouth as its arch becomes modified to share in the formation of the first true jaws to appear anywhere in the evolution of chordates. In all gnathostomes except placoderms the second pouch is also greatly reduced in size or absent as its arch becomes modified to assist in suspension of the jaws and in manipulation of food (tongue).

The remaining pouches and their supportive arches have retained a branchial function throughout fishes, with but few exceptions in which one or two have become functionless. In amphibians, however, the pouches went through rapid reduction, losing all resemblance to their former condition, the lungs and skin tending to replace them as respiratory organs. The supportive arches were left without function as pouch supports, but in many vertebrates they gained or perfected other functions essential to the new mode of land life with aerial respiration. In fact, it may be surmised that successful adaptation of tetrapods to terrestrial life would not have been possible, at least as now known, without the availability of arches freed from what previously had constituted a primary and probably sometimes a sole function. Thus the arches have not completely disappeared as they undoubtedly would, had they been left totally functionless by loss of branchial use, but they have become progressively modified and molded to perform other functions.

The tetrapod functions served by the rear arches are, primarily, support for the tongue (an increasingly important food-getting or food-manipulating device), and protection of the opening into the trachea.

Thus the derivatives of the visceral skeleton in gnathostomes may be placed in five groups (Fig. 7.2). They are (1) the *splanchnocranium*, including all contributions of the visceral skeleton to the skull or cranium; (2) the *hyobranchium*, all postcranial components in gill-breathing verte-

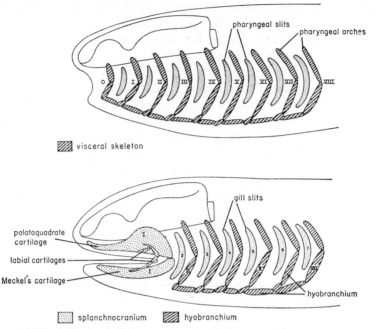

FIG. 7.3 (*Top*) Visceral skeleton of an agnathous vertebrate, side view, diagrammatic. Entire visceral skeleton in lined shading. Stage *a* of Fig. 7.2.

FIG. 7.4 (*Bottom*) Visceral skeleton of a placoderm, lateral view, diagrammatic: (*a*) splanchnocranium in open stipple, (*b*) hyobranchium lined. Stage *b* of Fig. 7.2.

brates, except for parts that in some may be entirely separate and modified for other functions (as for example the larynx in neotenic salamanders like Necturus); (3) the *larynx;* (4) *tracheal rings;* and (5) the *glossal skeleton.*

SPLANCHNOCRANIUM. Those parts of the visceral skeleton directly incorporated into and functioning as a part of the skull or *cranium* collectively constitute the *splanchnocranium.* The splanchnocranium first came into existence in the placoderms. In the Agnatha none of the visceral arches were associated with the cranium, and thus in them no splanchnocranium exists. In the placoderms the first arch lost its branchial function, or served that function only for the pouch posterior to it. It was modified as an internal part of the jaws—both upper and lower—and in this function it became integrated with the rest of the cranium. It thus constituted the original splanchnocranium, and in this capacity is known as the *mandibular arch.* All vertebrates derived directly or indirectly from the placoderms possess a splanchnocranium consisting of at least the mandibular arch.

In all postplacoderm vertebrates the upper part of the second arch has also lost its gill function, and has become incorporated with the cranial mechanisms. In this capacity the second arch is known as the *hyoid arch.* Only the upper part, known as the *hyomandibula* in postplacoderm fishes,

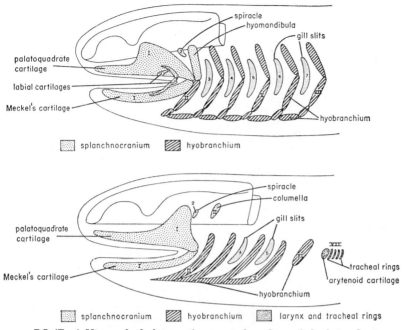

FIG. 7.5 (*Top*) Visceral skeleton of a post-placoderm fish, lateral view, diagrammatic: (a) splanchnocranium with open stipple, (b) hyobranchium lined. Stage c of Fig. 7.2.

FIG. 7.6 (*Bottom*) Visceral skeleton of primitive and larval amphibians, lateral view, diagrammatic: (a) splanchnocranium in open stipple, (b) hyobranchium lined, (c) larynx and tracheal rings in mixed stipple. Stage d of Fig. 7.2.

contributes to the splanchnocranium in most vertebrates; the rest of the hyoid arch forms a part of the tongue or gill-support apparatus.

In virtually all fishes and tetrapods the splanchnocranium thus consists at least of all of arch I, and the dorsal part of arch II. A third stage of splanchnocranial evolution is consummated in a few advanced mammals such as primates and ungulates, in which the median part of the hyoid arch is fused onto the skull in the otic region as the *styloid process*. This is the maximum extent of contribution of the visceral arches to the splanchnocranium in vertebrates.

LARYNX. Not until the vertebrates invaded land and came to depend largely upon air as a respiratory medium, and upon lungs as a respiratory organ, did the larynx appear on the scene. Amphibians were the first to develop the structure, which was primitively very simple and served only as a valve preventing entrance of foreign material into the trachea and lungs. In salamanders a very primitive condition is retained, of but one pair of cartilages (*arytenoids*), one on either side of the opening (*glottis*) into the trachea. These are formed from the seventh visceral arch, which lost its branchial function as the lungs increased in importance. The trachea is

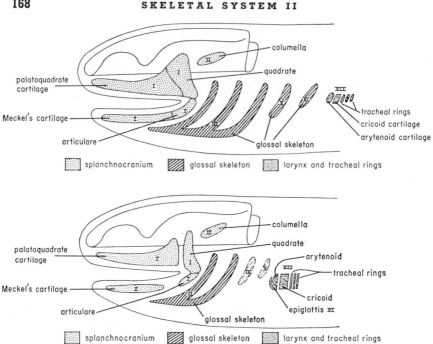

FIG. 7.7 (*Top*) Visceral skeleton of adult primitive amphibians, lateral view, diagrammatic: (a) splanchnocranium in open stipple, (b) glossal skeleton lined, (c) larynx and tracheal rings in mixed stipple. Stage e of Fig. 7.2.

FIG. 7.8 (*Bottom*) Visceral skeleton of primitive reptiles, lateral view, diagrammatic: (a) splanchnocranium in open stipple, (b) glossal skeleton lined, (c) larynx and trachea in mixed stipple. Stage f of Fig. 7.2.

strengthened by a series of bars or rings, also derived from the seventh visceral arch.

A second step is exemplified by anurans. An anterior tracheal ring has become enlarged as a *cricoid cartilage* situated immediately behind the arytenoid cartilages, strengthening the tracheal opening without interfering with the valvular action of the arytenoid cartilages. As a modified tracheal ring, the cricoid cartilage is, of course, regarded as a derivative of the seventh visceral arch.

A third step is exemplified by modern reptiles, at least some of which (for example, snakes) appear to possess a cartilage similar to and possibly homologous with the *epiglottis* of mammals. This is an extra valve protecting the glottis, now closed not only by drawing the bilaterally paired arytenoid cartilages together, but also by the epiglottal flap hinged on the cricoid cartilage at the lower (anterior) edge of the glottis, and swinging backward over the glottis and arytenoid cartilages. The epiglottis is thought to be derived from the sixth visceral arch.

Differentiation of an epiglottis sets the stage for development of vocal cords in mammals. Shortening of the arytenoid cartilages to allow de-

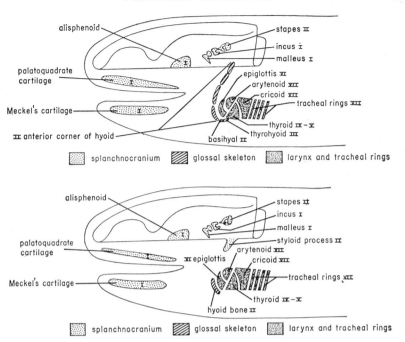

FIG. 7.9 (*Top*) Visceral skeleton of most mammals, lateral view, diagrammatic: (a) splanchnocranium in open stipple, (b) glossal skeleton lined, (c) larynx and tracheal rings in mixed stipple. Stage *g* of Fig. 7.2.

FIG. 7.10 (*Bottom*) Visceral skeleton of advanced mammals, lateral view, diagrammatic: (a) splanchnocranium in open stipple, (b) glossal skeleton lined, (c) larynx and tracheal rings in mixed stipple. Stage *h* of Fig. 7.2.

velopment of the vocal cords, extending from the lower edge of the arytenoids to the midventral line of the inner surface of the cricoid cartilage, would leave the glottis inadequately protected were the epiglottis not present. Of course, the epiglottis of reptiles, even if recognized, has not acquired the function, possessed in mammals, of closing the glottis. Likewise no, or very poorly developed, laryngeal vocal cords occur in reptiles. The importance of having an epiglottis in conjunction with laryngeal vocal cords is perhaps indicated by birds, which without an epiglottis (presumably also absent in their particular reptilian ancestors) developed (of necessity) a very different set of vocal cords situated in a special voice box, the *syrinx*, at the junction of the paired bronchi and the trachea.

A final stage is represented by mammals in which a U-shaped cartilage, the *thyroid* (meaning shield-shaped, not association with the thyroid gland) cartilage, is added to the ventral surface of the larynx. Its functional value is to provide the means for anchoring the larynx onto the base of the tongue. This arrangement is of great importance in the operation of the epiglottis to close the glottis. The thyroid cartilage is thought to be derived from the fourth and fifth visceral arches, fused.

GLOSSAL SKELETON. A primitive sort of tongue exists in fishes. It is supported by, and consists chiefly of, the median ventral element (*basihyal*) of the second (hyoid) visceral arch. This in turn is attached at its sides to the more dorsal elements of the hyoid arch, and, less directly, to all the more posterior visceral arches. The tongue is scarcely differentiated in fishes, as all the postcranial visceral arches still possess primarily a respiratory function. As a matter of fact, this situation persists in larvae and neotenic adults of modern amphibians.

In transformed amphibians and in all amniotes the visceral skeleton loses all branchial (gill) function. The parts not devoted in them to a laryngeal or cranial function remain for the most part attached to the basihyal, serving primarily as an elaborate *glossal skeleton*. The glossal skeleton of early amphibians and reptiles is far more elaborate and complex than necessary, it appears, consisting of the noncranial parts of arch II, and most or all of arches III–V, inclusive. At a theoretical and still earlier stage the glossal skeleton consisted of arch VI also, arch VII serving as the arytenoid cartilages; this may be regarded as the first stage in evolution of the glossal skeleton. The second stage is represented by primitive amphibians and reptiles, in some of which arch VI is lost (as in anurans, primitive lizards) or is retained as a primitive epiglottis (no living examples).

In the third stage, the glossal skeleton loses arches IV and V which either have been pressed into service as a thyroid cartilage (mammals) or have been lost (as in birds and most reptiles). Arch III in those mammals in which it persists (for example, carnivores) connects the basihyal and the rest of arch II with the thyroid cartilage (representing arches IV, V), as would be expected in a primitive condition; it is in the form of a single, short bar on either side, called the *thyrohyal*. It forms the posterior processes or cornua (horns) of the H-shaped tongue apparatus. The crossbar of the apparatus is formed of the basihyal, and the anterior cornua by the remainder of the postcranial parts of arch II.

The reptiles and birds representing stage three often have an elongate glossal skeleton, consisting of a Y-shaped element, the posterior horns of which are housed in sheaths in which they slide back and forth, giving the tongue great protrusibility. In birds the horns commonly curve over the rear of the skull; in some reptiles they may extend posteriorly for an enormous distance, even reaching the ilia of the pelvic girdle.

In the fourth stage, even arch III (*thyrohyal*) is lost, leaving only part of the components of arch II as the glossal skeleton (as in some mammals, such as man). Only the basihyal remains, fused onto parts of the anterior cornua and forming a curved *hyoid bone*. The upper ends of the anterior cornua are, in some types (primates, ungulates), fused with the temporal bone as the *styloid process,* thus becoming a part of the splanchnocranium.

The basic evolutionary trend of the glossal skeleton can be seen to be toward reduction in complexity, beginning with a maximal composition of five arches or parts thereof, and culminating with a minimal composition of only part of one arch.

Clearly also the evolutionary trend of the larynx almost perfectly complements that of the glossal skeleton: as one complex is reduced the other is expanded.

HYOBRANCHIUM. The hyobranchium is defined as all parts of the postcranial visceral skeleton of gill-breathing gnathostomes, except for that

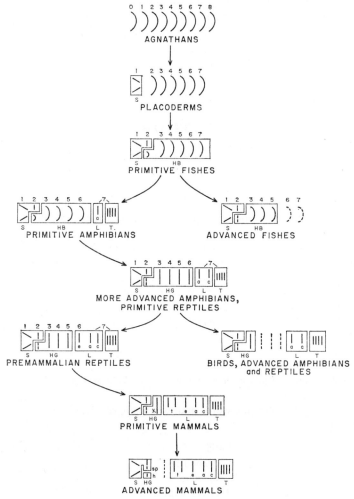

FIG. 7.11 A pictorial phylogenetic tree of the visceral skeleton of vertebrates. Curved lines represent arches having a branchial function, supporting gills; straight lines represent arches or parts thereof having lost their function as gill supports. Capital symbols: HB, hyobranchium; HG, hyoglossum; L, larynx; S, splanchnocranium; T, tracheal rings. Lower case symbols: a, arytenoid cartilages; c, cricoid cartilage; e, epiglottis; h, hyoid bone; sp, styloid process; t, thyroid cartilage; y, thyrohyal cartilage.

part, if any, serving as a larynx. A hyobranchium is thus not coexistent with a glossal skeleton, although in most amphibians a larval hyobranchium becomes in any individual a glossal skeleton in the transformed stage.

Phylogenetic Pattern. As shown in Figures 7.2–7.10, there are eight readily identifiable stages in evolution of the visceral skeleton in the mammalian line. Two other lines are conspicuously evident in the more specialized fish (Fig. 7.11) and in the advanced amphibians, reptiles, and birds (Fig. 7.11). In both of these groups certain arches have been completely lost, or have become functionless, contrary to the situation in all stages except the last of the mammalian line of evolution, wherein parts losing their respiratory functions have acquired other functions. The patterns of modification of the visceral skeleton in all the major vertebrate lines are suggested in Figure 7.11.

QUESTIONS

1. What basis distinguishes the visceral and pharyngeal skeleton?

2. Describe the pregnathostome arrangement of the pharyngeal skeleton.

3. What is the basic number of visceral arches in gnathostomes, and where do the pharyngeal pouches (or derivatives) of corresponding number lie?

4. Name the four groups of structures derived from the visceral skeleton in amniotes.

5. Briefly describe three stages in the evolution of the splanchnocranium.

6. Briefly describe four stages in the evolution of the larynx.

7. What anatomical adjustments in the larynx would have to be made to accommodate vocal cords in birds? What mechanism do birds actually use?

8. Briefly describe four stages in the evolution of the glossal skeleton, stating what has become of the elements lost at each stage.

9. Trace the evolution of the hyoid arch in tetrapods.

10. What is the name and function of the derivative of arch III in primitive mammals? What is its fate in more advanced mammals?

11. What special adaptation of the glossal skeleton occurs in reptiles and birds? Describe.

12. Define the following words and, where appropriate, state occurrence or give examples.

arytenoids	glottis	splanchnocranium
basihyal	hyobranchium	styloid process
cricoid cartilage	hyoid bone	syrinx
epiglottis	labial cartilages	thyroid cartilage
glossal skeleton	larynx	thyrohyal

Appendicular Skeleton

Origin. The appendicular skeleton apparently became differentiated from a ventrolateral, keellike flap of tissue on either side of the body, occurring in ancestral protochordates and agnathous vertebrates. The metapleural folds of Amphioxus are probably homologous with this hypothetical *fin fold,* but they differ in lacking muscularization. They are not well-developed in adult ostracoderms, although a controversial ostracoderm fossil, perhaps a larva, does appear to possess fin folds. In some adult ostracoderms there is a large spine on either side at the rear of the head, and these appear to be the same as the pectoral fins appearing in placoderms. The pelvic fin, also first appearing in placoderms, is not clearly evident in ostracoderms, but is thought to be derived from the same fin fold that in some remote form also gave rise to the pectoral fin (Fig. 7.12). There are too many similarities of the pelvic and pectoral appendages and girdles to believe they have differed much in origin, but both clearly did not differentiate in the trunk region: one (the pectoral fin) appeared as a cephalic structure, and only the pelvic fin differentiated as a trunk structure.

It is probable that the whole fin fold primitively possessed a series of primary endoskeletal supports (Fig. 7.12), perhaps much like the series of *basal* and *radial* cartilages (*fin rays*) seen in the dogfish fins. These became enlarged to form the pectoral and pelvic fins at the positions of greatest hydrodynamic stress, the intervening parts becoming reduced in size. Some placoderms exhibit vestiges of finlets intervening between the main paired fins, apparently representing a stage of fin-fold degeneration. Enlargement of some basal elements, forming a primitive girdle, subsequently provided a better anchorage on the trunk.

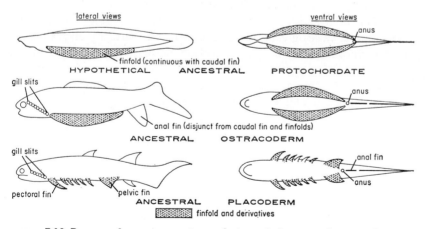

FIG. 7.12 Presumed sequences in evolution of the paired appendages, showing reduction of parts of finfold not forming appendages.

This version of the fin-fold theory is largely conjectural, because very few fossils are known of types close to the common stem of protochordates and vertebrates. Westoll has reviewed the evidence bearing on the theory, and concludes that although the fin-fold theory may be acceptable it "must be rather carefully rephrased. In the writer's opinion it would be unwise to suppose that all the chordates . . . are descended from an ancestral type with continuous paired fin folds with segmental endoskeleton and segmental muscles. But that there was a paired line of potential skin folding, from which keellike structures could develop, is entirely probable. The earliest such structures in many groups appear to have been stiff, and became variously modified. In many groups the fully controlled flexible fin capable of giving the animal a more perfect control of movement is a late development." The fact remains, however, that the mode of appearance of the "potential skin fold" is not known, and could reasonably be as previously described. The similarity of cephalochordates and vertebrates, the fin fold of the (larval?) ostracoderm *Jaymoytius,* and the acknowledged (White, 1958) rarity of fossilization of types that would be expected to exhibit the fin fold are convincing arguments favoring exercise of caution in discarding the conventional fin-fold theory in its gross form.

Two transitions are of major significance in the evolution of the appendicular skeleton: that from the fin folds to fins, and from fins (*ichthyopterygia*) to limbs (*cheiropterygia*). There is relatively little evidence upon which a picture of the first transition can be reconstructed, but more evidence exists of the other. Some fossil crossopterygians (especially Sauripterus and Eusthenopteron) have fins built along remarkably tetrapodlike lines (Fig. 7.13).

Ichthyopterygium

Structure and Evolution. The fins of fishes consist of a series of supportive bars or strands radiating from the body at the girdle. The nature of these supports varies greatly in different fishes. In virtually all fresh-water fishes the *integumentary fin rays* (mostly of dermal origin) occupy the entire distal, vanelike part of the fin, and *primary fin rays* of varying size and number are either absent or hidden within the axial musculature of the body wall, where the fin articulates with the girdle. These are *lobeless fins;* only the vanelike part projects from the body wall.

In chondrichthyans, primitive Actinopteri and in choanichthyans the fins remain fleshy at the base; they are *lobed fins,* and they appear to be primitive not only to limbs but also to the actinopteran lobeless fin. Lobed fins consist of (1) a fleshy base formed by muscles attached to primary fin rays or *pterygiophores,* and (2) a vanelike distal part consisting of the thin integument draped over a series of thin, flexible integumentary fin rays. Primitively the pterygiophores were organized into a series of three large basals and several series of small radials. The basal pterygiophores in-

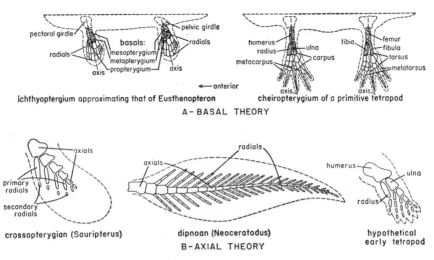

ichthyoptergium approximating that of Eusthenopteron

cheiropterygium of a primitive tetrapod

A – BASAL THEORY

crossopterygian (Sauripterus)

dipnoan (Neoceratodus)

hypothetical early tetrapod

B – AXIAL THEORY

FIG. 7.13 Transitional stages from the ichthyopterygium to the cheiropterygium, according to the basal (A) and axial (B) theories. (From Goodrich and Eaton.)

cluded the small *propterygium* anteriorly and *metapterygium* posteriorly, and the large *mesopterygium* centrally. Although as fishes the crossopterygians were not particularly successful, their place being taken by teleosts with their more efficient vanelike fins, their clumsy fins were an indispensable basis for the appearance of tetrapods. According to the *basal* theory, in some, like Eusthenopteron, the mesopterygium became recognizable as the femur and humerus, the propterygium as the radius or tibia, the metapterygium as the ulna or fibula, and the radials as a series of distal elements more or less approximating the number of digits tetrapods possess (Fig. 7.13A). According to the *axial theory* (Fig. 7.13B), the basal pterygiophores became arranged in a longitudinal axial series (as in Sauripterus), and two lines of modification followed. In one line the axial pterygiophores became a central series, with a set of radials attached on either side, as in modern dipnoans. In the other line, the axials formed the single proximal element and all the elements along the rear edge of the appendage, while the radials formed the other elements. Regardless of which theory is correct, wholly or in part, it is evident that the forerunner of the cheiropterygium was of relatively powerful construction, making it possible for some weight or stress to be placed upon the fins. In amphibians the fins became altered by loss of the dermal fin rays and by reduction of the distal primary elements to form the typical tetrapod cheiropterygium. The selective pressures that channeled evolution of the cheiropterygium can only be surmised, but a reasonable inference is that conditions of progressively decreasing rainfall favored improvement of devices enabling the ancestors of amphibians (1) to burrow in the mud at the bottom of the pools in order to survive periods of drought in a state of estivation much as in modern lungfish; and (2) to escape to other, less crowded bodies of water during

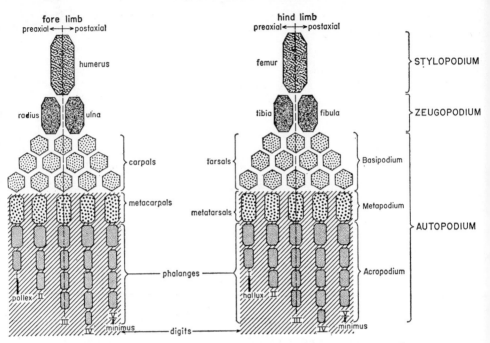

FIG. 7.14 Basic primitive organization of the cheiropterygium, schematic.

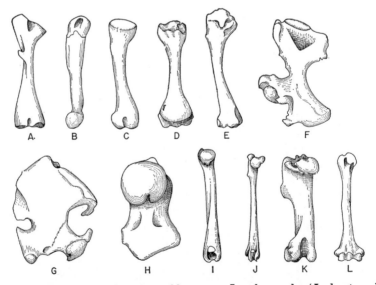

FIG. 7.15 Variations in the tetrapod humerus. A, salamander (Ambystoma); B, frog (Rana); C, alligator; D, beaded lizard (Heloderma); E, chicken; F, spiny anteater; G, mole (Scalopus); H, dolphin; I, dog; J, rabbit (Lepus); K, horse; L, gorilla. (From Adams and Eddy.)

periods of light rainfall insufficient to fill their own, overpopulated pools.

The six basic stages in evolution of the appendicular skeleton can be summarized as follows. The first stage is characterized by a *continuous even fin fold,* the second by pectoral and pelvic *enlargements,* the third by *girdle formation,* the fourth by formation of *lobed fins.* The fifth and sixth stages are concurrent and not successive, with the fifth characterized by formation of the *lobeless fin* and loss of the pterygiophores, and the sixth by formation of the *cheiropterygium* and loss of the integumentary fin rays.

Cheiropterygium

Basic Structure and Origin. The organization of the two limbs is remarkably similar. There seems, as a matter of fact, to be a complete parallelism of structure (Fig. 7.14). Each possesses a proximal component (*stylopodium*) of a single element (*humerus* in pectoral limb, *femur* in pelvic limb); a median component (*zeugopodium*) of two elements (an anterior *radius,* posterior *ulna,* in the pectoral limb; and anterior *tibia,* posterior *fibula* in the pelvic limb); and a distal component (*autopodium*)

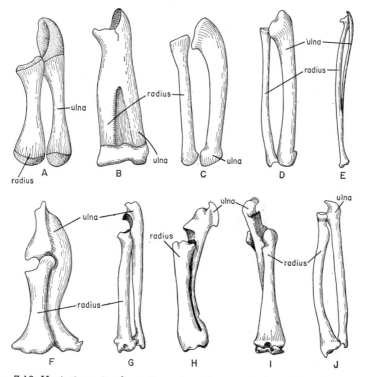

FIG. 7.16 Variations in the tetrapod radius and ulna. A, salamander (Necturus); B, frog (Rana); C, alligator; D, turkey; E, bat (Pteropus); F, mole (Scalopus); G, cat; H, cow; I, horse; J, ape (orangutan). (From Adams and Eddy.)

of some 35 elements (forming the hand or *manus* in the pectoral limb, the foot or *pes* in the pelvic limb).

STYLOPODIUM AND ZEUGOPODIUM. The stylopodium and zeugopodium are subject to relatively little variation among tetrapods. In those groups (such as snakes, whales, etc.) subject to reduction of either or both pairs of limbs, the humerus and femur are the last elements to disappear (Figs. 7.15, 7.17); they are never fused with the more distal components. The two elements of the zeugopodium are not infrequently fused with each other as, for example, in frogs with their *radioulna* and *tibiofibula* (Figs. 7.16, 7.18). The radius and ulna are fused also in ungulates, bats, and certain other mammals. In birds the tibia and the proximal ankle bones are all fused as one (*tibiotarsus*). In ungulates and birds the fibula tends to become degenerate, being either vestigial or absent.

AUTOPODIUM. This consists of three basic divisions. The *basipodium* (*carpus* or wrist, *tarsus* or ankle) is proximal in position, and consists of some twelve elements in each limb (*carpals* or wrist bones in the pectoral limb, *tarsals* or ankle bones in the pelvic limb). Five elongate elements comprising the *metapodium* articulate with the basipodium; they are the *metacarpals* of the manus, the *metatarsals* of the pes. The most distal com-

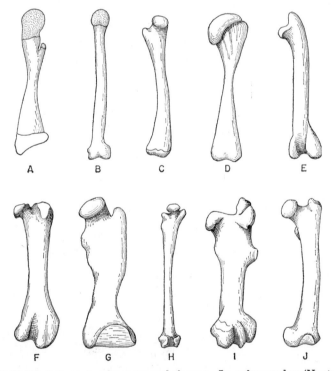

FIG. 7.17 Variations in the tetrapod femur. A, salamander (Necturus); B, frog (Rana); C, lizard (Phrynosoma); D, turtle (Chelydra); E, chicken; F, pelican; G, spiny anteater; H, bat (Pteropus); I, horse; J, ape (orangutan). (From Adams and Eddy.)

ponent is the *acropodium*, consisting of five series of short bones, each articulated with one of the metapodial bones; these are the *phalanges*. Each metapodial element and its attached series of phalanges constitute a *digit*, of which the anterior on the pectoral limb is called the *pollex*, that on the pelvic limb the *hallux*. The posterior digit of either limb is the *minimus*.

The axis of the limbs primitively extends down the center of each appendage, from the median line of the humerus or femur through the middle of the third digit; the limbs are visualized in an outstretched horizontal position at right angles to the body axis and with the primitive dorsal surface uppermost in all parts (elbow and knee directed dorsally). The anterior half of each limb, in front of its median axis, is the *preaxial* half; the posterior half is *postaxial*. Asymmetrical loss of preaxial or postaxial elements in various vertebrate lines has resulted in shift of the limb axes, particularly in distal parts.

ACROPODIUM AND METAPODIUM. The number of phalanges varies considerably in tetrapods (Figs. 7.19, 7.20). The primitive number in tetrapods appears to have been, for the digits of the manus in order from front to rear, 2–3–4–5–3; for the pes the number was 2–3–4–5–4. Still more phalanges were certainly present in ancestral crossopterygians and in very primitive amphibians. In some reptiles (fossil) and mammals (marine carnivores, cetaceans, sirenians) the number secondarily has been in-

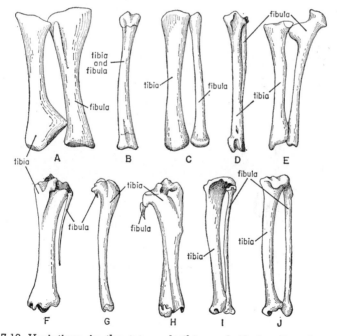

FIG. 7.18 Variations in the tetrapod tibia and fibula. A, salamander (Necturus); B, frog (Rana); C, alligator; D, turkey; E, pangolin; F, horse; G, antelope; H, cow; I, cat; J, ape (orangutan). (From Adams and Eddy.)

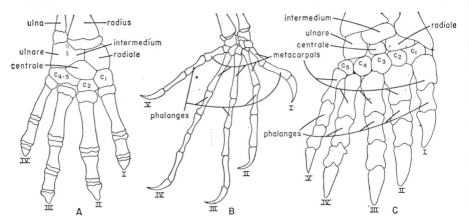

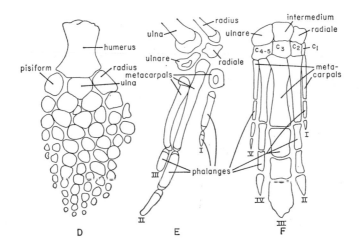

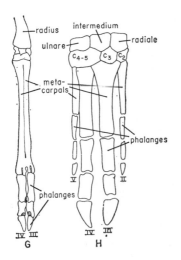

FIG. 7.19 Variations in phalanges and digits of the tetrapod manus. A, salamander (Necturus); B, lizard (Sceloporus); C, turtle (Pseudemys); D, ichthyosaur (fishlike) fossil reptile (Ichthyosaurus); E, chicken (just hatched); F, generalized perissodactyl; G, artiodactyl (antelope); H, generalized artiodactyl. (From Romer, Adams and Eddy.)

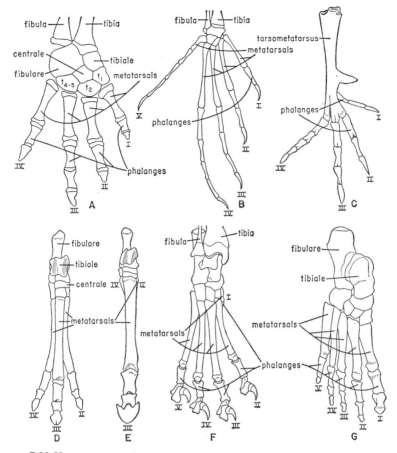

FIG. 7.20 Variations in phalanges and digits of the tetrapod pes. A, sala-mander (Necturus); B, lizard (Sceloporus); C, chicken; D, fossil horse; E, modern horse; F, cat; G, man. (From Adams, Eddy, Romer, and Senning.)

creased. However, the general trend throughout tetrapods is toward de-crease in number. For example, the generalized phalangeal formula for primitive mammals is 2–3–3–3–3; in birds, 1–2–1–0–0 for the manus (four and fifth digits lacking), 2–3–4–5–0 for the pes (fifth digit lacking). Various reptiles and mammals have formulae much more reduced than these. A notable extreme occurs in many ungulate mammals: but one (the third) or two (third and fourth) digits remain, each with three phalanges.

The reduction in number of phalanges in tetrapods is duplicated by the reduction in number of digits. Evidence of even more than the char-acteristic five digits in primitive amphibians exists, and is, of course, to be expected in view of the many radials that fishes possess. All modern am-phibians have lost the fifth digit on the foreleg; many lizards and all snakes have few or no digits; birds have lost two (fourth and fifth) in the pectoral and one (fifth) in the pelvic limb; and many mammals have nearly if not completely lost one or more digits, usually in the sequence 1, 5, 2, 4, 3. The supposition that in birds the first and fifth digits have been lost is not borne out by the fossil record.

Opposability of digits has evolved in numerous groups of vertebrates, and by several different combinations of digits (Fig. 7.21). A few anurans have an opposable thumb, or hallux, or both; true chameleons have both fingers and toes opposable (2–3 and 3–2); birds usually have opposable toes (2 or 3 directed forward, 1 or 2 directed backward); and some mammals have an opposable thumb, or an opposable hallux, or both.

BASIPODIUM. The proximal components of the basipodium are organized into a proximal series of three *basalia,* a medial series of four *centralia,* and a distal series of five *distalia* (*carpalia,* pectoral; *tarsalia,* pelvic). The anterior and posterior basalia bear the name of the zeugopodial bone associated with it (that is, *radiale* and *ulnare, tibiale* and *fibulare*); the median one is the *intermedium.* The centralia and distalia are simply numbered in sequence from anterior to posterior.

This primitive tetrapod basipodial arrangement is, of course, modified freely in different vertebrates, mostly by fusion or loss of various elements. In the wrist two sesamoid bones are commonly present, one anterior to the radiale, called the *radial sesamoid,* and one posterior to the ulnare, called the *ulnar sesamoid* or *pisiform.*

The variation in modification of the basipodium in different tetrapods is much too long a story to explore here, but modifications occurring in man,

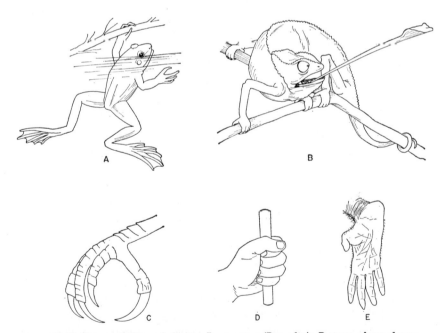

FIG. 7.21 Opposability of digits. A, anuran (Pseudis); B, true chameleon; C, avian pes; D, human manus; E, orangutan pes. (From Barbour, Gadow, Sayles, Walter and Young.)

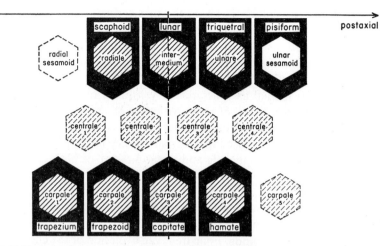

FIG. 7.22 Hypothetical primitive pectoral basipodium or wrist (equilateral hexagons) and its derivatives in man (black enclosures). Unshaded hexagons represent sesamoid bones, and dashed lines bones lost.

as an example, may be of interest (Fig. 7.22). In the wrist, the radiale persists as the *scaphoid* (improperly, the navicular); the intermedium forms the *lunar;* the ulnare remains unmodified as the *triquetral;* the pisiform is present; all centralia are lost; the first carpale is the *trapezium,* the second the *trapezoid,* the third the *capitate,* the fourth the *hamate,* and the fifth is lost. The cat is little different, having the scaphoid and lunar fused, and a radial sesamoid.

The ankle of man (Fig. 7.23) is formed, it is thought, from the tibiale, the intermedium and fourth centrale being fused as the *astragalus;* the fibulare, as the *calcaneus;* the first and second centralia, fused as the *navic-*

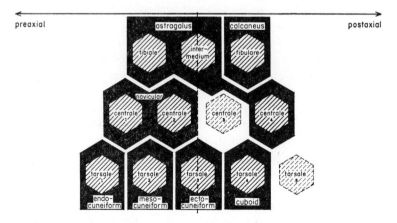

FIG. 7.23 Hypothetical primitive pelvic basipodium or ankle (equilateral hexagons) and its derivatives in man (black enclosures). Dashed lines represent bones lost.

ular (the third centrale is lost); the first tarsale, as *endocuneiform;* the second tarsale, as the *mesocuneiform;* the third tarsale, as the *ectocuneiform;* the fourth as the *cuboid;* and the fifth tarsale is lost. The cat is the same. Unfortunately the composition of the astragalus, navicular and cuboid is yet questionable.

Other basipodial and metapodial variations meriting special note include the *"cannon bone"* of most Artiodactyla (third and fourth metatarsals or metacarpals being fused, others lost or vestigial—see Fig. 7.19G), the *carpometacarpus* (fused metacarpals and distal carpals) and the *tarsometatarsus* (fused metatarsals and distal tarsals) of birds. In anurans the proximal row of ankle bones is commonly reduced to but two elongate rods, usually regarded as astragalus and calcaneus, and in some even these are fused to form a single elongate rod; the distal basipodials are commonly reduced to three small elements.

Evolutionary Trends. Four trends in evolution of the cheiropterygium are clearly discernible: (1) a decrease in number of elements, evident in the digits, the basipodium, the zeugopodium, and in the appendage as a whole; (2) a progressive subaxial flexion, effected by withdrawal of the limbs under the body, thus providing a more efficient support for the body; (3) a progressive elevation of the body on the appendages, providing a speedier locomotion; and (4) a functional diversification of the long bones. The first trend has been discussed adequately in previous paragraphs. The others require further discussion.

SUBAXIAL FLEXION. Primitively limbs simply stuck out at the sides of the body much like the fins from which they were derived. Amphibians rather rowed themselves along, almost dragging the belly on the ground. Sinuous body movements also helped. Even today, salamanders move in much the same fashion, and so do many lizards and crocodiles. In some of the "lower" vertebrates the awkward limbs were almost or quite entirely eliminated, thus placing all reliance upon the sinuous movements alone (for example, the wholly or partly limbless salamanders, lizards, and snakes are almost entirely dependent on sinuous movements).

The general trend of tetrapods (Fig. 7.24) was, however, to bring the limbs more nearly under the body, thus greatly improving the efficiency of the limbs as locomotor organs. It was necessary to keep the original ventral surface of the basipodium to the ground, and, in order that the force be applied in moving the body forward, to turn the basipodium forward. Thus the preaxial border of the basipodium faces inward in advanced tetrapods; the first digit is then medial, the fifth lateral.

In bringing the limbs under the body the dorsally directed joint at the knee and elbow necessarily had to be swung either forward or backward to avoid projection outward or upward. The two limbs generally responded differently, the knee rotating forward in the same direction as the basipodium, the elbow rotating backward. Since the pectoral rotation resulted at the elbow with the original dorsal surface facing backward whereas at the basipodium it still faced upward, there is a 180-degree twist

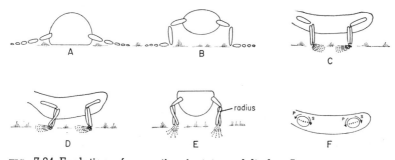

FIG. 7.24 Evolution of pronation in tetrapod limbs. A, anterior view of primitive condition as in ancient amphibians; B, flexion of limbs to support body, anterior view; C, position of limbs (lateral view) were axial torsion nonexistent; D, axial torsion (pronation) of anterior limb, as seen in lateral view; E, same as D, anterior view; F, lateral view, limbs outstretched directly laterally. Symbols: P, pronation; S, supination. (From Walter and Sayles.)

in the lower foreleg. Some vertebrates, as man, retain the ability to rotate the manus either outward (*supination*) into line with the remainder of the limb, with the ventral surface (for example, the palm) up, or inward (*pronation*) into the secondary position (palms down). In some other mammals the pronate position is more or less fixed.

The terms pronation and supination are applied to any of the rotational movements about the limb axes. With the limb in its primitive position (that is, outstretched at right angles to the body, dorsal surface uppermost), forward rotation of any part or all is *pronation* and rotation posteriorly is *supination* (Fig. 7.24F).

The maximum amount of rotation normally involved in the forelimbs of vertebrates is 180 degrees of pronation because the elbow faces posteriorly, the back of the manus anteriorly. In certain positions an additional 90 degrees of pronational rotation is possible in man. In the hind limb in most vertebrates the rotation is only 90 degrees of pronation, since the knee and the back of the pes both face anteriorly. The rotation of the hind limb is entirely restricted to the body junction of stylopodium and girdle. In the forelimb the rotation at the junction of stylopodium and girdle is 90 degrees of supination; and, therefore, 90 degrees of pronational rotation in the limb itself is necessary in compensation, as well as 90 degrees more for turning the preaxial surface parallel with the median axis.

Bats are of special interest in limb rotation since their hind limbs face posteriorly instead of anteriorly. Although the same amount of rotation of the hind limb has occurred in them as in other vertebrates, it is 90 degrees of supination instead of pronation.

ELEVATION OF BODY. Obviously primitive vertebrates walked flat-footed; they are *plantigrade*. As a matter of fact, only mammals, birds, and reptilian groups ancestral to those two classes have been able to diverge from this condition. To add spring and speed, some have become *digitigrade* (Fig. 7.25), walking with only the phalanges on the ground (carni-

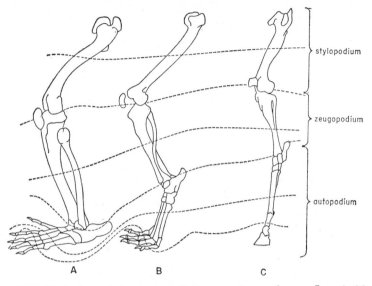

stylopodium

zeugopodium

autopodium

A   B   C

FIG. 7.25 Evolution of the autopodial supportive column. A, primitive *plantigrade* condition, without autopodial contribution to the supportive column; B, intermediate *digitigrade* condition, with a partial autopodial contribution to the supportive column; C, extreme *unguligrade* condition, with a full autopodial contribution to the supportive column. (From Rand.)

vores, birds) and an extreme is reached in the *unguligrades* (ungulates), which walk on the tips of the digits.

FUNCTIONAL DIVERSIFICATION. The primary functions of the long bones throughout vertebrates are locomotor and supportive. Varied additional functions exist in different groups of vertebrates, particularly in connection with the elongate cavity that typically exists within the center of each long bone.

In embryogenesis of long bones the elements first appear as cartilage. As they grow larger the cartilage is replaced by bone, beginning at one or more centrally located *centers of ossification* (Fig. 7.26). Typically the bone replacing the cartilage is very porous and spongy (*cancellous*). However, *cavitation* typically occurs in an elongate central region in the bone where the cancellous tissue breaks down and is not replaced by skeletal tissues. The space is the *marrow cavity,* and in most vertebrates it is filled with *yellow marrow,* a soft mass of fat, nerves, blood vessels, and a type of loose connective tissue (reticulo-endothelial). This same tissue permeates the spaces within the cancellous bone. The long bones in ectotherms, therefore, serve additional functions for the storage of fat and for white blood cell formation.

Some of the central cavities of the long bones of birds are air filled. The air spaces serve to reduce the weight of the wings, and they are actually connected with the lungs. The other central cavities remain as yellow marrow cavities.

In mammals essentially the same structure exists as in other vertebrates, but the marrow cavity is filled with a *red marrow* that is unique to mammals, since only in them does the marrow have the additional function of formation of red blood cells.

Compensation for the loss in strength accompanying loss of bone from the center of the long bones has been provided by substitution of membrane bone for chondral bone along much of the length of the shaft of the bone. Membrane bone is laid down layer by layer, forming *compact* bone which is very different from and much stronger per unit volume than the cancellous bone of replacement origin.

The economy of bone construction is amazing and has been the subject of very involved investigation. A safety margin of about one third of maximal single-direction stress is apparently maintained fairly rigidly. For example, the femur of man is known to break under a pressure of about 1650 pounds. The muscles attached to the femur are capable of exerting a pressure of about 1220 pounds, in normal maximal contraction. Ordinarily, of course, only one set of muscles contracts at any one time. If—in fright or for other reasons—under circumstances causing maximal contraction of one set of muscles the antagonistic set is also contracted, even to as much as half of its maximal potential, the femur fractures. Broken bones sustained in car accidents frequently are caused by this means. It is apparent why persons unaware of impending danger escape serious injury more frequently than those who freeze in horror of anticipation.

EPIPHYSEAL GROWTH. One of the peculiarities of endotherms (and their extinct reptilian forerunners) for which no functional superiority is clearly evident is the differentiation of *epiphyses* and a *diaphysis* on all long bones and on the vertebrae. The diaphysis is the central shaft, the epiphyses the two ends. In some bones (for example, the femur) two or more epiphyses may be present at one end of the bone, but in most cases there is but one at each end. The diaphysis and each epiphysis arise from separate centers of ossification rather than from one for the entire bone as in

FIG. 7.26 Ossification and growth in mammalian long bones. Cartilage in open stipple, membrane bone in solid black, replacement bone in reticular stipple. (From Walter and Sayles.)

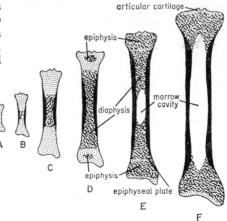

other vertebrates. The shaft and epiphyses are separated from each other in immature developmental stages by a cartilaginous layer, the *epiphyseal plate*. This plate remains as long as growth persists, but disappears with cessation of growth as the epiphyses and diaphysis fuse inseparably with each other (Fig. 7.26). The time of fusion differs in different bones, so that in man the age of any given skeleton can be determined accurately to within 3–6 months, at least up to an age of about 25 years. Ankylosis of other parts (for example, sternum, internal parts of cranial sutures) permits a less accurate determination up to an age of about 80 years.

Mammals did not evolve the complex growth mechanism of epiphyses for the benefit of criminologists, however. In all vertebrates growth in length of limb bones takes place by transformation of cartilage, and the primitive location for the "growth cartilage" is at the tips of the long bones. With a single center of ossification near the middle of the bone, growth proceeds as long as cartilage remains toward the tips of the bones. Thus, as is well known, lower vertebrates tend to grow, at least slowly, throughout life, for a thin layer of articular cartilage is essential to operation of the synovial joints. Both birds and mammals attain maturity and then cease to grow. They are capable of doing this through a restriction to the limited zone of the epiphyseal plate of sensitivity to the growth hormone of the pituitary gland. Some species of herpetozoa virtually cease to grow after reaching a certain size; but since all herptiles lack epiphyses, these particular species presumably simply cease to produce the growth hormone. In fact, all existing vertebrates seem to grow in proportion to the volume of growth hormones produced by the pituitary gland. If control of volume had already evolved in the ancestors of endotherms, as it apparently has in some modern herptiles, it is difficult to imagine what survival value there could possibly have been in selection for, and establishment of, multiple centers of ossification. Presumably at the time that endotherms were evolving, growth hormones were produced as long as the animals lived; under such conditions multiple centers of ossification, accompanied by restriction to the synovial plate of sensitivity to growth hormones, would have definite survival value if indeed establishment of a definite limit to growth has in itself some survival value.

Girdles

Pectoral. The pectoral girdle in primitive fishes consists of some seven paired bones—a total of fourteen elements (Fig. 7.27). Only four of these are cartilage bones (*scapula, coracoid*), thus constituting the *primary girdle,* and belonging to the primary endoskeleton. The remainder (in order from midventral line toward skull, the paired *clavicles, cleithra, postcleithra, supracleithra* and *postemporals*) comprise the *dermal girdle*.

In primitive amphibians the postemporal and postcleithra are lost (except in a few very early examples), and an unpaired, median ventral,

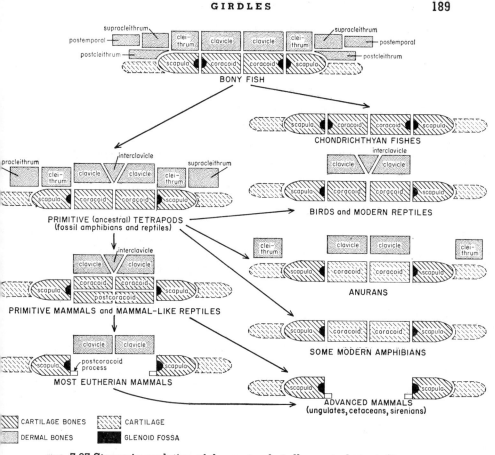

FIG. 7.27 Stages in evolution of the pectoral girdle, ventral view, diagrammatic. All components consist of cartilage in chondrichthyan fishes.

dermal *interclavicle* is added. The cleithra and supracleithra persist in primitive reptiles and amphibians, but they are present in no living vertebrates except anurans in which the cleithra persist. The extreme of elimination of all dermal bones of the pectoral girdle has occurred in salamanders and some mammals. Anurans retain only the cleithrum and the clavicle of the dermal series; caecilians as well as snakes and certain lizards completely lack the girdle. The clavicle and interclavicle persist in most reptiles, and are fused in birds as a single bone, the *furcula* ("wishbone"). Even primitive mammals (for example, monotremes) possess an interclavicle, but most mammals retain only the clavicle. This likewise disappears in those mammals whose mode of life involves throwing much of the body weight upon the forelegs.

In tetrapods the primary girdle consists basically of a pair of large cartilaginous structures, the *scapulocoracoids,* located on each side of the body. The two scapulocoracoids are fused medially in primitive groups, but broadly overlap or are even separated medially in more advanced types. Each scapulocoracoid consists of a *scapular cartilage,* often surmounted by a *suprascapular cartilage,* approaching but not in contact with the vertebral column, and lying external to the ribs or transverse processes and their musculature. The scapular cartilage is regarded as ending ventrally at the *glenoid fossa,* a depression receiving the humerus. A broad *coracoid cartilage* extends medially from the glenoid fossa, and often there is a *procoracoid cartilage* projecting forward from the glenoid fossa or the coracoid cartilage.

In both amphibians and reptiles much of the primary pectoral girdle remains unossified in adults. In salamanders only a scapular ossification is present, but in other herptiles a coracoid as well as scapular ossifications are generally present and in some a *suprascapula* bone ossifies in the suprascapular cartilage. In birds only the scapula and coracoid are present. Premammalian reptiles differ from others of their class in possessing not only a coracoid but also a *postcoracoid* bone ossifying in the rear part of the coracoid cartilage. The coracoid became progressively less important in these reptiles, and had been replaced entirely by the postcoracoid by the time the mammalian level in evolution was reached. Even in mammals the postcoracoid persisted as a separate element only in primitive types. It is represented in most mammals by the small *postcoracoid* process on the scapula. This process is usually termed the coracoid process, but this is in-

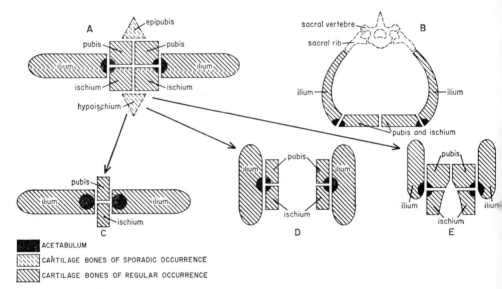

ACETABULUM
CARTILAGE BONES OF SPORADIC OCCURRENCE
CARTILAGE BONES OF REGULAR OCCURRENCE

FIG. 7.28 Stages in evolution of the tetrapod pelvis, diagrammatic. A, primitive condition in ventral view, with 6 bones well developed and 2 others present or not; B, same, cross section showing relation to vertebral column; C, anuran, showing reduction of ischium and pubis (ventral view); D, bird, showing loss of puboischial symphysis and reduction of pubis and ischium (ventral view); E, specialized mammal (as primates, insectivores), with loss of ischial symphysis (ventral view).

correct since the coracoid of nonmammalian vertebrates is definitely not homologous with the postcoracoid and postcoracoid process of mammals and premammalian vertebrates. The coracoid of premammalian vertebrates appears to be homologous throughout, although in reptiles and birds the bone is often called elsewhere the "procoracoid"—a term we shall regard here as a synonym of coracoid.

Pelvic. The pelvic girdle is much simpler than the pectoral girdle in fishes. No dermal elements whatever are present. In most fishes the pelvic girdle is represented by a single, undivided element on each side, the *puboischium.* Generally the two puboischia are not even in contact ventrally. On the contrary, the two halves are fused in all chondrichthyan fishes; this exception seemingly constitutes a strengthening device compensating for the relatively weak cartilaginous construction occurring in these fishes.

In tetrapods, three paired, primary girdle bones almost universally ossify in the embryonic cartilage of the girdle: the *ilium, pubis,* and *ischium* (Fig. 7.28). In some amphibians large parts of the girdle are not ossified, and some centers fail to develop at all. Modern salamanders, for example, lack pubes and the ischia are small. In most tetrapods, however, the girdle is entirely ossified or only narrow symphyses persist in adults. In frogs both the pubis and ischium are vestigial, and in birds the pubis is vestigial. In all tetrapods having a girdle, except birds, the pubis, or the ischium, or both, of the two sides meet midventrally at a symphysis; the absence of a symphysis in birds is an adaptation to their relatively enormous eggs, and mammals have not lagged far behind in reducing the length of the pelvic symphysis to a minimum to facilitate birth of their large young. In man only a narrow pubic symphysis occurs, and in breeding female pocket gophers no midventral symphyses remain.

Commonly in mammals the bones of either half of the pelvic girdle are fused inseparably (and often indistinguishably except in the very young or embryos) as the *innominate* bone and in old individuals the two innominates may be fused. They remain connected by a symphysis throughout the reproductive period.

In some primitive vertebrates a single or paired, median ventral bone or cartilage may form in contact with the anterior edge of the pubis (the *epipubis*) and another with the posterior edge of the ischium (the *hypoischium*). A very well-developed epipubic bone of certain salamanders is called the *ypsiloid bone,* serving when depressed or elevated to shift the center of gravity and thus the angle of the body when floating free in water. The baculum (penis bone) may be derived from the epipubis.

Comparisons and Contrasts in Tetrapods. The girdles in tetrapods are alike (a) in possessing primitively three pairs of primary endoskeletal bones, (b) including one dorsal and (c) two ventral pairs, (d) articulating with the limb bones at or near the junction of the three primary bones, and (e) in forming a nearly complete ring about the body. The girdles in tetrapods differ (a) in constancy of components, (b) in mode of articulation with the axial skeleton, (c) in the presence of dermal bones actually or in phylogeny, (d) in completeness of the ring about body, and (e) in position on body axis. Most of these similarities and differences have been treated adequately heretofore. The limb-girdle articulation and axial-appendicular articulation require further elaboration.

LIMB-GIRDLE ARTICULATION. The points of articulation of the girdles with the limbs are depressions called the *acetabulum* in the pelvic girdle and the *glenoid fossa* in the pectoral girdle. The acetabulum is almost always located at the point of junction of the three pelvic bones, where present. Sometimes a spurious *acetabular bone* forms separately at this point, contributing to the inner wall of the acetabulum.

The glenoid fossa is equally fixed in position, always occurring at or near the junction of whatever bones may be present in the primary girdle. In premammalian reptiles it forms at the point of junction of the three primary girdle bones—a position comparable to that of the acetabulum. In birds and most reptiles it lies between the scapula and coracoid, in primitive mammals between the postcoracoid and scapula, and in eutherian mammals on the scapula only.

AXIAL-APPENDICULAR ARTICULATION. The axial attachments are importantly different in the two girdles. In all tetrapods where the pelvic girdle is well developed, it is articulated with the sacrum, providing a solid framework for support of the entire weight of the body. The pectoral girdle, on the contrary, is not directly attached to the vertebral column in tetrapods, although it does generally possess an indirect attachment to the sternum by way of the clavicles and (where present) the interclavicle. The mammals (like ungulates) that lack clavicles do not have even an indirect articulation with the axial skeleton. The trend throughout tetrapods, in every class, is toward divergence in functions of the limbs, the pelvic appendages becoming better adapted to support the weight of the body, the pectoral appendages facilitating maneuverability. Almost without exception the hind limbs are more powerful than the forelimbs. That more bipedal animals have not evolved is indeed puzzling. A number of species of lizards and mammals are capable of bipedal locomotion for brief periods, but only birds and a few primates (of existing forms) regularly practice it. The very complexity of adaptation in all respects to the erect position is presumably the factor that has prevented other groups from exploitation of bipedal possibilities.

SIGNIFICANCE OF DIFFERENCE IN DERMAL COMPONENTS. Parallelism in basic structure of the pectoral and pelvic appendicular skeleton exists not only in the limbs but also in the girdles, with the astonishing exception of the dermal elements. Just why a dermal component should have developed in either girdle, or in the pectoral and not in the pelvic girdle, is an intriguing question. The answer presumably lies in the facts that (1) pectoral fins are consistently larger in fishes, therefore presumably requiring a firmer anchorage than the weaker pelvic fins; and that (2) when fins were evolving, the endoskeletal supports were rudimentary, whereas the dermal armor was well developed. Firm anchorage of the pectoral girdle early in its evolution perforce required utilization of the dermal armor, whereas the pelvic girdle needed no support other than its intrinsic skeleton.

In tetrapods the trend occurring in fishes has been reversed; in them the pelvic girdle, rather than the pectoral, became the chief supportive girdle. However, the need for pelvic anchorage came at a time when the dermal armor was on its way out. Thus tetrapods achieved axial integration of the pelvic girdle by hypertrophy of the endoskeletal components alone.

Simultaneously the need in tetrapods for exceptional strength, and thus anchorage of the pectoral girdle, disappeared; in fact, flexibility became of survival value. The dermal elements, previously serving chiefly as the anchoring component, thus tended to disappear. Articulation with the skull disappeared in the very earliest known tetrapods, and a reduction in number of dermal elements has been the rule in almost all tetrapod lines of evolution. Complete loss of dermal components without comparable reduction of the primary elements has been achieved, among living vertebrates, in salamanders and in some mammals.

Evolutionary Trends. In fishes there is a general trend toward increase in size and maintenance of axial anchorage (with the skull or vertebral column) of the pectoral appendages, and toward decrease in size and firmness of union of the pelvic appendicular skeleton with the axial skeleton. These trends reflect the relatively great importance of the pectoral fins in propulsion or guidance of movements (or both) of the body in water. In tetrapods, on the contrary, the pelvic appendages are the most important in locomotion, and thus the trends are reversed: the pectoral appendages tend to be relatively smaller and less well anchored to the axial skeleton, and the pelvic appendages tend to be relatively larger and more firmly attached to the axial skeleton.

In advanced members of both tetrapods and fishes the extent of midventral union of the two halves of both the pectoral and pelvic girdles tends to decrease.

Unpaired Appendages

The unpaired appendages consist solely of the medial fins in fishes; none persist in tetrapods. They have, presumably, evolved from a continuous *primitive dorsal fin* extending the length of the tail to the anus. From this have differentiated in various fishes one, two, or several separate dorsal fins, the caudal fin, and an anal fin. In some only a caudal fin persists (cyclostomes); in others not only are numerous subdivisions present but they may be strengthened by a variety of spines and rays, some dermal, others outgrowths of the neural or hemal spines of the vertebrae.

Tail Types. One of the most useful characteristics in classifying fishes is the shape of the tail. The tail is of relatively little value, however, in classifying tetrapods, primarily because of the universal lack of a fin in adults. Nevertheless the tail does vary greatly in length, size, and function in tetrapods; it is even lost or reduced to an almost unrecognizable vestige in some groups, as, for example, caecilians, anurans, birds, and some primates.

Fish, on the other hand, always possess a tail, and it usually is provided with a fin either above or below, or both. Most larval amphibians have a fishlike tail also. A number of types of tails are recognized, differing primarily in respect to symmetry. For our purposes six different types may usefully be distinguished (Fig. 7.29). The most primitive is the *protocercal* tail, known to occur only among protochordates; no vertebrate ever

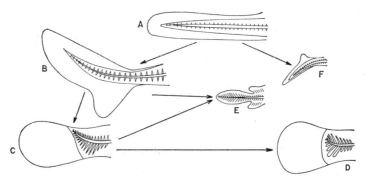

FIG. 7.29 Evolution in types of caudal fin. A, protocercal (protochordates); B, heterocercal (Chondrichthyes and primitive ostracoderms); C, abbreviate heterocercal (Holostei); D, homocercal (most teleosts); E, diphycercal (later dipnoans and crossopterygians, and in Polypterus, Calamoichthys, cyclostomes, a few teleosts); F, reverse heterocercal (some ostracoderms).

had a truly protocercal tail, so far as can be surmised. In this type the body axis extends straight posteriorly and the dorsal and ventral fins are equally developed.

Most astonishingly, all primitive fishes (the most primitive ostracoderms, placoderms, crossopterygians, chondrosteans) possessed an asymmetrical fin with the upper lobe longer than the lower and penetrated by the upturned vertebral axis. This is termed a *heterocercal* tail or, more strictly designated, a *fully heterocercal* tail. The same type occurs also in the specialized class Chondrichthyes, but in all other advanced groups of fishes one of several possible modifications have evolved.

In most modern fishes (most teleosts) the tail has become *homocercal*. In this type the fleshy part is not slender and elongate but is broad and ends quite bluntly, being evenly rounded off at the base of the tail fin. The tail fin itself is symmetrical but is highly varied in shape. The internally asymmetrical caudal vertebrae in these fishes, however, as well as of annectent living and fossil types, reveal that the homocercal tail has evolved from the fully heterocercal type. As a matter of fact an intermediate ancestral stage between these two is represented by a type still in existence in a few rather primitive living fishes (all members of the Holostei): the *abbreviate heterocercal* tail. Superficially the abbreviate heterocercal and homocercal tails are closely similar, the fin itself being virtually, if not quite, symmetrical in the former type, but the two can be distinguished by the fact that the fleshy base of the abbreviate heterocercal type extends farther posteriorly at the upper edge than at the lower.

Two other types of relatively rare occurrence among fishes are *diphycercal* and *reverse heterocercal*. The latter is the reverse of the fully heterocercal type, the caudal axis being directed ventrad instead of dorsad. It occurs only in some ostracoderms. The diphycercal type is indistinguishable morphologically from protocercal tails, but differs prominently in phylogeny since it evolved from the heterocercal type. Diphycercal tails occur in advanced crossopterygians, cyclostomes, Polypterus, and eels. The tails of tetrapods have clearly evolved from this type and may, in fact, be regarded as diphycercal if classified with piscine tails.

QUESTIONS

1. How do the pectoral and pelvic fins differ in region of body from which they evolved?

2. Describe the fin-fold theory of the origin of the paired appendages, noting intermediate stages.

3. What selective pressures may conceivably have channeled evolution of the cheiropterygium?

4. Diagram and name the components of the cheiropterygium, as in Figure 7.14.

5. Briefly summarize stylopodial and zeugopodial variation.

6. It has been said that man owes his intelligence, at least in part, to his opposable thumb. List other vertebrates also possessing opposable digits, briefly describing the combination occurring in each.

7. Show by labeled diagrams (as in Figs. 7.22, 7.23) how the primitive tarsus and carpus has been modified to produce those of man.

8. Contrast the tarsals of birds and anurans with the primitive tarsus.

9. Subaxial flexion of the forelimbs required a 180-degree twist, but in the hind limbs required only 90 degrees in most mammals. Carefully explain the difference.

10. Name four evolutionary trends in the cheiropterygium.

11. What functional value did cavitation of the long bones have in birds? In mammals?

12. By what means was loss of osseous strength accompanying cavitation compensated in birds and mammals?

13. Explain how a frightened person is more likely to suffer bone fractures in an accident than one unaware of the danger.

14. Explain the role of the epiphyseal plate in body growth in endotherms. Why does the synovial cartilage not play a similar role?

15. Account for the continuous growth characteristic of ectotherms in terms of growth centers. Account for the evolution of epiphyses.

16. Diagram and label the bones of the pectoral or pelvic girdles in fishes, distinguishing dermal from nondermal bones.

17. Trace the occurrence of each bone of the girdles through vertebrates.

18. Name the bones present in each part of the appendicular skeleton in each vertebrate type studied in the lab, distinguishing dermal bones, membrane bones, and cartilage bones.

19. What selective pressures may account for fusion of the two halves of the pelvic girdle in chondrichthyan fishes, whereas they are disjunct in most other fishes?

20. What adaptive value may there be in absence of pelvic symphyses in birds?

21. List similarities and dissimilarities of the pelvic and pectoral girdles.

22. What is the general rule of location of the acetabulum and glenoid fossa?

23. Contrast tetrapods and fishes in relative development of pectoral and pelvic appendages, accounting for the differences.

24. With what functional situation has the dermal girdle been eliminated in mammals?

25. What theoretically may account for the presence of a pectoral dermal girdle and the absence of a pelvic dermal girdle?

26. Similarly, what theoretically may account for the progressive degeneration of the pectoral dermal girdle in tetrapods?

27. Define the following words and where possible state occurrence or give examples.

abbreviate heterocercal	centrale	femur
acetabular bone	cheiropterygium	fibula
acetabulum	clavicle	fibulare
acropodium	cleithrum	fin fold
astragalus	compact bone	fin rays
autopodium	coracoid	fully heterocercal
axial theory	coracoid process	furcula
baculum	cuboid	glenoid fossa
basale	cuneiform	hallux
basal fin ray	dermal fin ray	hamate
basal theory	dermal girdle	heterocercal
basipodium	diaphysis	homocercal
brachial	digit	humerus
calcaneus	digitigrade	hypoischium
cancellous bone	diphycercal	ichthyopterygium
cannon bone	distale	ilium
capitate	ectocuneiform	innominate
carpal	endocuneiform	integumentary fin rays
carpale	epiphyseal plate	interclavicle
carpometacarpus	epiphysis	intermedium
carpus	epipubis	ischium
cavitation	Eusthenopteron	lobed fins

lobeless fins
lunar
manus
marrow
marrow cavity
mesocuneiform
mesopterygium
metacarpal
metapodium
metapterygium
metatarsal
minimus
navicular
pes
phalanx
pisiform
plantigrade
pollex
postaxial
postcleithrum
postcoracoid
postemporal

preaxial
primary fin ray
primary girdle
procoracoid cartilage
pronation
propterygium
protocercal
pterygiophores
pubis
puboischium
radial fin ray
radial sesamoid
radiale
radioulna
radius
red marrow
reverse heterocercal
Sauripterus
scaphoid
scapula
scapulocoracoid
stylopodium

subaxial flexion
supination
supracleithrum
suprascapula
tarsal
tarsale
tarsometatarsus
tarsus
tibia
tibiale
tibiofibula
tibiotarsus
trapezium
trapezoid
triquetral
ulna
ulnar sesamoid
ulnare
unguligrade
yellow marrow
ypsiloid
zeugopodium

8

SKELETAL SYSTEM III

Skull

BASIC COMPONENTS. On reasonably sound embryological and anatomical grounds it is thought that the skull or *cranium* began in the early chordates ancestral to vertebrates as a simple structure whose chief and virtually sole function was protection and support for the brain. This is the *neurocranium proper*. It soon received a contribution in the form of the three pairs of *sensory capsules,* thus acquiring a second function of protection of the three primary, paired sense organs of the head (olfactory, optic, otic organs). Both the neurocranium proper and the sensory capsules are commonly referred to collectively as the *neurocranium*.

A third component (Fig. 8.1) is the *dermocranium,* serving as a protection for the neurocranium and as an aid in capturing food. A fourth component is the *splanchnocranium,* consisting of that part of the visceral skeleton added to the skull. It serves various functions, chief of which are embryonic bases for the jaws (or, in Chondrichthyes only, the jaws themselves), suspensors for the jaws, accessories for hearing, and support for the brain.

Of these divisions the dermocranium alone belongs to the secondary endoskeleton, and its components thus are dermal bones and form directly from mesenchyme. The other three divisions (comprising the *endocranium* or *primary cranium*) belong to the primary endoskeleton, and the bones comprising them are preformed in cartilage. However, not all parts of the primary cranium are necessarily ossified.

The *chondrocranium* is a term used in reference to those parts of the cranium persisting as cartilage in any given animal at any given stage of life. In embryonic stages all primary endoskeletal components are repre-

198

sented by cartilage, but a large proportion is usually replaced by bone in adults. Little cartilage remains in the skulls of most amniotes and teleost fish. On the other hand, in the Chondrichthyes none whatsoever is ossified; the entire cranium is a chondrocranium. In various other fishes and in amphibians different degrees of ossification occur in adults. That part of the cranium represented by bone at any given stage constitutes the *osteo-cranium*. The components of the dermocranium never form a part of the chondrocranium, whereas all parts of the endocranium are at one stage or another a part of the chondrocranium.

The Neurocranium and Sensory Capsules

Basic Development. The early embryonic form of the neurocranium is thought to parallel phylogenetic history more or less exactly. The neuro-cranium proper forms from two pairs of cartilages situated below the brain and to either side of the notochord (Fig. 8.2). These primordia are (1) the

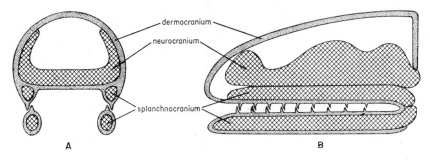

FIG. 8.1 Schematized cross section (A) and parasagittal section (B) of a vertebrate skull, showing relation of dermocranium, neurocranium and splanchnocranium.

parachordal bars, lying to either side of the anterior tip of the notochord, and (2), just in front of them, the *prechordal bars.* Spaced about these bars, to the side and in front, are six sensory capsules—the olfactory, optic, and otic capsules. From enlargement of these primordia the entire cra-nium, exclusive of the dermal and visceral crania, forms in all vertebrates.

Typically the neurocranial bars expand only to form a more or less complete floor for the brain, extending upward on the sides to a varying degree. The roof in most vertebrates is formed by other parts—the dermo-cranium. In the Chondrichthyes and to a lesser degree in some other fishes, the neurocranium also develops a roof for the brain.

The procedure of early neurocranial expansion is more or less stereo-typed (Fig. 8.2). The parachordals and prechordals on each side fuse to form a single bar, the *trabecula,* between which a fusion occurs trans-versely at the rear, involving the notochord, termed the *basal plate.* A

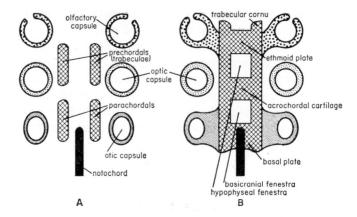

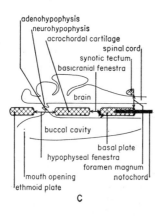

FIG. 8.2 Formation of a platytrabic neurocranium, schematic. Sensory capsules stippled, neurocranium proper lined. A, early embryonic or phylogenetic stage, dorsal view; B, later stage, same view, showing fusion of all separate parts save optic capsules; C, midsagittal section of a somewhat later stage, showing positional relation of brain, neurocranium and buccal cavity.

comparable fusion occurs across the middle of the bars (the *acrochordal cartilage*) and another near the anterior tips (*ethmoid plate*). Two openings are thus formed; the rear is termed the *basicranial fenestra,* the anterior one the *hypophyseal fenestra* in reference to the hypophysis or pituitary gland which forms through this aperture. The free anterior tips of the trabeculae are the *trabecular cornua.*

The otic capsules fuse with the rear of the parachordals, the olfactory capsules with the middle of the prechordal cartilages. The optic capsules never actually fuse with the neurocranium, inasmuch as mobility of the eyes is of great survival importance.

A transverse fusion occurs dorsal to the brain between the rear of the otic capsules; this is the *synotic tectum.* Thus a vertical foramen, the *foramen magnum,* is found at the rear of the cranium.

All vertebrates follow more or less this pattern in their embryogeny, except that the prechordals are fused in most amniotes and in most teleost fishes to form a *trabecula communis.* These vertebrates are said to have a *tropitrabic* (tropibasic by older terminology) neurocranium (Fig. 8.3), as opposed to the more primitive *platytrabic* (platybasic) type of most anamniotes. The latter type is distinguished not only by having paired instead of single cornua, but also by having a flat skull with the eyes wide

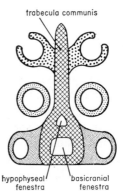

trabecula communis

FIG. 8.3 A tropitrabic neurocranium, dorsal view, schematic. Sensory capsules stippled, neurocranium proper lined.

hypophyseal   basicranial
fenestra   fenestra

apart and the brain case extending forward between the orbits. In the tropitrabic amniotes the orbits are separated only by a narrow septum, formed in part by the trabecula communis; the brain cavity is wholly posterior to the orbits.

Bones Contributed by the Neurocranium Proper. The bones ossified in the neurocranium proper include four groups: the occipital group, the posterior sphenoids, the anterior sphenoids, and the mesethmoid (Fig. 8.4). The occipital group includes (1) the *supraoccipital,* formed in the synotic tectum, bordering the foramen magnum middorsally, and absent in all living bony fishes except the teleosts, all living amphibians except the caecilians, and in *Sphenodon;* (2) the *exoccipitals* bordering the foramen magnum on either side, and present in all vertebrates; and (3) the *basioccipital,* derived from the basal plate, forming the ventral border of the foramen magnum, and absent only in the Choanichthyes, urodeles, anurans, and many extinct amphibians.

The *occipital condyles* of tetrapods are projections of the skull articulating with the first vertebra. They always include at least a small part of each exoccipital; and in modern amphibians (lacking a basioccipital), as well as primitive fossil amphibians, amphisbaenids (a group of lizards), a

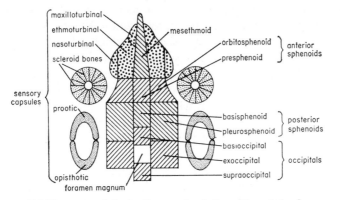

maxilloturbinal
ethmoturbinal
nasoturbinal   mesethmoid
scleroid bones   orbitosphenoid } anterior
                                        presphenoid   } sphenoids
sensory
capsules
          prootic
                                        basisphenoid   } posterior
                                        pleurosphenoid } sphenoids
                                        basioccipital }
                                        exoccipital   } occipitals
opisthotic   supraoccipital }
foramen magnum

FIG. 8.4 Diagram of derivation and relationships of the bones of the amniote neurocranium and sensory capsules. Capsular derivatives stippled, neurocranial derivatives lined.

few fossil reptiles, and in mammals, they are formed only from the exoccipitals, and are thus paired. The primitive tetrapod condition exhibits an unpaired condyle. Single condyles persisted or redeveloped in seymouriamorph amphibians, all modern reptiles save amphisbaenids, and in birds. In these groups the condyle is formed chiefly from the basioccipital. Fishes lack true condyles, but possess homologous, single *occipital processes* (see Vertebral Column, p. 181).

The posterior sphenoids include the median *basisphenoid,* absent in modern Choanichthyes and in amphibians. It is situated over the hypophyseal fenestra, and in mammals bears on its dorsal surface a deep pocket, the *sella turcica,* in which the pituitary gland is located. On either side of the basisphenoid are, in all osteichthyans except the Dipnoi, in caecilians, reptiles, and in birds, the *laterosphenoids* or *pleurosphenoids.* In mammals their place is taken by bones of quite different origin (*not homologous*), the *alisphenoids.*

The anterior sphenoid group is composed of the *presphenoid* (sphenethmoid of nonmammalian vertebrates) in the middle, and the *orbitosphenoids* on either side. The occurrence of either bone is rather variable, but both are present in all mammals and birds.

The sphenoids usually are fused to a greater or lesser degree. In adults what appears as a single bone thus may actually represent three or more bones. Such composite bones are usually called "sphenoids" (anterior or posterior, or both, if the two groups are separate).

The *mesethmoid* is ossified in the trabecula communis, the remainder of which extends forward as the nasal septum between the nasal capsules. The mesethmoid is a thin, vertical bone of spotty occurrence, being present only in the Dipnoi, teleosts, and in eutherian mammals.

Bones Contributed by the Sensory Capsules. The otic capsule has two important and nearly universal centers of ossification: the *prootic* and *opisthotic.* In mammals the prootic is better known as the *petrous* bone (housing the inner ear) and the opisthotic as the *mastoid* bone. Commonly the two are fused together as the *petromastoid* bone. Another bone present in most vertebrates but not in mammals is the *epiotic.* When present it is usually fused with the prootic and opisthotic, forming a composite called the *periotic.* In bony fishes two additional bones may be present: the *pterotic* and *sphenotic.* Any of the bones of the otic complex may be, and usually are, fused with adjacent bones, whatever they may be.

The optic capsule actually never fuses with the neurocranium, but is housed in a chamber (orbit) in which it can readily be rotated. The capsule is not formed of cartilage, as a rule, but of a heavy connective tissue making up the *scleroid* coat of the eyeball. In some vertebrates (such as owls, hawks, some lizards), thin, overlapping plates (*scleroid bones*) occur in the scleroid coat. Most fossil reptiles and birds possessed them, suggesting that their presence is not so much an adaptation to specific modes of life as to some general situation, probably associated with the mechanics of focusing the eye (see Chap. 17).

The olfactory capsule ossifies in mammals as unique *turbinate* bones, thrown into complex folds and branches, forming a sort of scroll-like maze into which air is drawn upon "sniffing." The upper and posterior surfaces of this maze are covered with olfactory epithelium, which is thus enormously increased in area (and efficiency) without marked increase in size of the olfactory capsule. A perhaps even more important function is to facilitate preconditioning (by warming and filtering) of the inhaled air. The turbinate bones contributed by each capsule are the *ethmoturbinal* (*ectethmoid*), the *nasoturbinal,* and the *maxilloturbinal.* These are more or less fused with each other, and the elements of the two capsules are also typically fused with the mesethmoid (and sometimes also with the vomer), forming a complex often called simply the *ethmoid* bone. Homologies in other classes of the mammalian elements are uncertain.

The Splanchnocranium

The Mandibular Arch. The visceral arches or parts thereof that contribute directly to the cranium make up the splanchnocranium. One or two *labial cartilages* present near the angles of the jaws in elasmobranchs possibly represent the most anterior arches contributing to the cranium in any gnathostome. No other gnathostomes possess any vestiges whatsoever of these premandibular arches, if indeed that is what the labial cartilages represent, and therefore little importance is attached to them.

The most anterior arch, with the possible exception cited, that contributes to the cranium is the mandibular arch (No. 1). This arch forms a nearly or quite complete ring, contrary to the other visceral arches which are U-shaped. The ring is split and bent in the middle on either side, the two halves (dorsal and ventral) swinging forward toward each other. Each half is also split at the midline, thus forming typically a bar on either side dorsally (the *palatoquadrate cartilages*), and another pair ventrally (*Meckel's cartilages*). These are often looked upon as upper and lower jaws, respectively, but they are not actually the jaws in any vertebrate except the Chondrichthyes, in which dermal bone becomes degenerate. They do serve in all other vertebrates as (in addition to other more specialized functions in various groups) a vitally important framework about which the usual tooth-bearing dermal bones are organized. Remains of them, in the form of cartilage if not of bone, persist in at least the lower jaw in adults of all tetrapods. They may thus be considered *part,* but only part (except as noted), of the jaws of all gnathostomes.

One has only to reflect upon the heavy armor of primitive vertebrates such as the ostracoderms and placoderms, and upon the existence of that armor about the mouth, to realize that the visceral skeleton did not bear the teeth, and did not serve directly as grasping devices. The same remains true in all subsequent groups (except Chondrichthyes); in fact a progressive reduction in the visceral arch component and a corresponding increase in the dermal component have been common trends, reaching a maximum expression in mammals. A perhaps useful distinction is to recognize three kinds (actually parts) of the jaw in vertebrates: (1) "visceral jaws" (mandibular arch only and derivatives thereof); (2) "dermal jaws" (dermal bone components only); and (3) "epidermal jaws" (enamel of teeth, and rhamphotheca). Excepting the teeth, chondrichthyans possess visceral jaws only, turtles and birds possess all three types, and all other gnathostomes possess only visceral and dermal jaws.

The visceral jaws actually have had three main functions, as jaws, in the history of vertebrates: (1) support for teeth and for tooth anchorage in dermal bone; (2) articulation for the jaws; and (3) provision of the muscles for operation of the jaws (adapted from the portion of the segmental gill-arch musculature associated with the mandibular arch). The supportive function in an embryonically "organizing" sense is maintained in all vertebrates, but in a literal sense it was lost very early. The articular function has been particularly tenacious and essential, but is finally lost in mammals. Even direct association with the muscular contribution was lost as early as in the primitive fishes, in which the attachment of the muscles has shifted from the visceral arch to the encasing dermal bones. Little superficial evidence thus remains in most living vertebrates of the critically important roles the mandibular visceral arch has played in the evolution of their jaws.

PALATOQUADRATE DERIVATIVES. In the palatoquadrate cartilages two or more bones form in most gnathostomes. In bony fishes as many as five bones may form on each side. Most constant in occurrence is the element called a *quadrate* in nonmammals, becoming the *incus* in mammals. As a quadrate it articulates the skull with the lower jaw; as the incus it serves as one of the three ear ossicles (the middle one), and thus plays an auditory role, aiding in the transmission of sound vibrations to the inner ear. Next most constant is the *epipterygoid,* present in primitive examples of all tetrapods; it exists in all mammals, in which it is known as the *alisphenoid.* This bone forms a part of the brain case, occupying in mammals the place of the pleurosphenoids, which are absent. Both occur in the skulls of primitive reptiles. The *autopalatine, suprapterygoid,* and *metapterygoid* are bones limited to teleost fishes.

DERIVATIVES OF MECKEL'S CARTILAGE. In Meckel's cartilage the *articular* (*malleus* in mammals) is the most constant of all derivatives, being present in all the bony vertebrates except some amphibians. Its history parallels that of the quadrate. As the articular it serves to articulate the lower jaw with the skull at the quadrate bone; this relationship, of articular of lower jaw articulating with the quadrate of the skull, is amazingly constant in nonmammalian vertebrates. In the mammals, however, the articular (fused with the *prearticular,* a dermal bone) joins the quadrate in the middle ear, becoming the *malleus,* the outermost bone in the chain of three mammalian middle ear ossicles. Other bones ossify at various places along Meckel's cartilage in various vertebrates, but none are of much significance in tetrapods; they include a *retroarticular* at the rear, a *mentomeckelian* at the anterior tip (the only one persisting in amphibians), a *coronomeckelian,* and *mediomeckelian.*

Cranial Contributions of the Hyoid Arch. The second or hyoid visceral arch contributes to the splanchnocranium in all gnathostomes except placoderms, in which the hyoid arch is still branchial in function. The contribution is small, however. The dorsal tip, lying against the skull, aids primarily in primitive gnathostomes in articulation of the jaws with the skull. It ossifies as two bones, the *symplectic* (less regularly present) and *hyomandibula* (regularly present) in fishes, and is represented in the Chondrichthyes by the hyomandibular cartilage. The aid of the hyomandibular element is apparently not essential, for considerable variation exists even among fishes in method of jaw articulation. In tetrapods the hyomandibula is divorced completely from its formerly primary articular functions and retains as its sole function the formerly secondary and very different function of conducting sound vibrations across the middle ear cavity to the inner ear. In deference to this change of emphasis in function, the hyomandibula is termed the *columella* in all tetrapods except mammals, in which it is called the *stapes*. The columella is the only middle ear ossicle in nonmammalian tetrapods; as the stapes it is the innermost of three in mammals. Throughout tetrapods it fits into the same opening, the fenestra ovalis, in the otic capsule.

The only other contribution of the hyoid arch to the splanchnocranium is the *styloid process* of the temporal bone in some mammals. This process is the result of fusion of the upper ends of the anterior cornua of the glossal skeleton to the skull. The remainder of the cornua is reduced to small size and commonly, as in man, fuses with the basihyal to form a U-shaped *hyoid bone* which is not part of the splanchnocranium.

The Dermocranium

The dermal bones of the skull of endotherm vertebrates are considerably reduced in comparison with those of primitive vertebrates. The following summary includes all the dermal bones of modern tetrapods and the major elements present in fishes and fossil tetrapods. The arrangement is approximately the same in all. The dermal bones are laid down over, or are added to, the primary endoskeletal components of the skull (neurocranium and splanchnocranium). Thus they can best be grouped in accordance with the components with which they are associated: (1) the additions to the neurocranium, and (2) the additions to the splanchnocranium.

Additions to Neurocranium. Two major groups may be recognized: the dorsal roofing bones, and the ventral flooring bones.

Four series make up the roofing bones (Fig. 8.5): a median series, an orbital series, a lateral series, and an opercular series. The median series consists, from front to rear, of the *nasal, frontal, parietal,* and *postparietal* (or *dermsupraoccipital*). All are primitively paired, and all are present in most vertebrates including all mammals. The postparietals are fused in mammals as a single bone, the *interparietal,* which in turn is often fused in adults with the occipital bone. As an anomaly, a separate center of ossification occasionally appears embryonically at the junction of the suture between the parietals and the frontals. It may be regarded as a spurious bone (*Wormian bone*). Other spurious bones form occasionally as individual anomalies in the junctions of other sutures.

The orbital series consists of the *lacrimal* forming the front border of the orbit; the *postorbital* forming the rear border of the orbit; and the *prefrontal* and *postfrontal* forming the medial border. The *palpebral* bone

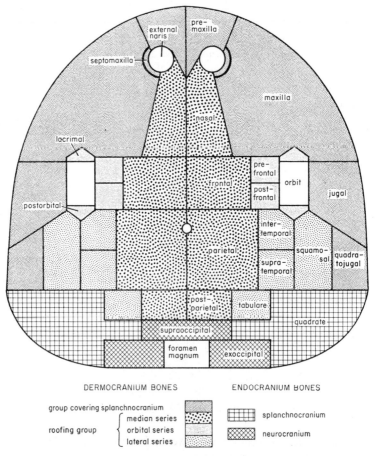

FIG. 8.5 Dermocranium and associated bones of a primitive tetrapod skull, dorsal view, schematic.

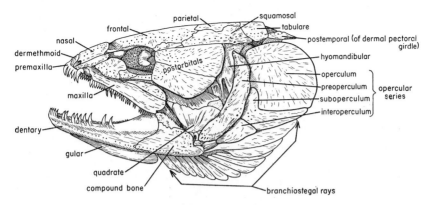

FIG. 8.6 Lateral view of skull of the bowfin, Amia, showing the opercular series of dermal roofing bones and relative position thereof. (From Goodrich.)

is another of the orbital series, but is of limited occurrence (in the upper eyelid of crocodilians, etc.) The lateral orbital border is commonly formed by the jugal and maxillary bones (not of this series). All except the lacrimal, of the orbital series, are lost in mammals.

The lateral series includes an *intertemporal, supratemporal, squamosal,* and *tabular,* posteriorly; and a *septomaxilla* bordering the nostril. All are lost in mammals except for the squamosal, which is fused with the composite bone, called a *temporal,* in mammals. The latter bone is in no way homologous with the nonmammalian temporals, which are single elements. With the lateral series articulates, in fishes, a series of dermal bones (the dermal girdle) associated with the pectoral girdle.

The opercular series (Fig. 8.6) is entirely confined to fishes, with the single exception of one of the four elements (*preoperculum*) remaining in the most primitive known fossil amphibians. The series includes an *operculum, suboperculum, interoperculum,* and *preoperculum,* all lying at the rear lateral corner of the skull and extending as a protective cover over the gill region.

The ventral flooring bones, forming the primitive or *primary palate,* include a median series and a lateral series (Fig. 8.7). In the median series, from front to rear, are the *prevomers, pterygoids,* and *parasphenoid* (only the latter unpaired). The lateral series includes, anteriorly, the *palatines;* posteriorly, the *ectopterygoids.* The prevomers are thought to be represented in mammals by the palatine processes of the premaxillae; the pterygoids by the hook-shaped *hamulus* protecting the pharyngeal opening of the Eustachian tube; the parasphenoid by the *vomer* (the latter actually may represent the fused prevomers); the palatines usually by separate bones bearing the same name; and the ectopterygoids by the so-called (mammalian) pterygoid bones (or processes, if fused with other bones) exclusive of the hamulus. In various vertebrates teeth are borne upon all the palatal bones. Parasphenoid and prevomerine teeth are

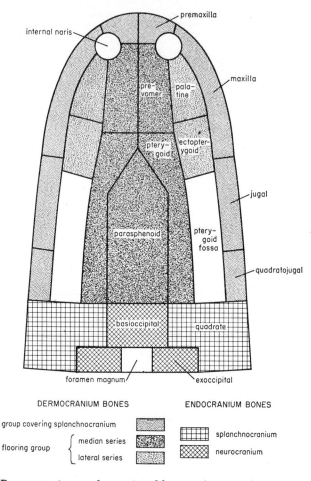

FIG. 8.7 Dermocranium and associated bones of a primitive tetrapod skull, ventral view, schematic.

common in modern amphibians, palatine and pterygoid teeth in modern reptiles. Birds and mammals have lost them entirely.

Additions to the Mandibular Arch. The dermal upper jaw, added to the palatoquadrate cartilages, consists of, in succession from front to rear, the *premaxilla* (right and left commonly fused), *maxilla, jugal* or *malar,* and *quadratojugal.* Only the first two bear teeth. Mammals lack the quadratojugal, and often the premaxilla and maxilla are fused together. Other vertebrates vary markedly in composition of the upper jaw, some retaining only a premaxilla, others only a maxilla.

The dermal lower jaw (Fig. 8.8), added to Meckel's cartilages, consists, on either side and more or less from front to rear, of the *dentary, splenial, postsplenial, coronoid* (several in some reptiles), *angular, surangular* and *prearticular.* Only the dentary bears teeth, except for the splenial and coronoid in certain amphibians. In mammals the dentary is the only bone left in the lower jaw, but the angular and prearticular are nevertheless represented elsewhere by vestiges. The angular or the surangular, or both, have become the ectotympanic bone (a part of the complex mammalian temporal), and the prearticular accompanies the articular to form part of the malleus.

Evolutionary Trends in the Vertebrate Cranium

A number of general trends or "laws" exhibited in evolution of the vertebrate cranium have already been discussed in connection with a review of the basic structure of the cranium. Others have not yet been mentioned. All are listed and, where necessary, discussed below.

1. PROGRESSIVE ASSIMILATION OF CRANIAL COMPONENTS. The neurocranium proper was the earliest component of the cranium; the sensory capsules then joined the neurocranium; the dermocranium, segregated from the dermis, was probably next to be added, followed in the placoderms by the splanchnocranium, appropriated from the visceral skeleton. A fifth noteworthy addition occurred with differentiation of the amniotes, two anterior vertebrae apparently fusing with the rear of the skull. No discernible skeletal evidence of these vertebrae remains in the skull of adults, although the number of cranial nerves (twelve in amniotes, ten in most anamniotes) does reflect the fusion.

2. MULTIPLICATION OF CHONDRAL ELEMENTS. Elements of the primary cranium tend to become increased in number in advanced verte-

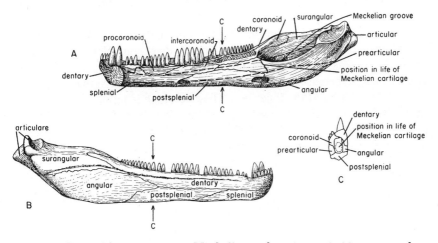

FIG. 8.8 Dermal bones encasing Meckel's cartilage in a primitive tetrapod skull. Only the articular is not a dermal bone. A, medial view; B, lateral view; C, cross section. (From Williston.)

brates. Teleosts and mammals possess the greatest number, and progressively fewer occur in more primitive types.

3. WILLISTON'S LAW. Dermal bones tend to become fewer throughout vertebrates. Primitive fishes have the most. Groups of bones conspicuously exhibiting this trend are the opercular series, the dermal jaw bones, the lateral roofing series, and the orbital series. Mammals and modern amphibians probably represent the greatest extremes in this evolutionary trend.

4. REDUCTION OF VISCERAL JAWS, RECIPROCAL HYPERTROPHY OF DERMAL JAWS. See preceding discussion of the mandibular arch.

5. EVOLUTION OF SOUND-CONDUCTION ROUTES. One of the most convincing examples in vertebrate history of specialization along lines of preadaptation is to be found in the remarkable alterations occurring in the parts of the splanchnocranium articulating with the otic capsule. Since the mandibular and hyoid arches articulate with the skull at the otic capsule, it follows as a matter of course that they carry sound vibrations to that area, whether they have other functions or not. As a matter of fact any part of the body in contact with the ground can carry sound vibrations to other parts, but the unique situation that led to actual specialization of parts of the hyoid and mandibular arches for sound conduction was the articulation of these arches on the walls of the otic sense organ. Although in early vertebrates this organ was not adapted for sound perception, it gained that function in many advanced types because its structure is preadapted to detection of sound waves. The otic organ is essentially a fluid-filled sac, the walls of which are provided in various spots with sensory receptors in the form of hairlike projections that perceive any movement in the surrounding fluid. These sensory patches can thus readily be modified to perceive movements resulting from sound vibrations; they are in this sense "preadapted" for hearing.

Many fishes are thought to be deaf, and it is true that most have no gross morphological adaptations for sound detection. Yet many teleost fishes do possess three or four special ossicles (*Weberian ossicles*), derived from the hemal spines of anterior trunk vertebrae, situated between the swim bladder and the inner ear. The otic organ is termed the inner ear in those cases in which it possesses auditory functions. Such fishes have a grossly evident structural adaptation for hearing, and have been proved to possess acute hearing, but many other fishes lack such apparent hearing aids. Nevertheless, it is thought that even the types that lack obvious adaptations for hearing may, in many cases, be able to hear at least moderately well. As a matter of fact, since the entire body can conduct sound vibrations received from the water to the inner ear, no particular specialization for conduction is necessary. The internal specialization needed for actual perception of sound waves by the sense organs within the inner ear need not be conspicuous either, and in fact is not conspicuous even in sharp-eared fishes or amphibians. A gross specialization would be expected among fishes only were there some means for augmenting the sound vibrations. This is precisely the function that a taut resonous swim bladder can perform, and it is clearly because of this capacity that the Weberian ossicles became specialized to transmit those augmented sound waves directly to the inner ear.

In tetrapods sound waves could be detected either through the ground or through the air. Detection of air-borne sound waves, however, requires specializations not already developed by fishes, for the intensity of such waves is not great enough to permit the waves to be picked up readily and transmitted by solid parts of the body. Therefore, in the most primitive tetrapods sound waves are transmitted by the most direct route possible— from the ground to the inner ear. In more advanced types, both ground and air-borne sounds are perceived, and in still more advanced types hearing is limited almost entirely to air-borne sounds. We can thus recognize four stages in the evolution of hearing routes in vertebrates: the *first* is comprised of fishes which hear water-borne sound *via,* generally, all parts of the solid body structures; the *second* is represented in living vertebrates by salamanders, which hear ground-borne sounds *via* special routes (forelegs or jaws) that carry the waves to the ear across the mandibular suspensorium; the *third* is represented by all other tetrapods save mammals which hear largely air-borne sounds, but to a certain degree also ground-borne sounds, both *via* the mandibular suspensorium; and the *fourth* is represented by endotherms, which are specially adapted only to hear air-borne sounds, although, as in all other vertebrates, waves received under unusual conditions directly by the body can also be heard. It is reasonably speculated that all vertebrates capable of hearing, except mammals, must hear a remarkable roar as they work their jaws. In some salamanders, which are unique in having strong sound-conductive ligaments and muscles connecting the pectoral girdle and columella, there may well be also a comparable roar with every movement of the forelegs.

6. FUNCTIONAL EVOLUTION OF THE MANDIBULAR SUSPENSORIUM. The transition in adaptation among tetrapods from detection of sound waves received through solids (that is, gross structures of the body) to detection of sound waves received through the air was not and could not be sudden; it was a gradual transition involving dual functions of the conducting system in intermediate stages. Since the conducting system in all vertebrates has involved the mandibular arch and its attachments to the skull (that is, its *suspensorium*), we can most effectively treat the evolution of the middle ear ossicles on the basis of the stages of evolution of the mandibular suspensorium (Fig. 8.9).

The earliest stage of evolution of the mandibular suspensorium is represented by the agnathans, in which none of the arches are associated directly with the skull. This condition is called *paleostyly,* literally meaning the "ancient suspension."

Placoderms have become *autostylic;* in them the mandibular arch is attached to (or suspended from) the cranium by itself ("auto"), without intervention by the hyoid arch.

It was in the primitive postplacoderm fishes that the critically important intervention occurred of the upper part of the hyoid arch (the hyomandibula) between the skull and the rear of the mandibular arch. In this, the third stage, the mandibular arch is *euamphistylic,* since it has a double ("amphi") suspension from the skull: one contact directly with the skull, the other *via* the hyomandibula. The implication of the prefix meaning "true" (*eu*) is that the mandibular arch actually forms an important part of the jaws; in contrast see discussion of cranioamphistyly following.

In a fourth stage, the advanced fishes (elasmobranchs, teleosts) all became *hyostylic,* having a mandibular suspension solely *via* part of the hyoid arch (hyomandibula). In both this stage and the preceding it is evident that the hyomandibula, attached as it was to the otic region of the skull, served as a conductor of sound waves as well as a suspensor.

In the fifth stage (derived directly from the third, not from the fourth which was a concurrent evolutionary line), the hyomandibula was modified exclusively as a sound conductor, and no longer aided in mandibular suspension; it became the usually slender *columella,* a middle ear ossicle and the only one of nonmammalian tetrapods. Having lost its hyoid support, the mandibular suspension reverted to *autostyly,* a type grossly characteristic also of more primitive fishes and an earlier stage of evolution. While it is risky to surmise now what selective forces were involved in the specialization of the hyomandibula for hearing as its articular functions were lost, it seems highly probable that the strong survival value of its complete adaptation for hearing of the more delicate air-borne sound waves far exceeded the survival value of persistence as an articulating element. An accident of great importance in this connection was the existence of the spiracular cavity against the anterior border of the hyomandib-

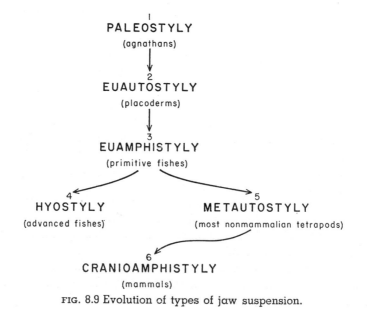

FIG. 8.9 Evolution of types of jaw suspension.

ula and the side of the otic capsule. That cavity provided a space which in aerial situations could be and was used as an indispensable aid in relaying air-borne sound waves without diminution to the otic capsule. The outer opening of the spiracular cavity became closed by a thin "eardrum" (tympanum), and the hyomandibula at the same time moved somewhat to extend from the eardrum across the cavity to the wall of the inner ear. In such a position it became a middle ear ossicle, since it extended across the spiracular cavity, now known as the middle ear cavity.

The final stage is the stage of *cranioamphistyly,* characteristic of mammals. In this stage the columella was joined in the middle ear by the incus and the malleus, derived, respectively, from the quadrate bone of the dorsal half of the mandibular arch and the articular of the ventral half of the mandibular arch (fused with the adjacent prearticular, a dermal bone). Although the transition of function may seem almost unbelievable, it is authenticated by both the fossil record and the embryogenic pattern of living mammals. It is evident that in the crawling reptiles ancestral to mammals the lower jaw still served an important function in conduction of sound waves, which passed from the articulare to the quadrate, and thence to the columella *via* a number of cartilaginous struts between the quadrate and columella. Virtually all nonmammalian tetrapods possess this sort of anchorage for the columella, which thus can readily pick up ground-borne waves as well as air-borne waves.

The factors involved in accentuation of the hearing function and loss of articular function of the quadrate and articular seem to be two: for one, mammals became less of a ground-crawling type of animal, and the jaws thus rarely could serve as an aid to hearing; and, secondly, selective pressures led toward shortening of the lower jaw as a means for increasing its leverage—its efficiency as a gnawing and chewing organ. The articulation therefore tended to extend farther forward, involving not only the progressively smaller articular and quadrate, but also the bone in front of the articular (and prearticular)—the dentary—and the bone in front of the quadrate—the squamosal. Ultimately, in all true mammals, the jaw articulation became restricted exclusively to the squamosal and dentary, leaving the articular and quadrate functionless except for their formerly minor role in sound conduction.

Since the articular and quadrate in most reptiles lie very close to the tympanum, it is not surprising that the most distal bone, the articular, should come to lie against the tympanum and serve to receive the sound waves. The quadrate retained its ancient relation to the articular as it became the incus, and the columella lost its tympanic connection in becoming the stapes, while retaining its ancient relation to the otic capsule and its more recent anchorage with the former quadrate.

Two other bones of the lower jaw became, perhaps coincidentally, involved in the "otic capture" of the articular in mammals. The prearticular, a dermal bone, remained fused with the articular and shared with it in the composition of the malleus. The angular or the surangular, or both (varying in different mammals), other dermal bones just anterior to the prearticular, also moved into the otic region, becoming the ectotympanic bone of the tympanic bulla.

This general picture of ear-ossicle evolution is agreed to by all students of vertebrate anatomy and evolution. Some uncertainty still surrounds certain details, however. Tumarkin (1955) has summarized most of the points of difference of opinion from the preceding account, and his views are depicted for comparative purposes in Figure 8.10. Certain aspects of his theory have been soundly criticized but there is still much more to be learned before the details of this evolutionary sequence will be completely clear.

7. DISSOCIATION OF SKULL AND PECTORAL GIRDLE. There seems to be little question that the pectoral girdle evolved in close association with the dermocranium. In placoderms the pectoral fins emerge from the cranium, and in many modern bony fishes the dermal girdle still retains an articulation with the temporal region of the skull (Fig. 8.11). All cranial association is lost in the tetrapods, however, and also most of the elements—especially the dorsal elements—of the dermal girdle.

8. REDUCTION OF THE INTERORBITAL SPACE. Most anamniotes possess a broad interorbital space, as is characteristic of the platytrabic chondrocranium; in teleost fishes and most amniotes, with development of a trabecula communis, the interorbital space becomes very narrow and is occupied by a thin septum, as is characteristic of the tropitrabic chondrocranium.

9. PROGRESSIVE COMPOUNDING OF BONES. Fusion of bones, to form *complex bones,* is not a particularly conspicuous trend in fishes or even in amphibians, but is increasingly so in reptiles, mammals, and birds. In mammals, examples are the occipital complex (of some four to seven

MIDDLE EAR OSSICLE	TETRAPOD GROUPS	EVOLUTIONARY ORIGIN
PSEUDOCOLUMELLA	ANURA	footplate from otic capsule stylus from quadrate
PARACOLUMELLA	REPTILES, AVES, most FOSSIL AMPHIBIA	footplate from hyomandibula stylus from (a) quadrate in reptiles, amphibians (b) hyoid arch in birds
EUCOLUMELLA	SALAMANDERS, CAECILIANS	entirely from hyomandibula
STAPES	MAMMALS	footplate from hyomandibula stylus from quadrate
INCUS	MAMMALS	quadrate
MALLEUS	MAMMALS	articular and prearticular

FIG. 8.10 Evolution of middle ear ossicles as envisioned by Tumarkin.

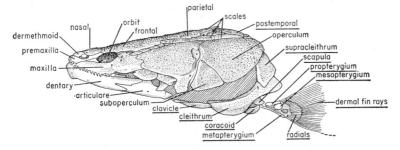

FIG. 8.11 The relation of skull and pectoral girdle in a bony fish. Names of parts of the girdle and fin are underlined. (From Gregory.)

bones: basioccipital, two exoccipitals, supraoccipital, interparietal), the sphenoid (of six bones), the ethmoid complex (of some five to eight bones: one mesethmoid, one vomer, two ectethmoids, two maxilloturbinals, two nasoturbinals) and the temporal (of four to six bones: the squamosal, petrous, mastoid, ectotympanic, and in some the endotympanic—a cartilage bone of unknown homology forming a tympanic bulla—or the styloid process, or both).

It is in the birds, however, that the extreme in fusion of skull bones is reached. Virtually every bone in the adult skull is fused with adjacent bones; the sutures that remain are for the most part incomplete. Thus the identity of the bones in most areas of the adult bird skull is difficult to determine.

10. DIVISION OF OCCIPITAL CONDYLES. See discussions in preceding pages of this chapter and under the Vertebral Column for a review of evolutionary trends and their functional bases. The advantage of development of two condyles from the single forerunner in tetrapods varies according to group. Modern amphibians necessarily have two, since they possess only the exoccipitals of the occipital series. Mammals possess a complete complement of occipital bones, but in them the labor of head movement is divided, nodding movements occurring between skull and atlas, rotation between the atlas and axis. In amphisbaenids (burrowing wormlike reptiles) acquisition of two condyles would seem essential to their mode of life, serving to strengthen the head-neck attachment and rendering possible more powerful burrowing movements. The functional advantages that led to retention of single condyles in various tetrapod lines remain, however, largely unknown.

11. FORMATION OF TEMPORAL FOSSAE. Since the dermocranium was laid down on top of other components of the cranium and originally lacked muscle of its own, it, of course, covered the muscles attached to and operating movable parts of the cranium. The arrangement can be visualized in cross section, the neurocranium appearing as a U-shaped structure, the muscles attached to its outer surface, and then covered by the dermocranium. A double skull, with muscles between, is simulated (Fig. 8.13).

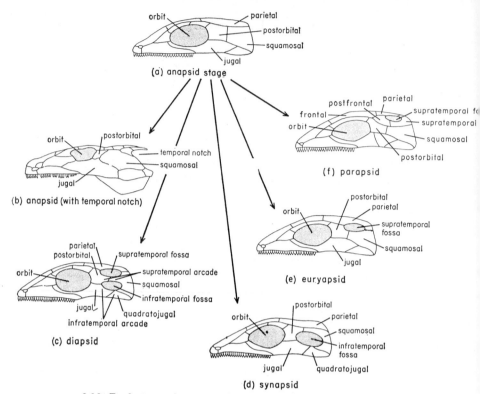

FIG. 8.12 Evolution of temporal accommodation in tetrapods. (From Romer.)

Fishes have retained, for the most part, a solid outer cranium, and are thus *anapsid;* but in primitive amphibians the interference of the outer cranium with operation of the muscles became serious, perhaps because the dermocranium was progressively more fully integrated with the rest of the skull. In any event, to allow room for expansion at the belly of the jaw muscles as they contract, a *temporal notch* (Fig. 8.12B) developed in some fossil amphibians at the rear of the skull on either side. The same sort of adjustment occurs in most living turtles (Fig. 8.13) although the ancient and odd sidenecked turtles evolved a still different but analogous *zygomatic notch.*

Primitive reptiles, lacking any sort of temporal gap, evolved from amphibians that still possessed a solid dermocranium. Postorbital and temporal notches of turtles thence evolved independently, while in other groups of reptiles, a pair of openings, called *temporal fossae (supratemporal* and *infratemporal*), developed on either side near the rear of the skull, in the temporal region (Fig. 8.12). This is the *diapsid* condition, retained in all living reptiles except turtles and passed on to all their avian descendants. Among extinct reptiles, however, some groups lost (or did not develop) the lower fossa, retaining only the single pair of upper fossae;

these are *parapsids,* or *euryapsids;* the supratemporal fossa is bounded medially by the parietal in both, but is bordered extensively elsewhere by the postfrontal and supratemporal in parapsids, just as in diapsids, but by the postorbital and squamosal in euryapsids. Seemingly these two lines evolved independently and not one from the other. In another line, the upper fossa disappeared (or failed to develop), leaving the single pair of lower fossae; these are *synapsids.* The infratemporal fossa increased greatly in size in this line of evolution, which gave rise to mammals although all reptilian representatives have become extinct.

Although both the chelonian notches and temporal fossae appear to have developed primitively to provide space for expansion of the belly of the temporal muscles in contraction, the temporal muscles tended to shift their attachment from the neurocranium to the edges of the fossae (Fig. 8.13). This shift has progressed but little in the crocodilians, but in lizards and snakes it involves not only the edges of the fossae but also the upper surface of the dermocranium dorsal to the upper fossa. The shift is complete in mammals.

12. FORMATION OF A SECONDARY PALATE. The bones of the primary palate have already been listed. They form a complete roof for the mouth, broken only by the two internal nares anteriorly (absent in most fishes). Fishes and amphibians retain the primary palate unmodified, but certain deficiencies inherent in this structure became evident with adoption of terrestrial life. The most conspicuous deficiency was the almost complete interference with breathing caused by having the mouth open, or by manipulation of food in the buccal cavity.

Reptiles have attempted to hurdle this handicap in a number of ways. In snakes the trachea extends far forward ventrally so breathing can continue while food is being swallowed—often a long process. In some turtles and lizards a shelf has grown over the primary palate anteriorly

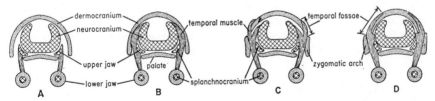

FIG. 8.13 Shift in attachment of temporal muscles in conjunction with formation of temporal fossae as seen in cross section of the skull. A, primitive condition, with muscles attached only to the parts of the mandibular arch, as are the serially homologous adductors of other visceral arches; B, extension of attachment of muscles to sides of neurocranium, favoring a thinning of the sides of the dermocranium to accommodate muscular contraction; C, perforation of the fossae, with encroachment of muscles onto dorsal surfaces of dermocranium; D, development of extensive attachments to outer surfaces of dermocranium and to inner surface of zygomatic arch.

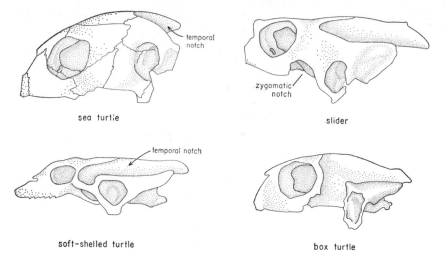

FIG. 8.14 Various stages in hypertrophy of the temporal and zygomatic notches in turtles. (From Adams and Eddy.)

from the maxillary and premaxillary bones, involving also the palatine bones to a small degree. This is the *secondary palate* (Figs. 8.15, 8.16), which forms a new part of the roof of the mouth. In crocodilians this bony, secondary palate has been perfected by its extension over the entire primary palate; crocodilians thus have a completely new roof for the mouth. It is even a more complete bony, secondary palate than mammals have, for in the latter group the rear half or third of the secondary palate is a *soft palate* (as opposed to the anterior *hard palate*); the two together are the equivalent of the completely bony, secondary palate of crocodilians. In both animals the nasal passage is completely (or very nearly so, in mammals) separated from the buccal cavity. In crocodilians this facilitates manipulation of food while under water. It does not concern breathing, for crocodiles breathe at long intervals and can easily refrain from breathing for several hours if necessary.

In mammals the secondary palate serves a different function, permitting breathing while eating. This is an absolutely necessary adjunct of

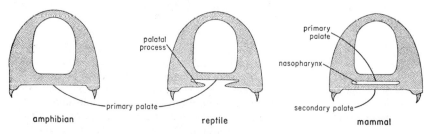

FIG. 8.15 Schematic cross sections of the crania of a series of tetrapods, showing evolution of the secondary palate.

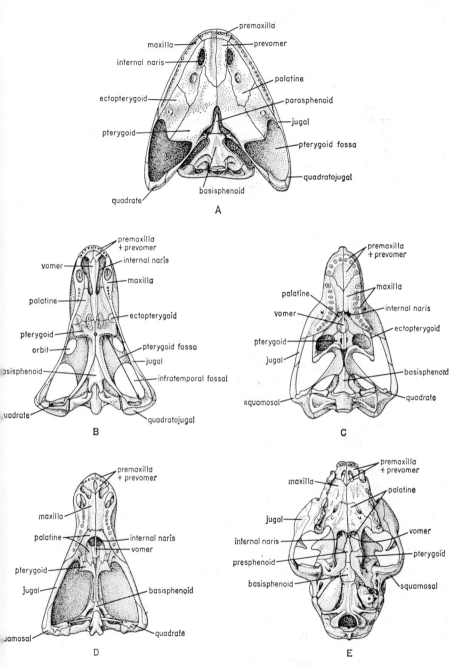

FIG. 8.16 Palatal views of a series of tetrapod skulls showing evolution of the mammalian secondary palate. A, amphibian; B, C, D, successive reptilian stages; E, cat. (From Romer and Senning.)

their high rate of metabolism and coincident rapid rate of breathing, high body temperature, and endothermic temperature control.

Occasional anomalies, involving arrested development of the secondary palate, occur in mammals. They reflect ancestral conditions to a considerable degree, and may thus be regarded as atavistic. Among these are the "harelip" of man (the vertical groove or *philthrum* on the nose of cats is basically the same thing), and a "cleft palate," in which the outgrowths from the maxillary bones fail to meet medially. No serious interference with normal function results. This condition is typical, as a matter of fact, of the lizard palate.

If a secondary palate is so essential to the mammalian endothermic achievement, it may be viewed as equally essential for birds with their even higher rate of metabolism. Actually birds do possess a secondary palate, but in the interest of weight reduction (presumably) it is largely soft, having a longitudinal bar on either side of the median line to serve as support.

QUESTIONS

1. Name and state the functions of the four major components of the cranium. To wnat division of the endoskeleton does each component belong?

2. Sketch and label a neurocranium with its sensory capsules.

3. What are the two basic types of neurocrania and how do they differ? In what vertebrate groups does each type occur?

4. Name the bones ossified in the neurocranium proper, associating them by groups, and stating in which vertebrate groups and by what name each occurs (with special attention to the elements present in mammals).

5. In what division of vertebrates did occipital condyles appear, from what did they evolve, and what was their selective value?

6. Briefly discuss the evolution of condyles in tetrapods, accounting for the changes that took place.

7. Name the bones ossified in each sensory capsule, stating in which vertebrate groups each occurs and giving the name applied in mammals (if distinctive).

8. What is presumed to have been the function of scleroid bones? Turbinate bones?

9. What is the possible significance of the occurrence of labial cartilages in elasmobranchs?

10. Name the three major components (or kinds) of jaws in vertebrates, stating in what groups each occurs.

11. What are the three functions of the visceral jaws, as such, in vertebrates?

12. Name the bones ossified in the mandibular arch, stating in which vertebrate groups each appears, and giving the distinctive names, if any, applied in different classes.

13. Name the contributions of the hyoid arch to the splanchnocranium, giving the groups in which each occurs and synonyms where applied.

14. Name in their proper series the dermal roofing bones added to the neurocranium, stating which occur in mammals.

15. Which series of roofing bones is a piscine adjunct? What vestige if any remains in tetrapods?

16. Name the dermal flooring bones of the cranium, state which are dentigerous in different vertebrates, and specify what homolog of each remains in mammals.

17. Name the dermal bones added to the parts of the mandibular arch, and specify which (and under what name) persist in mammals.

18. Name twelve evolutionary trends in the cranium of vertebrates. Discuss each.

19. How do dermal and chondral elements of the skull differ in their evolutionary trends?

20. As the visceral jaws diminished in importance, what took their place?

21. State the characteristics of the four stages in evolution of the sound-conduction routes in vertebrates.

22. Name and explain the six stages in functional evolution of the mandibular suspensorium; draw a phylogenetic tree of the stages.

23. In what vertebrates are skull and pectoral girdle coarticulated?

24. Name and describe the components of four compounded cranial bones in mammals. Which class represents the extreme in the trend toward bone fusion?

25. Trace the evolution of temporal fossae, temporal notches, and postorbital notches.

26. Name the bones contributing to a secondary palate.

27. What is the function of a secondary palate in mammals? Birds? Crocodilians? Of what does it consist in each?

28. Describe the secondary palate as it exists in various vertebrates.

29. What is the evolutionary significance of harelip? Philthrum? Cleft palate?

30. Describe three stages in evolution of attachment of mandibular muscles.

31. What was the initial value of temporal fossae? Their subsequent utilization?

32. Classify all bones of skulls studied in the lab; be able to state for each whether it is a cartilage bone or dermal bone, and to which cranial division and subdivision it belongs.

33. Define the following words, and where possible give examples and state occurrence.

acrochordal cartilage	basioccipital	dermsupraoccipital
alisphenoid	basisphenoid	diapsid
amphistyly	chondrocranium	ectethmoid
anapsid	columella	ectopterygoid
angular	complex bone	ectotympanic
articular	coronoid	endocranium
autopalatine	coronomeckelian	epidermal jaw
autostyly	cranioamphistyly	epiotic
basal plate	dentary	epipterygoid
basicranial fenestra	dermal jaw	ethmoid

ethmoid plate

ethmoturbinal

euamphistyly

euryapsid

exoccipital

fenestra ovalis

foramen magnum

frontal

hamulus

hard palate

hyomandibula

hyostyly

hypophyseal fenestra

incus

infratemporal fossa

interoperculum

interparietal

intertemporal

jugal

lacrimal

laterosphenoid

malar

malleus

mandibular arch

mastoid

maxilla

maxilloturbinal

Meckel's cartilage

mediomeckelian

mentomeckelian

mesethmoid

metapterygoid

nasal

nasoturbinal

neurocranium

neurocranium proper

operculum

opisthotic

orbitosphenoid

osteocranium

palate

palatine

palatoquadrate
    cartilage

paleostyly

palpebral

parachordal

parapsid

parasphenoid

parietal

periotic

petromastoid

petrous

philthrum

platytrabic

pleurosphenoid

postfrontal

postorbital

postparietal

postsplenial

prearticular

prechordal

prefrontal

premaxilla

preoperculum

presphenoid

prevomer

primary palate

prootic

pterotic

pterygoid

quadrate

quadratojugal

retroarticular

scleroid bone

secondary palate

sella turcica

septomaxilla

soft palate

sphenoid

sphenotic

splenial

squamosal

stapes

suboperculum

supraoccipital

suprapterygoid

supratemporal

supratemporal fossa

surangular

suspensorium

symplectic

synapsid

synotic tectum

tabular

temporal

temporal fossa

temporal notch

trabecula communis

trabeculae

trabecular cornua

tropitrabic

tympanum

turbinate bone

visceral jaw

vomer

Weberian ossicles

Wormian bone

9

MUSCULAR SYSTEM

MOST PARTS of the vertebrate body lend themselves rather well to an evolutionary analysis. Homologies are for the most part adequately clear. When doubts of homology exist, we know that generally a few more facts will make the true course of evolution apparent.

Such is not the case for the muscular system. With a very few exceptions it is impossible to follow homologies through even the members of a single class. In comparisons of members of two or more classes, only the crudest sort of homology can be recognized. The factors that make this so are discussed at the end of this chapter.

In the absence of a satisfactory means for tracing individual muscle homologies, we must perforce turn our attention to the grouping (classification) of muscles, for in most cases only groups of muscles can be traced from one class to another. Embryonic origin is of prime importance in grouping muscles, and thus we delve more than usual into embryological facts in studying muscles.

A certain amount of descriptive anatomy must be known before the grouping (classification) of muscles may be effectively studied. A part of the essential knowledge of muscles is ordinarily secured in elementary zoology courses. This will not be repeated here. The student should be certain, however, that he is familiar with this basic information before going on, even if it is necessary to return to an elementary text for review. Essential basic facts are: (1) the role of the muscular system in bodily functions; (2) the microscopic structure of muscle fibers; (3) the three main types of muscle tissue, and (4) their anatomical and (5) physiological differences.

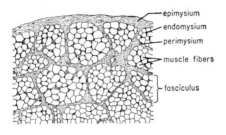

FIG. 9.1 Organization of muscle fibers and their enveloping connective tissue sheaths as seen in cross section of a small part of a voluntary muscle. (From Bailey.)

Our own description shall start with the gross anatomy of skeletal muscle, with which we are chiefly concerned. Evolution of smooth and cardiac muscle—as muscle—has little interest within the vertebrates. We study the evolution of the heart as a whole with the circulatory system; and as the heart goes, so goes cardiac muscle tissue. The same thing may be said of smooth muscle: as the organs with which it is concerned evolve, so evolves the muscle. Thus as we study the digestive system, or circulatory system, we, in effect, follow a part of the evolution of smooth muscle. Skeletal muscle tissue, on the contrary, comprises organs that are the muscles themselves. Muscles, as distinct organs, do not hinge directly upon other organs in their evolution. They can be and are traced in evolution as structures and groups of structures quite apart from other structures. To be sure, all parts of the body are interrelated and no one part changes without compensatory alterations occurring in others to some degree; but the point is that voluntary muscles are organs and are just as independent as any other organs of the body, whereas smooth muscle tissue is found exclusively as part of the tissue of various organs that are otherwise nonmuscular.

Internal Anatomy of Voluntary Muscle

Each voluntary muscle consists of many fibers, the number differing according to the size of the muscle. Regardless of muscle size, the fibers are organized in bundles of 20 to 30 fibers, called *fasciculi* (Fig. 9.1). These fasciculi are of about the diameter of a slender pin and, when the overlying fascia of a muscle are removed, are clearly evident to the naked eye. These are the strands the direction of which gives a clue to the limits of adjacent muscles in gross dissection. Each fasciculus is encased by a connective tissue sheath called the *perimysium*. Within the bundles, each fiber is surrounded by a very thin layer of connective tissue, the *endomysium*. An *epimysium* covers the entire muscle or division thereof.

Thus were all muscle tissue removed from a muscle, the connective tissue would perfectly reproduce its form, even to the detail of external form of each individual fiber. Connective tissue extends throughout the body from the skin to the innermost parts, and voluntary muscle is no exception.

External Anatomy of Voluntary Muscle

A muscle commonly consists of a (1) *belly,* or *gaster,* to which muscle fibers are limited, and on either end of the belly a (2) *tendon* consisting solely of a tough connective tissue by means of which the muscle is attached (Fig. 9.2). Contraction of the muscle exerts an equal pull upon each attachment.

Not all muscles have attachments effected by the cordlike tendons characteristic of most of them. A tendon may be absent, either because the fasciculi are attached directly (as, for example, to the epimysium of another muscle, or to the periosteum of a bone), or because the fasciculi terminate in sheets of connective tissue (fascia) not specially modified for reception of a muscular force (as, for example, on the subcutaneous fascia). Furthermore, the tendon may be so expansive as to constitute a membrane, distinctive by its function chiefly as a conductor of muscular force. Such membranelike tendons are *aponeuroses.*

The bellies of muscles likewise differ greatly in form. Many are spindle-shaped, continuous into cordlike tendons, but others are spread sheetlike over considerable expanses, and frequently are attached at one end to an aponeurosis. These are *panniculate* muscles (Fig. 9.4). Most muscles consist of a single belly (*monogastric*), but some consist of two bellies (*digastric*) (Fig. 9.3), others of still more numerous bellies (*polygastric*) (Fig. 9.4). Each gaster, if more than one is present, is separated from the next by a complete, very narrow partition of connective tissue called a *tendinous inscription*. It should be emphasized that subdivision of a muscle into any number of components lying *side by side* (and thus with multiple heads or slips) does not mean that the muscle is polygastric; many

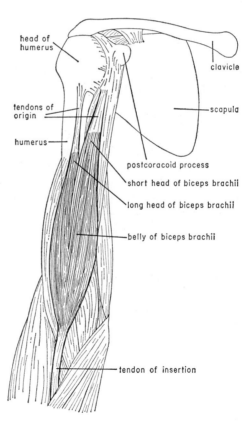

head of humerus

clavicle

tendons of origin

scapula

humerus

postcoracoid process

short head of biceps brachii

long head of biceps brachii

belly of biceps brachii

tendon of insertion

FIG. 9.2 A monogastric muscle: biceps brachii of man. (From Quain.)

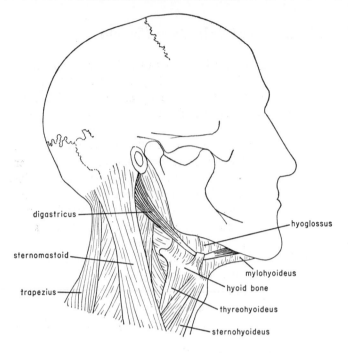

digastricus

hyoglossus

sternomastoid

mylohyoideus

hyoid bone

trapezius

thyreohyoideus

sternohyoideus

FIG. 9.3 A digastric muscle: digastricus of man. (From Quain.)

monogastric muscles are thus subdivided. Such muscles are designated as *complex* (Fig. 9.5). Only when the fasciculi are interrupted at a single plane along their lengths is the muscle regarded as consisting of more than one belly.

Tendinous inscriptions (Fig. 9.4) are of special interest as representing hypertrophied myosepta. Primitively all voluntary muscles were segmentally divided, the fibers being no more than one segment in length. In modern tetrapods most muscles have become differentiated and modified in part by fusion of segmental fibers and loss of the myosepta. The retention of myosepta by any muscle is thus a primitive characteristic. The rectus abdominis and most of the epaxial muscles may for this reason be regarded as the least modified of all the muscles of the mammalian body.

Actions of Voluntary Muscles

The two points or areas of attachment of any voluntary muscle are known as the *origin* and the *insertion*. The end of the muscle toward the origin is the *head;* the end toward the insertion may be subdivided as a number of *slips,* although the terms are frequently used interchangeably. In the performance of any given function the origin is the fixed end and the insertion is the moving end. Rarely does a muscle have a single function.

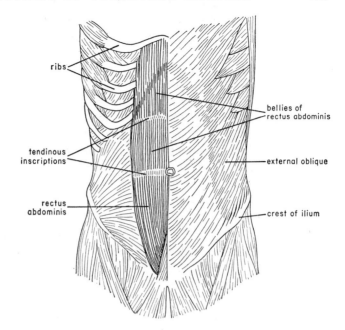

ribs

bellies of
rectus abdominis

tendinous
inscriptions

external oblique

rectus
abdominis

crest of ilium

FIG. 9.4 A polygastric muscle: rectus abdominis of man; and a
panniculate muscle: external oblique of man. External oblique removed to expose rectus abdominis
on left side of figure. (From Quain.)

FIG. 9.5 A complex muscle: serratus
ventralis (= serratus magnus) of
man. (From Quain.)

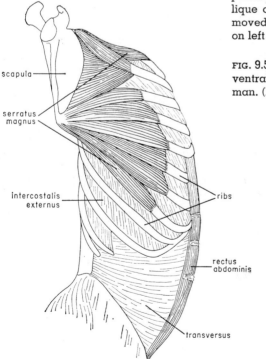

scapula

serratus
magnus

intercostalis
externus

ribs

rectus
abdominis

transversus

It usually has a principle or *primary function,* and the origin and insertion are usually specified upon the basis of that function. Most muscles have a number of *secondary functions,* in which they act as a *synergist* in support of the function of some other muscle or group of muscles. In some synergic functions the origin and insertion of a muscle may be reversed as compared with orientation in performance of the primary action. For instance the geniohyoid of mammals serves chiefly to move the larynx forward, thus having its origin on the mandibular symphysis and insertion on the hyoid bar (which in turn is bound to the larynx). It may also, however, be synergic with the digastric in depression of the lower jaw, in which action the origin is the hyoid and the insertion the mandibular symphysis.

Muscles are capable of exerting force only in contraction. They cannot extend themselves. Thus muscles perforce are arranged almost without exception in opposing (*antagonistic*) groups performing opposite functions. The functioning members (*agonists*) always are opposed by passive members (*antagonists*). Often both members of an antagonistic pair contract at once, although to a different extent for each, thus producing controlled (coordinated) movements. Only rarely do both exert maximal contraction, and when they do the result is often a broken bone, for simultaneous maximal contraction of all members of an antagonistic group can exert a greater force than the skeleton is adapted to withstand (see Appendicular Skeleton, p. 187).

Commonly recognized antagonistic functions include *sphincters,* which constrict openings, and *dilators,* which enlarge them; *retractors,* which retract the base of some structure (as, for example, the sternohyoid, which retracts the tongue), and *protractors,* which extend the base of some structure (as for example the geniohyoid, which protrudes the tongue); *levators,* which raise a part in reference to another (as the masseter and temporal muscles, which close the jaws by raising the lower), and *depressors,* which lower a part in reference to another (as, for example, the digastric, which lowers the lower jaw); *abductors* (a special kind of levator), moving appendages away from the ventral surface, and *adductors* (a special kind of depressor) moving them toward the ventral surface; *extensors,* derived from the dorsal muscle mass of an appendage and usually extending (straightening) an appendage or part thereof, and *flexors,* derived from the ventral muscle mass of an appendage and usually flexing (bending) an appendage or part thereof; and *supinators,* which turn the dorsal surface of the distal part of a limb posteriorly, and *pronators,* turning the dorsal surface anteriorly.

Naming of Muscles

Although the variety of names given to muscles may suggest that there is little system involved, actually the selection is guided by established and reasonable policies.

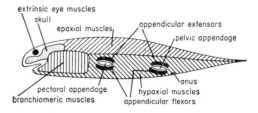

FIG. 9.6 Arrangement of voluntary muscles in primitive vertebrates, diagrammatic.

Most commonly muscles are named (1) by a combination of *origin and insertion* (for example, sternohyoid) as determined by the primary function, the origin invariably being given first. Thus in at least a gross way the attachments of a muscle may actually be given in the name. They are also named (2) upon the basis of *function*—for example, flexor and extensor (digitorum longus); (3) *position*—internal (oblique), external (intercostals), pectoralis (major), (transversus) abdominis; (4) *shape*—deltoid, trapezius, teres; (5) *direction of fibers*—rectus (abdominis), (external) oblique, transversus (abdominis); (6) *size*—vastus (lateralis), (pectoralis) major, (gluteus) maximus; (7) *structure*—biceps (brachii), quadriceps (femoris), digastric; and (8) *fancied resemblances* (lumbricales).

The Musculature of Primitive Gnathostomes

In the most primitive vertebrates with paired appendages the body musculature is extremely generalized, with relatively little differentiation of small muscles of specialized function (Fig. 9.6). The voluntary musculature can readily be summarized as follows: (1) a generalized trunk mass, in the body wall, with a subdivision only into epaxial and hypaxial masses; (2) limitation of fibers of the axial musculature to one segment, the fibers extending longitudinally only the distance between adjacent myosepta; (3) the paired appendages, each provided with a generalized, undifferentiated, dorsal muscle mass and a similar ventral mass; (4) a set of branchiomeric muscles, limited to the visceral skeleton of the pharynx; and (5) a set of extrinsic eye muscles.

The five groups indicated are to be found in all modern vertebrates, usually with much more complex subdivisions.

Methods of Later Modification

Transformation of the highly specialized musculature of higher tetrapods has come about by a number of processes. All trunk muscles are characterized by (1) *fusion* of myotomes, so that a single muscle may extend over the length of many segments. Concomitantly (2) a *splitting* into superimposed layers has been the rule; the thoracic and abdominal hypaxial muscles of mammals are an excellent example. Furthermore, (3) through *expansion* some muscles, primitively of limited size, subsequently cover a considerable area (as, for example, the platysma, derived from the inconspicuous and small sphincter colli of primitive amphibians; or the large mammalian trapezius, derived from the relatively small piscine gill levators). Some (4) by *shifting* have been greatly altered in position (diaphragm muscles from neck hypaxial muscles; the temporalis from the angles of the visceral jaws). Appendicular muscles have undergone (5) extensive *multiplication or fusion of attachments,* in accordance with the multiplication or reduction in number of digits. Finally, (6) by *subdivision* many muscles develop two or more sections, in turn often as distinct from each other as are muscles that are commonly recognized as separate structures (for example, subdivisions of the pectoralis major and minor or of the serratus dorsalis, commonly present among mammals).

Basic Conformation of Axial Musculature

The postpharyngeal trunk region in all vertebrates is markedly different in basic muscular structure from the craniopharyngeal region. The former is the simpler and perhaps more basic, and may be discussed first.

The Postpharyngeal Trunk Region. Three myogenic (muscle-forming) areas occur in this region. The splanchnic wall of the hypomere gives rise to the smooth muscle of the alimentary tract and certain large blood vessels, and to cardiac muscle: all of involuntary muscle. No muscle is formed from the parietal hypomeric wall.

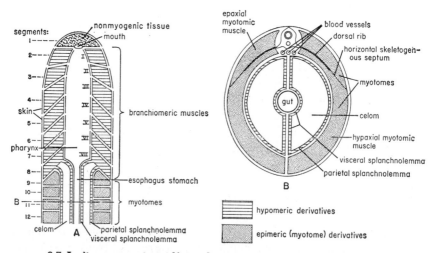

FIG. 9.7 A, diagrammatic midfrontal section of an adult hypothetical primitive vertebrate, showing arrangement of voluntary muscles. B, same, cross section through trunk at level of dashed line shown in Fig. A.

The bulk of the body wall musculature forms from the myotomes. Other muscle tissue is formed from the dermatome (in mammals, the arrectores pilorum, moving the hair). The myotomic muscle is primitively (and embryonically) segmented, whereas the dermatomic and hypomeric muscle, of the trunk, is not. The relative positions of these parts are indicated diagrammatically in Figure 9.7.

The Craniopharyngeal Region. The number of segments comprising the head and pharynx varies considerably in vertebrates. Adult modifications and to a lesser extent embryonic modifications are so extensive that the actual number of segments incorporated into the craniopharyngeal region, in the course of evolution of a given vertebrate, is difficult to determine. It is believed, however, that the basic number in gnathostomes is eight (Fig. 9.8). The identities of the derivatives of the first three (*antotic*) segments is well established for all vertebrates; they are homologous throughout. The two *otic* segments (fourth and fifth) are likewise rather constant. The greatest variation concerns the *metotic* segments, which vary from none to ten in living vertebrates. Three (sixth, seventh, eighth) are thought to be basic in vertebrates. The skull itself typically terminates with the fifth segment in anamniotes (leaving typically three postcranial pharyngeal segments), with the seventh segment (leaving typically one postcranial pharyngeal segment) in amniotes. All our consideration of muscle derivatives will be based upon the hypothetical prototypic cranial segmentation.

In the craniopharyngeal area the most conspicuous contrast with the trunk region is the substitution of hypomeric muscle for the myotomic body wall muscles. No celom extends into the pharyngeal region. The hypomere there remains solid, rather than forming thin walls about a central cavity. The hypomere becomes very thick walled, as a matter of fact, and gives rise chiefly to *branchiomeric* muscles, indistinguishable from skeletal muscle save by embryonic origin and innervation. The innermost hypomeric wall gives rise to involuntary muscle, contributing to the pharynx wall lining, but the greatest thickness of the hypomere is concerned with formation of the branchiomeres.

Segmentation of the pharyngeal hypomere is not considered homologous with segmentation in the trunk elsewhere, and rightfully so, because the segmented materials are not the same in the two cases. The hypomeric pharyngeal segmentation is *branchiomerism;* the myotomic segmentation, *metamerism.*

The branchiomeres extend almost or quite completely around the pharynx ventrally, but do not meet middorsally, where either the cranium or axial musculature interrupts the branchiomeres. The first segment of the head lacks a branchiomere (Figs. 9.9, 9.13); the first branchiomere really lies in the second segment. Care should be taken to observe that the branchiomeric number for any given segment is one less than the segmental number.

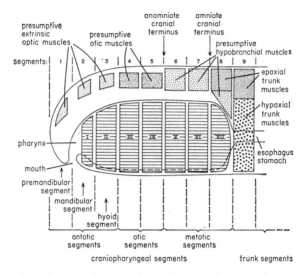

FIG. 9.8 Diagrammatic phantom lateral view of craniopharyngeal segments, showing embryonic relationships of myogenic components. Contrast with Fig. 9.9.

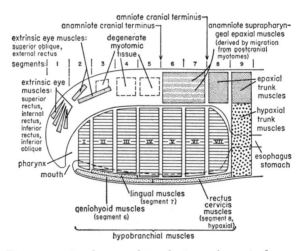

FIG. 9.9 Diagrammatic phantom lateral view of craniopharyngeal segments, showing adult relationships of myogenic components. Modifications from Fig. 9.8 of embryonic stage include (1) shift of hypobranchial muscles; (2) loss of all myotomic tissue in segments 4 and 5, and the dorsal part of that in segment 3; (3) division of eye muscles; and (4) in anamniotes only, migration forward of the trunk epaxial muscles to reach the rear of the skull.

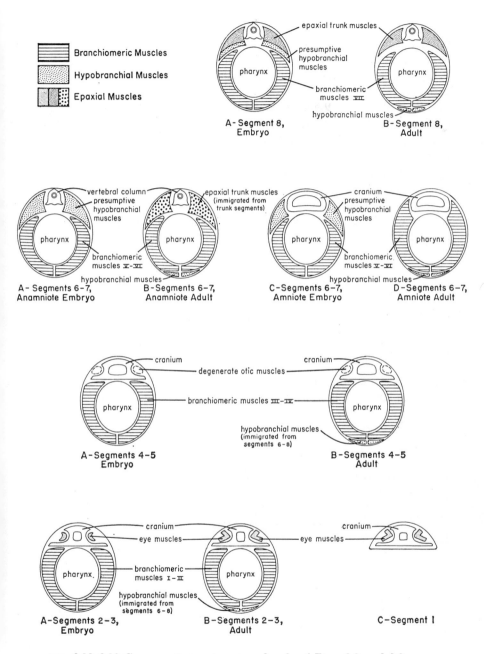

FIG. 9.10–9.13 Cross sections at various levels of Figs. 9.8 and 9.9, contrasting amniote and anamniote, embryonic and adult conditions, in different segments.

Although the lateral pharyngeal musculature is exclusively branchiomeric, myotomic muscle does form in most of the craniopharyngeal segments. The myotomes of the first three segments form eye muscles exclusively (Figs. 9.8, 9.9, 9.13). In the fourth and fifth segments the myotomes
either do not appear or else give rise to connective tissue (Figs. 9.8, 9.9,
9.12). These segments correspond with the bulbous otic region of the
cranium.

The sixth and seventh myotomes give rise exclusively to hypobranchial muscles in most vertebrates (also to epibranchial muscles in elasmobranchs) (Figs. 9.8, 9, 11). These thus move bodily in embryonic development from a dorsal to a ventral position below the pharynx. The ventral
half of segment eight likewise contributes to the hypobranchial musculature, migrating ventrally with myotomes six and seven. The dorsal half of
segment eight (Figs. 9.8, 9.9, 9.10) gives rise to axial muscles identical
with those of the trunk. The accompanying diagrams illustrate the basic
components and their changes in each segment (Figs. 9.8 through 9.13).

Classification of Muscles

The following classification concerns muscles as seen, and as situated,
in adult animals. The embryonic source is a very helpful guide in grouping
them, but not an exclusive one since so many types are differentiated from
essentially single, gross embryonic sources. Embryonic source of any muscle, regardless of the adult group in which that muscle may be placed,
should be known, but care should be taken not to be misled into erroneous

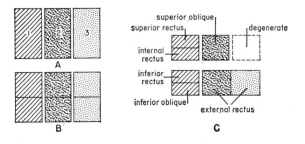

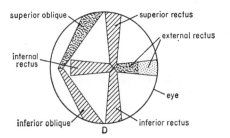

FIG. 9.14 Embryonic origin of the
eye muscles, in successive stages
A-D. Each myotome and derivatives
thereof is shaded distinctly and
consistently throughout. D represents a medial view of the right
eye and its attached muscles removed from the orbit.

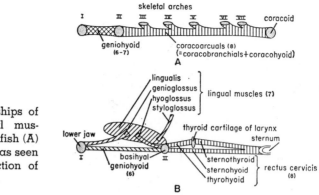

FIG. 9.15 Relationships of the hypobranchial muscles in a primitive fish (A) and a mammal (B) as seen in midsagittal section of ventral body wall.

definitive grouping because of the embryonic source. Ten definitive groups of muscles may be recognized: (1) intrinsic eye muscles; (2) extrinsic eye muscles; (3) hypobranchial muscles; (4) axial branchiomeric muscles; (5) epaxial trunk muscles; (6) hypaxial trunk muscles; (7) appendicular muscles; (8) integumentary muscles; (9) visceral muscles; and (10) electric organs.

Intrinsic Eye Muscles. There are two sets of intrinsic eye muscles: (1) the *iris* muscles, lying within the iris and consisting of both dilator and constrictor fibers that control the diameter of the pupil; and (2) the *ciliary* muscles that, being attached to and controlling the shape or position of the lens, focus the eye. Both are involuntary and consist of smooth fibers only. The iris muscle is unique, being the only muscle of the body formed from ectoderm; all others develop from mesoderm. The ciliary muscle is derived from mesenchyme of indeterminate source.

Extrinsic Eye Muscles. The anterior three craniopharyngeal myotomes give rise only to the extrinsic eye muscles (Fig. 9.14). The first myotome forms four eye muscles (*superior rectus, internal rectus, inferior rectus,* and *inferior oblique,* in order from dorsal to ventral surface). The second myotome forms one and one half muscles (*superior oblique* from dorsal half, part of *external rectus* from lower half). The third myotome forms only the remainder of the external rectus, the dorsal half of the myotome degenerating into connective tissue. All these muscles are constant in all vertebrates, with the exception of those with degenerate vision. A few other extrinsic eye muscles are of scattered occurrence in limited groups of vertebrates.

Hypobranchial Muscles. This group is formed from segments six, seven, and the ventral half of myotome eight (Fig. 9.15). From the sixth myotome is formed the *geniohyoid* muscle, extending from the mandibular symphysis to the basihyal cartilage or equivalent thereof. This muscle is present in most vertebrates. From segment seven is derived the tongue musculature in tetrapods; in fishes it contributes to the geniohyoids. The tongue musculature includes the *genioglossus, styloglossus,* and *hyoglossus*

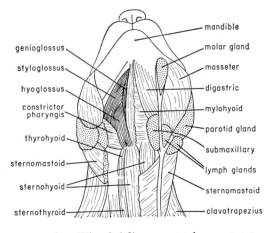

genioglossus
styloglossus
hyoglossus
constrictor pharyngis
thyrohyoid
sternomastoid
sternohyoid
sternothyroid

mandible
molar gland
masseter
digastric
mylohyoid
parotid gland
submaxillary
lymph glands
sternomastoid
clavotrapezius

FIG. 9.16 The extrinsic tongue muscles of the cat: genioglossus, styloglossus, hyoglossus. (From Hyman.)

muscles (Fig. 9.16), present in most tetrapods; and the *lingualis* muscle, which is unique to mammals and forms the bulk of the tongue. From segment eight form, in fishes, the *coracoarcuals,* extending forward from the pectoral girdle (coracoid bar) to the anterior level of the pharynx. In tetrapods the coracoarcuals are little modified primitively from the piscine condition, but in reference to their continuity with the rectus abdominis, they are termed the *rectus cervicis.* The rectus abdominis, rectus cervicis, and geniohyoid, in order from rear to front, thus form a more or less continuous belt of longitudinal muscle fibers on the ventral body surface. In different tetrapods the rectus cervicis is differently modified and the differentiated parts are given distinctive names in each group. In mammals it is split (or partially so) into the *sternohyoid, sternothyroid,* and *thyrohyoid* muscles.

Axial Branchiomeric Muscles. Two groups of muscles are derived from the hypomere: (a) the *visceral* muscles, and (b) the *branchiomeric* muscles. The former are derived from the visceral wall of the hypomere, and the latter are sometimes regarded as having been derived from the parietal wall. Actually there is little real evidence that even in evolution the branchiomeric muscles have developed exclusively from the parietal wall. It is perhaps best to follow embryological evidence, which points toward absence of any differentiation whatsoever between parietal and splanchnic walls in the pharyngeal region. It is, nevertheless, true that the innermost cells of the hypomere in the pharyngeal region, as well as elsewhere, give rise to smooth, involuntary muscle.

The branchiomeric muscles are all voluntary and composed of striated skeletal muscle tissue. These muscles probably first appeared, as such, in early vertebrates or late protochordates, with loss of the atrium and assumption of a chiefly respiratory rather than chiefly alimentary function by the pharynx. They are segmented embryonically in all vertebrates, in adults of all fishes, and in some amphibians. The segmented condition is thus clearly primitive. Furthermore, the complicated operation of the elaborate gill apparatus in primitive vertebrates (fishes) is reflected in

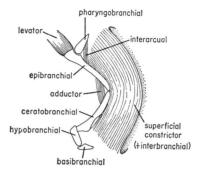

FIG. 9.17 A single gill arch musculature in a shark. (From Romer.)

subdivision of each branchiomere into parts serving specialized functions (Fig. 9.17). These parts, represented in each branchiomere, include (a) *dorsal constrictors* (dorsal to the level of the gill slits) and (b) *ventral constrictors* (ventral to the level of the gill slits), which surround the pharynx and serve to compress it; (c) the *levators,* attached to the dorsal ends of the skeletal arches, which elevate the gills, operating in conjunction with the constrictors to effect a compression of the pharynx; (d) *adductors,* which bend each arch at the middle on each side, drawing dorsal and ventral halves forward and together; (e) *interarcuals,* which similarly bend the upper ends of the skeletal arches backwards; and (f) a variety of less constant components, such as subarcuals of teleosts, coracobranchials of elasmobranchs, etc. The first four components named are the most constant in occurrence throughout fishes.

In amniotes, as we have already seen, the pharynx has lost its respiratory function, and with it the need for a complex gill skeleton with its associated musculature. Both have been utilized for other functions, often very far afield from the original respiratory one. The mandibular skeletal arch has been modified to serve as jaws or as the framework about which jaws are formed, and its branchiomere (the first) naturally operates the parts of that arch; the mandibular branchiomere thus differentiates in mammals as the *temporal, masseter,* and *pterygoid* muscles (all from the adductor series), as well as the *mylohyoid* and *anterior belly of the digastric* (from the ventral constrictor series).

The second or hyoid branchiomere is represented in mammals by the *stapedius* (from the levator series), and by the *posterior belly of the digastric* and the *stylohyoid* (from the ventral constrictor series). The digastric muscle is unique to mammals; and in other vertebrates its anterior belly is represented by part of the intermandibularis, the posterior belly by the interhyoideus. The analog in other amniotes, serving to depress the lower jaw, is the *depressor mandibulae,* also derived from the second branchiomere, but not represented by a homolog in mammals.

Another important derivative of the constrictor series of the second branchiomere is the *sphincter colli,* first evident in amphibians. This becomes an integumentary muscle in reptiles, and that association persists in all reptilian derivatives, including birds and mammals. Thus in amniotes the sphincter colli and its derivatives (including the *platysma*) cannot be listed as an *axial* branchiomeric muscle, since they belong with the *integumentary* group; nevertheless the embryonic and phylogenetic origin should be known.

From the third branchiomere in mammals the *stylopharyngeus* muscle is apparently derived; from the fourth, the *cricoarytenoid* and *thyroarytenoid* muscles; and from the fifth branchiomere, the *cricothyroid* muscle. From the sixth and seventh branchiomeres (levator series) four muscles are derived, only one of which (the *sternomastoid*) remains an axial muscle; the other three (*trapezius, levator scapulae ventralis, cleidomastoid*) belong to the appendicular muscles. The trapezius is represented in tetrapods other than mammals by a small muscle termed the *cucullaris*.

Epaxial Muscles. The epaxial muscles are those muscles posterior to the cranium that lie dorsal to the horizontal skeletogenous septum. Despite a superficial similarity of the subdivisions of some of the myotomes of the anterior seven craniopharyngeal segments to the epaxial-hypaxial subdivision of more posterior myotomes, there is no fundamental similarity. Epaxial and hypaxial divisions are not recognized anterior to the eighth segment.

Since the eighth segment contributes to the epaxial series, epaxial muscles actually are derived not only from the trunk segments but also from a single posterior craniopharyngeal segment. The posterior end of the amniote skull is thus immediately adjacent to the anterior epaxial muscles. The anamniote skull, however, ends at the rear of the fifth segment, and only by migration forward of the eighth and anterior trunk myotomes is a junction of epaxial muscles with the skull effected.

In anamniotes there is relatively little differentiation of the primitive epaxial mass into recognizable groups of muscles; the mass as a whole is referred to as the *dorsalis trunci*. In amniotes generally there is a differentiation into five series named on the basis of origin and insertion of the fibers (Fig. 9.18). In all these series, since neither end of any muscle is actually fixed, the origin is arbitrarily defined as the posterior attachment, and the insertion as the anterior attachment. The *spinotransversalis* series originates on the spinous processes of various vertebrae, and inserts on the transverse processes of *more anterior* vertebrae, or on the skull. The *splenius* of mammals belongs in this series. A second group is the *spinospinalis* system (originating and inserting on spinous processes) lacking in mammals. The *transversotransversalis* system, with fibers originating and inserting on transverse processes, is exemplified in mammals by the *iliocostalis, longissimus,* and the lateral part of the *sacrospinalis*. A fourth group is the *transversospinalis* system, having fibers originating on transverse processes posteriorly and inserting on spinous processes anteriorly; the *semispinalis, multifidis,* and medial part of the *sacrospinalis* belong to this group in mammals. Finally, the *intervertebrals* comprise a group whose fibers extend only between the centra of adjacent vertebrae.

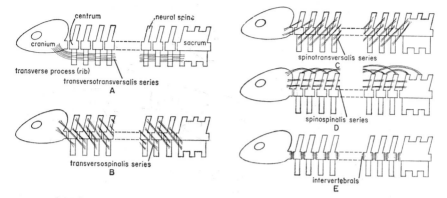

FIG. 9.18 Diagrams of the amniote components of the epaxial division of the trunk muscles, on a schematic axial skeleton, lateral view.

Hypaxial Muscles. The hypaxial muscles are derived only from the trunk myotomes (of segment nine and posterior thereto), and from the tissue lying ventral to the horizontal skeletogenous septum. They fall into three groups.

The *rectus abdominis* group includes the muscle of the same name, and in mammals the *diaphragm* muscle, derived from a few cervical myotomes.

The *flank* muscles include the *external oblique, internal oblique,* and *transverse* series. In the abdomen these three are represented in most tetrapods, including mammals, by muscles bearing the same name (some are subdivided into two layers in some reptiles). In the chest region the external oblique sheet becomes subdivided to form the *scalenes, serratus dorsalis, transversus costarum,* and *external intercostals;* the internal oblique sheet is represented by the *internal intercostals;* and the transverse sheet is represented by the *subcostal* muscles (or *transversus thoracis*).

Finally, the third hypaxial group is the *subvertebrals,* which are attached to the ventral surfaces of the transverse processes of the vertebrae (therefore below the horizontal skeletogenous septum, which corresponds in position with the transverse processes). An example of the subvertebrals is the *longus colli.*

Appendicular Muscles. Appendicular muscles generally are defined as any extending from body wall to the paired appendages or girdles (*extrinsic*), or extending from one part of the appendicular skeleton (including girdles) to another (*intrinsic*) (Fig. 9.19).

There are two main groups of appendicular muscles. They differ both in embryonic (Fig. 9.20) and in phylogenetic origin. The *primary appendicular* muscles are derived embryonically from undifferentiated dorsal and ventral masses of mesenchyme (called *blastemata*) in the appendage buds. In amniotes this mesenchyme is not of determinable source, but in some anamniotes it is clearly derived by slips that separate off from the ventral ends of the trunk myotomes as they grow ventrad toward the me-

FIG. 9.19 Schematic representation of certain types of
extrinsic (A) and intrinsic (B)
appendicular muscles. A: 1,
rhomboideus; 2, rhomboi-
deus capitis; 3, pectorals; 4,
ischiocaudalis; 5, caudofem-
oralis. B: 1, biceps brachii;
2, flexor carpi ulnaris; 3,
gracilis; 4, gastrocnemius; 5,
peroneus.

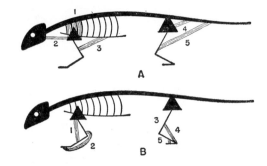

dian ventral line. Thus phylogenetically the primary appendicular muscles
can at least be said to be of myotomic origin. Most muscles differentiating
from the blastemata are intrinsic, although a few are extrinsic; in this respect and in embryogeny the primary appendicular muscles are so distinctive that some authorities accept only these as true appendicular muscles.

The *secondary appendicular* muscles form relatively late in embryonic
development. They are derived from trunk muscles lying adjacent to the
appendages, and thus may be of *epaxial myotomic* origin (for example,
rhomboideus), *hypaxial myotomic* origin (for example, all the *pectoralis*
muscles), or of *branchiomeric* origin (for example, *trapezius*). Most secondary appendicular muscles are extrinsic, but some exceptions occur.

Integumentary Muscles. The integumentary muscles are those having
one or both attachments (origin, insertion) on the skin. We may recognize
two groups: *intrinsic* and *extrinsic integumentary* muscles. Muscles of the
intrinsic type are completely imbedded within the skin, and thus have both

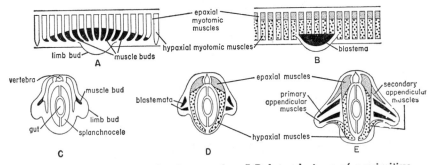

FIG 9.20 Origin of appendicular muscles. A-B, lateral views of a primitive
vertebrate showing two embryonic stages: A, an early stage with muscle
buds forming downward-growing myotomes; B, a later stage, with muscle buds separated from myotomes and fused to form a dorsal blastema
(ventral blastema not shown). C-E, cross sections of primitive vertebrate
embryos: C, early stage, showing delamination of muscle bud; D, later
stage, showing separation of muscle buds from myotomes and their division into dorsal and ventral blastemata; and E, a later stage with formation of secondary as well as primary appendicular muscles. The primary
muscles or their anlagen are shown throughout in black.

origin and insertion in or on the dermis. They are also involuntary, smooth muscles derived from the dermatome itself, not from the myotomes or branchiomeres.

Extrinsic integumentary muscles, on the contrary, have only one attachment—the insertion—on the dermis, the other being on the adjacent axial or appendicular musculature. They are voluntary and striated, and are derived from either myotomic or branchiomeric sources.

The intrinsic group exists only in the endotherms. It consists of microscopically tiny muscles, each associated with a single feather or hair. The hair-moving muscles are the *arrectores pilorum* (Fig. 9.21), and those

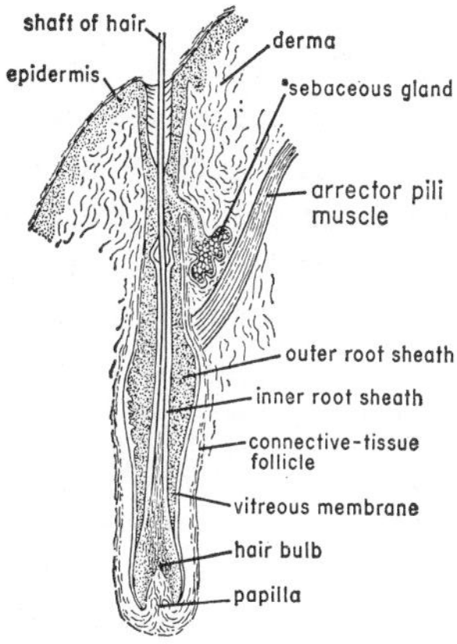

FIG. 9.21 Arrector pili muscle of mammalian skin. (From Bailey.)

moving feathers are the *arrectores plumarum*. Normally, in the relaxed state of these muscles, the feathers or hairs lie almost flat against the skin. Contraction of the muscles "erects" the feathers or hairs, causing them to stand more nearly straight out from the skin. When contracted in man they cause the area immediately surrounding each hair follicle to project slightly above the level of the surrounding skin, producing "goose pimples." The primary survival value of this action is, apparently, to increase the thickness of the insulating dead air space trapped by the feathers or hairs, thus conserving body heat. In most endotherms this constitutes an important means of temperature control, but, of course, in man the function is lost since the hair coat has become too sparse to influence effectively body temperature; nevertheless the mechanism still remains in man in testimony of the existence in his ancestors of a denser coat of hair that did have functional value in temperature control.

The phylogeny of the arrectores is not clearly evident. They possibly evolved in conjunction with the epidermal scales originating in reptiles, since they are present in both classes derived from reptiles but in no other groups. They may well have been essential in ancestral reptiles for moving individual scales to loosen the exuvia in the important process of moulting. In modern reptiles the exuvia is freed by rubbing, by pulling it free with the

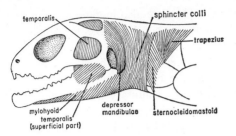

FIG. 9.22 Sphincter colli of a primitive reptile (Sphenodon). (From Romer.)

mouth, or by popping it free as the underlying part—such as the head—is caused to swell slightly by damming the blood in the venous system draining these parts. Sphincter muscles around the entire neck and also in the walls of the jugular veins create the temporary obstruction to normal blood flow. It remains uncertain, however, whether these processes replaced the ancestral arrectores somewhere in the phylogeny of modern reptiles, or were never present in ancestral types. Certainly the arrectores must have been present in at least the reptilian ancestors of both birds and mammals, and it is likely that they were present also in the reptilian ancestors of modern reptiles and were subsequently lost.

All the other integumentary muscles are extrinsic. We may recognize three groups: the *sphincter colli, panniculus carnosus,* and *miscellany.* The most ancient of these, and in fact of all integumentary muscles, is the *sphincter colli,* which first appears as an integumentary muscle in reptiles (Fig. 9.22). It is derived from the interhyoideus muscle of the second branchiomere, and its function originally was perhaps to assist in the moult-

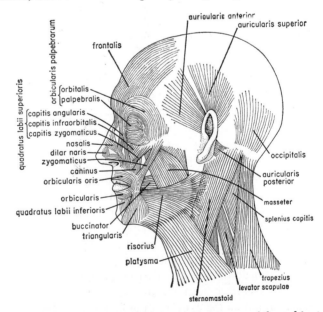

FIG. 9.23 The platysma and other derivatives in man of the sphincter colli. Only the masseter, sternomastoid, levator scapulae and trapezius are shown as muscles not derived from the platysma. (From Quain.)

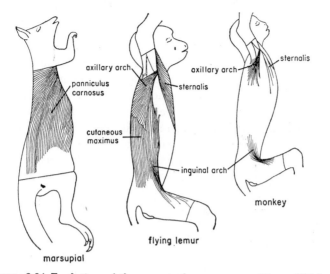

FIG. 9.24 Evolution of the panniculus carnosus. (From Wilder.)

ing process on the head and neck region. The muscle is restricted to the neck region in living reptiles, but has expanded in mammals—where it is known as the *platysma*—to cover much of the head (Fig. 9.23). In mammals it serves as a skin-moving muscle. Because of its extension into the head, the muscle makes possible facial expressions that are totally impossible in other vertebrates. Even in those mammals with a relatively limited range of facial expression such as the cat, the platysma is subdivided into some 10 or 15 muscles. In man, in which facial expression reaches its peak, there are some 26 named subdivisions of the formerly single platysma, in addition to the vestige which retains the latter name.

The panniculus carnosus is apparently unique to mammals and is well developed in the most primitive of all, the monotremes. It is an extraordinarily extensive sheet (Fig. 9.24), restricted in eutherians to an only somewhat less extensive *cutaneus maximus*. This muscle differs from the sphincter colli and derivatives thereof in position, occurring in the thoracic and lumbar regions, and in origin, being derived from the pectoralis minor and latissimus dorsi. The muscle is thus myotomic, not branchiomeric, in origin. Its function is analogous to that of the sphincter colli, moving the skin. In contrast to the sphincter colli, the cutaneus maximus has become degenerate in primates. Vestiges persist only as diaphanous sheets in superficial fascia in the axilla (*axillary arch*), groin (*inguinal arch,* absent in man), and on the ventral surface of the chest (*sternalis,* Fig. 9.25).

Other extrinsic integumentary muscles occur in nonmammalian vertebrates. An example is the small muscles present in some snakes, extending from the ventral ends of the ribs to the large ventral scales that are slowly moved back and forth across the ribs to slide the body forward in a straight line.

Electric Organs. Perhaps the strangest types of structures ever evolved in vertebrates are the electric organs of certain species of fishes. No other vertebrates have ever evolved them. A surprisingly wide variety of fishes, both marine and fresh water, possess electric organs. Included are a number of skates and rays (such as Torpedo and Astroscopus, the stargazer), certain African fishes (mormyrids) and certain South American eels. In almost every case the electric organ has convincingly been demonstrated to have evolved from muscle fibers. In some it appears that the organs have evolved from motor end plates of nerves to certain muscles, the muscles themselves having disappeared. In one case (Malapterurus) the organ has been shown to have formed from a modified gland of some sort; at least it is a motor organ, and the nerve supplying it played a primary role in the specialization of the structure as an electric organ.

The anatomy of the electric organ has been described by Keynes as follows. "The common feature shared by all electric organs is that they are built up from a large number of disclike cells called electroplaxes or *electroplates,* arranged in a more or less orderly fashion so that, in a given species, all face in the same direction, and thus give additive effects. Each electroplate is embedded in a jellylike extracellular material, and enclosed within a compartment of connective tissue. Nerves and blood vessels enter each compartment, and the nerves are distributed to one face of the electroplate, while the blood vessels branch to form a network of capillaries in the jelly layer. The electroplates are single cells, although, like muscle fibers, they are multinucleate, the nuclei generally being located just beneath the two surfaces. The cytoplasm of the electroplates is relatively transparent, so that in all electric fishes the electric organs form clear gelatinous masses which can readily be distinguished from the surrounding muscle." (Fig. 9.26.)

The mode of evolution and transformation of these motor organs into electric organs remains largely obscure. All muscles in all vertebrates receive impulses, at least partly of electric composition, causing contraction. Voluntary muscles are always, furthermore, provided with insulating ma-

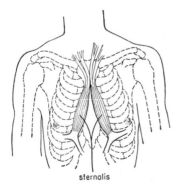

sternalis

FIG. 9.25 A rare atavism in hypertrophy of the sternalis muscle in man. (From Wilder.)

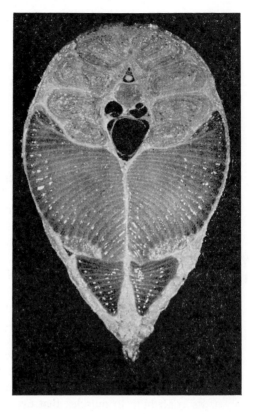

FIG. 9.26 Cross section of the tail of the electric eel, showing the two major divisions of the paired electric organs and the plates (electroplaxes) of which they are composed. (From Keynes.)

terial about each fiber, in the form of connective tissue. Thus all voluntary muscle is preadapted, in part, to serve as a storage battery of electric energy. It is perhaps strange that an electric defense has not evolved in more animals.

A variety of muscles has been modified as electric organs. The jaw muscles (branchiomere 1) of one species of ray, the eye muscles (epimeric) of another ray, the tail muscles of another, and the epaxial trunk muscles of an eel have been thus modified. The modified tissues are of complex organization, profoundly altered from their original condition (Fig. 9.26). The organ is not well developed in all fishes; in a number of species it is a small, less fully differentiated structure capable of emission of but 1 or 2 volts, whereas in the electric eel 600 volts can be produced. The ray generates the greatest power of all—several amperes at about 250 volts.

The survival values of electric organs are three: offense, in capturing food; defense, in warding off enemies; and direction finding, especially and perhaps solely in the fresh-water varieties. The organs have evolved independently in several groups, seemingly with different functions. Fishes with electric organs also have an ability to detect the presence of and distinguish between conductors and nonconductors; the sense organs involved are not known.

Visceral Muscles. The visceral muscles are those derived from the visceral wall of the hypomere. Without exception they are involuntary, and all except the cardiac muscle are smooth. Included in this group are not only the heart muscle but also the smooth muscle of the gut, of organs derived from the gut, of many blood vessels, and of the organs derived from the mesomere.

The Laws of Myology

As mentioned previously, homologies of muscles are very difficult to determine in comparison of members of different classes, subclasses, and even orders, suborders, or sometimes genera. The difficulty is particularly great in reptiles, amphibians, and fishes, less so in birds, and still less in mammals, but it is a source of at least some uncertainty in every class of vertebrates.

One reason for this difficulty is the fact that neither the position nor size of limbs is fixed. In one group a given range of variation occurs in number of trunk segments (say 45 to 48), and in other groups, even related, quite a different range of variation may occur (say 38 to 40). If the limbs are of approximately the same size in the two groups, the segments contributing to the limbs cannot be the same. The same thing is true of the axial muscles, which are not of the same composition in the two groups. How can such muscles be considered truly homologous? When different segments contribute to muscles that even look alike in two different animals, those muscles are not identical. Their innervation will be as different as their embryogeny.

Not only does the number of trunk segments vary, but the appendages may and do shift in evolution from one position to another, backwards or forwards along the trunk. In some fishes the pelvic girdle is situated actually in front of the pectoral girdle. Such shifts result in different embryonic sources for the muscles concerned. Finally, the size of appendage, and with it the number of segments contributing muscles to it, varies even among species of a single genus. The apparently universal ability of trunk myotomes to contribute in their evolution to appendicular musculature may be stated as the *law of uniform appendicular potentiality of axial musculature*.

These and other considerations render all statement of homology of any muscles derived from the trunk myotomes extremely vulnerable to question. This may be regarded the *law of limited homology of muscles*. Phylogenetic homology of muscles, with few exceptions, cannot in the strictest sense be traced through all vertebrates nor even outside the limits of compact groups of related forms (orders, families, or even genera); most so-called homologies are based in reality upon analogy, or partial homology, involving *grossly* (not specifically) (1) similar embryonic source,

(2) similar innervation, (3) similar positions and relationships to other structures, and (4) similar function. The most readily traceable of all muscles are those of the cranial myotomes, and the branchiomeric muscles. Homologies even of some of these are open to question in numerous animal groups.

One of the most useful tools in arriving at the most reasonable approximations of homology is expressed in the *law* of *nerve-muscle relation:* The nerve of a given body segment or of a major division thereof almost invariably continues to supply the muscles derived from that segment (or part) through all their changes. Thus, for example, with few exceptions all derivatives of the hypaxial myotomes, no matter how much modified, are innervated by ventral rami of the spinal nerves, and all derivatives of the epaxial myotomes by the dorsal rami. The blastemata that result from fusion of the appendicular contributions of the myotomes are thus not the block to identification of the source of subsequently differentiating muscles that it might be, because the segment of origin of each part is revealed by innervation.

QUESTIONS

1. How do the three types of muscle tissue differ in their integration as distinct organs in their own right?

2. Describe the organization of voluntary muscles, naming the recognized coverings and subdivisions.

3. What is the evolutionary significance of tendinous inscriptions?

4. Name six agonist functions and the antagonist counterpart of each; cite an example of each.

5. Name eight procedures by which muscles are named, with an example of each.

6. Summarize the basic musculature of a primitive gnathostome.

7. Describe six methods whereby the basic musculature of primitive gnathostomes has been modified to produce the musculature of the later gnathostomes. Give examples of each.

8. State precisely what two main sources of myogenic tissue forms muscles in the craniopharyngeal region of the hypothetical prototypic vertebrate, state to which muscles each group gives rise, and state which segments are represented in each group.

9. What are the segmental limits of the skull in the hypothetical prototypic amniote? Anamniote?

10. To what muscles does ectoderm give rise? Endoderm?

11. Name the ten groups of muscles based upon relationships in adults.

12. Name and differentiate the intrinsic eye muscles.

13. Distinguish extrinsic and intrinsic appendicular muscles. List examples of each type from the cat.

14. How are the two main groups of appendicular muscles differentiated and what is their relation to the intrinsic and extrinsic types?

15. Trace the evolution of each of the two groups of mammalian extrinsic integumentary muscles.

16. How do the two groups of mammalian extrinsic integumentary muscles differ in position and origin? Where does each first appear and as what are they seen in man?

17. What relation do electric organs have to muscles?

18. Name and give the embryonic origin of the extrinsic eye muscles.

19. Name and give the embryonic origin of the mammalian hypobranchial muscles; trace their evolution.

20. How do the epaxial trunk muscles of amniotes and anamniotes differ?

21. What are the amniote divisions of the epaxial trunk muscles? Give examples in mammals.

22. Name the three groups of hypaxial trunk muscles.

23. What muscles of mammals belong to the rectus abdominis group? To the subvertebrals?

24. Name the three series of flank muscles and their representatives in the thoracic and abdominal regions.

25. Name five divisions of the branchiomeric muscles in fishes.

26. Name the mammalian axial and nonaxial branchiomeric muscles and specify the branchiomere from which each has been derived.

27. What name is given the homolog in other amniotes of the mammalian trapezius?

28. Name and explain the three laws of myology.

29. Be able to allocate any muscle dissected in the laboratory to the proper group of the ten here recognized, and be able to specify the myotome, branchiomere, or subgroup to which it belongs or from which it was derived.

30. Define the following words; where appropriate list examples and state origin, classification and occurrence.

abductor	coracoarcual	external intercostals
adductor	craniopharyngeal	external oblique
agonist	segments	external oblique series
antagonist	cricoarytenoid	external rectus
antotic segments	cricothyroid	extrinsic appendicular
aponeurosis	cucullaris	muscles
appendicular muscles	cutaneus maximus	extrinsic eye muscles
arrectores pilorum	depressor	extrinsic integumentary
arrectores plumarum	depressor mandibulae	muscles
axial branchiomeric	diaphragm muscle	fascia
muscle	digastric	fasciculi
axial muscles	dilator	flank muscles
axillary arch	dorsal constrictors	flexor
blastemata	dorsalis trunci	gaster
branchiomeric muscle	ectodermal muscle	genioglossus
branchiomerism	endomysium	geniohyoid
ciliary muscle	epibranchial muscles	head
cleidomastoid	epimysium	hyoglossus
complex muscle	extensor	hypaxial muscles

hypobranchial muscles
iliocostalis
inferior oblique
inferior rectus
inguinal arch
insertion
interarcual
internal intercostals
internal oblique
internal oblique series
internal rectus
intervertebral
intrinsic appendicular
  muscles
intrinsic eye muscles
intrinsic integumentary
  muscles
iris muscle
law of limited muscle
  homology
law of nerve-muscle
  relation
law of uniform appen-
  dicular potentiality
  of axial musculature
levator
levator scapulae
  ventralis
lingualis
longissimus
longus colli
masseter

metamerism
metotic segments
monogastric
multifidis
mylohyoid
myogenic
origin
panniculate
panniculus carnosus
perimysium
platysma
polygastric
postpharyngeal
  segments
primary appendicular
  muscles
primary function
pronator
protractor
psoas
pterygoid muscle
quadratus lumborum
rectus abdominis
rectus cervicis
retractor
sacrospinalis
scalenes
secondary appendicular
  muscles
secondary function
semispinalis
serratus dorsalis
slip

sphincter
sphincter colli
spinospinalis
spinotransversalis
splanchnic muscles
splenius
stapedius
sternalis
sternohyoid
sternomastoid
sternothyroid
styloglossus
stylohyoid
stylopharyngeus
subcostal
subvertebral
superior oblique
superior rectus
supinator
synergist
temporal
tendinous inscription
tendon
thyroarytenoid
thyrohyoid
transverse series
transversospinalis
transversotransversalis
transversus abdominis
transversus thoracis
trapezius
ventral constrictors
visceral muscle

10

SPLANCHNOCELE

THE EARLY HISTORY of the celom, at the prechordate and protochordate levels, is, as true of so many other systems, uncertainly revealed by information now known. Through the vertebrates, however, the evolutionary sequence is rather clear. There are some seven stages through which mammals have passed, and unlike most systems the celom does not exhibit markedly different deviations in other evolutionary lines. The celom thus appears to have been relatively conservative. Its changes, few as they have been, appear very clearly to have been responses to functional needs for success in specific environmental situations. The chief factor involved throughout its evolution *in the vertebrates* seems to have been the provision of a certain amount of physical freedom from bonds of connective

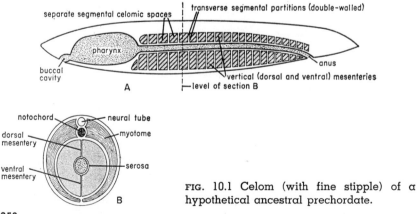

FIG. 10.1 Celom (with fine stipple) of a hypothetical ancestral prechordate.

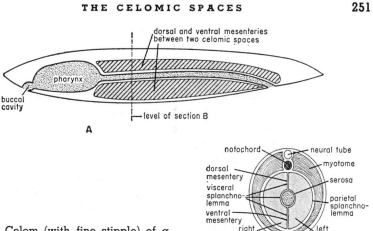

FIG. 10.2 Celom (with fine stipple) of a hypothetical ancestral protochordate.

tissue that would otherwise be present between internal organs that must move considerably in performance of their functions. Every new major set of mobile internal organs is provided, more or less from the time of its earliest appearance, with a celomic compartment for its operations. Alterations in conjunction with the excretory and reproductive functions seem to have been restricted largely to prevertebrate stages of evolution.

The Celomic Spaces

The Hypothetical Ancestral Prechordate Stage. The ancestral prechordate is thought to have possessed segmental, paired celomic cavities (Fig. 10.1). This would be a condition much like that of living annelids. Some evidence suggests on the other hand that vertebrates were derived from nonsegmented ancestors. The true course of this phase of our ancestry will likely never be unequivocably established. The belief in the segmental mode of origin is most widely held at the present time and integrates well with beliefs concerning the early stages of other systems (especially of the kidneys).

The Hypothetical Ancestral Protochordate Stage. The segmental partitions are lost in this stage, thus reducing the number of celomic spaces to a single pair, one on either side of the body (Fig. 10.2). A complete dorsal mesentery and a complete ventral mesentery separate the two celomic spaces from each other. There is no separation anteroposteriorly into specialized pericardial or other cavities. This is the complete, undivided, paired *splanchnocele,* which is retained intact in no living vertebrate.

No living protochordate possesses exactly this conformation of the celom, although Amphioxus differs chiefly in the pharyngeal area where an atrium exists. It seems very likely, however, that in very ancient times ancestral protochordates must have possessed the described arrangement. The functional significance of the change seems probably to have been linked with improvement of the excretory and reproductive systems, both of which in early stages of evolution depended upon the celom as a means of conveyance of metabolic wastes and reproductive cells, respectively. Loss of the segmental transverse partitions greatly simplified this role for the celom.

The basic structure of the celom throughout vertebrates is clearly evident in this stage. The walls are the *splanchnolemma,* the spaces the *splanchnocele.* The median walls of the two celomic cavities are the *visceral* walls, as opposed to the *parietal* walls that lie against the lateral, dorsal, and ventral body walls. The visceral walls typically consist of two recognizably different parts: the *serosa* lying against various organs protruding into the celomic spaces, and the *dorsal* and *ventral mesenteries.* Either or both mesenteries may be wholly or partly lost in adults, but both are present embryonically. Rarely are paired mesenteries formed from the parietal walls by protrusion of lateral organs into the celom. With rare exception all organs encased by the celom fail actually to penetrate the interior of the cavity, since a wall of the celom is always pushed in front of any organ forming either between or to one side of the cavities.

The Piscine Stage. In the earliest known vertebrates the pharynx has become chiefly a respiratory organ rather than a food-catching device as in earlier chordates. A chambered heart evolved to provide the necessary force to drive the blood through the branchial capillaries. Situated just in front of the anterior end of the celomic cavity, the tubular heart of ancestral protochordates was in a perfect position to be protected by a forward extension of the celom and thus to surround the chambered heart as it evolved in fishes. This, apparently, is precisely what happened. A *pericardial cavity* appears for the first time on the scene (Fig. 10.3), providing a special chamber in which the rhythmic contractions of the heart can occur unhampered by bonds to other unrelated structures.

A second innovation at the piscine stage is the formation of a *transverse septum* separating the pericardial cavity from the remainder of the splanchnocele. It is double walled as would be expected of a membrane formed by infolding of the parietal walls of the splanchnocele. It is of double utility as a protective posterior wall for the pericardial cavity and as a pathway for veins carrying blood to the heart. In embryogeny it is also a locus for initial formation of the liver, although such a role in phylogeny is doubtful. In later vertebrates the transverse septum is drafted into service in a variety of other roles, chiefly as certain celomic walls as well as the rear wall of the pericardial cavity, which it continues to form throughout vertebrates.

A third piscine innovation is differentiation for the first time of a *pleuroperitoneal cavity,* which is that part of the splanchnocele remaining after separation of the pericardial cavity. The name is somewhat in-

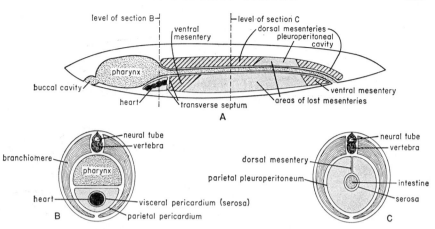

FIG. 10.3 Celom (with fine stipple) at the piscine evolutionary stage.

appropriate in the sense that a large proportion of animals possessing the structure have no lungs (to which "pleural" refers). The pleuroperitoneal cavity is, however, homologous with the separate pleural and peritoneal cavities of later vertebrates and the name is thus acceptable.

A fourth modification is loss in the pleuroperitoneal cavity of a small part of the dorsal mesentery most of which, however, is generally retained nearly or quite intact throughout vertebrates. Definably different sections, even though continuous with each other, have evolved in later vertebrates. The supportive value of this mesentery would seem to be of the utmost importance as evidenced by its preservation throughout vertebrate evolution.

Fifthly, the ventral mesentery of the pleuroperitoneal cavity is extensively reduced, leaving only a relatively small anterior and posterior part. This situation is duplicated in most vertebrates, although in some (for example, salamanders) the ventral mesentery may be nearly complete. Lack of supportive need and derivation of greater freedom of movement for the gut would seem to have been factors involved in loss of the ventral mesentery. A completely different sort of evolution would be expected had primitive vertebrates been of erect posture. The mesenteries provided by the vertebrate ancestors of species that are now of erect posture (as man) are certainly not especially adaptive, even though generally adequate, for the newly acquired stance.

Finally, the pericardial mesentery is wholly lost, being present only embryonically in all vertebrates. The heart, a primitively median structure, is, however, covered by the visceral layer or serosa, specifically referred to here as the *visceral pericardium*. As there are no pericardial mesenteries (with rare vestigial exceptions—for example, the *gubernaculum cordis* of snakes—a slender cord between the apex of the ventricle and the rear pericardial wall), the serosa constitutes the entire visceral pericardium, and the two terms are thus synonymous. The functional advantage in loss

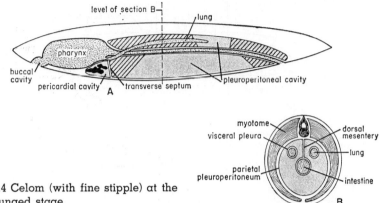

FIG. 10.4 Celom (with fine stipple) at the early lunged stage.

of the pericardial mesenteries is obvious. As is the case for virtually every structure that is wholly or partly encased by the celom, the heart does not lie on the interior of the celomic space within the celomic walls.

Thus in the piscine stage two celomic cavities exist. Two cavities also exist in the ancestral protochordate stage, but the arrangement is totally different in the two stages. The cavities are bilaterally paired in the earlier stage (protochordate), tandem (anteroposterior) to each other in the later stage.

The Early Lunged Stage. Choanichthyan fishes and salamanders exemplify a step toward adaptation to the air-breathing life through which all tetrapods must have passed at one time. The typical fish arrangement exists in these, with the sole modification being the lungs which protrude into the celom from the pharynx (Fig. 10.4). At this stage the lungs, still an adjunct of other respiratory systems (chiefly the gills), are not provided with special celomic chambers.

The Primitive Reptile Stage. In virtually all reptiles and in anurans a special celomic accommodation is made for the lungs, which for the first time in these groups assume a major if not exclusive role in respiration. Several changes actually are involved in the process (Fig. 10.5).

For one, the pharynx becomes greatly reduced in size, due to loss of the bulky gill apparatus. Second, the lungs become larger and capable of considerable expansion and contraction, occupying most of the space formerly used by the pharynx. Third, the anterodorsal part of the celom pushes forward into the area formerly occupied by the pharynx, surrounding the lungs and providing for their free, unrestricted movement. Fourth, two *pleural pouches* are formed in this process. These pouches simply constitute two lobelike projections forward of the pleuroperitoneal cavity; they may be in contact with each other but are not fused medially. The *area* between them is called the *mediastinum*. Fifth, in extension forward of the dorsal anterior part of the celom, the pericardial cavity comes to lie *ventral* instead of anterior to the forepart of the celom. Finally, this forward

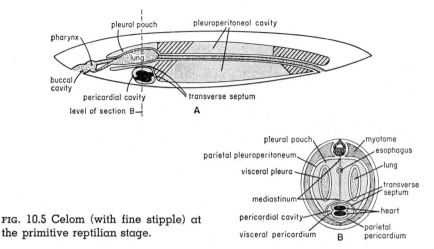

FIG. 10.5 Celom (with fine stipple) at the primitive reptilian stage.

development is accompanied by a partial rotation of the pericardial cavity resulting in assumption of an *oblique position* by the transverse septum. This membrane still bounds the pericardial cavity posteriorly as before, but in this stage it also forms at least a part of the dorsal wall of the pericardial cavity and a part of the ventral walls of the pleural pouches.

The Advanced Reptile Stage. In the higher reptiles (crocodilians and, oddly enough, snakes and some lizards, presumably also therapsids) and in birds the lungs are finally awarded a completely separate set of chambers (Fig. 10.6). The changes hinge upon the formation of a new structure, the *oblique septum.* This is composed in part of a section of the transverse septum (posterior wall of pericardial cavity), but chiefly of a new, double-walled membrane infolded from the dorsal and lateral parietal pleuroperitoneum. The fused structure is the oblique septum.

Second, formation of this septum results in complete isolation of the former pleural pouches as separate *pleural cavities,* whose medial walls are not fused and are separated in part by structures such as the esophagus, blood vessels, and pericardial cavity.

Third, the posterior part of the pleuroperitoneal cavity remaining after isolation of the pleural cavities is now called the *peritoneal cavity.*

Thus in the advanced reptiles as well as in the two classes (birds and mammals) to which their fossil ancestors gave rise, there are four major

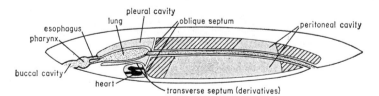
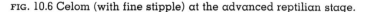

FIG. 10.6 Celom (with fine stipple) at the advanced reptilian stage.

celomic cavities: a pericardial cavity, a peritoneal cavity (in both of which the median mesenteries are partly or wholly reduced to produce a single cavity rather than paired ones), and a pair of pleural cavities. The initial advantage gained by separation of the pleural cavities is not clearly obvious. Subsequently, however, the oblique septum assumes major importance in mammals, supplying a basis for formation of the very important accessory respiratory organ, the diaphragm. But in birds and reptiles the oblique septum is initially nonmuscularized and does not aid in respiration. The initial advantage must simply have been a perfection of isolation of the lungs from the other viscera. This advantage is real, but not overwhelming as is indicated by (1) the very long evolutionary history of vertebrates with open pleural pouches, and (2) the fact that vertebrates with an anomalously incomplete pleural cavity do manage to survive an average lifetime. Even incomplete pericardial walls are not an insuperable handicap. Such animals are, however, undoubtedly more liable to early demise, through fatal irritation in critical periods, than are others. Such a disadvantage soon becomes obvious in competition with better-adapted animals: without such competition even the existence of the defect would receive little attention.

In birds a rather extraordinary subdivision of the pleural and peritoneal cavities occurs. Some ten cavities are more or less separate, corresponding for the most part with the air sacs.

The Mammalian Stage. Three major advances are evident in celomic structure of mammals. First, the oblique septum becomes extensively muscularized, forming the *diaphragm*. This structure is thus enabled to assist actively in respiration, although it is not a wholly indispensable adjunct. Abdominal and thoracic muscles also are important in performance of respiratory movements. There is no equally specialized functional counterpart in birds, which, like most other tetrapods, utilize a variety of devices to introduce air into the lungs. Most important among these are the various septa subdividing the celom; these assist in the mechanical processes of exhalation and inhalation. The diaphragm is an arched, not a flat, partition, with the concavity facing the abdominal viscera. Upon

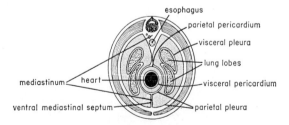

FIG. 10.7 Celom (with fine stipple) at the mammalian stage, as seen in cross section of the thorax at the level of the heart.

contraction it flattens, forcing the abdominal viscera posteriorly and creating a slight thoracic vacuum to which adjustment is made by prompt inflow of air into the enlarging lungs.

A second mammalian alteration is formation of a *ventral mediastinal septum* by means of enlargement of the pleural cavities into the area between the heart and ventral thoracic wall (Fig. 10.7). Two factors seem to be involved in this modification: (1) accommodation for the lungs, which are proportionately larger in mammals than in any other vertebrates, and (2) protection for the pericardial cavity. Mammals have larger lungs than other vertebrates because of their high metabolic rate combined with relatively inefficient lung structure. Birds, with a still higher metabolic rate, have a marvelously efficient forced-draft system requiring only rather small lungs. The mammalian lung is much less efficient, and thus needs a disproportionately large volume to maintain the required metabolic rates.

Protection of the pericardial cavity becomes of importance as the crawling habits of reptilian ancestors are put aside. Most ectothermic tetrapods habitually lift the body but slightly from the ground, and thus the pericardial cavity is in no particularly vulnerable spot. Advanced reptiles as well as birds and mammals raise the body well onto the limbs, thus exposing the ventral surfaces to greater dangers than do the lower tetrapods. Furthermore the flying, jumping, and running habits into which the limb-supporting innovation leads greatly increases the hazards to ventral structures. Enlargement of the pleural cavities to occupy the area between the pericardial cavity and chest wall can scarcely do other than cushion all shocks for the heart.

The third mammalian novelty is the *greater omentum,* another adaptation to the active life of endotherms. It forms as a posteriorly directed pocket in the mesogaster, which is preadapted for this change by the transverse position assumed by the stomach (to which the mesogaster is attached). The initially slight concavity thus eventually becomes greatly enlarged by extensive pocketing posteriorly, covering most of the intestines and lying as a protective pad between the viscera and ventral abdominal wall. Some fat, often in large quantities, is stored in the greater omentum, which thus serves the better for protection, and also for food storage.

If mammals have been faced with the necessity for protection of the ventral surfaces, it would seem that birds also would be faced with the same problems, for their risks are equally great if not greater. Yet birds lack the ventral extensions of the pleural cavities, as well as a protective omentum. The answer seems to be, in part, the greatly enlarged sternum with its thick muscular covering. Immediately above it lies an air sac. These structures could scarcely fail to function as an excellent thoracic protection. The avian analog of the mammalian omentum seems to be simply a specialization of the ventral peritoneal wall itself, which is very tough and serves also for fat storage; both features parallel the functions of the greater omentum.

The Mesenteries

Derivatives of the Dorsal Mesentery. Numerous subdivisions of the dorsal mesentery are commonly recognized. They are distinguished from each other chiefly by the parts to which they are attached. Thus that of the stomach is the *mesogaster;* of the small intestine, the *mesointestine;* of the colon, the *mesocolon;* of the rectum, the *mesorectum,* etc. Due to the convolutions that occur in the digestive tract, folds and fusions likewise occur. Inasmuch as gut variations are numerous, the variations in the mesenteries are nearly equally as great.

The mesogaster is further subdivided, one segment being differentiated as a ligament between the stomach and spleen (*gastrosplenic ligament*). This arrangement follows from the fact that as a general rule the spleen actually forms within the dorsal mesentery. In addition, in mammals, the *greater omentum* becomes differentiated from the mesogaster. Although collapsed and appearing superficially sheetlike, the greater omentum is actually a baglike structure, the two walls of which can with care be separated from each other, and the communication of which with the rest of the peritoneal cavity is often reduced to a narrow opening (foramen of Winslow). The space within the greater omentum is called the "lesser peritoneal pouch" (not a cavity, a term implying equivalence with the four primary cavities of the splanchnocele).

Derivatives of the Ventral Mesentery. The ventral mesentery is very greatly reduced in size. Only a few specialized mesenteries commonly remain. Remnants are the *falciform ligament,* which connects the anterior end of the liver with the midventral wall; the *lesser omentum* or *gastrohepatoduodenal ligament* between stomach-duodenum and liver; and the *median ligament* of the bladder (in mammals).

Derivatives of the Transverse Septum. In mammals the transverse septum forms the (1) dorsal and (2) posterior walls of the pericardial cavity, (3) part of the anterior wall of the peritoneal cavity, (4) part of the ventral walls of the pleural cavities, (5) part of the diaphragm (the central tendon), (6) the mesoderm components of the liver, and some other structures with which we are not directly concerned here.

QUESTIONS

1. What has been the chief factor involved in evolution of the celom throughout the history of vertebrates?

2. What is thought to have been the nature of the celom in chordate ancestors just before chordates appeared on the scene?

3. Diagram and label completely a cross section and a sagittal section through the body of a hypothetical protochordate ancestral to vertebrates showing the arrangement of the celomic spaces relative to gut structures and the recognized parts of the splanchnocele and splanchnolemma.

4. What selective pressures seem to have been responsible for the loss of segmental celomic partitions?

5. Diagram and label a sagittal section through the body of a fish, showing the arrangement of the celomic spaces relative to gut arrangement.

6. Name and give the functional advantages for each of the six advancements of the piscine celomic conformation over the protochordate type.

7. How are lungs accommodated by the celom when they first appear?

8. What celomic adjustments accompany complete loss of the branchial system of respiration? Account for the functional advantage of each.

9. Describe the advanced reptilian transformations of the celom, and the functional advantages of each.

10. Describe the mammalian transformations of the celom, and the functional advantages of each.

11. What analogous substitute is made by birds for each of the mammalian celomic alterations? Explain.

12. Name the derivatives in mammals of the dorsal mesentery; of the ventral mesentery; of the transverse septum.

13. Distinguish fishes, choanichthyans + salamanders, anurans + primitive reptiles, advanced reptiles + birds, and mammals, on the basis of their unique celomic conformation.

14. How many celomic cavities exist in the (a) prechordate, (b) protochordate, (c) piscine, (d) primitive reptilian, (e) crocodilian, (f) avian, and (g) mammalian stages of evolution?

15. Define the following words as given, and where possible state occurrence and give examples.

diaphragm
dorsal mesentery
falciform ligament
foramen of Winslow
gastrohepatoduodenal
   ligament
gastrosplenic ligament
greater omentum
gubernaculum cordis
lesser omentum
lesser peritoneal pouch
mediastinal septum

mediastinum
mesocolon
mesogaster
mesointestine
mesorectum
oblique septum
parietal
   splanchnolemma
pericardial
pericardial cavity
pericardial sac
peritoneal

peritoneal cavity
pleural cavity
pleural pouch
pleuroperitoneal cavity
serosa
splanchnocele
splanchnolemma
transverse septum
ventral mesentery
visceral
   splanchnolemma

11

DIGESTIVE
AND RESPIRATORY
SYSTEMS

THE RELATION OF RESPIRATORY AND DIGESTIVE SYSTEMS. We are accustomed to think of the respiratory system as a discretely modified part of the primordial gut or alimentary tract, and, therefore, as a readily distinguishable and coherent entity. It is true that in most vertebrates respiration is accomplished through either pharyngeal gills or lungs—both gut derivatives. On the other hand, protochordates (at least primitive types) and most living amphibians respire chiefly if not wholly through the integument, and other respiratory organs are utilized in certain groups of amphibians and turtles. The system responsible for respiration is thus not a single entity throughout chordates, nor as such can its evolution be traced. Nevertheless, the respiratory system in chordates is largely limited to parts derived from the gut.

Even though thus limited, the respiratory system is so completely integrated on an anatomical basis with the digestive system as to render the two systems inseparable in any evolutionary account. The most ancient vertebrate respiratory structures, the internal pharyngeal gills, acquired in their long existence in aquatic animals a highly complex structure (Fig. 11.21) reflected in virtually every other system of the body—nervous, circulatory, skeletal, and so on. Adaptation to terrestrial life, with the mandatory air

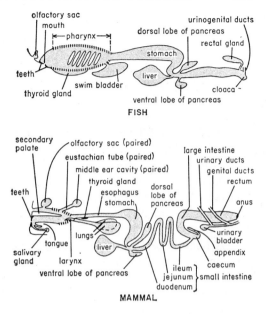

FIG. 11.1 The digestive and respiratory systems of fish and mammal schematically contrasted.

breathing that goes along with it (Fig. 11.1B), meant loss as respiratory accessories of nearly all of these specialized components of the gill system, a respiratory function being retained by only a limited section. Such a complex organization did not degenerate, however, without divergence into other avenues of function. Parts formerly respiratory in function evolved into structures of auditory, endocrine, metabolic, digestive, and other functions. In tetrapods their only common feature is that they are all derived from the gut.

For these reasons we are not segregating the discussions of the digestive and respiratory systems. The functions of respiration and digestion are quite distinct and separate, but our concern here is primarily with anatomy and evolution; and anatomically no segregation of the two systems approaching the dichotomy of the two functions themselves exists in chordate or even in vertebrate phylogeny.

Features of the Generalized Vertebrate Gut. Anteriorly the gut opens to the exterior by a *mouth,* leading into an expanded *buccal cavity. Teeth,* situated on *jaws* that serve to close the mouth and operate the teeth, guard the buccal cavity. A variety of *buccal glands* secrete fluids of various sorts into the buccal cavity and become modified in tetrapods as *salivary* and *mucus* glands. *Taste (gustatory) organs* line parts of the buccal cavity and, in most tetrapods, a *tongue* is usually present to aid in manipulation of food. A *secondary palate,* complete or incomplete, occurs in amniotes (Fig. 11.1).

The buccal cavity is continuous with the *pharynx,* whose limits are defined by the paired *pharyngeal slits* piercing the lateral walls. Typically seven pairs of slits existed in primitive gnathostomes. A ventral evagination of the pharynx, the *thyroid gland,* is present in all vertebrates. The *lungs* and *swim bladder* are also pharyngeal derivatives, but are not present in all vertebrates. *Pharyngeal teeth* exist in some fishes on the gill bars; their development, requiring both ectoderm and mesoderm, is made possible by invasion of the pharyngeal area by oral (stomodaeal) ectoderm.

The pharynx is continuous posteriorly into an *esophagus,* primitively short and little reduced in diameter. In later types it becomes elongate and slender. The esophagus empties into a *stomach,* which may be a single baglike structure as in most mammals, or subdivided into two to four parts.

An *intestine* follows the stomach, emptying into the *cloaca,* a terminal chamber receiving not only fecal materials but also reproductive and urinary products. The cloaca is lost in some fishes and in most mammals, as the opening of the intestinal tract to the exterior is separate from the reproductive and urinary opening, which in some mammals also is divided. The intestine is commonly subdivided into a *large intestine* at the rear, and a *small intestine,* each in turn divisible in some vertebrates into lesser parts.

A number of diverticula from the gut may occur between the esophagus and cloaca. The *liver* (lacking a gut connection in mature cyclostomes) regularly occurs. Most vertebrates also have a *pancreas,* a gland formed by both dorsal and ventral evagination from the gut. A *urinary bladder* is present in most tetrapods, and embryonically a yolk sac and allantoic membranes exist as gut diverticula. *Ceca* may occur at various points, as at the pyloric end of the stomach (fishes, vampire bats), at the cloaca (birds), and at the beginning of the large intestine (*colic* ceca, as of mammals).

Types of Modification. Perfection of digestive processes has required not so much an improvement of chemical processes as an increase in the quantity of secretion and in the length of time of exposure of food materials to the digestive actions of different parts of the alimentary tract. Both alterations were accomplished by increase in surface area. The primitive gut is quite simple, consisting essentially of a straight tube more or less uniform in diameter. Later animals have evolved increased surface area by (1) lengthening of various parts, necessitating some sort of looping or coiling; (2) formation of diverticula or enlargements of various sorts (stomach compartments, crop, liver, pancreas, ceca, etc.); and (3) development of internal folds or projections (as of ridgelike *rugae* in the stomach; *papillae* in the esophagus; a *typhlosole,* spiral valve, and papillalike *villi* in the intestine).

Mouth

At least three clearly distinct mouths seem to have existed in vertebrates and their ancestors. The *primary mouth,* found in all archeostomes, either is a direct transformation of the embryonic blastopore or forms in the same position (Fig. 11.2). Unquestionably the remote ancestors of chordates possessed such a mouth, but in these as well as in all other deuterostomes the blastopore becomes, or lies close to, the anus. A new opening at the opposite end of the alimentary tract serves as the mouth. As stated previously (see Chap. 2) the common ancestry of the advanced, bilaterally symmetrical archeostomes such as annelids or arthropods, and the deuterostomes, is to be sought in radially symmetrical animals (proctostomes) at the earliest stage of invasion of the realm of axial orientation—one group (archeostomes) retaining the oral function of the postembryonic remnant of the blastopore and forming an anus at the opposite end, the other (deuterostomes) retaining the anal function for the blastopore derivative and forming a mouth at the opposite end. It is thus clear that at an early evolutionary stage (proctostomes) the primary mouth is also the primary anus, and that in archeostomes a *secondary anus* instead of a secondary mouth is the new formation. The primary anus is retained in all deuterostomes.

The *secondary mouth,* functional in all deuterostomes save vertebrates, cephalochordates, and urochordates, comes into existence with the function of the postembryonic remnant or equivalent of the blastopore restricted to that of an anus.

A *tertiary mouth,* functional in vertebrates, cephalochordates, and urochordates, forms a relatively short distance posterior to the secondary mouth. It has been altered slightly in gnathostome vertebrates by fusion with one or more anterior pharyngeal pouches. Inasmuch as the number of pouches involved is uncertain, and since none significantly alters the original definitive mouth or its position, it is satisfactory to disregard such modification at least as a major step in oral evolution.

Vestiges of the secondary mouth are differently manifest in chordates possessing a tertiary mouth in adult stages. In amphioxus the secondary

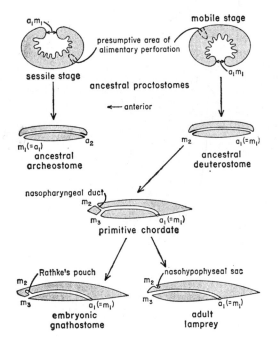

FIG. 11.2 Evolution of three mouths in vertebrate phylogeny, schematized. Symbols: a_1, primary anus; a_2, secondary anus; m_1, primary mouth; m_2, secondary mouth; m_3, tertiary or definitive mouth.

mouth is represented in adults by Hatschek's pit, a minute structure of un-known (and perhaps no) function. Embryonically Hatschek's pit is contin-uous with the gut.

In hagfishes the secondary mouth is retained in adults as a large ante-rior opening (even larger than the more ventrally situated definitive mouth) entering the *nasopharyngeal duct.* The latter communicates directly with the gut.

In adult lampreys the nasopharyngeal duct is blind, the connection with the alimentary tract being lost.

In gnathostomes the nasopharyngeal duct is represented by the inner end only, the outer part and the opening to the exterior being completely lost. The posterior end, termed *Rathke's pouch,* appears embryonically as a hollow evagination from the roof of the presumptive buccal cavity. In subsequent embryonic stages it becomes thickened, loses its connection with the gut, and curiously enough becomes associated with a ventral divertic-ulum (the *neurohypophysis*) of the brain as the *anterior lobe* (or *adeno-hypophysis*) of the *hypophysis.* Thus cyclostomes and cephalochordates lack this anterior lobe, although they possess the equivalent of the posterior lobe. Urochordates seem to possess no vestige whatsoever of the secondary mouth, although they possess a ringlike *subneural gland* thought to repre-sent the neurohypophysis. The urochordates are regarded as having a de-finitive mouth rather than a secondary mouth chiefly because of their close relation to, and presumably degenerative evolution from, somewhat ceph-alochordatelike ancestors.

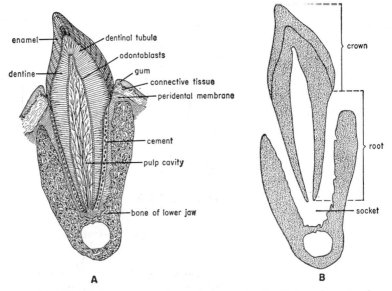

enamel
dentine
dentinal tubule
odontoblasts
gum
connective tissue
peridental membrane
cement
pulp cavity
bone of lower jaw
crown
root
socket

A

B

FIG. 11.3 Vertical sections of mammalian teeth. A, in place in the socket, with adjacent tissues; B, removed from socket, adjacent tissues not shown. (From Bailey.)

The embryonic, ectoderm-lined invagination that becomes the mouth opening and mouth cavity in adults is the *stomodaeum,* a structure present in all chordates as well as other deuterostomes. The endoderm-lined gut does not embryonically reach the exterior at either the oral or the anal end. Relatively deep invaginations from the exterior complete the gut at both ends during relatively late developmental stages.

Teeth

With equally valid reason teeth could be treated in connection (1) with the integumentary system, because they have clearly evolved from integumentary structures—the dermal denticles; (2) with the skeletal system, because in most vertebrates they have become directly anchored to, and therefore a part of, the skeletal system; and (3) with the digestive system, because they function primarily in alimentation—as grasping and chewing devices. For the sake of convenience and conformance with common policy they are considered here with the digestive system.

All vertebrates except the Agnatha either possess teeth or have evolved from toothed ancestors. Toothless or partly toothed vertebrates have often compensated for their deficiency with deceptively toothlike structures. Some of these substitutes are the horny tubercles of the lamprey; conical bony projections on the lower jaw of a few anurans; various types of bony projections on the jaws of certain teleost fish; serrations on the beaks of turtles; and the enamel-coated, bony ridges on the jaws of Sphenodon.

Structure. True teeth (Fig. 11.3) are separate structures consisting of an outer unique layer of *enamel,* a deeper and thicker layer of *dentine,* and an inner *pulp* containing connective tissue, blood vessels, and nerves. The enamel is exceedingly hard, composed of about 96 percent inorganic matter —the greatest percentage of inorganic matter found in any vertebrate structure. Much of the volume of enamel in any tooth is made up of elongate crystals of carbonate apatite aligned at right angles to the surface; the remainder (about one third) is calcium phosphate. It contains no living matter.

Dentine is very bonelike, having about the same proportion of inorganic and organic matter as bone (72 vs. 66 percent); but its canaliculi run directly outward from the pulp cavity, where the bodies of all its secretory cells (*odontoblasts*) lie in a layer against the inner wall of the dentine. Unlike enamel, dentine contains living matter (and can, therefore, register pain), since each canaliculus houses a fine protoplasmic strand originating at one of the odontoblasts. Enamel is an ectoderm product; presence of true teeth thus requires the presence of ectoderm. The remainder of the tooth is of mesoderm origin. Growth is by accretion toward the root, the tip of the tooth first forming and having full size.

Evolutionary Trends. Many characteristics of teeth have been subject to change. Trends of change are clearly evident in six characteristics worthy of special attention: (1) location of the teeth, (2) their cycles of replacement, (3) their number, (4) their form, (5) the number of replacement sets, and (6) their mode of anchorage.

LOCATION. The embryonic source of teeth may be regarded as a reflection of their evolutionary source. Teeth are thought to be the modified denticles originally found on all the integumentary scales or plates over all the body in early fishes. The plates disappeared about the mouth, leaving the denticles, which invaded not only the periphery of the mouth but also as far into the gut as ectoderm is invaginated. Many fishes possess true teeth as far posteriorly as the branchial bars. A general trend toward limitation of the area of dispersal seems to exist in vertebrates: most palatal and jaw bones are toothed in fishes; only the splenial, dentary, premaxilla, and maxilla, as well as miscellaneous palatal bones, in amphibians; the palatine, pterygoid, dentary, premaxilla, and maxilla, in modern reptiles; and only the dentary, premaxilla, and maxilla in modern mammals. In the sawfish, teeth occur even outside the mouth, on either side of a long, flattened snout; such variations make the distinction of teeth from scales an arbitrary matter.

NUMBER. No specific number of teeth can be selected as primitive for vertebrates, but certainly ancestral gnathostomes possessed many teeth. They were *polyodont,* as indeed would be expected in view of the origin of teeth from numerous, small dermal denticles. In general the trend in all vertebrates has been toward a reduction (*oligodonty*) in number of teeth, undoubtedly in correlation with general trends toward increase in size and in firmness of attachment of the teeth. Even in mammals the general trend is toward reduction in number, although in some lines (for example, the toothed whales) there has been a reversal with an increase in number as the teeth have become smaller and less firmly ankylosed to the jaw. Primitive mammals had eleven teeth on each side of each jaw (Fig. 11.4), whereas, for example, man has but eight, with a frequent reduction to 7 (Fig. 11.5).

The extreme of oligodonty occurs in certain mammals, such as the female narwhal (a kind of whale), which is toothless; the male of this species is not much better provided, as it has but a single large incisor protruding swordlike straight forward from the head. Lack of teeth in certain other

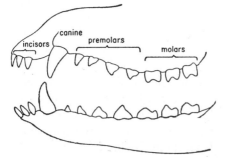

FIG. 11.4 Diagram of fully heterodont tooth arrangement primitively characteristic of eutherian mammals. (From Romer.)

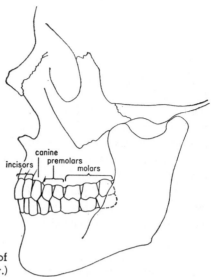

FIG. 11.5 Diagram of arrangement of permanent teeth in man. (From Gray.)

edentulous (toothless) groups—for example, modern birds, turtles and certain anurans—is clearly the result of a trend toward reduction in size of the teeth, not reduction in number, since a number of teeth are present embryonically in certain turtles and birds.

Other clear-cut cases of reduction in number of teeth occur in all classes of vertebrates, certain bones normally toothed lacking teeth in these exceptions. Larval amphibians tend to have more teeth than adults, and embryonic caecilians of certain viviparous species have a very extensive dentition loss in adults. Teleosts tend toward reduction of the jaw teeth and elaboration of palatal and pharyngeal teeth. Anurans, with rare exception, lack teeth in the lower jaw, and many reptiles have no palatal teeth whatever.

CYCLES OF REPLACEMENT. In early vertebrates tooth replacement was continuous and essentially unlimited. Several sets of replacement teeth are always present at the bases of the functional teeth (Fig. 11.6). As the functional teeth become disengaged from the tooth-bearing bone, the replacement tooth next in line moves into the vacated spot and becomes loosely anchored there, as the other replacement teeth move another notch toward the functional tooth, and a new bud forms at the outer end of the series.

Tooth replacement does not, however, take place at exactly the same time for all teeth along the edge of the jaw. In primitive vertebrates *polymodal* replacement is the rule, with several waves of replacement progressing simultaneously down the length of each jaw. Mammals and a few reptiles, on the contrary, are *unimodal,* having but one wave of replacement progressing down the length of each jaw. The significance of the difference between unimodal and polymodal tooth replacement may best be appreciated by the realization that in a vertebrate with numerous teeth the replacement process could scarcely occur simultaneously for all teeth, or continuously from front to rear, or haphazardly; for large toothless gaps would at least occasionally result, and they would seriously impair the ability of the animal to feed or defend itself. Accordingly, every second to sixth tooth (or more) in most vertebrates is replaced more or less simultaneously, followed by the next tooth in line after each new one, and so on until the cycle is complete and ready to repeat (Fig. 11.7). In this way no large part of the jaw is left toothless at any one time despite the continuous replacement that is going on. In effect, several waves of replacement, two to six or more teeth in length, succeed each other from front to rear of the jaw. In mammals and a few reptiles, all with a permanent dentition as well as one or more deciduous sets of teeth, there is but one wave, very slow to be sure, for the entire jaw. It is a mode of replacement primitive vertebrates, with their loosely anchored teeth, could not afford to use.

FORM. Concerned as they are chiefly with diet, the teeth are extensively modified in different vertebrates (Fig. 11.8) from the primitive conical shape. Crushing types, of rounded, flattened shape, occur in some sharks and reptiles (lizards); grinding types, in various mammals; slashing types (canines), in some reptiles and most mammals; poison-conducting types (fangs), in certain snakes and lizards; and shearing types (*carnassials*), in carnivorous mammals. The occurrence of two or more types of teeth in a single individual is *heterodonty;* the more primitive condition, of more or less uniform jaw teeth, is *homodonty* (or *isodonty*). Most mammals are heterodont, but some (for example, toothed whales) are homodont. Most toothed nonmammalian vertebrates are essentially homodont,

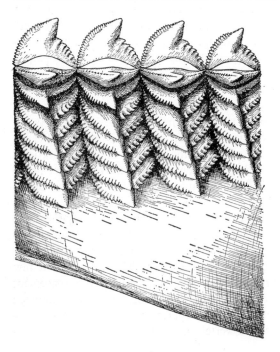

FIG. 11.6 Replacement teeth in a shark, showing the several replacement sets of teeth characteristic of polyphyodont vertebrates.

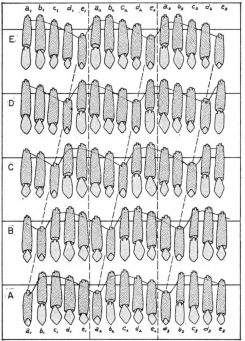

FIG. 11.7 Diagram of poly-modal tooth replacement along medial edge of dentary (upper edge shown by straight horizontal line) in a eupleurodont vertebrate such as a lizard, showing changes taking place at successive time levels, A-E. The three straight oblique lines connect tooth loci which, at the indicated time levels, have just lost the functional tooth and have a replacement tooth ready to grow into functional position. Length of each replacement wave is represented by five tooth loci; three waves are initiated in the groups a_1—e_1, a_2—e_2, and a_3—e_3.

but crocodilians and numerous lizards, snakes, and fishes are clearly hetero-dont, at least to a degree. Nonmammalian vertebrates with a recognizable degree of tooth differentiation may be regarded as *subheterodont* (or *subis-odont*).

Mammalian heterodonty is uniquely complete; mammals are the only *fully heterodont* vertebrates, in the sense that they typically possess, suc-cessively from front to rear, *incisors, canines, premolars,* and *molars,* each modified for performance of special functions.

Primitively, mammals are thought to have had three incisors, one canine, four premolars, and three molars on each side of each jaw (Fig. 11.4). This number is expressed as a formula in fractional form, the nu-merator representing one side of the upper jaw, the denominator one side of the lower jaw. Thus the formula for primitive mammals would be $\frac{3-1-4-3}{3-1-4-3}$; that for the cat is $\frac{3-1-3-1}{3-1-2-1}$; for the rabbit $\frac{2-0-3-3}{1-0-2-3}$; and for man $\frac{2-1-2-3}{2-1-2-3}$ (Fig. 11.5).

The four types are readily distinguished from each other except for the premolars and molars (collectively referred to as *cheek teeth*). Canines are always either single or absent on either side of either jaw, have a single root, are pointed, and usually are projected above the level of adjacent teeth. Incisors are commonly flattened anteroposteriorly, and have a single root. Even premolars and molars can, in any single given species (as man) or group of species, be distinguished morphologically, but only one feature will distinguish the two types in all mammals collectively: premolars are moulted once, molars are never shed. There is no fundamental difference between them in shape. Primitively all the cheek teeth possessed three or four *cusps* or rounded humps on the occlusive surface of the crown, and any tooth still bearing this shape or some other complex form derived from it is called *molariform*. Often, however, as in man, the permanent premolars are only *bicuspid,* although the deciduous premolars are molariform. Thus shape is no criterion of distinction between molars and premolars. The form of the roots is no better a criterion, for premolars have one or two roots and the molars have one, two, or three roots.

The spacing and actual appearance of the four basic tooth forms in mammals vary greatly in different groups (Fig. 11.9): the narwhal has already been mentioned; in rodents and rabbits the incisors are modified as continuously growing, gnawing teeth, widely separated from the more posterior premolars (in elephants they are tusklike); canines are often absent (rodents, etc.) or knifelike (hogs, carnivores, etc.); and the molars and premolars may be elaborate grinding teeth in herbivores (elephants, ruminants), or shearing devices (carnassial teeth—the last upper premolar, the first lower molar) in carnivores.

NUMBER OF REPLACEMENT SETS. In primitive reptiles, as well as in primitive fishes and in most amphibians, the small, numerous, functional teeth project but little beyond the level of the labial (outer) flange of the jaw (Fig. 11.10C). Some modern reptiles (several lizard families) still retain this primitive condition, but two trends of modification from it are conspicuously evident (others exist but are of minor importance). In one trend the labial flange itself became enlarged and assumed the function of the teeth, which in turn disappeared. Turtles and birds exemplify this trend.

On the contrary, in other lines of reptiles, including the one leading toward mammals, the teeth became enlarged and more firmly anchored to the jaws. In all primitive vertebrates the replacement teeth are numerous and lie concealed by the gums below the functional teeth on the lingual side of the jaws (as in Fig. 11.6). The functional teeth remain in place a relatively short time, then become loosened, drop off, and are replaced by the adjacent replacement teeth, which in turn are continually replenished by small tooth buds forming at the bases of the replacement series. Animals having continual tooth replacement are *polyphyodont* (Fig. 11.11B).

Enlargement and firm attachment of the teeth to the jaws in more advanced types could not be accomplished, however, without a sacrifice of perpetual replacement, which requires ease of displacement and thus a relatively loose attachment of functional teeth. The first step toward solution to this dilemma was to utilize the ancient system of frequent replacement for the rapidly growing stages, but at maturity to retain one set as *permanent* teeth, never again to be replaced. The permanent teeth thus could and did become solidly anchored, as the replacement teeth never could be. Several lizard families as well as the crocodilians exemplify this condition of *oligophyodonty* (Fig. 11.11C), having several sets of *deciduous* teeth (baby or "milk" teeth in man) followed by a single complete set of permanent teeth.

In mammals there is a still further reduction in number of sets of teeth. In one extreme, as in moles, but one set occurs, and it is, of course, permanent. Moles are thus *monophyodont* (Fig. 11.11F). Presumably, ancestral mammals were fully diphyodont (Fig. 11.11D), having one complete deciduous set and one complete permanent set. All recent mammals with a well-developed dentition, however, although usually called diphyodont, are

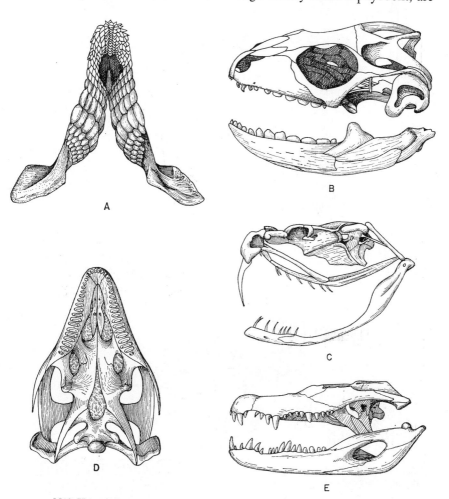

FIG. 11.8 Heterodonty in some ectotherms. A, lower jaw of Port Jackson shark; B, a teid lizard, with rear molariform teeth; C, a rattlesnake, with enlarged paired fangs; D, a fossil lizard, Polyglyphanodon, with anteroposterior compression of rear teeth; E, an alligator with large and small caniniform teeth. (From Bronn, Gilmore, Kingsley, Klauber, and Romer.)

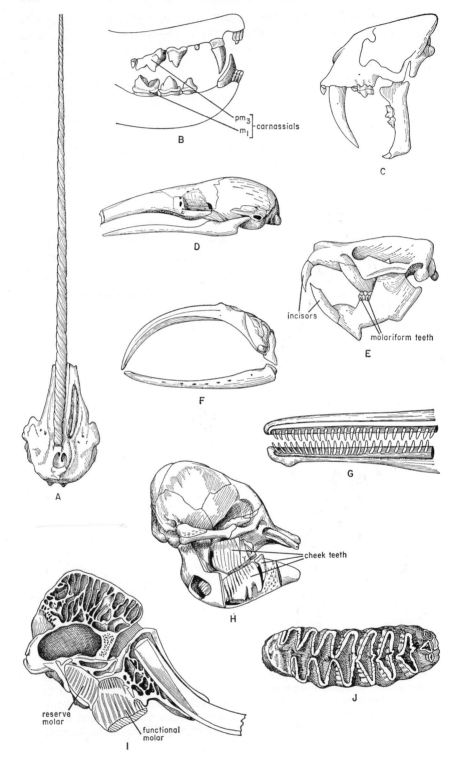

B

pm₃
m₁ carnassials

C

D

incisors

molariform teeth

E

F

G

cheek teeth

H

reserve
molar

functional
molar

I

J

FIG. 11.9 (*Left*) Variations in tooth form in mammals. A, male narwhal with left incisor only, forming a tusk; B, cat, with a typical carnivore dentition, including carnassial teeth; C, sabre-tooth tiger, an extinct Californian carnivore with hypertrophied canines; D, hairy anteater, with no teeth; E, rodent, with hypertrophied gnawing incisors; F, right whale, toothless; G, toothed whale (porpoise), as seen in sagittal section of skull with lower jaw, showing essentially homodont dentition; H, immature elephant with roots of teeth exposed; I, mature elephant, showing hypertrophy of incisors as tusks, and pattern of molar succession; J, occlusive surface of a molar of an elephant, showing an extreme in adaptation for the grinding function. (From Adams and Eddy, Flower and Lydekker, Parker and Haswell, Reynolds, Young and Zittel.)

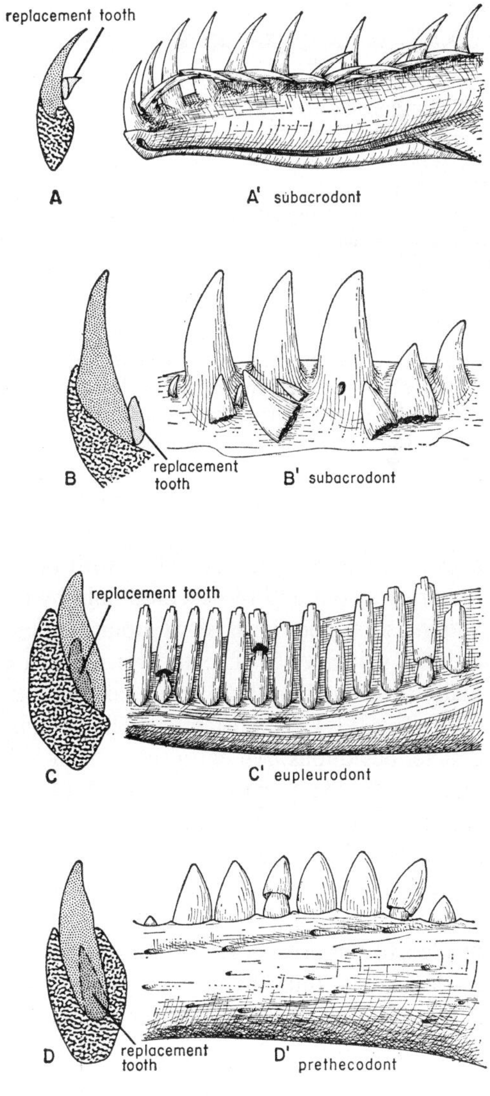

FIG. 11.10 Evolution in modes of replacement and attachment of teeth. A, a snake (Agkistrodon) with subacrodont teeth and intercalary replacement; B, a lizard (Varanus) with subacrodont teeth and intercalary replacement; C, a lizard (Sceloporus) with eupleurodont teeth and vertical replacement; D, a crocodilian (Alligator) with prethecodont teeth and vertical replacement.

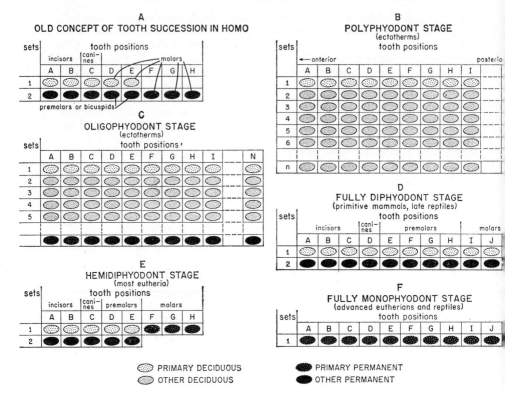

FIG. 11.11 Comparison of concepts of tooth succession in man and other vertebrates. A, former nonevolutionary concept; B-F, successive stages in attainment of the condition in man (E) and more advanced mammals (F), according to the evolutionary concept.

actually either fully monophyodont or partly so, and most fall into the latter category. The partly monophyodont types—most mammals—are thus *hemidiphyodont* (Fig. 11.11E), with the secondary set being on its evolutionary way out and represented only by the permanent premolars, canines, and incisors. The single set of molars is permanent but, of course, represents the first primary set of teeth even though eruption of the rear molars normally is delayed until the secondary set has appeared in the fore part of the jaws (Fig. 11.12). All teeth of the primary set, except the molars, are, of course, deciduous. An extra set, partial or complete, occurs rarely in mammals (including man) as an anomalous atavism. Obviously there is a trend toward the entire elimination of the rear teeth of the jaw in man, the delay in eruption being so great for the rear molars that they never do erupt in some individuals. The fact that the molars, which are permanent, erupt after the more anterior permanent teeth of the secondary set are in place has led to the erroneous conclusion that the molars actually belong to the secondary set, thus envisioned as consisting of all the permanent teeth. Such is not the case. Part of the primary set is deciduous, part permanent. The secondary set is entirely permanent, but includes only part of the permanent teeth, and represents only those teeth anterior to the molars.

The extreme in the trend toward reduction in number of replacements is *aphyodonty,* in which no teeth whatever appear. This is clearly a trend occurring in man, the wisdom tooth (last molar) occasionally failing completely to erupt. None of the teeth erupt in armadillos, anteaters, and whalebone whales, and in the narwhal only one tooth (the left upper incisor) erupts in one sex (male). Not all loss of teeth among vertebrates has been achieved along a line of successive diphyodonty, monophyodonty, and aphyodonty, however; the principle of aphyodonty can be accepted with assurance only for certain mammals. Other toothless vertebrates presumably lost the teeth by progressive reduction in their size or number (Fig. 11.13).

All deciduous teeth, when fully developed, possess a complete root and crown just as do the permanent teeth. As any given replacement tooth develops underneath, however, the root of the deciduous tooth gradually is resorbed; the part remaining when the tooth actually is shed is little more than the crown.

ANCHORAGE. Three types of tooth anchorage are conventionally recognized. The *pleurodont* type is characterized by attachment of the teeth along the lingual side of the jaws, much as in Figures 11.6 and 11.10C, C¹. Two types have independently been derived from that primitive type in reptiles and mammals: the *acrodont* type, with the teeth attached at the crest of the jaw bone (Figs. 11.10A, A¹, 11.14), and the *thecodont* type (Fig. 11.10D, D¹), with the *roots* (often multiple) of the teeth attached in sockets, and the *crown* projecting above the socket. Both of the latter types evolved in correlation with the trends toward a firm anchorage of a permanent set of teeth. Their mode of evolution is a fascinating study.

Replacement teeth in primitive reptiles were arranged in either oblique (Fig. 11.10B¹) or vertical (Fig. 11.10C¹) series below the functional teeth. Firm anchorage was achieved from each condition, but the mode of attachment evolved differently in each. In the evolutionary line of the ob-

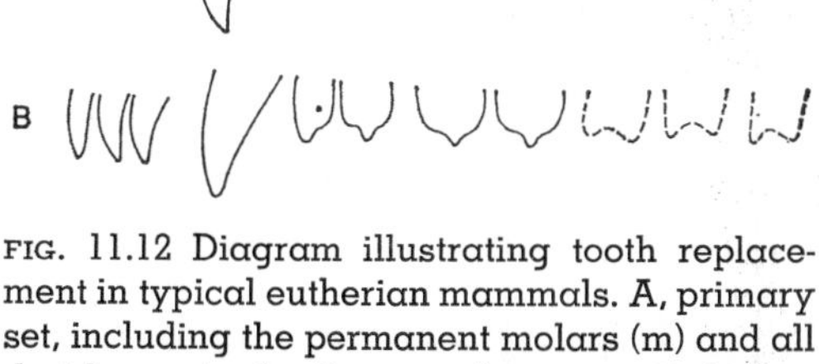

FIG. 11.12 Diagram illustrating tooth replacement in typical eutherian mammals. A, primary set, including the permanent molars (m) and all deciduous teeth; B, secondary set, including replacement, permanent teeth for all types except molars. (From Romer.)

liquely arranged replacement teeth, enlargement of the functional teeth required greater spacing between the teeth to accommodate the developing replacement teeth, which assumed a clearly *interdental* position. The firmest anchorage possible for teeth becoming specialized along this line was at the crest of the jaw bone—the acrodont attachment. In extreme types the teeth are also monophyodont, as in Sphenodon and apparently in certain lizards (agamids and chameleontids). As in the thecodont teeth of mammals, the acrodont teeth of reptiles erupt slowly, beginning at the front of the jaw and slowly involving additional teeth toward the rear. In the fully acrodont lizards (as the agamids) the rear teeth can be seen in their formative stages, preceded anteriorly by teeth only partly ankylosed, and these in turn preceded by firmly attached, truly acrodont teeth. The "younger" teeth at the rear of the jaws form in an essentially pleurodont position; in the process of becoming completely ankylosed they assume the appearance of acrodonty (Fig. 11.14).

In the evolutionary line of vertical or *subdental* replacement, however, a firm anchorage is made possible by the enlargement of the lingual flange of each jaw bone, and the formation of a bony partition between the roots of the successive teeth, forming sockets. Such extremes are thecodont—and examples include many archosaurian reptiles (including modern crocodilians) as well as mammals. The advantage of thecodonty is the same as for acrodonty—it provides for a firm dental anchorage. However, thecodonty could not have evolved in the interdental line of specialization because it would have interfered with tooth replacement in formative stages. Only in those types with vertical (subdental) displacement could partitions between tooth attachments be formed without interference with the replacement process. Numerous lizard and snake families, recognized as *subpleurodont* or *subacrodont* (Fig. 11.10A, B), exemplify various intermediate stages between the primitive pleurodont types with either vertical or interdental replacement and the extremes of acrodonty and thecodonty. Pleurodont types with interdental replacement may usefully be termed subpleurodont,

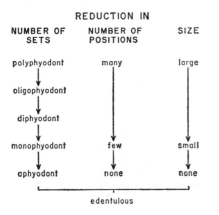

FIG. 11.13 Three modes of evolution of the edentulous condition in vertebrates.

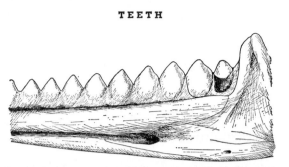

FIG. 11.14 Medial aspect of part of lower jaw of a euacrodont lizard, showing the firmly ankylosed anterior teeth, less well-ankylosed teeth toward rear, and a developing "wisdom" tooth at extreme rear. As in man, the teeth erupt progressively later toward the rear of the jaw.

since this condition is a prelude to acrodonty. *Eupleurodont* types possess subdental replacement. Acrodont types that seemingly remain polyphyodont may usefully be termed subacrodont, whereas those that develop ontogenetically a permanent dentition are strictly acrodont, or *euacrodont* (Fig. 11.14). Young crocodilians exhibit a *prethecodont* stage (Fig. 11.15), with a deep dental groove bordered by high lingual and labial ridges, but no interdental partitions.

Dental Terminology in Man. A confusing disparity exists between the names applied to human teeth by comparative anatomists and by human anatomists (Fig. 11.11A). In the terminology of human anatomy, any molariform tooth is termed a molar tooth. Since the deciduous premolars are molariform instead of bicuspid, they are erroneously regarded as deciduous molars, despite the facts that (a) they occupy the position of the permanent, bicuspid premolars, and (b) they have the same complex form as the other members of the primary set of cheek teeth. Thus in human anatomy the premolars ("bicuspids") are almost universally regarded as permanent teeth lacking deciduous forerunners; the anterior two molars are regarded as having both deciduous and permanent representatives; and the third molar is regarded as being permanent only, lacking a deciduous forerunner. Clearly the terminology and concepts currently applied to the premolars and molars of man require modification to make them conform with knowledge of other mammals. The two premises responsible for the unique

FIG. 11.15 Dorsal aspect of lower jaw of an alligator, showing a prethecodont condition in most of the dentigerous zone. True thecodonty occurs at the anterior end, where separate sockets are present.

features of the usual human terminology are (1) assumption that all permanent teeth must belong to the same set, and (2) that molars and premolars can be defined and distinguished, as natural groupings, on the basis of shape (not position). Both premises are obviously wrong.

Other Buccal Structures

Glands. Integumentary glands are present in the buccal cavity chiefly, like teeth, because of extensive invagination of the ectoderm into that area. In fishes these glands are little modified (with rare exception), mucus-secreting structures, but in tetrapods they become reduced in number, enlarged, and specialized for various functions. In some amphibians they are specialized to produce a mucous substance rendering the surface of the tongue sticky. In reptiles some become specialized as true *salivary glands,* numerous and well developed in some modern representatives. Mammals have inherited five pairs of salivary glands that are commonly present: the *submaxillary, sublingual, parotid, molar,* and *suborbital* glands. In birds, on the contrary, the glands have become reduced in number and size and apparently are of no digestive importance.

Salivary glands presumably served a function originally of simply keeping the buccal cavity and esophagus moist, but in some amphibians and reptiles a digestive function becomes evident and in mammals attains a real importance. The secretions of these glands are in many cases poisonous to other animals, even though in some cases that property is of no significance to the owner. The saliva of man is at least occasionally poisonous when introduced into the circulatory system of another human; that of shrews is highly potent, and of course the parotid salivary secretion of some (perhaps all) snakes is more or less poisonous to other animals. In most snakes the saliva, where strongly venomous, is introduced into the flesh by *fangs.* No such teeth, modified for conduction of venom, exist in any other vertebrates.

Taste Organs. Taste buds originally were scattered over the surface of the body as well as in the buccopharyngeal region. In amphibians they are restricted to the mouth and pharynx, and in mammals have become restricted chiefly to the tongue. Like most other strictly buccal (or integumentary) structures, they are restricted primarily to regions of occurrence of ectoderm. For more detail in this connection see the discussion of the sensory system (p. 407).

The Olfactory Organs. The nasal organs exist in virtually all vertebrates as paired sacs located just in front of the mouth. They were primitively open only to the exterior (*via external nares*) just as they still exist in most fishes. In such a state they play no role in connection with the digestive and respiratory systems.

In choanichthyan fishes and tetrapods the nasal capsule opens not

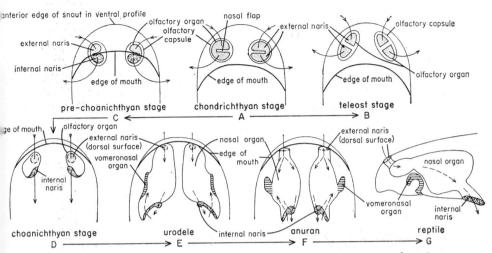

FIG. 11.16 Stages in evolution of the olfactory openings, organs, and cavities. (From Romer.)

only externally but also into the buccal cavity (at the *internal nares*), thus effecting a direct passageway through the olfactory capsule (Fig. 11.16) from the external nares to the buccal cavity. Because internal nares first appeared in fishes—ancient ones at that—there is good reason to believe that they originally were of value in quite a different fashion than in tetrapods. They presumably served as a passageway for fluids, improving olfaction by permitting a direct flow through the sense organ. The blind capsules of other fishes undoubtedly were less efficient, but other devices similarly improving the sense of smell were adopted in them to produce an essentially tubelike conformity of even the blind capsule. The survival value of a continuous olfactory current is evident. Only by minor coincidence did the posterior opening in one group of fishes come to lie within the mouth, rather than outside it as in other fishes.

With invasion of land the internal nares of the Choanichthyes were found to be a highly useful preadaptation for air breathing, serving as passageways for air instead of water.

In all tetrapods save those with a secondary palate, the internal nares open into the anterior end of the buccal cavity. Presence of a secondary palate results in separation of the nasal chamber from the buccal cavity as far posteriorly as the region of the glottis.

Secondary Palate. In the anamniotes the roof of the buccal cavity is the primary palate. In the air-breathing anamniotes this means there is a common passageway for air and for food and water extending from the internal nares, at the anterior end of the buccal cavity, to the glottis. Most amniotes, on the other hand, possess at least a partial subdivision of this common passageway in the form of a secondary palate, which becomes complete only in crocodilians and mammals (see discussion of skull, p.

217). The benefits are dual: the vital sense organs and glands of the buccal cavity are released from exposure to desiccation, and manipulation of food by the tongue and teeth is made possible without interference with the process of breathing. The trend in tetrapods is thus toward as complete a separation as possible of the respiratory and alimentary tracts. In the forms with a so-called "complete" secondary palate there remains only the shortest possible common passageway (Fig. 11.1). Only to the relatively insignificant (1) location of the olfactory capsules in front of the mouth, rather than back or to the sides of it or (2) failure of the attachment of the lung progenitor to the gut to be shifted dorsally (like the swim bladder) rather than ventrally can the failure of the two tracts to become completely

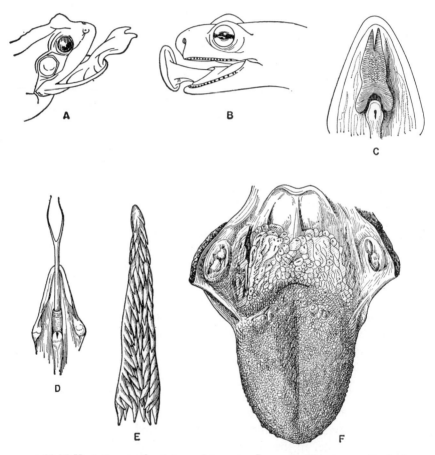

FIG 11.17 Variation in the tetrapod tongue. A, a primitive type, attached at front of mouth, found in most frogs and salamanders; B, a mushroom-shaped (boletoid) type found in some advanced salamanders; C, type found in many lizards; D, type found in a few lizards and in all snakes; E, a type found in birds; F, a type found in mammals. (From Hilzheimer, Neal, Noble, Rand, Walter, and Wiedersheim.)

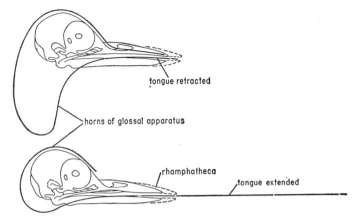

tongue retracted

horns of glossal apparatus

rhamphatheca

tongue extended

FIG. 11.18 Tongue action in a bird. Note that when the tongue is retracted the glossal cornua extend almost to the tip of the upper jaw, in a subcutaneous sheath; when protracted, the glossal cornua are not only pulled forward in the throat but slip backward in the supramandibular sheaths so far that the cornual tips lie near the orbits. (From Hilzheimer.)

separate be attributed. In a way the present impasse in the trend toward separation is regrettable, for now an elimination of the hazard of choking is inaccessible. However, the existence of a substitute aperture (mouth) for intake of air, to take the place of a temporarily clogged nasal passageway, has undoubtedly been of survival value in the history of all mammals, including man.

Tongue. A tongue is often regarded as existing in fishes, but actually they possess at most only a slight pad or projection on the basihyal bone or cartilage. Not until amphibians evolved did a true lingual apparatus, free of branchial function, appear on the scene. Not even larval amphibians possess a true tongue; it is a feature of adults (transformed individuals) only (Fig. 11.17).

The evolution of the skeletal support of the tongue is discussed in connection with the skeletal system. For the most part the skeleton consists of the branchial or hyoid arches, or both, but an important component is the basihyal, which is either a transverse bar or is extended forward as a *processus lingualis* supporting the center of the tongue and in many types extending actually to its free tip.

The fleshy part consists chiefly of muscle fibers and, to a lesser degree in various vertebrates, of lymphatic or blood sinuses. The muscles are of hypobranchial origin, and in most vertebrates serve without other aid to protrude and otherwise manipulate the tongue. Mammals are unique in possession of a *lingualis* muscle constituting the bulk of the tongue; in other classes the paired hyoglossus muscles comprise the fleshy part of the tongue. In mammals the hyoglossus is but one of the extrinsic muscles aiding in tongue movement, other extrinsic muscles assisting in all tetrapod classes.

In some vertebrates tongue protrusion is effected, at least in part, by instantaneous flooding of lymph or blood sinuses; this is so of anurans and the true chameleons.

Shape of the tongue varies greatly. It is an elongate, slender, highly protrusible structure (Fig. 11.18) in some (snakes, some lizards, birds, anteaters), fleshy and only slightly protrusible in others; it is usually attached at the rear near the hyoid bar, as it is primitively. Secondarily it has become attached to the anterior floor of the mouth in most anurans (other rare species either lack a tongue or have it attached at the rear of the mouth) and a few salamanders.

Respiration

Definition. The word "respiration" is used in a number of senses, only one of which is involved in the present discussion of the respiratory system. We are concerned with *exchange* of gases, always occurring across a moist membrance in close contact with blood vessels. This respiratory membrane simply helps maintain an approximate physical equilibrium between the carbon dioxide and oxygen of the blood and the levels of concentration that exist in the surrounding medium of air or water. The blood usually has an excess of carbon dioxide, which diffuses off through the respiratory membrane due to the lesser concentration in the surrounding medium. It usually has a deficiency of oxygen, which diffuses from the external area, where greater concentration occurs, through the respiratory membrane into the blood.

This sort of respiration clearly should occur at *any* body surface where the epithelium is thin and moist. This is not only theoretically but actually true. Respiratory surfaces occur at a variety of locations in the body in different vertebrates, but most vertebrates cannot afford to leave the external body surface unprotected to an extent that would permit respiration to occur. Thus in all vertebrates except amphibians, which do rely heavily upon the skin for respiration, the respiratory membranes are restricted in occurrence to small regions of the body such as the gills or lungs.

Two other definitions of respiration are (1) actual oxidation of sugars, fats, or proteins (some other substances also in some other organisms, but not in vertebrates) as a means of producing energy, and (2) the mechanical operation serving to circulate air (inhalation, exhalation) or water about the respiratory membranes. We can distinguish the first as *internal respiration,* the second as *breathing* or *mechanical respiration,* and gaseous exchange as *external respiration.*

External respiration exploits two media: air and water. Some respiratory organs—for example, the body skin—serve equally well in either, but the two definitive respiratory organs of vertebrates (gills and lungs) are specifically adapted for one medium or the other, not both.

Organs for Aquatic Respiration. At least five different organs have been evolved in different chordates for exploitation of water as a respiratory medium: the integument, internal pharyngeal gills, external gills, the buccopharyngeal epithelium, and cloacal bursae.

The earliest chordate respiratory membrane seems to have been the integument, which in primitive protochordates was thin enough to permit gaseous exchange. Subsequently early vertebrates developed a bony, absolutely nonrespiratory integument, and adopted the pharyngeal slits as bases for substitute respiratory organs, the *internal gills*. The gills adequately served the needs of all fishes, but they could not serve for aerial respiration in tetrapods. As amphibians cast about for efficient aerial respiratory organs they reverted to use of the skin, having lost the heavy primitive armor. This is, of course, a strictly secondary function of the skin, particularly appropriate for amphibians with their bimodal way of life, since the skin is equally efficient as a respiratory membrane in water and in air (so long as it is moist). It is thought that the skin also serves the respiratory needs of hibernating soft-shelled turtles, which differ from other turtles by having none of the skin of the shell cornified. The buccopharyngeal epithelium is likewise extensively vascularized in many amphibians, serving as another respiratory surface and like the skin effective in either air or water. Larval amphibians, having lost the effectiveness of their ancestral internal gills, have developed epithelial growths from the outer surface of the gill bars, forming *external gills* (Fig. 11.19). They are vascularized from the same aortic arches as their forerunners, the internal gills, but like the latter are effective only in water. Thus salamanders such as Necturus can respire by four means—external gills, lungs, skin, and the buccopharyngeal epithelium; however it has been proved experimentally that the latter two alone can suffice for respiration.

Most fresh-water turtles, derived from ancestors long adjusted to respiration by means of lungs only, in some cases have, in adaptation to hibernation under water, evolved an accessory device for aquatic respiration—paired bladderlike *cloacal bursae* evaginated from the cloaca. Water drawn into and forced out of the cloacal bursae enables aquatic turtles

FIG. 11.19 Diagrammatic frontal section through Necturus, showing the external gills.

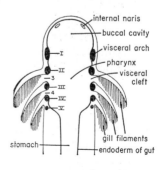

to live under water for longer periods, particularly in hibernation, than would otherwise be possible. All other vertebrates that lack gills and hibernate under water must respire through the skin or the buccopharyngeal epithelium.

Organs of Aerial Respiration. At least four structures have evolved in vertebrates to serve in adults as aerial respiratory devices: the skin, buccopharyngeal epithelium, nasal epithelium, and lungs. Major utilization of the first three occurs only in amphibians, which pay a penalty for such respiratory protection by the necessity of keeping the body surfaces moist all the time. In amphibians lack of moisture means not only failure of the respiratory membranes but also rapid desiccation of the entire body, as fluid can pass equally well in either direction. The skin also cannot be protected by scales or keratin that would hinder passage of gases. None of the aerial respiratory organs accessory to lungs can thus be regarded as successful for tetrapods as a whole, although they probably served an essential function in the stage of transition from aquatic to aerial respiration. Even in mammals the skin serves a slight respiratory function, since it excretes small quantities of carbon dioxide through the sweat glands.

Lungs are the primary aerial respiratory organs. All tetrapods save one rather large group of salamanders (plethodontoids) possess them. The adults of this group also lack gills, so respiration is exclusively integumentary and buccopharyngeal save in a few species that have the external nares extraordinarily enlarged with their walls vascularized to permit a unique type of nasal respiration.

Since internal gills, the most important organs of aquatic respiration, and lungs, the most important organs of aerial respiration, are pharyngeal derivatives, a discussion of their evolution follows the ensuing survey of the pharynx.

Pharynx

Definition. The pharynx is that part of the alimentary tract posterior to the buccal cavity whose wall is pierced by paired slits in at least embryonic stages. It constitutes a large area of the alimentary tract in primitive chordates, but becomes greatly restricted in amniotes by (a) shifting anteriorly of the glottis, and (b) formation of a secondary palate (Fig. 11.1).

Evolution in Function of Primary Pharynx. Originally a food filter (in protochordates), the pharynx has been extensively altered in various vertebrates to serve a vast variety of functions. Its derivatives (including the walls) aid in active capture and manipulation of food (jaws); as a regulator of rates of metabolism (thyroid gland); as a regulator of calcium and phosphorus metabolism; as a regulator of rate of breathing; as an aid to hearing (middle ear cavity and ossicles); as a support for the

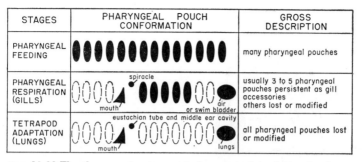

STAGES	PHARYNGEAL POUCH CONFORMATION	GROSS DESCRIPTION
PHARYNGEAL FEEDING		many pharyngeal pouches
PHARYNGEAL RESPIRATION (GILLS)	spiracle mouth air or swim bladder	usually 3 to 5 pharyngeal pouches persistent as gill accessories others lost or modified
TETRAPOD ADAPTATION (LUNGS)	eustachian tube and middle ear cavity mouth lungs	all pharyngeal pouches lost or modified

FIG. 11.20 The three main stages of pharyngeal evolution in chordates.

tongue (lingual apparatus); as an aid in production of voice (larynx); as a means of expression (facial muscles) and communication; as a means of respiration by gills and lungs; and many others. *No structural feature has even approached the importance of the pharynx in providing materials for evolution in vertebrates and for their successful invasion of myriads of worldly habitats.*

Three successive stages of dominant pharyngeal function are apparent in chordate evolution: (1) pharyngeal feeding (protochordates); (2) gill respiration (fishes); and (3) intake regulation (tetrapods) (Fig. 11.20). In tetrapods the pharynx is scarcely more than a crossroads—a chiasma— of respiratory and alimentary tracts. Its utility is chiefly that of maintaining a control of the air or food and water taken into the body, directing each into the proper channel. On the contrary the basic structure of the pharynx under conditions of gill respiration is highly complex.

It is of interest that acquisition of an alimentary function by the pharynx may well have followed the use of a preoral lophophore for food capture in early prechordates.

Basic Gill Structure. The structure of the pharynx varies considerably in different fishes. Gills presumably evolved, after all, in descendants of a group of protochordates (or stage of protochordate embryogeny) in which a series of simple paired slits, separated by pharyngeal bars, connected the anterior gut cavity (pharynx) directly with the exterior.

This simple system, serving as a food filter, is transformed into a gill system by the device of staggering the internal and external slits, so that a canal of some length separates the two. This canal becomes baglike, its walls complexly folded and vascularized, producing a *gill chamber*. Each fold (*lamella*) is provided with a system of blood vessels where respiration occurs. The lamellae are narrow, closely placed, straight ridges projecting at right angles from the anterior and posterior walls of each chamber, their inner ends lying near the skeletal pharyngeal bar (Fig. 11.21). The bar is curved, following the contours of the pharynx wall, and thus the lamellae appear to radiate from the vicinity of the pharyngeal bar. The connective tissue between successive gill chambers forms a tough *intra-*

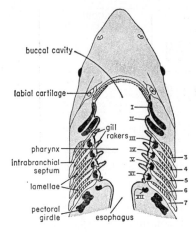

FIG. 11.21 Diagrammatic frontal section through the pharynx of a dogfish, showing a primitive internal gill construction. (From Senning.)

branchial septum (erroneously called interbranchial septum) into which penetrates a series of supportive bony or cartilaginous *gill rays* attached to the pharyngeal bars. Thus the adjacent walls of any pair of juxtaposed gill chambers are united as a single structure, the *gill* or *holobranch*. The lamellae on any one wall are collectively referred to as a *demibranch,* two adjacent ones comprising a holobranch. Not all demibranchs are paired to form holobranchs, however; often the first and the last are unpaired.

The internal gill slits are often protected by a series of projections (*gill rakers*) extending forward over the slits from the anterior edges of the pharyngeal bars. Primitively no protection was present, however, for the external openings.

LINES OF MODIFICATION. Three conspicuous lines of modification of the gill system in fishes are evident. Originally a series of at least twelve pairs of gill chambers existed in vertebrates. Progressive improvement of their respiratory efficiency set the stage for (1) *progressive reduction in number of all chambers.* The primitive number was reduced to between three and seven pairs in various gnathostome fishes (only the sharks Hexanchus and Heptanchus have more than five, among living vertebrates) and to zero in tetrapods. The fate of the structures eliminated as gills requires separate treatment in the following pages.

The gills remaining in different fishes have in some retained more or

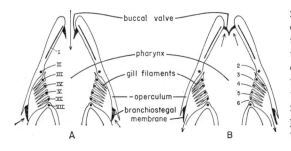

FIG. 11.22 Schematic diagram in frontal section through the pharynx of a teleost, showing the basic gill system and the function of the reciprocal valves facilitating movement of water through the pharynx. (From Schimke-witsch.)

FIG. 11.23 Evolution of the intrabranchial septum in fishes. A, primitive condition (lamellate), as in elasmobranchs; B, intermediate stage, as in holocephalans; C, advanced stage (filamentous), as in teleosts. (From Weichert.)

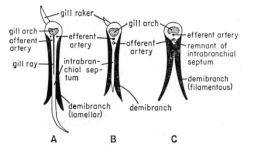

less the primitive structure, as in elasmobranchs, but in most fishes they have been modified in various ways (Figs. 11.22, 11.23). A common alteration was (2) *formation of a protective operculum* covering the entire gill region on each side and attached to the rear of the head. The operculum is fleshy in the ratfishes, but at least partly bony in all osteichthyans. It eliminates the separate external gill slits, the internal slits opening instead into a common opercular chamber communicating with the exterior by a single, usually large opening.

A third trend was toward *reduction of the intrabranchial septa* (Figs. 11.22, 11.23), leaving the lamellae attached only at the branchial bars and resulting in loss of identity of the separate gill chambers. Gills of this sort are termed *filamentous,* in reference to the appearance of the lamellae as filaments, attached at only one end. In one small group of teleosts (of which the Siamese fighting fish or Betta, popular among home aquarists, is an example) a unique accessory branchial chamber (*suprabranchial chamber*) exists as a deep pocketlike evagination from the dorsal wall of the branchial chamber on each side. Its walls in some members are thrown into complex lamellae or folds, forming an accessory "gill" known as the *labyrinth organ* (Fig. 11.24). Bony outgrowths from the third visceral arch help to support the vascular structures. The function of this chamber is to make aerial respiration possible; labyrinthine fishes gulp air at the surface when they find themselves in oxygen-deficient water, and gaseous exchanges take place *via* the labyrinth organ. This structure thus serves the same function that the air bladder did in earlier types.

Gill Derivatives

Pouch Cavities. In the transition to and perfection of the gill function in fishes of a pharynx, formerly a food-gathering device, a reduction in number of segmental parts is the rule (Fig. 11.25). Loss of pouches, as well as skeletal supports, occurred at both the anterior and the posterior ends of the series. Not all parts involved were completely lost, however; such a complex system could scarcely fail to yield useful components even though the original or primary function might be lost. A rear pair of pouches, behind the last functional gill pouch of gnathostome fishes, be-

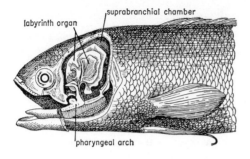

labyrinth organ

suprabranchial chamber

pharyngeal arch

FIG. 11.24 The labyrinth organ of an aberrant teleost fish (Anabas). (From Schimkewitsch.)

came closed off at the external gill slits and altered to serve as *air bladders,* or was lost. These are discussed in detail later.

An anterior pair of pouches (the first of the seven regularly present in gnathostomes) was either lost or fused with the buccal cavity; the latter is generally accepted as the more likely fate.

A third alteration appearing in the evolution of fishes is the loss or transformation into a *spiracular cavity* of the second gill pouch. Teleosts lack this pouch completely, leaving them with but five functional gill pouches and four holobranchs; this number is reduced in a few extremes to two holobranchs and three gill pouches. Tetrapods evolved from piscine ancestors possessing a spiracular cavity; this was transformed in tetrapods to serve a very important function in hearing, being the *middle ear cavity* and the *Eustachian tube,* the latter connecting the former with the pharynx. In some tetrapods these derivatives of the second gill pouch are lost, but such animals are deaf to airborne sounds and are considered degenerate in the sense that they evolved from tetrapod ancestors that did have the second gill pouch well developed in the adult stage.

The serial pharyngeal structures passed through a second critical period of shift in function as land life was explored by tetrapods. No longer were gills an essential part of the animal's structure, their respiratory function now having been assumed by the skin, buccopharyngeal lining, and, primarily, the lungs. The gill pouch linings, the branchial muscles, aortic arches, and skeletal arches all found other functions under the new regime, but not so the pharyngeal pouch cavities. All, from number three through seven, are completely lost in adults. Of the primitive chordates' pharyngeal pouch cavities, adult tetrapods retain only vestiges of the parts reduced at the first period of reduction (formation and perfection of gills): part of the buccal cavity, the lung cavities, and (except in a few nearly or quite deaf animals such as snakes, some lizards, some anurans) the middle ear cavity and Eustachian tube. Nothing is retained of parts eliminated in the second period of reduction (formation of lungs). The structures have been retained in reserve in tetrapods, however, for future reference as it were, should a use become survivally important, for gill slits and cavities are recapitulated to a certain degree in the embryogeny of all tetrapods. All five pairs of pouches persist in embryos of reptiles, four in embryos of mammals and birds.

Pouch Slits. The internal and external slits for the pharyngeal pouches remain where the gill pouches persist in the second (piscine) stage of pharyngeal evolution, except for the external slit for the pouch giving rise to the air bladder or its derivatives. In every case the *external* slit for this pouch is lost. In some teleosts having no duct, or a closed one from the

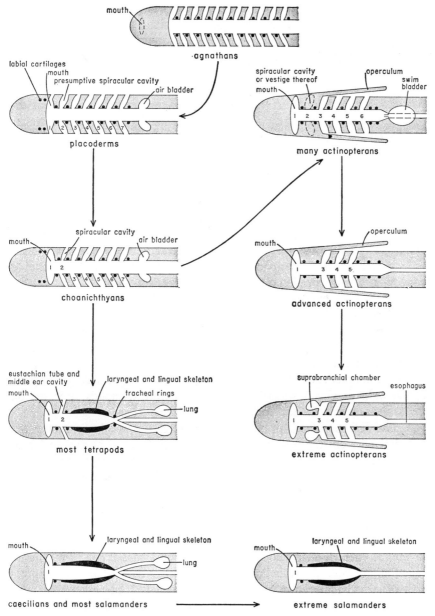

FIG. 11.25 Phylogeny of the pharyngeal pouch cavities in vertebrates.

swim bladder to the gut, the *internal* slits also are lost. In primitive teleosts and in all tetrapods the internal gill slits of this pouch are fused as a single opening (*glottis* in tetrapods). In higher fishes, off the line of evolution of tetrapods, both the internal and external gill slits for the second pouch are lost with the pouch. Presumably the external slit for the first pouch is represented by at least part of the mouth opening, and the internal slit by some undefinable part of the buccal cavity. All other slits are lost as the pouches are lost or retained where the pouches persist.

In the tetrapods the external gill slit of the second pouch is closed usually by the tympanic membrane but sometimes also by muscle or even bone; the internal slit is also closed in a few animals, all quite or virtually deaf, such as salamanders, snakes, and some lizards and anurans which completely lack a Eustachian tube and middle ear cavity. Internal slits persist in conjunction with those pouches present embryonically, but external slits are not normally present in adults except in some salamanders and caecilians. As rare anomalies one or more slits persist into postembryonic stages as *cervical fistulae* in the throat. Larval amphibians have a number of gill slits and pouches, which retain a branchial function, but all true adults of this class lack them as do other tetrapods. Salamanders retaining gills or gill slits in reproductive stages are *paedomorphic,* attaining sexual maturity in at least a partially larval form. Such animals deceptively appear to represent an intermediate stage of evolution of the tetrapods, and actually there is undoubtedly an extensive similarity to ancestral forms linking well-adapted tetrapods and fishes, but the similarity is one of convergence. All paedomorphic salamanders are thought, on reliable grounds, to have evolved from ancestors that did transform to a terrestrial body form as sexually mature adults.

Pouch Walls. Even though the walls of the pharyngeal pouches were highly vascularized, especially after being adapted to serve as gills, it is not without reason that with the loss of respiratory function other functions would be adopted. As a matter of fact, the process of specialization of parts of the walls as glands was under way long before tetrapods appeared on the scene—even with the earliest known fishes.

The *thymus gland,* primitively consisting of several separate parts, one derived from the wall of the dorsal pocket (ventral in mammals) of each pouch on each side, becomes progressively more compact and more limited in its source throughout vertebrates. All pouches produce thymus gland tissue in cyclostomes. In gnathostome fishes typically four pairs of pouches contribute to the thymus; in amphibians three pairs (except anurans, with one); and in amniotes two pairs, although in mammals one of the two pairs contributes virtually nothing. As constantly present as the thymus is through all vertebrates, it must be an essential cog in vertebrate function, but what that function is remains to this date unknown. Suppression of sexual maturation in early development is a suggested role, supported by the fact that the gland becomes reduced in size or even lost in sexually mature animals, but no experimental evidence supports the idea. Some regard it as lymphoid in function, since it is lymphoid in tissue structure. Since ducts are absent an endocrine or lymphoid function seems the only possible value unless indeed the glands now serve merely as a developmental trigger essential to the embryogeny of other organs.

A second set of derivatives is the *tonsils,* of which the earliest to appear are *pharyngeal tonsils* of amphibians (Fig. 11.26) located in the rear roof of the buccal cavity. These apparently persist in amniotes, and in man are known as *adenoids. Palatine tonsils* located at the rear of the soft palate and the *lingual tonsils* located at the base of the tongue are also pharyngeal-tonsil derivatives that are present in mammals. Only palatine tonsils (sometimes, therefore, called *true* tonsils) are definitely known to be derived from the pharyngeal pouch walls. Since they are composed of lymphoid tissue, the chief (if not exclusive) function of all is thought to be lymphoid, and accordingly it has been thought that, like most other lymph nodes, they can be removed with little, if any, harm to the owner.

Other glandular derivatives of the pouch walls are modified from the ventral pockets, as opposed to the thymus and tonsils (Fig. 11.27) that are derived from the dorsal pockets as noted previously. In the cyclostomes the ventral derivatives are presaged by rudimentary epithelial thickenings called *epithelial corpuscles* of unknown function. In living gnathostome fishes the epithelial corpuscles, with the exception of the *postbranchial bodies,* have disappeared; but that they existed in primitive fishes is implied by their persistence as *parathyroid* and *carotid glands* in tetrapods.

The *parathyroid glands* are present in all tetrapods. They develop as specialized outgrowths of the dorsal (mammals only) or ventral pockets of two or three pairs of pharyngeal pouches. The glands are thus often seen as two or three discrete structures on each side, less often a single pair. They are partially imbedded in the thyroid gland in mammals, situated close to that gland in reptiles and birds, and are located at various positions in the neck in amphibians. As regulators (by means of a hormonal secre-

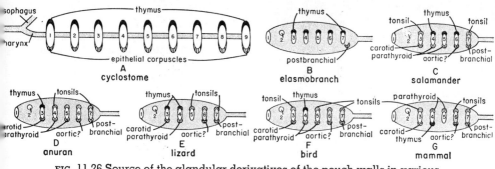

FIG. 11.26 Source of the glandular derivatives of the pouch walls in various vertebrates.

tion) of the amount of calcium and phosphorus in the blood, the parathyroids are absolutely essential to life, at least in most mammals; removal
results in death within a few days (not in the rat). Whether they are equally
essential in other tetrapods is unknown. Presumably some other mechanism
of calcium and phosphorus control exists in fishes as it must be a function
of equal importance in them as in tetrapods. A gradual replacement of
that mechanism throughout tetrapods culminates with an almost complete
shift of control to the parathyroids in the more advanced groups such as
mammals.

The *carotid glands* (or *carotid bodies*) are present in all tetrapods
where they function as sense organs detecting the oxygen tension in the
blood; this complements in all vertebrates the action of the brain centers
sensitive to the concentration of carbon dioxide. Decrease in oxygen concentration or increase in carbon dioxide content initiates a motor response
of increase in rate of mechanical respiration. In endotherms the carotid
body has acquired the additional function of detecting variation in cranial
blood pressure.

Another mammalian structure, the *aortic body* situated at the arch of
the aorta, has much the same function as the carotid body and may, like the
latter, have evolved from pharyngeal-pouch walls.

The *postbranchial* or *ultimobranchial bodies,* arising presumably
from the seventh or even more posterior pharyngeal pouches, are present
in all gnathostomes but are situated in different positions in different classes.
In mammals they are imbedded in the thyroid gland, but in other groups
they lie more posteriorly in the neck or thoracic region. Their function is
unknown.

Thyroid Gland. Most of the structures derived from the pharynx have

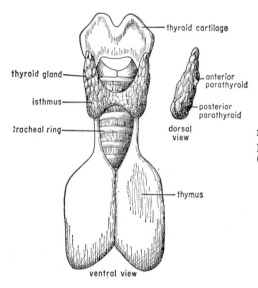

FIG. 11.27 Thyroid, thymus, and
parathyroid glands in man.
(From Adams and Eddy.)

been discussed in connection with the pouch wall, cavities, and slits. The thyroid gland is an exception. It has evolved, at least in part, from the endostyle of protochordate ancestors, as is clearly shown in the embryogeny of lampreys. In vertebrates it forms as a midventral evagination from the pharynx wall in the same position the endostyle occupies in protochordates. It has secondarily become paired in some vertebrates. Much new glandular material was added in the course of evolution, but the original source of the thyroid from the endostyle can scarcely be questioned. Its close functional association with the digestive tract in primitive chordates is reflected by the unique capacity of its hormone, thyroxin, to resist digestive action of the alimentary tract; no other hormone can be taken by mouth.

The functions of the thyroid gland appear to be mediated in all vertebrates by its hormonal secretion, *thyroxin*. By this means the thyroid gland appears to serve in all vertebrates as a regulator of rate of metabolism. It possesses still other functions at least in classes other than mammals, playing a key role in the processes of transformation in amphibians and moulting in both amphibians and reptiles.

Air Bladder and Derivatives

Early History. Paired air bladders seem to have existed in placoderms. Evidence produced by embryonic caecilians, as well as other indications, leads to the fairly secure inference that air bladders were derived from a rear pair of gill pouches—perhaps the eighth, ninth, or tenth. Presumably, in the course of reduction in number of gill pouches as they became more efficient as respiratory organs, some rear pair lost its external gill slits and became useful as storage organs for air or gas (Fig. 11.28). They may have evolved either as aids in respiration, or as a device for adding buoyancy to the body in response to the fresh-water habits the placoderms appear to have developed. The latter appears the more probable.

Subsequently the air bladder became modified in different groups in three different ways: (1) lost in chondrichthyans and some teleosts; (2) specialized as a *swim bladder* in most Osteichthyes; and (3) specialized as a *lung* in some choanichthyans and in their tetrapod derivatives (Fig. 11.28).

A true or definitive swim bladder is characterized by (1) fusion of the originally paired chambers with each other dorsally, (2) loss or dorsal shift of attachment to the gut, (3) absence of a pulmonary vein or artery, (4) absence of internal subdivision, and (5) function as a modifier of specific gravity. True or definitive lungs have (1) no fusion of the originally paired chambers, (2) a shift ventrally of attachment to the gut, (3) paired pulmonary veins and arteries, (4) internal subdivisions of some sort, often complex, and (5) a function as an organ for aerial respiration.

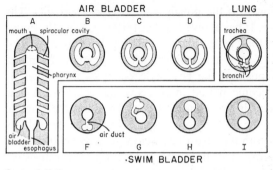

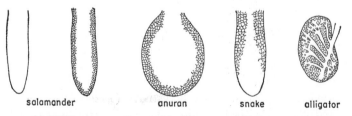

FIG. 11.28 Hypothetical evolution of the swim bladder and lungs of vertebrates. B-I, cross sections at level of air bladders or derivatives thereof. B-D, successive stages in perfection of air bladders; E, transformation of air bladders to lungs; F-I, transformation of air bladders to a swim bladder. Air bladder walls, and their derivatives, bordered by a fine line.

Intermediate types exist even in primitive living fishes and render conclusive the supposition of common origin of the two structures.

Lung Structure. Primitive lungs are baglike structures with simple walls. A short *trachea* extends from the glottis to the forked *bronchi* that in turn lead to each lung. Evolution of efficient structure was a long process. Anurans possess a few ridges about the inner lung surface, forming shallow pockets (Fig. 11.29). In reptiles the trachea and bronchi are larger and the lung pockets more numerous and deeper, with a central duct leading to them. In mammals the central duct has acquired a wall and become highly branched, the fine terminal branches leading into millions of tiny pouches (*alveoli*), where gaseous exchange occurs (Fig. 11.30). Being blind, however, there cannot be a complete exhaustion of air from the respiratory chambers with each exhalation; a certain amount of residual, inert air remains.

The most efficient lung structure occurs in birds, in which the alveoli are replaced by tiny tubes, called *air capillaries*, where respiration takes place (Fig. 11.31). These tubes occur as numerous crescent-shaped loops along the length of larger ducts, the *parabronchioles*, branching from bronchi in the lungs. Each end of each air capillary opens into a parabronchiole, and the loop between extends parallel with the parabronchiole. Open at both ends, the air capillaries permit a complete circulation of

FIG. 11.29 Diagrammatic section illustrating the gross internal structure of the lungs in various vertebrates. (From Wiedersheim.)

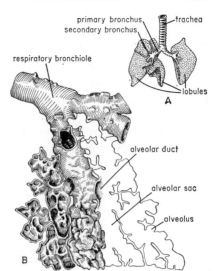

primary bronchus
secondary bronchus
trachea
respiratory bronchiole
lobules
A
alveolar duct
alveolar sac
alveolus
B

FIG. 11.30. Mammalian lung structure. A, trachea and lungs of rat;
bronchioles leading to lobules not
shown. B, a single lobule enlarged.
(From Bremer, Adams, and Eddy.)

air over their surfaces. Air replacement is not complete with each breath,
however, for there is no means whereby the air can be forced through these
capillaries; it perforce rushes through the parabronchioles with each breath,
but maintenance of favorable gaseous tensions in the air capillaries undoubtedly is largely a matter of diffusion. Avian lungs do possess a forced-
draft architecture, but curiously enough the effectiveness extends only to the
parabronchiole level of subdivision and not to the level of actual gaseous
exchange (that is, to the air capillaries). In this respect the avian lung is not
greatly superior to the mammalian lung. It has been estimated that lung
efficiency in birds approximates 25 percent, whereas that of mammals is
around 10 percent.

The structure and function of avian lungs are not wholly understood.
Usually five pairs of air sacs are placed about the lungs; one or more air
sacs are usually connected with cavities in certain adjacent bones such as
the humerus, sternum, coracoid, furcula, scapula, ribs, and pelvis. The
lungs are more or less constant in size at all times in a given adult specimen,
contrary to the situation in all other vertebrates depending upon the lungs
for gaseous exchanges. It is the air sacs that expand and deflate, forcing
air back and forth over the pulmonary respiratory surfaces. The *trachea*
forks into two *primary bronchi,* one entering each lung. This, in turn,
branches into *afferent bronchi,* leading on the one hand into the air sacs
via *air sac bronchi,* and on the other into *parabronchioles.* The parabronchioles are finely branched tubes circling through the lung tissue
dorsally and there reuniting in *efferent* bronchi, which in turn join the primary bronchus. Most air sacs have an exit that is separate from the entrance
for the air: the *recurrent bronchi,* uniting with the afferent bronchi or
independently branching into parabronchioles. With inhalation, air passes
through the primary bronchus into the afferent bronchi and thence chiefly

into the air sac bronchi, but partly into the parabronchioles. At exhalation air leaves the air sacs via the recurrent bronchi (where present) or air sac bronchi, thence is forced through the parabronchioles into the efferent bronchi, primary bronchus, and ultimately to the exterior. As thus conceived air circulation in the avian lung is simple and straightforward enough; unfortunately, however, such a circulation requires the existence of reciprocal valves which have not as yet been demonstrated to exist. The details of the mechanism of avian respiration remain to be established.

Birds are also unique in possessing a *syrinx* at the union of the primary bronchi. This is a cartilaginous "voice box," totally lacking homology with the "voice box" (larynx) of other vertebrates.

The Breathing Mechanism. A complicated system of branchiomeric muscles enables fishes to circulate water over the gills; but adaptation to terrestrial life increased dependence for respiration upon the lungs and a new system became necessary. No single method was immediately impressed into service, perhaps because evolution of a truly efficient breathing mechanism required a series of alterations, each hinging upon the preceding one. Mammals and birds have evolved a peak of efficiency not matched by other vertebrates.

Modern amphibians breathe chiefly by buccopharyngeal movements; the floor of the mouth is depressed, increasing the volume of the buccal cavity and causing inhalation of a quantity of air to occupy the increased volume. The external nares are then closed, the buccal floor is elevated, and the air is forced into the lungs. Because of an extensive buccopharyngeal vascularization, amphibians can omit for considerable periods the step of forcing air into the lungs by simply forcing air out of and into the buccal cavity. One group of lungless salamanders breathes solely by this method. One group of anurans scarcely breathes at all, respiring chiefly through the skin; the members of this group are highly aquatic animals. The buccopharyngeal breathing mechanism undoubtedly was the standard among ancient primitive amphibians. The highly efficient branchiomeric pumping system of fishes was of no use since it was (and is) restricted to the pharyngeal area, whereas the lungs lie posteriorly. The capacity to move the ribs had not evolved in fishes, and thus the buccopharyngeal mechanism was an important stopgap. It was highly inefficient, however, for it required the mouth to be closed; animals with a buccopharyngeal breathing mechanism cannot breathe while feeding.

Thus among reptiles the rib muscles came to act generally as a subsidiary of buccopharyngeal muscles; in turtles, however, without movable ribs, breathing is accomplished by contraction of several celomic membranes invaded by specialized hypaxial trunk muscles; the girdles move passively as breathing occurs but are not instrumental in effecting breathing movements.

Birds have adopted much the same system as turtles, breathing chiefly by means of contraction of specialized hypaxial muscles that cause exertion and release of pressure upon the visceral air sacs.

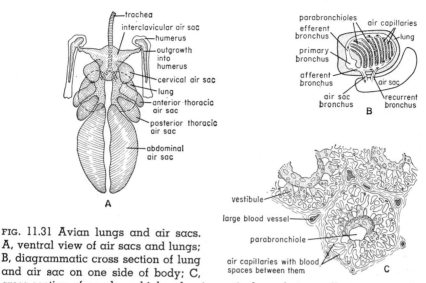

FIG. 11.31 Avian lungs and air sacs. A, ventral view of air sacs and lungs; B, diagrammatic cross section of lung and air sac on one side of body; C, cross section of parabronchioles showing reticulum of air capillaries surrounding each. (From Thomson and Goodrich.)

In mammals intercostal, diaphragm, and abdominal muscles all aid in breathing. Contraction of the diaphragm and external intercostals enlarges the pleural cavity, drawing air into the lungs; relaxation of these muscles causes exhalation to the point of equilibrium of internal and external tensions. A forcible exhalation beyond the point of equilibrium is brought about by contraction of abdominal muscles and the internal intercostals, which by relaxation permit inhalation until a point of equilibrium is again reached. Breathing in mammals can thus be carried on completely below or completely above the point of internal and external equilibrium, or overlapping that point to a considerable degree. The same situation, with, of course, different mechanics, undoubtedly exists in all breathing tetrapods.

The Swim Bladder. The crude air bladders of placoderms, choanichthyans, chondrosteans, and holosteans, serving perhaps a dual function as organs of buoyancy and of respiration, became specialized in most teleosts for the function of buoyancy, or were lost. Chondrichthyan fishes, limited to the oceans, lost them completely, as they had no need for either respiratory accessories or buoyancy aids (the dense salt water serving the latter purpose). Many marine teleosts, as a matter of fact, have likewise lost the air bladder. Fresh-water teleosts, which need a compensation for the relatively light medium they live in, have this air bladder highly specialized to serve in reduction of their specific gravity.

As stated previously, intermediate types between swim bladders and lungs occur in some living primitive fishes (Fig. 11.32). These are well adapted to serve either as swim bladders or as lungs. In dipnoans and Polypterus the air bladders are attached to the gut midventrally by a common trachealike tube and are internally subdivided; in the Holostei they also possess internal compartments. Paired bronchuslike structures are present in some dipnoans and in Polypterus, but in Neoceratodus a single tube leads from the gut to the bladder, which while single shows clear evidence of its paired origin. One teleost fish has the bladder tube attached to the side of the gut, in a position intermediate between that of the primitive air bladder (and retained by the lungs) and that of the swim bladder. In other teleost fish the bladder attachment is lost (*physoclistous*) or is dorsal in position in adults. Some marine and bottom-dwelling types have lost the bladder entirely.

The hydrostatic function is, to a small degree, performed in those fishes (*physostomous*) with an intact bladder duct by the simple expedient of gulping air at the water surface and releasing it as needed by exerting muscular pressure upon the bladder. To a greater degree in all, and entirely in those teleosts without a bladder duct in adults, one or more *red glands* or *red bodies* actively secrete gases (chiefly oxygen, partly carbon dioxide, nitrogen, and other atmospheric gases) into the bladder, whence it is re-absorbed into the blood by other tissues about the swim bladder.

Swim bladders serve secondarily in some species as devices for making sounds; as muscles contract against the membrane of the bladder, vibrations, differing with species, are produced. In certain species the swim bladder has also acquired an auditory function, passing sound vibrations to the inner ear by way of a series of *Weberian ossicles*—small bones modified from the anterior vertebrae.

Esophagus

The esophagus is very short in fishes and amphibians, longer in amniotes (Fig. 11.33). Its elongation can chiefly be attributed to the necessity in amniotes of bypassing the newly enlarged lungs, situated about the heart, and of traversing a newly evolved neck, also a necessary adjunct of successful life on land. The lamprey, with a separation of pharynx and alimentary tract, like amniotes has a long esophagus bypassing the pharyngeal region. The similarity is clearly a parallelism, not a product of common origin.

Presumably the esophagus was originally provided largely, if not wholly, with smooth muscle fibers, and thus was subject only to involuntary control. In later types the upper end is invaded to varying degrees with striated muscle fibers subject to voluntary control. Ordinarily only the upper end, if any, of the esophagus has striated fibers, but in ruminant mammals voluntary fibers extend even into the so-called stomach.

In many birds a specialized pouch in the esophagus for storage of food, the *crop,* has evolved with the function of enabling them to feed quickly and well when the opportunity presents itself.

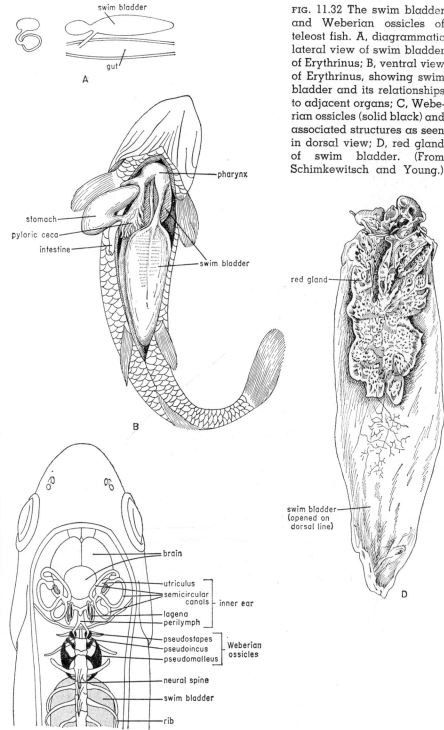

FIG. 11.32 The swim bladder and Weberian ossicles of teleost fish. A, diagrammatic lateral view of swim bladder of Erythrinus; B, ventral view of Erythrinus, showing swim bladder and its relationships to adjacent organs; C, Weberian ossicles (solid black) and associated structures as seen in dorsal view; D, red gland of swim bladder. (From Schimkewitsch and Young.)

Stomach

Originally simply a storage organ, the stomach has secondarily adopted digestive functions in most fishes and in all tetrapods. In all a sphincter called the *pylorus* separates the stomach from the intestine; there is no comparable delimitation of stomach and esophagus (Fig. 11.34).

Originally a simple bag, the stomach is virtually nonexistent in various groups of fishes (cyclostomes, holocephalans, dipnoans, some teleosts), but elsewhere there is a general trend toward increase in complexity, with special functions served by each part. This trend is especially conspicuous in herbivorous vertebrates, to a lesser extent in carnivorous animals. The regions of the stomach commonly recognized are, in order from esophagus to pylorus, the *esophageal* (with nonglandular, stratified epithelium),

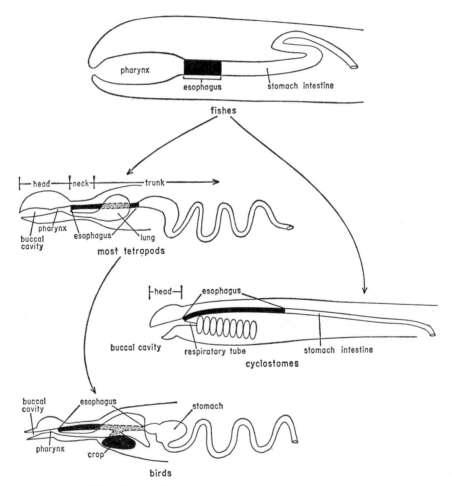

FIG. 11.33 Evolution of gross features of esophagus in vertebrates.

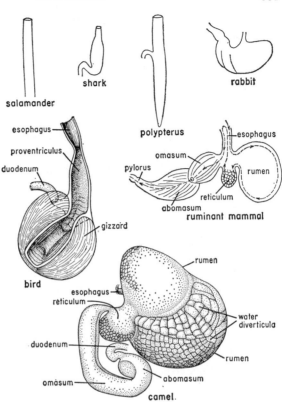

FIG. 11.34 Variation in shape of the stomach in vertebrates. (From Kingsley, Hilzheimer, Adams, and Eddy.)

cardiac (with columnar epithelium possessing nondigestive glands, present in mammals only but not in all mammals), *fundus* (with columnar epithelium possessing digestive glands), and *pyloric* (with columnar epithelium possessing nondigestive glands). These regions, as defined by histomorphology, are but little correlated with gross form. The esophageal region, actually representing an enlarged part of the esophagus, is absent in some but comprises most of the stomach in other vertebrates.

Gross features of the stomach bear little constancy among vertebrates. Crocodilians have a thin-walled anterior chamber, the *proventriculus,* followed by a thicker-walled *gizzard* or *ventriculus.* Birds have much the same sort of specialization, although the demarcation between the two parts is not always clear. In ruminant mammals a still greater subdivision occurs. Ruminants are the artiodactyls with a stomach subdivided into not less than three chambers. Pigs, peccaries, and hippopotami lack these subdivisions. Typically the stomach of ruminants consists of four well-defined chambers of which the anterior three (*rumen, reticulum, omasum*) are thought to be in reality modifications of the esophagus, only the posterior chamber (*abomasum*) constituting the cardiac, fundus, and pyloric parts of the stomach. Ruminants bolt their food, storing it in the rumen. Then at their leisure they regurgitate the poorly chewed food in small balls and

FIG. 11.35 Spiral valve in an elasmobranch. (From Kingsley.)

chew them as "cuds." The food is then returned to the reticulum. In camels a series of *water diverticula* aid digestion but do not serve for storage of water. A pyloric enlargement, often cecumlike, occurs in some mammals as, for example, the blood-lapping vampire bat.

Intestine

Originally, in protochordates and cyclostomes, a straight tube with little modification, the intestine in gnathostomes is subdivided into an anterior *small intestine* and a posterior *large intestine*. The latter ends at the cloaca or, in forms having the intestinal opening separate from the reproductive and urinary ducts, at the anus. A terminal part, the *rectum,* is often distinguishable. The small intestine is modified in primitive fishes as a *spiral valve* (Fig. 11.35), an ingenious device that greatly lengthens the passageway (and thus digestive surface) without increasing the length of the intestine. It is a much neater solution to the problem of increasing the digestive area than that of most other vertebrates whose lengthy intestine is folded and twisted randomly in the abdomen. A rudimentary spiral valve may be represented by the only slightly spiraled low ridge called a *typhlosole* in cyclostomes. For some reason the spiral valve was gradually abandoned in fishes, perhaps because of the gradually bulkier food and the necessity for more efficient peristalsis. It is absent in teleosts, and no tetrapods retain it in any form.

Increase in length of intestine is the rule in herbivorous vertebrates, whereas in carnivores the intestine may remain but little longer than the body. Digestion of plant tissue is obviously more difficult than digestion of animal tissue. The correlation is nowhere more striking than in many anurans, whose herbivorous tadpoles have intestines many times longer than the body, whereas the adults are carnivorous and have intestines but two or three times the body length (Fig. 11.36).

A *duodenal* (anterior) section of the small intestine is commonly recognized in all gnathostomes, but mammals are unique in possessing a further subdivision of the rear part of the small intestine into the more anterior *jejunum* and a posterior *ileum*.

Cloaca

Primitively the excretory, genital, and intestinal canals open into a common chamber, the *cloaca,* whose opening to the exterior is the *anus*.

The urinogenital ducts open into the rear dorsal wall of this chamber. A ridge within or constriction of the cloacal cavity often partially separates an intestinal part from the urinogenital part. The *coprodaeum* is the division receiving the intestine; the *urodaeum* receives the genital and reproductive ducts. The coprodaeum is anterior in anamniotes, posterior in amniotes.

In many fishes and in mammals except monotremes, the cloaca is nonexistent, the intestine and urinogenital ducts opening separately to the exterior at the anus. In such fishes the intestinal opening is anterior, whereas in mammals it is posterior. The shift from the piscine arrangement is attributable to the development of a ventral cloacal diverticulum, the *urinary bladder,* in amphibians. The urinogenital ducts eventually establish contact with this urinary bladder in mammals. Thus as a separation of the bladder and intestine is effected in mammals, the urinogenital ducts open anterior to the anus rather than posterior to it as in the fishes with a completely divided cloaca.

Embryonically in all vertebrates an ectoderm-lined invagination, the *proctodaeum,* forms at the rear of the body. In vertebrates with a cloaca the proctodaeum is altered but little in adults, becoming the cloaca itself. In vertebrates lacking a cloaca the proctodaeum becomes subdivided and disappears in late embryogeny.

Gut Diverticula

Liver. The liver forms embryonically as a ventral outpouching from the gut whose connection persists in all gnathostomes as the *bile duct.* It

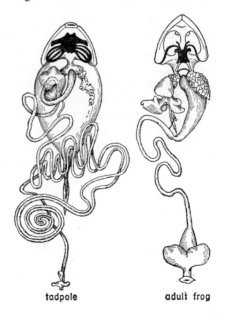

FIG. 11.36 Contrast in lengths of alimentary tracts in a tadpole and an adult frog. (From Wilder.)

tadpole   adult frog

varies greatly in size and conformation in different vertebrates, but as a vitally important structure is present in all vertebrates.

The liver has digestive functions but it also has numerous other functions. In lampreys, as a matter of fact, the digestive function is lost, for the bile duct is absent and the liver is accessible only by way of the circulatory system. The bile, a product of digestive value, is in most vertebrates stored in a pouch, the *gall bladder,* evaginated from the bile duct. It is not essential, when present can be removed without harm, and is normally absent in some groups of mammals and birds.

Rather constant in form throughout vertebrates, the liver appears in cephalochordates as a hollow diverticulum from the gut immediately posterior to the pharynx. If this indeed is homologous with the vertebrate liver, it obviously lacks many of the functions of that organ. With good reason it is often referred to as an *hepatic cecum* because of its difference from the true vertebrate liver.

Both the urochordates and hemichordates have digestive glands of somewhat different character, appearing as a series of small pouches along the anterior part of the intestine. Whether these are homologous with the vertebrate liver or pancreas is uncertain.

The chief digestive function of the liver is secretion of bile, the primary effect of which is to emulsify fats as a mechanical aid to their chemical breakdown by pancreatic enzymes. Some other functions known in various vertebrates are detoxification of many poisons, formation especially in embryos and destruction in adults of red blood cells, storage of glycogen and fatty substances, production of heat, and secretion into the blood of an enzyme essential for carbohydrate and protein metabolism. No gland of the vertebrate body has more varied functions than the liver, although it curiously has never acquired any endocrine function.

Pancreas. All vertebrates and only vertebrates possess a pancreas. In some vertebrates, however, it is diffuse and sometimes partly imbedded in other organs. It arises in all as a dorsal and usually also ventral outpouching from the gut. The organ maintains union with the gut through one or more *pancreatic ducts*. The ducts may enter the small intestine with the bile duct or separately.

A *parapancreas* of unknown function and origin occurs beside or within the ventral lobe of the pancreas in certain sea snakes. As described by the discoverer, Bergman (1938), it possesses a separate duct emptying into the duodenum in common with or near the bile duct. It may well be an evolutionary and embryonic derivative and specialization of the ventral lobe of the pancreas.

The pancreas is essentially a digestive gland, secreting a number of digestive enzymes adapted to fractionation of proteins, carbohydrates, fats, proteoses, or peptones. It is also an endocrine gland, certain groups of its cells (*islands of Langerhans*) secreting a hormone, *insulin,* which regulates the storage of glycogen in the liver, the level of concentration of sugar in the blood, and the oxidation of the sugar by body cells in general.

Ceca. In many teleost fishes one or more (up to 200 or so) slender diverticula called *pyloric ceca* are attached to the small intestine near the pylorus. The number is often used as a means of distinguishing species. A *colic cecum,* rarely two, is present in most mammals. It is sometimes of very large size. In some vertebrates (for example, man) the distal end is degenerate and is distinguished as the *appendix.*

Cloacal ceca are present in birds and most turtles. Those of turtles are bladderlike *cloacal bursae* and appear to be of respiratory function (see p. 283). The avian homologs are *Fabrician bursae.* They lie dorsal to the large intestine and like the cloacal bursae in some turtles they open into the dorsal cloacal wall by a single aperture. The large internal cavity of each bursa is lined by columnar epithelium, and numerous branching tubules imbedded in lymphatic nodules open into each cavity. The avian bursae presumably function as "cloacal tonsils," but may also have other functions.

Anal or *cloacal glands* are accessories commonly present in all tetrapod classes. They serve primarily as protective structures in some species, as a sexual lure in others.

Urinary Bladder. In amphibians a urinary bladder first appears as a ventral outpouching from the rear of the large intestine. Although not directly connected with the urinary ducts in amphibians, it still serves in them for storage of urine. It persists in primitive reptiles and in mammals, but in snakes, crocodilians, and birds is lost. In the latter group, snakes and in lizards, the urinary wastes are solid and eliminated with the feces, thus rendering a urinary bladder an unnecessary adjunct. In amphibians, turtles, and mammals excreting a fluid urine, the urinary bladder has been preserved as a useful storage organ. Ammonia is too toxic to be stored.

Extraembryonic Membranes. In all vertebrates with telolecithal eggs the *yolk sac* is continuous with the cavity of the small intestine. All trace of the yolk stalk is ordinarily lost in adults; abnormally a short diverticulum may persist.

The *allantois,* restricted in occurrence to the amniotes, forms as a ventral evagination of the gut, utilizing as a matter of fact the urinary bladder already present in amphibian ancestors. The structure disappears in adults except for (1) the base which becomes the urinary bladder in those amniotes possessing one, and (2) a ligament connecting the bladder with the midventral body wall at the umbilicus.

QUESTIONS

1. Name and give examples of the three types of modification in the gross anatomy of the alimentary tract as seen in chordate evolution. What is the survival value of such modifications?

2. State what structures in embryonic and adult tetrapods represent each of the mouths that have evolved in chordate phylogeny. In cyclostomes? In protochordates?

3. State which groups of animals utilize as mouths each of the three mouths evident in chordate phylogeny.

4. Characterize teeth.

5. How do enamel, bone, and dentine differ?

6. How does the general pattern of growth of a tooth differ from, say, that of a phalangeal bone?

7. What was the evolutionary source of teeth?

8. State the general trend of change in tooth location in vertebrates, and give supportive examples.

9. State the general trend of change in number of teeth in vertebrates and give supportive examples.

10. State the general trend of change in cycles of tooth replacement in vertebrates and give supportive examples.

11. State the general trend of change in form of teeth in vertebrates and give supportive examples.

12. Name, distinguish, give the occurrence, and trace the evolution of the various stages in reduction of number of tooth replacements.

13. Name, distinguish, give the occurrence, and trace the evolution of the various types of tooth anchorage.

14. What is the primitive tooth formula for mammals? For man? For the cat?

15. Briefly state how the formerly standard medical views and the hypotheses of comparative anatomy differ in reference to the premolars and molars. State the two premises responsible for the unique features of the former terminology for man.

16. Briefly discuss the origin, original survival value, and evolution in function of salivary glands.

17. What has been the evolution in distribution of taste buds?

18. What was the original survival value of internal nares?

19. What are the survival values of the secondary palate?

20. To what facts of anatomical heritage can the failure of complete separation of respiratory and alimentary tracts of "higher" vertebrates be attributed?

21. How might the present impasse in progressive separation of respiratory and digestive tracts be regarded as either fortunate or unfortunate?

22. How do the tongues of mammals and other vertebrates differ in intrinsic musculature?

23. Briefly discuss variation in shape, attachment, and method of protrusion of the tongue in different vertebrates.

24. Distinguish three kinds (definitions) of respiration.

25. Name the seven organs used for respiration and the groups of vertebrates in which each is used.

26. Which class of vertebrates possesses the greatest array of different respiratory organs? What evolutionary significance may this have?

27. Name the three successive stages of dominant pharyngeal functions and the chordates of which they are characteristic.

28. Explain three major lines of modification of the gill respiratory system in fishes.

29. Distinguish and state the evolutionary relationships of lamellar, filamentous, and labyrinthine types of gills. What is the function of the labyrinth organ?

30. Describe three alterations in fishes commonly involved in reduction in number of gill pouches. How are the same cavities altered, if at all, in tetrapods?

31. What alterations of other pouches (that is, those not involved in the preceding question) occurred with emergence of tetrapods?

32. What is paedomorphosis? Is the larval body form in such a condition primitive? Explain.

33. Trace the evolution of the thymus gland in vertebrates.

34. Name the structures derived from the gill pouch walls, the function of each, and the vertebrate group in which each occurs.

35. What protochordate structure appears to be the forerunner of the vertebrate thyroid gland?

36. What functions of the thyroid gland are known?

37. In gross terms, what was the fate of the air bladder in the descendants of the earliest vertebrates?

38. How do the definitive lung and swim bladder differ?

39. What are the anatomical peculiarities that render avian lungs potentially more efficient than any others, and how do they operate?

40. How does voice production in birds differ from that in mammals?

41. Describe the breathing process of amphibians; of reptiles; of various groups of birds; of mammals.

42. What variation in form and attachment of the air bladder and its derivatives occurs in fishes?

43. What are the functions of the swim bladder of fishes and how are these reflected in their habitat?

44. Describe the mechanism of gas control in the piscine swim bladder.

45. What are Weberian ossicles, in what do they occur, and where are they located?

46. How does the esophagus differ in length in fishes and in tetrapods, and to what may this difference be attributed?

47. How is the esophagus of most birds unique?

48. Discuss variation in muscularization of the esophagus. What unique function is served by the extreme of full voluntary muscularization?

49. What is distinctive about the esophagus of the lampreys?

50. Name and characterize the regions of the stomach.

51. How are birds and crocodilians similar in stomach structure?

52. Describe the function of the ruminant stomach, naming the parts in proper order.

53. How is the mammalian small intestine unique?

54. What conformation of the small intestine is evident in elasmobranchs?

55. How do the positional relations of intestinal and urinogenital openings, where separate, differ in mammals as compared with nonmammalian vertebrates?

56. Name and locate the major diverticula of the alimentary tract in vertebrates, stating in which groups each is found.

57. Define the following words and where appropriate state occurrence or cite examples:

abomasum
acrodont
adenohypophysis
adenoids
afferent bronchi
air bladder
air capillary
air sac
air sac bronchi
alveolus
aortic body
aphyodont
appendix
bicuspid
branchial
branchial chamber
bronchus
buccal cavity
canine
cardiac stomach
carnassial
carotid body
cecum
cervical fistula
cheek teeth
cloaca
cloacal bursa
colic ceca
coprodaeum
crop
crown
cusp
deciduous teeth
demibranch
dentine
diphyodont
duodenum
edentulous
efferent bronchi
enamel
epithelial corpuscles
esophageal stomach
esophagus
euacrodont
eupleurodont
Eustachian tube
external gill
external respiration
Fabrician bursa
fang

filamentous gill
fully heterodont
fundus
gill
gill rakers
gill slit
gizzard
gustatory organs
Hatschek's pit
hemidiphyodont
hepatic cecum
heterodont
holobranch
homodont
ileum
incisor
insulin
interdental
   (replacement)
internal gill
internal respiration
intrabranchial septum
islands of Langerhans
isodont
jejunum
labyrinth organ
lamella
liver
lung
mechanical respiration
middle ear cavity
molar
molar gland
molariform
monophyodont
nasopharyngeal duct
neurohypophysis
occlusion
odontoblasts
oligodont
oligophyodont
omasum
operculum
paedomorphosis
pancreas
papilla
parabronchioles
parapancreas
parathyroid
parotid gland

peristalsis
permanent teeth
pharynx
physoclistous
physostomous
pleurodont
polymodal
   (replacement)
polyodont
polyphyodont
postbranchial bodies
premolar
prethecodont
primary anus
primary bronchi
primary mouth
primary set (teeth)
proctodaeum
proventriculus
pulp cavity
pyloric stomach
pylorus
Rathke's pouch
rectum
recurrent bronchi
red gland
reticulum
root
rugae
rumen
ruminants
salivary gland
secondary anus
secondary mouth
secondary palate
secondary set (teeth)
spiracle
spiral valve
stomodaeum
subacrodont
subdental
   (replacement)
subheterodont
subisodont
sublingual gland
submaxillary gland
subneural gland
suborbital gland
subpleurodont

suprabranchial
   chamber
swim bladder
syrinx
tertiary mouth
thecodont
thymus gland

thyroid gland
tonsils (lingual,
   palatine, pharyngeal,
   true)
trachea
typhlosole
ultimobranchial bodies

unimodal
   (replacement)
urodaeum
ventriculus
villa
water diverticula
Weberian ossicle

12

ENDOCRINE SYSTEM

THE PLACE OF AN ENDOCRINE SYSTEM IN VERTEBRATE ANATOMY. The endotherm vertebrates have achieved the maximum degree of coordination existing in chordates. This achievement has been brought about not by any abrupt improvement but rather by gradual changes whose initial effects are evident early in vertebrate phylogeny.

Coordination has been effected in vertebrates by two systems: (1) the nervous system, wholly dedicated to the functions of directing and integrating activity, and (2) sets of a certain kind of secretory cells constituting endocrine glands. It is to be understood that all aggregations of actively secretory epithelial cells are *glands*. Two major types are recognized. Glands that liberate their secretions into ducts carrying those products to the surface of the epithelial membrane from which the gland has been formed are *exocrine* glands. Those whose secretions are liberated directly into the blood system are *endocrine* glands. The endocrine glands collectively constitute the *endocrine system*.

The endocrine system acts as a coordinator only through assistance of the circulatory system, which carries the endocrine secretions (hormones) indiscriminately throughout the body, even though they may be destined to affect only a few organs. Cells capable of producing substances having a beneficial effect elsewhere in the body have evolved in a seemingly haphazard fashion, with absolutely no anatomical relationship *inter se* whatsoever, save that they are all supplied by the circulatory and nervous systems—scarcely a unique feature. Yet the endocrine organs function as an integrated group, maintaining certain controls on each other as well as upon other organs. They, thus, collectively constitute a true system, nebulous though it may be on an anatomical basis.

310

An endocrine function—that is, secretion into the blood of a substance producing an effect elsewhere—is the sole function of the *pituitary, thyroid, parathyroid,* and *adrenal* glands, as they exist in tetrapods. The *pancreas* is not only an endocrine but also an exocrine gland, secreting substances onto an epithelial surface (in this case into the duodenum). The *gonads, hypothalamus, duodenum,* and *placenta* are all of endocrine function, but they have other important functions as well; the gonads are cytogenic (producing reproductive cells); the hypothalamus is of nervous function; the duodenum of digestive function; the placenta of nutritive, excretory, and other functions. A number of other organs are thought possibly to have endocrine functions, but are more likely of lymphoid function or are totally useless; the *thymus* and *pineal* glands are especially suspect. Tissues apparently capable of producing substances identical with certain hormones, but differing from endocrine tissue in the sense that the substances have an effect only in the immediate vicinity of release, are found in many places in the body; many if not all end plates of effector (motor) neurones, and special cells in the cervix of the uterus, in the prostate glands, in the carotid glands, and elsewhere, are examples.

Like other systems the endocrine system has evolved tremendously in vertebrates, but the trends are chiefly toward (1) segregation of hormone secreting tissues as discrete organs, (2) elaboration of new hormones, and (3) increase in the role of certain hormones. Most of the changes are thus physiological and do not grossly involve apparent anatomical adjustments. No survey of comparative anatomy should fail to take cognizance of the functional values of anatomical succession, but physiological succession of itself is not here considered to be within the province of comparative anatomy.

The major facts in anatomical phylogeny of most of the organs known or suspected to have endocrine function are dealt with elsewhere in this book in connection with the anatomically recognizable systems with which they have been associated in vertebrate phylogeny. The adrenal glands are an exception.

Adrenal Gland Evolution

Adrenal glands may be characterized as organs located near the kidneys in all tetrapods and consisting of interrenal and suprarenal tissues. The interrenal tissue secretes a complex of hormones (including cortisone), and the suprarenal tissue produces epinephrin ("adrenalin" is a commercial preparation). Embryonically the interrenal tissue forms from the mesodermal peritoneal wall, whereas the suprarenal tissue is formed from ectoderm derived from the neural crest cells. In mammals the interrenal tissue is restricted to an outer zone of the adrenal gland called the *cortex,* the suprarenal tissue to the inner *medulla.* In other tetrapods the two tissues are more or less heterogeneously intermingled.

The completely different embryonic origin of the two tissues of the composite adrenal glands is a reflection of their completely separate phylogenetic histories. In fishes the suprarenal tissue, commonly bright yellow in life, is scattered in small aggregations along either side of the dorsal aorta, very near the sympathetic ganglia from which those cells no doubt evolved, and with which there is a remarkable similarity of function. The interrenal tissue, commonly pinkish, is as the name implies usually scattered in clumps along the medial surfaces of the kidneys.

In amphibians, although the two tissues are intermingled to form grossly recognizable adrenal glands, the glands are elongate structures intermediate in form between the diffuse form of fishes and the compact form of amniotes.

QUESTIONS

1. What is the function of an endocrine system and how is it performed? On what basis can the endocrine organs be regarded as constituting a system?

2. Name the endocrine glands and specify the nature of their functions, if any, other than endocrine. What glands are suspected but not proved to be of endocrine function?

3. Are all chemical equivalents of hormones produced solely by endocrine glands? Explain.

4. How do the mammalian adrenals differ from those of other vertebrates in organization of tissue? Explain.

5. Distinguish the adrenal tissues in mode of origin and in function.

6. How may amphibians be considered intermediate between the more primitive fishes and more advanced amniotes with respect to the adrenals?

7. Define the following words:

adrenalin	endocrine gland	interrenal glands
cortex	epinephrin	medulla
cortisone	exocrine gland	suprarenal glands
cytogenic	hormone	

13

URINOGENITAL SYSTEM

THE URINARY AND GENITAL SYSTEMS are usually considered together because through much of the evolution of vertebrates one system has tended to usurp parts of the other; what is genital in function in one group may in some derivative group be urinary in function, and vice versa.

Evolutionary Succession of Vertebrate Kidneys

Four distinctive types of kidneys occur in adult stages of vertebrates: the *holonephros, opisthonephros, pronephros,* and *metanephros.* An understanding of the details of structure and evolution of these types cannot be acquired at this point, but an early appreciation of their evolutionary relationships is essential (Fig. 13.1). The *holonephros* is the most primitive type, occurring in fact in the adults of no living vertebrate. It is derived from the full length of the embryonic nephrotomal plate. The extreme anterior end of the holonephros has been lost in living primitive vertebrates, whose kidney in adults is derived from all the nephrotomal plate except that of a few segments at the anterior end of the celomic area; such a kidney is an *opisthonephros.*

The other two types evolved independently from opisthonephric animals. In a few teleost fishes an adult kidney was developed from only those anterior nephrotomes that were lost in their adult opisthonephric

313

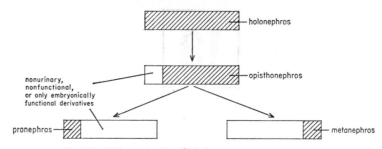

FIG. 13.1 The evolutionary sequence of the kinds of kidneys occurring in adult vertebrates, living and fossil. All four outlines are the same length and indicate the nephrotomal plate.

ancestors; such a kidney is a *pronephros*. In amniotes the adult kidney develops from the opposite extremity of the nephrotomal plate, representing the posterior end only of the opisthonephros of their ancestors; such a kidney is a *metanephros*.

Origin of the Holonephros

Perhaps the best perspective of the close relationship of urinary and reproductive systems can be obtained by tracing the phylogeny of the most primitive of all vertebrate kidneys, the holonephros.

Hypothetical Ancestral Prechordate Stage. Although the protochordates from which vertebrates evolved are unknown, there is good reason to believe they possessed a segmented celom and segmental gonads (Fig. 13.2). Each celom space is thought to have communicated more or less directly with the exterior by a *urinogenital pore* or *celomoduct* conductive of both excretory and gonadal products. Thus at this stage the celomic spaces already served two functions: the gathering and elimination of metabolic wastes, and elimination of reproductive cells.

Hypothetical Ancestral Protochordate Stage. Five alterations were involved in attainment of conditions that could be regarded as primitive among vertebrates (Fig. 13.3). First, the intersegmental septa disappeared, leaving only the vertical dorsal and ventral septa separating right and left celoms from each other. Second, the gonads fused into a single organ on each side, eventually shortening markedly. Many fish retain gonads of primitive form that extend nearly the full length of the body, whereas in other fish and in tetrapods generally they are greatly reduced in size and limited to a small part (primitively the anterior part) of the celom. Third, the rear pair of segmental urinogenital pores became reproductive only in function; they are *genital pores,* retained for reproduction in cyclostomes, but degenerate and nonfunctional in elasmobranchs, ganoids, turtles, and crocodilians, in which they are known as *abdominal pores.* Fourth, the other pores (now *urinary pores*) became connected with each other by a longitudinal groove forming in the outer body wall—a groove that eventu-

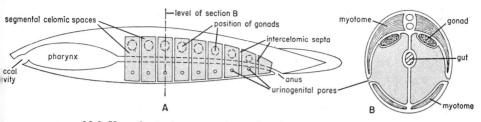

FIG. 13.2 Hypothetical ancestral prechordate stage of evolution of the kidney.

ally became closed as a tube opening to the exterior at the penultimate pore. The longitudinal tube thus formed is the *holonephric duct,* formed in response, no doubt, to the selective pressure favoring segregation of reproductive and urinary products. Fifth, the segmental connections of the celomic cavity with the holonephric duct became extended to form *uriniferous tubules,* opening into the celom at the *nephrostomes.*

Evolution of the Internal Glomerulus

Kidney function in vertebrates was not destined to be long dependent upon the celom. The indiscriminate loss of body fluids was far from efficient. A more efficient mechanism was early devised by substituting the circulatory system for the celom. As integration of kidney and circulatory system was gradually improved, the anatomical as well as functional association of the celom as a whole with the kidney was gradually eliminated entirely. We can recognize perhaps four conspicuous stages—acts—in this drama (Fig. 13.4).

Aglomerular Stage. To begin with, in the early evolution of the holonephros (the *aglomerular stage*) each uriniferous tubule soon came to drain a special pocket, the *nephrocele,* in the celom. The opening of the nephrocele into the splanchnocele is the *peritoneal funnel.* Operation of the early holonephros thus still required extraction of metabolic wastes from the celom, as in the hypothetical protochordate.

External Glomerular Stage. A second modification introduced in later holonephric animals was of major significance. A small capillary ball, the

FIG. 13.3 Hypothetical ancestral protochordate stage of evolution of the kidney.

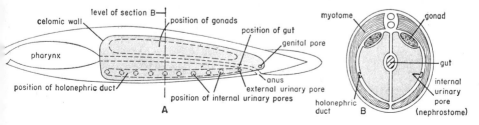

glomerulus, receiving blood from renal arteries of the dorsal aorta, and drained by renal veins, was developed to project tuberclelike into the nephrocele. Thus, for the first time the circulatory system came into effective relationship with the excretory system. Urinary products, in a crude filtrate of the blood, were released from the glomerulus into the nephrocele, thence swept into the uriniferous tubules and the holonephric duct. This sort of primitive arrangement of glomerulus and uriniferous tubule is termed the *external glomerulus.* Although not very closely duplicated in living vertebrates, this external glomerular stage was certainly an intermediate stage in intermediate and now nonexistent species.

Primitive Internal Glomerular Stage. An almost inevitable improvement followed as the nephrocele became constricted about the glomerulus (*internal glomerular stage with peritoneal funnel*). The glomerulus then became hidden within the kidney and outside of the splanchnocele, and in such relation is called an *internal glomerulus.* The peritoneal funnel is, in this third stage, restricted to a narrow duct between uriniferous tubule and splanchnocele. The nephrocele is restricted to a very narrow space, whose walls constitute *Bowman's capsule,* about the glomerulus. Capsule and glomerulus collectively constitute the *renal corpuscle.* At this stage very little excretory material is picked up from the celom; virtually all is extracted from the blood.

Advanced Internal Glomerular Stage. A final step in divorce of excretory system and the splanchnocele was taken in amniotes, with complete closure of the peritoneal funnel (*internal glomerulus without peritoneal funnel*).

FIG. 13.4 Evolution of the internal glomerulus. A, ancestral protochordate; B, aglomerular vertebrate; C, external glomerulus; D, internal glomerulus with peritoneal funnel; E, internal glomerulus without peritoneal funnel.

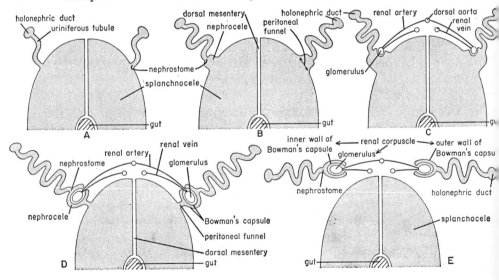

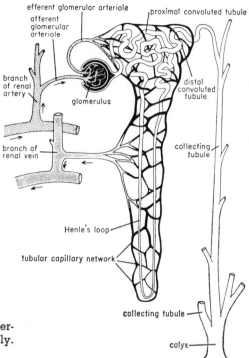

efferent glomerular arteriole

afferent glomerular arteriole

proximal convoluted tubule

branch of renal artery

glomerulus

distal convoluted tubule

branch of renal vein

collecting tubule

Henle's loop

tubular capillary network

collecting tubule

calyx

FIG. 13.5 The mammalian uriniferous tubule and its blood supply. (From Quiring.)

The Mammalian Kidney

STRUCTURE OF THE RENAL UNIT. A renal unit may be defined as a uriniferous tubule and its associated renal corpuscle. The mammalian renal units (Fig. 13.5) are essentially like those of other amniotes, consisting of extremely long uriniferous tubules and internal glomeruli without peritoneal funnels. A few relatively minor features are characteristic primarily of mammals. The most nearly unique feature is the presence of a slender, U-shaped *Henle's loop* in the middle of the uriniferous tubule. A small section in the avian uriniferous tubule is homologous. That part of the uriniferous tubule between Henle's loop and Bowman's capsule is the *proximal convoluted tubule,* the other part the *distal convoluted tubule.* About six uriniferous tubules empty into a single *collecting tubule,* tens of thousands of which are required to drain the uriniferous tubules of a single kidney.

Function of the Renal Unit. A consideration of the function of the uriniferous tubules must also embrace associated parts of the circulatory system. Two capillary networks are associated with each uriniferous tubule: the *glomerular capillary network* of the renal corpuscle, and the *tubular capillary network* enmeshing the uriniferous tubule. An *afferent glomerular artery* supplies the glomerulus, which is drained by an *efferent* *glomerular artery* in turn supplying the tubular capillary network. The latter is drained by the renal veins. A *glomerular filtrate* is obtained from the blood passing through the glomerulus; this filtrate differs from blood only in the absence of blood cells and of large molecules incapable of passing through the glomerular capillary walls. The amount of filtrate is directly proportional to blood pressure and extent of dilation of the capillary walls; the higher the pressure or the greater the concentration of *diuretic* drugs (such as caffeine, alcohol) the greater is the amount of filtrate. In the tubular capillary network useful components of the glomerular filtrate are extracted from the uriniferous tubule. Water is removed to the extent of physiological necessity primarily at Henle's loop, whereas solutes such as sugar are removed as the filtrate passes along the distal and proximal convoluted tubule. Since only mammals and birds possess a Henle's loop, and only this loop can extract water from the glomerular filtrate, only in these two groups is the concentration of urinary products in the distal tubule greater (only slightly in birds, with a small loop) than that of the blood. All recovery along the uriniferous tubule requires expenditure of energy since it is accomplished against an osmotic gradient. The fluid reaching the collecting tubule is *urine,* which undergoes little if any further change before expulsion from the body. At no point do cells of the kidney actually excrete general bodily waste products, despite the fact that the kidney as a whole serves as an excretory organ. In reality it acts more as an organ of *selective recovery* than as one of *selective elimination.*

Gross Structure. The mammalian kidney consists of a moderately thick, outer layer, the *cortex,* surrounding a large central *medulla* (Fig. 13.6). The uriniferous tubules lie exclusively in the cortex, except that the Henle's loops dip down into the peripheral areas of the medulla. The latter consists primarily of collecting tubules, whose fine distal tips lie, of course, in the cortex. The collecting tubules become progressively larger as they join with each other in passing toward one or more *renal papillae* on the surface of which they open into a large *renal pelvis* drained by the ureter. The pelvis and collecting tubules are continuous with the ureter embryonically, growing toward the initially quite separate uriniferous tubules that only relatively late in embryogeny effect connections with the collecting tubules.

The medullary tissue is somewhat varied in organization in mammals. In carnivores such as the cat there is no segregation of collective tubules, but in primates such as man the collecting tubules are aggregated in about a dozen groups, each with its renal papilla opening into the renal sinus. Each group of tubules is grossly visible and is designated a *pyramid;* the cat has but one pyramid, whereas man has about twelve. In primates there is relatively little external evidence of the internal subdivision of medullary tissue, but in many mammals such as ungulates the external surface is *lobulate* (Fig. 13.6B), each lobule corresponding to an internal pyramid.

In ventral view the mammalian kidney typically is somewhat bean-

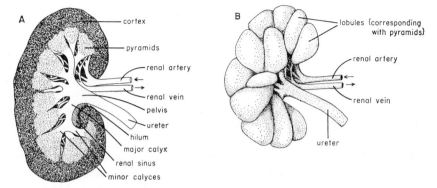

FIG. 13.6 Gross form of the mammalian kidney. A, frontal section, human, B, external view, bear. (From Weichert and Walter.)

shaped. The concave surface, where the ureter is attached, is the *hilus*. About the pelvis of the ureter pass the large renal arteries and veins, all collectively occupying a space within the kidney referred to as the *renal sinus*.

Evolution of the Tubular Capillary Network

All gnathostome vertebrates possess two renal capillary networks, essentially as in mammals. Cyclostomes, however, possess only the glomeruli, or neither set of capillaries, suggesting that agnathous vertebrates ancestral to gnathostomes passed through successive stages in which at first the kidneys (holonephros) possessed no renal capillary association whatever, and later only glomerular sets of capillaries (Fig. 13.7A). There was seemingly a significant lag between formation of the glomerular and the tubular sets of capillaries. It appears highly probable that the two sets of capillaries were independently evolved, not only because of the absence of the tubular network in living cyclostomes but also because of the independent venous connections of the two capillary networks in all the primitive gnathostomes (ichthyopsids) in which they occur.

Whether of later origin than the glomerular capillaries or not, the tubular capillary bed has a very different blood supply in ectotherms (Fig. 13.7B) than it has in endotherms (Fig. 13.7D). The functions of each set are the same in all vertebrates wherever they have been found, but the vascular connections have evolved extensively. There has been no marked change in glomerular blood supply, the evolution of which has already been discussed in sufficient detail for present purposes. It is the relationship of the two networks to each other that has undergone the most extensive change.

When the tubular capillary network first appeared in gnathostome fishes, it was supplied by *afferent renal veins* branching from two *renal portal veins,* one for each kidney. The network was drained by *efferent renal veins* which also collected the blood drained from the glomerular capillaries. The efferent renals in turn emptied into the posterior cardinal veins (or the equivalent thereof). This blood circuit was thus nearly completely separate from that serving the glomerulus. The renal portal system, of which the tubular network may be considered a part, was apparently preserved for so long and in so many types of vertebrates because of the essential role played by the tubular capillary network in the recovery of useful solutes and of water.

The dual vascular renal circuits persisted for millions of years, and are today retained in all amphibians, reptiles, and gnathostome fishes. Not until the Mesozoic, in certain higher reptiles now extinct but ancestral to modern mammals and birds, were steps taken to streamline renal circulation. The alterations ultimately effected were (1) anastomosis of the tubular capillary network with the base of the efferent renal vein (Fig. 13.7C); (2) transformation of the anastomosis and the part of the efferent renal vein between the glomerulus and the anastomosis into a single *efferent glomerular artery;* (3) loss of the part of the efferent renal vein between the anastomosis and the branch draining the tubular capillary network; (4) loss of the afferent renal veins; and (5) loss of the renal portal vein. The end result is the mammalian conformation. Living birds represent an intermediate condition, in which all but the final step in the chain of events has been taken: the renal portal veins persist, but play no role in kidney circulation. They carry blood directly through the kidneys, from rear quarters into the main abdominal vein (protopostcava), without passage through any capillary system. The renal portal veins persist, but the renal postal system, as such, has disappeared. Yet the basically essential component of the

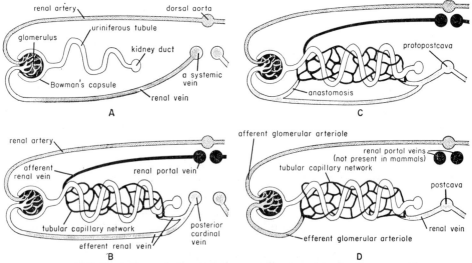

FIG. 13.7 Evolution of the tubular capillary network, in successive stages A-D. A, cyclostomes; B, gnathostome ectotherms; C, hypothetical intermediate stage between B and D; D, endotherms.

renal portal system, the tubular capillary network, remains intact both in birds and in mammals; only its vascular connections have been changed.

It may seem somewhat strange that circulation through the glomeruli and the tubular capillaries could not have been effected from the outset in a single vascular circuit as in mammals. This is a much more efficient system, but as has been abundantly demonstrated elsewhere efficiency is not readily and immediately arrived at: lengthy trial and error is almost invariably an adjunct of improvement and a necessary prelude to success in attainment of an efficient working system. What is available or is contrived in early formative periods of a structure may not, and usually is not, adapted to the best possible degree for a new function, for the obvious reason that it was formerly adapted for the performance of other functions.

In connection with the kidney, it is not surprising that initiation in gnathostome fishes of a recovery system, after a long period of early evolution without one in protochordates and agnathans, called into play a drainage system (the renal portal) completely different from that preoccupied already with another function (the glomerular system). It could hardly have been expected otherwise.

The adaptive value of the renal portal recovery system at the time it was instituted is open to some question. On fairly reliable grounds it is thought that need for conservation of transport materials, not the water, was the initial force. Primitive vertebrates, at least on the tetrapod line of evolution, are thought to have been inhabitants of fresh water. In these not so much conservation of water as elimination of it is the pressing physiological problem. In a fresh-water medium the vertebrate body fluid is strongly hypertonic. A rapid turnover of water, especially with indiscriminate removal of useful and only laboriously replaceable substances, creates a serious problem in conservation of blood components other than water. The renal portal recovery system was an effective and adequate solution. The uriniferous tubules with which it was associated have throughout all vertebrates save endotherms been effective from the beginning solely in extraction of transported materials, not water. In endotherms a specialized section of the tubule was evolved to extract water also (Fig. 13.5).

Maintenance of Water Balance

Water is essential for maintenance of vertebrate life. Species to which water is not readily available in their normal habitat must evolve special mechanisms to safeguard the water they do have. Terrestrial and marine animals (Fig. 13.8B, C) find this a pressing problem, and have evolved many devices to hoard their supplies.

On the other hand, vertebrates living in fresh water (Fig. 13.8A) have been faced with the converse problem—prevention of absorption of too much water.

The kidney has been of prime although not exclusive importance in

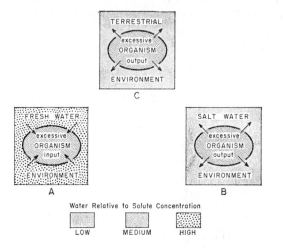

FIG. 13.8 Diagram of the water balance problems of vertebrates under various environmental conditions. Water-permeable areas in the otherwise essentially impermeable body wall permit passage of water (but not of solutes) in the direction that brings equalization of solute concentration on the two sides of the membrane.

the adjustment by all vertebrates to the problem of maintenance of water balance.

Adjustments to existence in a *hypotonic* fresh-water environment by various vertebrates include (1) a copious and effectively impervious mucoid skin secretion (as in cyclostomes, most osteichthyans, amphibians); (2) reduction of integumentary blood supply (as in all fishes); (3) a thick, bony armor (as in some ostracoderms, placoderms); and (4) increase in size of glomerulus (as in amphibians).

Adjustments to existence in a *hypertonic* marine environment include the first two modifications listed in the preceding paragraph, and in addition (3) decrease in size of the glomerulus (as in teleosts); (4) increase in bodily osmotic pressure to approximately that of the environs by means of a tolerance to a higher concentration of urea in the blood than in any other vertebrates (chondrichthyans); (5) excretion by the gills of the salts extracted from ingested sea water (as in teleosts); (6) excretion of salt by glandular tissue around the external nares in various marine birds; (7) excretion of salts in a hypertonic urine (as in marine mammals and birds); and (8) excretion of salts by the lacrimal glands in marine turtles. The means utilized by sea snakes and marine lizards for excretion of excess salts remains unknown; possibly the recently discovered parapancreas play a role in this connection.

Adjustments to the dehydrating existence of terrestrial vertebrates include (1) development of an impervious epidermal covering in the form of keratin (all amniotes); (2) reduction in vascularization of the integument (all amniotes); (3) decrease in size of the glomerulus (reptiles, birds); (4) absorption by cloacal walls of the water from excretory fluids stored in the cloaca in reptiles and birds; (5) formation of a specialized section (*Henle's loop*) of the uriniferous tubule for water extraction (especially mammals, rudimentary in birds); (6) evolution of a means of nitrogenous excretion (in the form of *uric acid*) that reduces water loss to a minimum (as in birds, some reptiles); (7) perfection of an antidiuretic hormone produced by the pituitary gland (as in mammals); and (8) perfection of the ability to produce "metabolic water" from dry food, making access to drinkable water or water-containing foods totally unnecessary (as in many desert-dwelling vertebrates). Some of the adaptations listed in the preceding paragraphs require further explanation.

Glomerular Size. Reduction in size of the glomerulus is a device to reduce water output. Thus it obviously is not a conspicuous trend in fresh-water inhabitants, but rather in tetrapods that cannot afford copious water loss and in marine vertebrates that live in a hypertonic medium tending to dehydrate the body (Fig. 13.9B). Fresh-water anamniotes have large glomeruli (Fig. 13.9A) dispensing body fluids with relative abandon since as a rule they need to get rid of an excessive intake of water. Even the marine chondrichthyans retain the primitive large glomerulus (Fig. 13.9A), as they solved the problem of water conservation in a hypertonic medium by increasing the concentration of (and tolerance to) urea in the blood to a degree sufficient to balance the osmotic pressure of the sea.

In other marine fishes, however, and in sauropsids, the elasmobranch solution was not discovered. Instead, in them the amount of water loss was cut down by actually cutting down the amount of filtrate, in extreme cases reducing the renal corpuscle to the diameter of the tubule itself, and eliminating the glomerulus.

Henle's Loop. In mammals, and to a much lesser extent in birds, the glomeruli have remained somewhat larger than in other amniotes because a new technique of water conservation was devised. In mammals a "hairpin loop" in the middle of the uriniferous tubule (Figs. 13.9C, 13.10) became greatly elongate and narrow (*Henle's loop*), adapted specifically for water recovery by means of a complex "counter-current multiplier" system. Thus in mammals the glomerulus retains what is essentially its original capacity for uninhibited filtration, while its possessors rest physiologically secure with a uriniferous tubule serving not only to extract transported materials as of old but also to extract water from the glomeru-

FIG. 13.9 Evolution in gross appearance of the uriniferous tubule in vertebrates. A, primitive type (as in fresh-water fishes, elasmobranchs, amphibians), with a large renal corpuscle and a proximal and distal convoluted tubule; B, intermediate type (as in marine actinopterans and in reptiles), with a small renal corpuscle; C, endotherm type, with a large renal corpuscle and Henle's loop. (From Romer.)

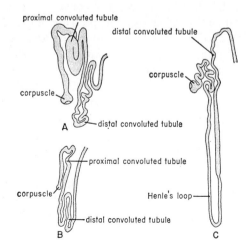

lar filtrate. The longer the loop, the more hypertonic the urine. In some types the loops reach into the renal papilla. Mammals are thus unique in their capacity to eliminate a hypertonic urine. They would thereby seem to be perfectly adapted to subsistence upon sea water, but in reality they are incapable of doing so because of inability of the alimentary epithelium to absorb the water against an osmotic gradient. Marine teleosts have evolved this capacity, as have perhaps a very few other marine vertebrates, but mammals in general—even most, if not all, marine types—have alimentary epithelia mortally sensitive to large quantities of hypertonic fluids.

Nitrogenous Excretion. Primitively nitrogenous wastes were eliminated in solution, and therefore probably as *ammonia,* the form in which it leaves the cells where metabolized. Teleosts, some turtles, and crocodilians excrete ammonia, as they occupy an aquatic environment facilitating prompt elimination of excreta from the body. In most other vertebrates, however, the ammonia is transformed into the less toxic *urea,* also a soluble compound, by the liver. Urea is eliminated in a water carrier as urine. This system is an improvement over the more primitive ammonia excretion, but still is highly profligate of water. Only in mammals is the concentration of urea in the urine greater than that of the blood. The Squamata, no doubt many fossil groups of reptiles, and birds solved the problem of water loss, and at the same time devised the most efficient means of nitrogenous excretion known in any vertebrates, by converting nitrogenous wastes into the almost completely insoluble and wholly nontoxic uric acid. Excretion of uric acid requires almost no water loss, since the acid is voided as a white solid, often with the feces. The whitish component characteristic of avian feces is uric acid, which is stored in the cloaca until voided. Thus urinary bladders are absent in most vertebrates excreting uric acid. Curiously many vertebrates excreting urea or uric acid as adults recapitulate this evolutionary sequence in their ontogeny, excreting in succession ammonia, urea, and uric acid.

Integumentary Controls on Water Balance. An effective nonrenal solution to the problem of conserving blood components in the presence of an unfavorable osmotic pressure might have been the simple expedient of cutting off infiltration of water. As a matter of fact the astonishing armor of primitive chordates (ostracoderms) is thought to have constituted just such an attempt. It was doomed early because the door to free infiltration was opened progressively wider by elaboration and perfection of the gill respiratory system. Here one evolutionary trend worked to undermine the other, and it was the respiratory need for integumentary permeability (in the limited gill region, to be sure, but nonetheless a completely open door for water intake) that proved the most demanding. The doomed armor disappeared in many groups, integumentary impermeability being provided even more effectively than with the clumsy armor by the development of many mucus-secreting integumentary glands, and by reduction in vascularization of the skin. Perversely enough the armor was gone when tetrapods, in becoming adapted to life on land, were faced anew with the

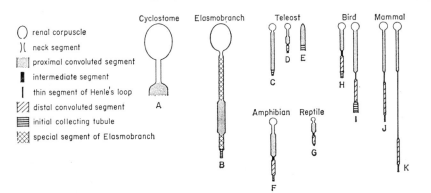

FIG. 13.10 Variation in composition of uriniferous tubules in vertebrates. Note reduction in size of renal corpuscle in tetrapods, and appearance of Henle's loop in birds and (especially) mammals. A, hagfish; B, skate; C, sculpin; D, catfish; E, toadfish; F, frog; G, turtle (Chrysemys); H, I, chicken; J, K, rabbit. (From Prosser.)

imperative need for integumentary impermeability (in this case to prevent loss, not gain of water) that a highly glandular skin could not provide, and a substitute (keratin) had to be exploited.

An extraordinary epithelial adaptation was evolved by marine teleost fishes, most if not all of which possess the capacity to secrete salt from the gill filaments. Thus these fishes can freely ingest sea water, promptly eliminating excess salts by way of the gills. Their kidney tubules are unable to excrete the salts without loss of at least as much water as is gained, and thus the branchial excretory device is an absolutely essential adjunct to the existence of teleosts in marine habitats.

Kinds of Kidneys

A kidney may be defined as a more or less definite body made up of a mass of uriniferous tubules, usually greatly coiled, together with supporting cells and blood vessels, all wrapped in or bordered by a peritoneal sheath. We are accustomed to seeing kidneys of small size and compact form, but this is true only of the latest type of kidney to evolve. The earlier kidneys were less compact, often extensive. It should be noted that the definition includes all of the uriniferous tubules, or at least all that retain some semblance of excretory function, *but excludes the kidney duct.* In discussing urinogenital evolution we shall carefully distinguish kidney and duct derivatives.

The five kidneys commonly recognized in vertebrate phylogeny differ primarily in (1) extent of association with the circulatory system (presence or absence of glomeruli, internal or external); (2) extent of association with the celom (presence, absence, diameter of peritoneal funnel); (3) number of tubules (whether corresponding in number to segments, or secondarily increased in number); (4) position in the body and in the nephrotomal plate (anterior, middle, rear); (5) identity of the drainage tube; (6) form (whether compact or diffuse); and (7) occurrence (vertebrate groups in which found, in either the adult or embryonic condition).

Holonephros. The holonephros varies at least theoretically from having no glomeruli whatever to having only external glomeruli. The only animals now known to possess a holonephros, the embryonic myxinoids, have external glomeruli posteriorly, none anteriorly. The peritoneal funnels are open and the tubules are strictly limited to one pair per segment. The kidney extends the full length of the abdominal cavity, and is drained by the *holonephric duct,* phylogenetically derived by invagination from the external surface of the body. The organ is not compact, but rather diffuse. It occurs in embryonic myxinoids and presumably was present in most ostracoderms and ancestral protochordates.

Opisthonephros. In this type, directly evolved from the holonephros, internal glomeruli are present throughout, and usually the peritoneal funnels are persistent but vestigial and narrow. The tubules are numerous, several pairs occurring in each segment. The kidney extends nearly the full length of the abdominal cavity, being derived from all the nephrotomal plate save that of a few anterior segments. The drainage duct is the *Wolffian* or *opisthonephric duct,* which represents the entire holonephric duct except its anterior end (only of embryonic function in most vertebrates). The form is elongate and not compact. This is the kidney of all adult anamniotes except myxinoids, a few teleosts, and presumably some ostracoderms. Embryos of opisthonephric animals utilize a pronephros, which becomes nonfunctional in adults. Two types of opisthonephros exist; in one, the most primitive, the adult kidney lacks reproductive function, whereas in the other type it serves to conduct sperm as well as excretory products. These two types are discussed later.

Metanephros. Directly evolved from the opisthonephros, this type is characterized by being fully provided with internal glomeruli completely lacking peritoneal funnels. The tubules are greatly increased in number (into the millions), but all are derived from a few posterior nephrotomes of the embryo. These commonly lie in adults near the middle of the abdominal cavity. Its drainage duct is the *ureter* or *metanephric duct,* apparently evolved by a split in the former drainage duct (opisthonephric duct), the remainder persisting as the Wolffian duct (in adults varying greatly in form, function, and terminology). This kidney is very compact in form, and occurs in all adult amniotes. Embryos of metanephric animals utilize a mesonephros, which becomes lost or nonexcretory in adults. The pronephros is vestigial and nonfunctional in early embryos, and disappears almost completely in adults.

Pronephros. Bypassed by the main stream of evolution, a few teleosts exist in which only the extreme anterior end of the nephrotome functions as the adult kidney. This was also true, apparently, of some ostracoderms. These aberrant fish undoubtedly evolved from opisthonephric animals, and retained in adults for some curious reason the embryonic pronephros, failing to develop the remainder of the nephrotome tissue as a kidney. They seem to verify the indication that vertebrates—and especially fishes—try almost anything in their trial-and-error approach toward improvement.

Since the adult kidney in the few teleosts mentioned is basically the same as the embryonic pronephros functional in prenatal opisthonephric animals, and vestigial in embryonic amniotes, the same name, "pronephros," is adopted for it. Nevertheless the tetrapod pronephros is not wholly the same as that of most fishes, for the anterior tubule is incorporated into the Müllerian duct in most tetrapods, not in most fishes.

The pronephros is characterized by having (1) external glomeruli, (2) open peritoneal funnels, (3) one pair of tubules per segment, (4) occurring only at the extreme anterior end of the abdominal cavity and being derived only from the anterior two to four segments of the nephrotome, (5) by retaining what is essentially the holonephric duct (now called the pronephric duct, however) for drainage, (6) having a diffuse form, and (7) by occurring in a few adult teleosts, as the functional kidney of embryonic opisthonephric animals, and as a nonfunctional vestige in embryonic amniotes.

Mesonephros. In amniotes the anterior tip of the nephrotomal plate is nonfunctional and represents the pronephros of earlier vertebrates. The rear few nephrotomes become the definitive adult kidney (metanephros), and the part between these extremes is functional embryonically as the *mesonephros*. It disappears or becomes nonexcretory in adults.

The mesonephros is often regarded erroneously as the same as the opisthonephros, the name "mesonephros" being applied to both. There is a marked difference between the two, however, since the nephrogenic tissue of ancestral opisthonephric animals gave rise in amniotes not only to the mesonephros but also to the metanephros.

The mesonephros can thus be characterized as being the same as the opisthonephros, *except* that it does not include the rear segments of the nephrotome and is functional only in embryonic amniotes.

Significance of Kidney Succession. The evolution of amniotes through three great levels of organization of the kidney (holonephros, opisthonephros, metanephros) appears to be more profound, perhaps, than it is in reality. Functional changes of possibly greater significance than the changes in gross form occur as modifications of each kidney type. Shift from one type to another seems, rather, to have been necessitated by (1) a series of changes, some somatic, some intrinsic, that collectively required alteration of gross kidney form; and by (2) a need for separation of urinary and reproductive ducts.

Progressively greater coordination of all parts of the body and progressively greater efficiency have been constant pressures upon all animals. Competition or, to regard it as a less conscious phenomenon, relative successfulness makes it inevitable that improvement be rewarded by perpetuation. The greater the degree of structural refinement, however, the greater the length of time needed for integration. It is axiomatic that there is a steady increase in length of the formative period in vertebrate life—an inevitable necessity imposed by the progressive increase in adult complexity. With increase in length of the embryonic period, a need arises for an efficient excretory system to serve during that period. Thus part of the kidney remains functional in relatively primitive form. Yet adults require a progressively more elaborate and efficient excretory system to serve their more complex, more active bodies. Thus in addition part of the kidney must be reserved to continue development of a definitive adult organization while the other part functions embryonically. *The increasing selective pressures favoring embryonically functional excretory organs, coincident with the increasing selective pressures favoring greater adult efficiency,* seems to be the most important factor involved in the successive shifts from one type of kidney to another in vertebrates.

A second possible causative force may have been the selective advantage of separating urinary and genital ducts. Causative or not, it is nevertheless true that each successive type is accompanied by marked improvement of duct specialization. In holonephric animals, abdominal pores are used as reproductive exits. In subsequent stages a new duct, the *Müllerian duct,* forms from the dorsolateral celomic wall. Possibly both sexes originally used this duct for exit of the reproductive cells, but ultimately only the female so utilized it (as an *oviduct*), the male usurping the kidney duct (opisthonephric duct). Then with appearance of the metanephros the kidney function shifts entirely to the ureter, leaving the former opisthonephric duct with but a single duty (sperm conduction) in but one sex, as indeed the Müllerian duct had previously been restricted (egg conduction). Whether these shifts of duct usage were actually causative, or were merely opportunist (making use of otherwise functionless structures) is not evident.

Kidney Derivatives

Holonephric Stage. The holonephros involves the entire nephrotomal plate (Fig. 13.11A). From it has evolved in later stages not only kidneys but reproductive organs and a variety of nonfunctional vestiges as described below.

Opisthonephric Stage. Actually the opisthonephric stage embraces three different sorts of kidney modification (Fig. 13.11B, C, E), but all three modifications possess a typical opisthonephros. In the most primitive stage, exemplified by lampreys (Fig. 13.11B), the anterior two to four tubules are functional embryonically as the *pronephros;* the others are functional in adults as the *opisthonephros.* In the piscine line of evolution and in most living actinopteran fishes (Fig. 13.11C), the pronephros is basically the same as in the lamprey stage, but the opisthonephros has become modified to serve both reproductive and urinary functions. The re-

productive section is the *epididymis,* consisting of the anterior opisthonephric tubules. Tiny *efferent ductules* lead from the testis through the
mesentery of the testis into the uriniferous tubules, which they join just
distal to the renal corpuscle. The efferent ductules are not a part of the
kidney, nor are they derived from it. The uriniferous tubules joined by the
efferent ductules have no urinary function, but instead serve for temporary
storage and conduction of sperm. Females lack an epididymis, of course,
but the equivalent part of the kidney is not functional and is designated
the *cranial opisthonephros.*

   In the tetrapod line of evolution, and in the living amphibians, chondrichthyans, and choanichthyans (Fig. 13.11E), the holonephric derivatives are essentially the same as in actinopteran fishes except that the anterior tubule of the pronephros is specialized for reproduction, and often
only the posterior part of the opisthonephros—the *caudal opisthonephros*—
retains a urinary function. Animals with a caudal opisthonephros presage
the appearance of metanephric types. In females with a caudal opisthonephros, the middle of the adult kidney is functionless, but in males it
functions by secreting a nutritive fluid for the sperm and is called *Leydig's
Gland.*

   The pronephros is lost completely in adult gnathostome fishes with an
opisthonephros, and in tetrapods only the most anterior tubule persists in

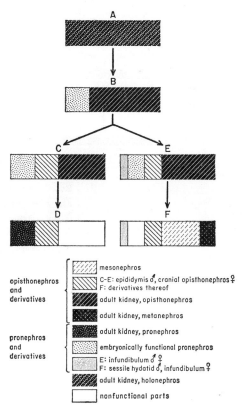

FIG. 13.11 Evolution of types of vertebrate kidneys and their derivatives. A, most ostracoderms and placoderms, embryonic
myxinoids; B, cyclostomes; C, most actinopteran fishes; D, aberrant teleosts; E, amphibians, choanichthyans, chondrichthyans; F,
amniotes. Oblique lines in F represent the epididymis, paradidymis and ductuli aberrantia in males, the epoophoron and paroophoron in females.

opisthonephros and derivatives

	mesonephros
	C-E: epididymis ♂, cranial opisthonephros ♀ F: derivatives thereof
	adult kidney, opisthonephros
	adult kidney, metanephros

pronephros and derivatives

	adult kidney, pronephros
	embryonically functional pronephros
	E: infundibulum ♂ ♀ F: sessile hydatid ♂, infundibulum ♀
	adult kidney, holonephros
	nonfunctional parts

adults. This and its peritoneal funnel become greatly enlarged to serve as the anterior end of the oviduct and the opening into it (*ostium tubae*), collectively referred to as the *infundibulum*. The modified tubule leads directly into the rest of the oviduct, from which it is morphologically indistinguishable. In males the infundibulum persists without function, with even an ostium; the rest of the duct disappears with the exception of vestiges at the rear to be mentioned later.

Metanephric Stage. In metanephric animals (Fig. 13.11F) the opisthonephros is found transformed into (1) a metanephros, derived from the extreme rear part, and (2) an embryonic mesonephros, representing the rest of the opisthonephros. The pronephros appears briefly in early embryogeny but then disappears without trace save for the infundibular part of the oviduct, which part in males is, of course, a functionless vestige and is known as the *sessile hydatid* (or hydatid of Morgagni, or appendix testis).

The mesonephros, serving embryonic excretory needs, also retains

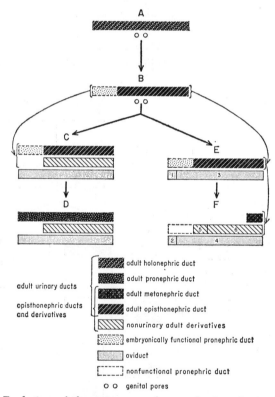

adult urinary ducts

opisthonephric ducts and derivatives

adult holonephric duct

adult pronephric duct

adult metanephric duct

adult opisthonephric duct

nonurinary adult derivatives

embryonically functional pronephric duct

oviduct

nonfunctional pronephric duct

o o genital pores

FIG. 13.12 Evolution of the urinary and reproductive ducts. A-F, stages corresponding to those of Fig. 13.11. 1, 2, part of oviduct (infundibulum, sessile hydatid derived from kidney; 3, 4, part of oviduct originating from abdominal wall; 5, nonfunctional tip of Wolffian duct in adult (appendix epididymis, appendix fimbriae); 6, functional part of Wolffian duct in adult (ductus deferens, Gärtner's duct).

the genital connections inherited from opisthonephric ancestors. Thus the anterior part of the mesonephros persists in adult males as the *epididymis;* it persists in adult females as the functionless *epoophoron,* consisting of tubules blind at the gonadal end (since there is no testis and no efferent ductules) and connecting with a short vestige of the Wolffian duct at the other end (Fig. 13.15). The middle part, just posterior to the epididymis, persists as functionless tubules. In males the anterior ones (comprising the *paradidymis*) are blind at the end toward the testis, and the posterior ones (*ductuli aberrantia*) are blind at both ends (Fig. 13.15). In females all are blind at both ends and constitute the *paroophoron.*

The Pronephric Stage. In the few teleosts with a pronephros functioning in adults, all except the extreme anterior part of the ancestral holonephros—and, therefore, all that in most anamniotes becomes the opisthonephros—fails to develop fully and is functionless. The embryonically functional pronephros, identical with that of other actinopteran fishes, remains as the functional kidney in the adult (Fig. 13.11D).

The Urinogenital Ducts

Holonephric Stage. In holonephric animals (Fig. 13.12A) the urinary duct is the holonephric duct, presumably derived in phylogeny from ectoderm (although, as the *archinephric duct,* from mesoderm in embryogeny). The reproductive organs do not possess a duct, but their products reach the exterior *via* the rear pair of abdominal pores.

Opisthonephric Stage. In all adult opisthonephric animals (Fig. 13.12B, C, E) the urinary duct is the *opisthonephric* duct, which is the same as the holonephric duct except that it lacks the part opposite the pronephros, since the pronephros is present only embryonically.

In the earliest opisthonephric animals, as in living cyclostomes (Fig. 13.12B), there are no genital ducts, the genital pores still serving as exits for the reproductive cells just as in the holonephric stage. However, in later opisthonephric stages, reproductive ducts are present, although their homologies in various fishes and in tetrapods are far from satisfactorily established. The currently most widely accepted theory is that they are all derived from the holonephric duct, but this now appears partly in error. Present evidence strongly indicates that the oviduct—and male homolog thereof—was of independent origin, perhaps having evolved *de novo* from the dorsolateral celomic wall as indeed it forms embryonically.

In all opisthonephric animals except the very earliest (cyclostomes; placoderms?) a female reproductive duct, the Müllerian duct, is present. It serves as an oviduct in females and is lost in males or represented by front and rear vestiges, the *infundibulum* and *sperm sacs,* respectively. In tetrapods (Fig. 13.12E) the infundibulum is derived from the anterior pronephric tubule, and the remainder of the oviduct from the celomic wall; but in actinopteran fishes (Fig. 13.12C) the entire oviduct is formed independently of the kidney and its duct and makes direct connection with the ovary without intervention of the pronephros. The actinopteran oviduct is entirely derived from the celomic wall.

The male reproductive duct in tetrapods (Fig. 13.12E) is the Wolffian duct itself (or most of it), termed the *ductus deferens* in males only, in reference to the function in sperm conduction. Its extreme anterior end, into which the tubules of the epididymis empty, is the *epididymidal duct*. The opisthonephric duct thus serves a dual function in males, only one (or none) in females. In actinopteran fishes, on the contrary (Fig. 13.12C), the ductus deferens becomes a structure separate from the kidney duct, the Wolffian duct apparently splitting to produce a separate duct for the testis (Fig. 13.13). No other vertebrates parallel this condition.

In some opisthonephric animals a split in the Wolffian duct occurs, forming a short tube (*accessory opisthonephric duct*) draining the caudal opisthonephros only. This seems to be homologous with the ureter of metanephric animals.

Metanephric Stage. The urinary function in metanephric animals (Fig. 13.12F) is performed by the *ureter,* thought to have been derived by a longitudinal split in the Wolffian duct (Fig. 13.14). It arises embryonically by evagination from the rear of the Wolffian duct, and grows toward the metanephric kidney with which it eventually establishes contact; this outgrowth even produces the collecting tubules of the kidney. This obviously is not a faithful recapitulation of mode of evolution, however.

Transportation of eggs remains a function of the Müllerian duct originating in opisthonephric animals. Parts of the oviduct are represented in

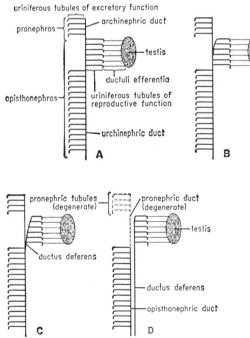

FIG. 13.13 Hypothetical origin of the ductus deferens in actinopteran fishes, in successive stages A-D.

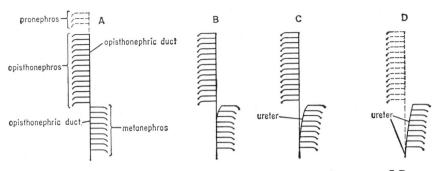

FIG. 13.14 Hypothetical origin of the ureter, in successive stages A-D.

males by a *prostatic utricle* (a blind evagination of the urethral canal) and the sessile hydatid previously mentioned (Fig. 13.15).

Transportation of sperm becomes the sole function of the Wolffian duct, now released from urinary function. An anterior tip, beyond the level of the epididymis, is represented by the vestigial and functionless *appendix epididymis* (or stalked hydatid) in males, by the *appendix fimbriae* (or appendix vesiculosa) in females (Fig. 13.14). The ductus deferens is in females represented by the short functionless *Gärtner's duct* (Fig. 13.15), blind at both ends and connected with the tubules of the epoophoron.

Pronephric Stage. The ducts of the few teleosts that retain a pronephros in adults are the same as in other teleosts except that the full length of the archinephric duct is retained, since the anterior part drains the pronephros. However, since this duct drains only the pronephros, it is designated the pronephric duct although it differs from the holonephric duct only in function and in having given rise to the ductus deferens.

Definitions. It is essential that the application of some of the terms for the more important types of ducts previously discussed be clearly limited.

MÜLLERIAN DUCT. The term is used for the duct of the ovary, or its counterpart in the male; it is the oviduct only in the female, but usually exists in at least a vestigial state in males.

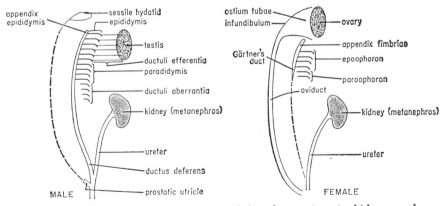

FIG. 13.15 Contrast of adult male and female amniote in kidney and urinogenital duct derivatives; gonads and ductuli efferentia added.

DUCTUS DEFERENS. Being the sperm duct, this term is applied only to males. It differs somewhat in composition in different vertebrates, in some representing almost the entire Wolffian duct, in others representing a tube split from the Wolffian duct.

WOLFFIAN DUCT. This is the duct of the opisthonephros, or its counterpart in metanephric animals. It occurs in adults of both sexes of opisthonephric animals, in the males of which it serves as the sperm duct. It occurs in embryos of both sexes of metanephric animals; in adult males it persists as the appendix epididymis and functional sperm duct, but only vestiges remain in adult female metanephric animals.

ACCESSORY OPISTHONEPHRIC DUCT. This duct splits from the opisthonephric duct that drains the posterior part of the opisthonephros in some groups of vertebrates. It is the forerunner of the ureter, and occurs in both sexes.

URETER. The duct of the metanephros, the ureter, is derived phylogenetically by a split in the opisthonephric duct, embryonically by evagination from the rear of the mesonephric duct.

MESONEPHRIC DUCT. The term is for the drainage tube for the mesonephros and is, therefore, of embryonic application only. It is the equivalent in metanephric animals of the opisthonephric duct, and is in metanephric animals the same as the Wolffian duct.

OPISTHONEPHRIC DUCT. This is the duct of the opisthonephros, and accordingly is the equivalent of the Wolffian duct in opisthonephric animals.

PRONEPHRIC DUCT. The term is used for the duct of the pronephros only. In pronephric animals it is essentially the equivalent of the holonephric duct (less the ductus deferens), but in opisthonephric and metanephric animals it is only that part of the kidney duct to which the pronephric tubules are attached; in both of these groups the duct is lost in adults.

Principle of Sexual Indifference. That any counterpart whatsoever of the ducts of one sex should appear in the other may be attributed to the origin of those ducts from parts essential to both sexes for urinary purposes (Fig. 13.15). Furthermore, parts specialized for one sex are occasionally adapted, at least in part, for use in the other sex. Sexually dimorphic parts are basically the same in morphology in both sexes, and are differentiated late in embryonic or early in postembryonic life. Early sexual indifference is not limited to the internal genital structures, but is equally true for external (intromittent) organs (see subsequent discussion). Comprehension of the significance of this principle renders immediately intelligible the cases of so-called "hermaphroditism" or "sex reversal" in humans.

Oviduct Evolution

Divisions. The oviduct commonly is more or less uniform throughout its length, but in various viviparous forms without evolutionary continuity there occurs a specialized enlargement, the *uterus,* adapted for retention and sometimes nourishment of the embryos. A vagina at the cloacal end of the oviduct is recognized in amniotes having a copulatory organ in the male, and is adapted for reception of the copulatory organ. The thick-walled uterus commonly projects slightly at its posterior end into the vagina as the *cervix.* The narrowed section of the oviduct between uterus and ostium is, in mammals, termed the *Fallopian tube;* no distinctive name is commonly used for the homologous section in viviparous nonmammalian vertebrates, but extension of application of the term for mammals to embrace other groups is reasonable.

A *shell gland* is developed along the oviduct in certain forms whose eggs are covered by a protective case.

Fusion. In mammals a unique general trend toward fusion of the oviducts exists. Six steps in this trend are easily recognizable (Fig. 13.16). In the prototherians, as in all nonmammalian vertebrates, there are two vaginae, two uteri, two Fallopian tubes: all parts of the oviduct are *duplex.* In the next stage represented by living mammals (marsupials), the vaginae are partly fused (*bicornuate*), the uterus and Fallopian tube remaining duplex. The penis in these two primitive groups is forked in adaptation to the forked or duplex condition of the vagina.

Rodents represent a third stage, in which the vaginae are wholly fused (*simplex*), the remaining parts duplex. In carnivores the posterior ends of the uteri become fused as the *body* of the uterus, but a short inner partition maintains a separation between the two anterior parts of the uterine body; this is referred to as a *bipartite* condition. Ungulates represent a true bicornuate uterus, lacking the inner partition. In primates the extreme in fusion is reached with the entire uterus, as well as vagina, becoming simplex.

Asymmetry. The right oviduct is lost in most birds.

Urinary Bladder

Urinary bladders are of wide occurrence and of varied types in different vertebrates. Teleosts have a *tubal bladder,* consisting simple of a saclike enlargement in the Wolffian duct. It is paired in some, single in others in

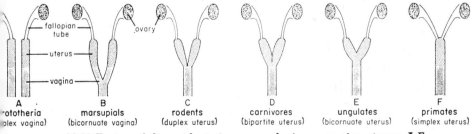

A	B	C	D	E	F
prototheria	marsupials	rodents	carnivores	ungulates	primates
(simplex vagina)	(bicornuate vagina)	(duplex uterus)	(bipartite uterus)	(bicornuate uterus)	(simplex uterus)

FIG. 13.16 Fusion of the oviducts in mammals, in successive stages A-F.

which the two ducts fuse at the bladder, a single duct leading to the exterior.

A *cloacal bladder* occurs in the choanichthyans and amphibians. It is a midventral evagination from the cloacal wall apparently serving principally to store water, and to a small extent for storage of urine released from the Wolffian ducts opening separately into the cloaca. This structure appears to be a forerunner of the *allantois* characteristic of all amniotes. The base of the allantois has been retained as the *allantoic* urinary *bladder* in adults of most amniotes, but not in birds, crocodilians, snakes, and some lizards; these exceptions have no urinary bladder, but instead excrete a relatively insoluble precipitate, uric acid (ammonia in crocodilians), which is stored in the rectum or cloaca. The duct, where present, extending from bladder to cloaca, vagina, or exterior is the *urethra*. Its terminal part, when fused with either the ductus deferens or oviduct, is the *urinogenital sinus* or *vestibule*.

The allantoic bladder is not directly attached to the urinary ducts except in mammals. In these the ureters, formerly opening dorsally, gain attachment to the bladder by passing on each side of the large intestine. Primitively among mammals they are attached to the urethra near its connection with the bladder (as in monotremes), but in most eutherians they empty into the bladder near the urethral exit. In some rodents they empty into the apex of the bladder.

Urinogenital Sinus

Not until mammals evolved did a urinogenital sinus become a constant anatomical feature of females. In nonmammalian females the oviducts open separately into the cloaca, free from contact with urinary ducts. In males, on the contrary, a urinogenital sinus is present in all amniotes and in a few anamniotes (sharks) with a ureter or forerunner thereof. There seems to be no trend in males toward elimination of the urinogenital sinus by separation of the urinary and reproductive ducts.

Establishment of a urinogenital sinus in the mammalian female may be regarded as a direct result of the establishment of a connection between the ureters and the urinary bladder. In nonmammalian amniotes the ureters open dorsally in the cloaca, but the urinary bladder is a ventral structure. Union of the bladder duct (urethra) with the oviduct, also ventral, is not unexpected. There is a trend toward separation of the urethra and oviduct, however, culminating in the rodents which have the urinary (anterior) and vaginal (posterior) openings wholly separate from each other. Primates closely approach a complete separation. In those mammals having a cloaca (monotremes) and lacking a separation of oviduct and urethra, the common urinogenital sinus of necessity resembles the vagina, serving as an intromittent duct and birth canal, but embryonically it is the base of the allantoic stalk and a part of the former cloaca, and thus is quite separate from the vagina, a division of the oviduct. In such mammals the vagina is to be regarded as opening into the urinogenital sinus. The *vulva* may be regarded as the external opening either of the urinogenital sinus or, if the reproductive and the urinary tracts are wholly separate, of the vagina. This actually dual use of the term is comparable with the similarly dual use of the term "anus," applied to the cloacal opening and also, in absence of a cloaca, to the rectal opening. Still another use of the term "vulva," embracing not only the opening but also the structures immediately adjacent to the opening, is common especially in reference to mammals.

Gonadal Evolution

Trends and Variations Exhibited by Both Testis and Ovary. Decrease in size and shift in position are two general trends in gonad evolution. Primitive vertebrates possess gonads of relatively large size. Both testis and ovary extend the length of the abdominal cavity. The ovary is the larger of the two gonads in most vertebrates (usually not in mammals) and in many fishes comprises 30 percent of the total weight of the animal when fully gravid. In higher vertebrates the ovary only attains a minimum of approximately 0.001 percent of the total weight of the animal. The trend from one extreme to the other is fairly continuous, with offshoot lines reversing or halting the trend here and there. The testis similarly decreases in size throughout vertebrates.

Decrease in size was accomplished in both gonads chiefly by loss of the rear portions. Thus the gonads that have passed the stage of full abdominal length lie in an anterior position in the celom and represent products of anterior mesomeres only. Gradually they tend to shift in evolution farther and farther posteriorly, coming to lie in advanced groups in the middle or posterior part of the celom. This shift is recapitulated embryonically.

In slender-bodied vertebrates, like snakes and some lizards, the gonads are staggered in position, the right commonly lying anterior to the left.

A cyclic period of activity of the gonads is evident in all vertebrates. The need for adequate developmental time at tolerable temperatures for eggs and young renders such a cycle absolutely unavoidable. There is only a seasonal limiting factor in the male, whose actual sexual activity nevertheless usually reflects more or less faithfully the female cycle. In some mammals, however, the reproductive cycle in males is little evident, a reproductive potential being maintained at all times. Repression of the male cycle is a result of attainment of independence from seasonal condition by *both* sexes for reproduction; nonhibernating species, in cooler temperature zones, form the bulk of the group. Despite the general independence of temperature exhibited by mammals as a class, many (including the hibernators) are completely controlled in reproduction by seasonal temperature succession.

Ovary. A curious variation of most birds and some teleosts is loss of the right ovary and oviduct. Presumably the large size of the eggs would occasion serious complications in the abdomen were the ovaries and oviducts on both sides functioning simultaneously.

The two ovaries are fused to varying degrees in some teleosts. They are hollow in many teleosts, in amphibians, and in the Squamata. This provides a place for storage and development of eggs, and in some teleosts a direct connection of this internal cavity with the oviduct is achieved.

Testis. One of the most astonishing modifications of the reproductive system is *testicular displacement* ("descent of the testis") in mammals. Ovarian displacement also occurs but is not carried to the extreme evidenced by the housing of the testes in an outpouching (*scrotal sac*) of the body wall.

The testicular displacement is accomplished by differentiation of a posterior section of the testicular mesentery (*mesorchium*) as a ligament (*gubernaculum testis,* homolog of the female *round ligament*) that fails to grow as other structures about it do. Remaining fixed at its posterior attachment, it causes the testis to shift posteriorly, relative to other structures. Eventually, in forms having a scrotal sac, the gubernaculum itself shortens and draws the testis through the body wall and into a position next to the skin of the scrotal sac where the gubernacular attachment is located (Fig. 13.17).

An evagination of the celomic cavity accompanies the testis into the scrotal sac, there forming a *vaginal sac* about the gonad. A mesenteric ridge extends from the abdominal cavity into the vaginal sac, and encloses the ductus deferens, blood vessels, lymphatics, and nerves supplying the testis. These structures collectively comprise the *spermatic cord*.

Various degrees of testicular displacement occur in mammals. In the extreme degree, the testes are permanently housed in the scrotal sac; ungulates and primates exemplify this extreme. Less extreme displacement occurs in rodents, insectivores, and bats, in which a periodic emergence (corresponding with the reproductive cycle) of the testes into the scrotal sac occurs. Still less extreme is the similarly periodic displacement from an abdominal position to a "pelvic" position, occurring in cetaceans. Only in elephants, conies, and most of the highly adapted aquatic mammals does no displacement, even periodic, of the testes to a position near the body wall occur. This is especially puzzling since the only known basic factor underlying the displacement is of significance throughout all other vertebrates: sperm are unable successfully to resist high temperatures such as those encountered within a warm-blooded animal. Eggs have been able to adapt themselves to the high temperature without difficulty; high tempera-

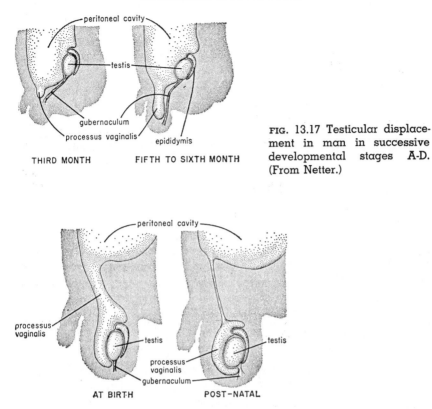

THIRD MONTH   FIFTH TO SIXTH MONTH

FIG. 13.17 Testicular displacement in man in successive developmental stages A-D. (From Netter.)

AT BIRTH   POST-NATAL

tures as a matter of fact are desirable in the developmental period of most vertebrates. Sperm have never, however, been able to overcome the early long history of adaptation to a relatively cool environment. It seems almost beyond question that the exceptional mammals in which no testicular displacement occurs must possess some device whereby testicular temperatures, at least periodically, are held below a certain critical maximum, although that device is not yet known.

Birds possess analogous devices which do, however, eliminate the necessity of extensive displacement. The testes are cooled in some cases by air sacs, against which the testes are known to be periodically displaced. Sperm are, furthermore, stored in the ductus deferens near the skin where temperatures are lower than that of the body, and spermatogenesis occurs when body temperatures are relatively low.

The effectiveness of temperature in rendering sperm sterile is illustrated by *cryptorchid* anomalies in which the testes fail to reach the scrotal sac as they normally do. Sterility is the invariable result. Similarly, very hot baths are said to have been an Oriental means of birth control. Fortunately high temperatures are deleterious only to fully formed sperm; spermatogonia remain unharmed unless the exposure is prolonged over several weeks. Even long exposure does not harm the hormone-producing cells.

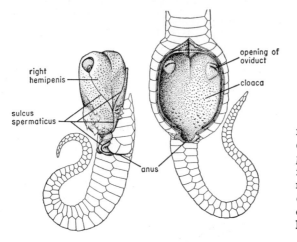

right
hemipenis

sulcus
spermaticus

opening of
oviduct

cloaca

anus

FIG. 13.18 Hemipenis of
a male snake (*Liophis
poecilogyrus*) dissected
from cloaca of its female
mate; the two were killed
and preserved in state
of copulation. (From
Pope.)

External Genitalia

External genitalia are copulatory organs, which in vertebrates include
only the intromittent organ or *phallus* and its counterparts, if any, in the
female. There are no elaborate copulatory accessories in the female for
clasping or guiding the phallus as exist in some invertebrates such as insects.

Male. Intromittent organs permit internal fertilization and constitute a
step forward from the more primitive method of external fertilization by
casting sperm over a batch of eggs in water. External fertilization is, of
course, impossible under terrestrial conditions; it requires a fluid medium.
Internal fertilization is, therefore, an adaptation to terrestrial conditions,
although in some aquatic vertebrates fertilization is internal. Internal
fertilization can be and is accomplished without a copulatory organ, however: in Sphenodon, most birds, and salamanders, sperm is transferred to
the female by contact of cloacae; and in many salamanders, the sperm are
deposited, in clumps called spermatophores, on the ground, under water,
or in moist situations, where they are picked up by the female with the
cloaca. Internal fertilization follows.

In most vertebrates internal fertilization is accomplished by intromittent organs. They are varied in structure. Part of the pelvic fins is used in
chondrichthyans; anal fin rays are used in some teleost fishes; hemal spines
back of the anal fin are used in other teleost fish; paired evertible sacs
called *hemipenes* (Fig. 13.18) on either side of the cloaca, housed in the
base of the tail, are utilized in the Squamata; and a true cloacal *penis* is
used in turtles, crocodilians, primitive birds, and in mammals.

The origin of the penis is unknown. It seems likely to have evolved
through ancestors utilizing a cloacal contact for internal fertilization, and
that a certain degree of protrusion of the whole cloaca, produced by blood
infusion, occurred at that (the first) stage. This is more or less the situation
in most birds.

Specialization of certain parts of the cloacal wall for blood infiltration and resultant protrusion would reasonably follow (Fig. 13.19). Presumably the peculiar hemipenes of squamate reptiles diverged in one direction at this stage, as other reptiles developed a forerunner of a single penis. Both structures are *erectile* by *hemotumescence*—they are protruded by blood infiltration.

Turtles possess a primitive penis probably illustrating a second stage of evolution of the mammalian structure. On either side of the midventral line of the cloacal wall a longitudinal band of porous, sinusoid tissue is developed; these two structures are the *corpora cavernosa*. Between them lies a groove, the *sulcus spermaticus*. When the sinuses are filled with blood the corpora enlarge as a single organ, protrude through the vent, and enclose the sulcus spermaticus in such a way as to form a duct whose inner end lies in close proximity to the end of the ductus deferens. A small sensory papilla, the *glans penis,* is situated at the posterior tip.

In mammals the two corpora cavernosa form the bulk of the penis. In addition some six major innovations have been introduced. The sulcus spermaticus has become permanently closed, forming the *cavernous urethra* continuous with the membranous urethra leading from the bladder and into which the deferent ducts empty. In the connective tissue between the corpora cavernosa a single elongate bone, the *baculum* or *os penis,* has evolved in a few orders (Fig. 13.20). Another cavernous body, the *corpus spongiosum,* evolved from the glans and surrounds the cavernous urethra. A skin flap (*prepuce*) covering the glans is present in some. Furthermore, the penis has evolved from a structure normally lying on and largely attached to the cloacal floor and has become free from the cloaca, since that structure disappears through separation of rectum and urinogenital sinus. Finally,

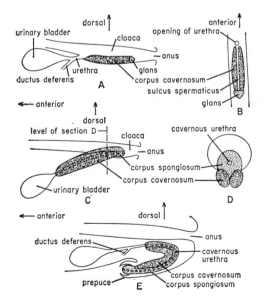

FIG. 13.19 Evolution of penis. A, turtle, sagittal section; B, turtle, dorsal view; C, D, early mammal; E, eutherian mammal.

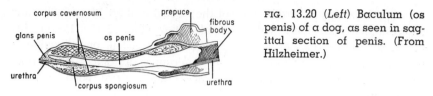

FIG. 13.20 (*Left*) Baculum (os penis) of a dog, as seen in sagittal section of penis. (From Hilzheimer.)

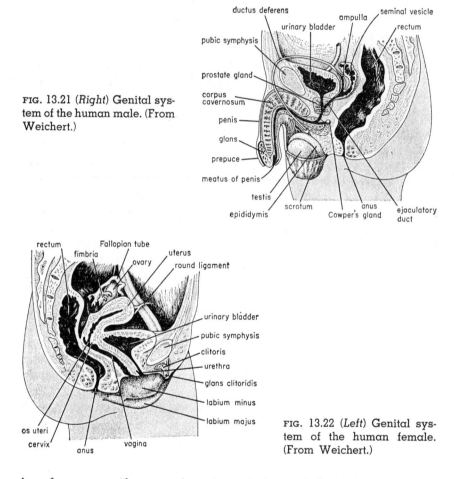

FIG. 13.21 (*Right*) Genital system of the human male. (From Weichert.)

FIG. 13.22 (*Left*) Genital system of the human female. (From Weichert.)

in a few groups (for example, primates) the penis has become separate even from the body wall, except at its base (Fig. 13.21).

Female. In mammals (Fig. 13.22) the female phallus consists of (1) a tubercle (*clitoris*), at the ventral border of the vulva, which represents the glans penis; (2) folds (*labia minora* and *labia majora*), bordering the vulva, that respectively represent the corpora cavernosa of the penis and the scrotal sac; and (3) in some an *os clitoridis* representing the os penis. Embryonically the external genitalia of the two sexes are astonishingly alike, up to a rather late stage (Fig. 13.23); then the various parts begin to develop in their own unique way for each sex. Occasionally development along somewhat male or female lines in the opposite sex produces anomalies referred to as "hermaphroditic," but which do not, of course, affect the true sex of the individual, determined by the sex cells of the gonads, not the external genitalia.

Similar vestiges of the penis occur in female reptiles and primitive birds.

Accessory Reproductive Glands

A large number of glands function as sexual accessories in various vertebrates. They may be grouped by function as *seminal, intromittent, hedonic,* and *mammary* glands.

Seminal Glands. Glands functioning primarily to contribute to a heterogeneous fluid (*semen*) of importance in transport of sperm are seminal glands. Leydig's gland, consisting of a large, medial section of the opisthonephros, is of such function in chondrichthyans. Mammalian examples (Fig. 13.20) are the *seminal vesicles* (not homologous with those of fishes), located at the bases of the deferent ducts, and the *prostate* glands, located at the point of union of the urethra and deferent ducts.

Intromittent Glands. These actually facilitate copulation, or are associated directly in some other manner with the intromittent organs. Mam-

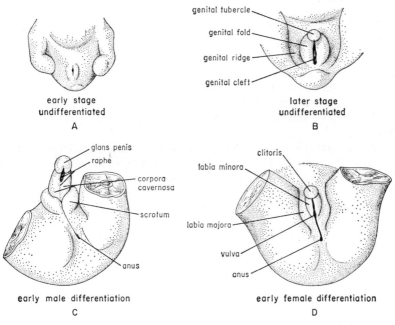

FIG. 13.23 Human sex differentiation. (From Wilder.)

malian examples are the *bulbourethral* (or *Cowper's*) glands (Fig. 13.21), emptying into the urethra where it passes into the penis; the *preputial* glands on the internal surface of the prepuce; the female homologs of these; and the seminal glands previously mentioned. In chondrichthyans the *water sacs* seemingly have an intromittent function.

Hedonic Glands. These are glands whose primary function is to stimulate sexual interest. A large number of integumentary glands of spotty distribution among vertebrates are of hedonic function. Supra-anal and chin tubercles are common among snakes, chin and lip glands in salamanders, anal and inguinal glands among mammals. Many nonglandular secondary sexual characters are at least partly of hedonic function.

Mammary Glands. These are restricted to mammals and are discussed elsewhere (see Integumentary System).

QUESTIONS

1. Describe the features and state the functions of the celom in the hypothetical prechordate stage ancestral to vertebrates.

2. Name and, where possible, give the functional value of the five major changes producing a holonephros in the hypothetical protochordate stage.

3. What are the four steps in evolution of the internal glomerulus? Of what value was the whole evolutionary process?

4. Name in proper order the recognized parts of the mammalian uriniferous tubule. What is the function of each?

5. Diagram and label the parts of the mammalian renal corpuscle.

6. What is the location and function of the capillary networks of the mammalian renal unit and by what vessels is each supplied and drained? Answer the above question for ectotherms. What is the function of the renal portal system in connection with the uriniferous tubules? To what extent, if at all, was this system discarded in "higher" vertebrates and to what extent was it retained? Contrast the mammalian and ectotherm kidney circulation, both in detail and in general operation, and describe by what changes the former evolved from the latter.

7. How did the needs for integumentary impermeability differ in ostracoderms and amniotes? Explain how the kidney may be regarded more as an organ of selective recovery than as one of selective elimination.

8. Explain the nature and cause of the problems of water balance faced by vertebrates under the three environmental situations of importance in this connection.

9. How is water output controlled (six ways) in different marine vertebrates (name them)? Output (six ways) in different terrestrial vertebrates? Input (four ways) in fresh-water vertebrates? Explain each.

10. In what three successively different forms are metabolic wastes excreted in vertebrates? What advantages does each successive form have over the preceding? Why was the particular form reasonable at the time it was first used? Of what groups is each form characteristic? What is the prime factor that prevents mammals from successful subsistence upon sea water? What enables mammals to eliminate a hypertonic urine?

11. Name and fully distinguish the five kinds of kidneys recognized in vertebrates. Diagram their evolutionary relationships.

12. Explain the supposed prime factor involved in the successive shifts from one type of kidney to another in the tetrapod line of chordate evolution. Explain a secondary factor also possibly involved.

13. Name the derivatives of the holonephros in each sex of opisthonephric animals; in metanephric animals.

14. Name the derivatives of the holonephric duct in each sex of opisthonephric animals (excluding actinopteran fishes); in metanephric animals.

15. Explain the principle of embryonic sexual indifference.

16. How does the oviduct differ in composition in teleosts and tetrapods?

17. Name and locate the nonexcretory derivatives of the holonephros in male and female anamniotes; in amniotes.

18. Name the vestiges in males of the female internal reproductive organs in opisthonephric vertebrates; in metanephric vertebrates.

19. Name the vestiges in females of male internal reproductive organs in opisthonephric vertebrates; in metanephric vertebrates.

20. Name and state the function and occurrence in different vertebrates of the three main divisions of the oviduct.

21. Describe in evolutionary sequence and give an example of groups possessing the different degrees of fusion of oviducts in mammals.

22. Name and distinguish the different kinds of urinary bladder, and specify the groups in which each occurs.

23. How do mammalian urinary bladders differ from other allantoic bladders so far as structures connected with them are concerned?

24. How do mammalian bladders vary in position of attachment of the ureters? Give examples.

25. In what vertebrates does a urinogenital sinus occur in males? In females? Describe and give examples illustrating stages or extremes in evolutionary trends, if any, exhibited in each sex.

26. What is the posterior limit of the vagina in females with a urinogenital sinus? Explain.

27. Explain two general trends in gonad evolution in vertebrates.

28. To what factors may a reproductive cycle be attributed in female vertebrates? Males? Any exceptions? How explained?

29. Describe briefly three variations concerning specifically the ovary in vertebrates.

30. What is the apparent functional value of testicular displacement? Describe the various degrees of displacement occurring in mammals, and cite examples. What is the avian analog of the mammalian method of testicular temperature control? What is cryptorchism and its relation to sterility and masculinity?

31. Name and state the occurrence of different types of intromittent organs in vertebrates.

32. Discuss the adaptive value of internal fertilization. How is it accomplished in different vertebrates (three ways)?

33. Describe three stages in the evolution of the penis giving the changes introduced at each stage and citing the groups in which each stage is exemplified in living vertebrates.

34. What are the female phallic counterparts of the amniote penis?

35. Name the groups of accessory reproductive glands and examples of each among mammals and other vertebrates insofar as possible.

36. How does the vas deferens of fishes and of tetrapods differ?

37. Name ten urinogenital structures of mammalian adults, or twelve of vertebrate adults in general, that are now vestiges or are now reproductive but were formerly excretory in function.

38. Define the following words, and where possible state occurrence and give an example:

abdominal pore
accessory
   opisthonephric duct
afferent glomerular
   artery
afferent renal vein
allantoic bladder
appendix epididymis
appendix fimbriae
archinephric duct
baculum
bicornuate
bipartite
body of uterus
Bowman's capsule
bulbourethral gland
caudal opisthonephros
cavernous urethra
celomoduct
cervix
clitoris
cloacal bladder
collecting tubule
corpus cavernosum
corpus spongiosum
cortex
Cowper's gland
cranial opisthonephros
cryptorchism
distal convoluted
   tubule
diuretic
ductuli aberrantia
ductus deferens
duplex
efferent ductules
efferent glomerular
   artery
efferent renal vein

epididymis
epoophoron
external glomerulus
Fallopian tube
Gärtner's duct
genital pore
glans penis
glomerular filtrate
glomerulus
gubernaculum testis
hedonic
hemipenis
hemotumescent
Henle's loop
hilus
holonephric duct
holonephros
hypertonic
hypotonic
infundibulum
internal glomerulus
intromittent gland
intromittent organ
labia majora
labia minora
Leydig's gland
lobulate kidney
medulla
mesonephric duct
mesonephros
mesorchium
metanephric duct
metanephros
Müllerian duct
nephrocele
nephrostome
opisthonephric duct
opisthonephros
os clitoridis

os penis
ostium tubae
oviduct
paradidymis
paroophoron
penis
peritoneal funnel
phallus
prepuce
preputial gland
pronephric duct
pronephros
prostate gland
prostatic utricle
proximal convoluted
   tubule
pyramid
renal corpuscle
renal papilla
renal pelvis
renal portal vein
renal sinus
renal unit
round ligament
scrotal sac
selective elimination
selective recovery
semen
seminal gland
seminal vesicle
sessile hydatid
sexual indifference
shell gland
simplex
sperm sac
spermatic cord
splanchnocele
sulcus spermaticus
testicular displacement

tubal bladder
tubular capillary
   network
urea
ureter
urethra

uric acid
urinary pore
urine
uriniferous tubule
urinogenital pore
urinogenital sinus

uterus
vaginal sac
vulva
water sac
Wolffian duct

14

CIRCULATORY
SYSTEM

CONSIDERATION of the circulatory system must include three distinct topics: (1) the blood vascular system, with the heart; (2) the lymphatic system; and (3) the hemopoietic (blood- and lymph-forming) organs. The blood vascular system, by far the most complex topic, involves many more impressive and striking phylogenetic trends than the others.

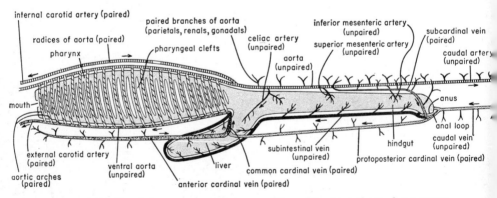

FIG. 14.1 Circulatory system of an amphioxuslike hypothetical primitive prevertebrate, lateral view.

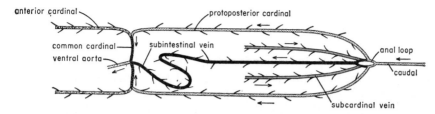

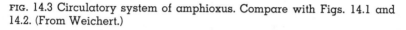

FIG. 14.2 Veins of a hypothetical primitive prevertebrate, ventral view.

FIG. 14.3 Circulatory system of amphioxus. Compare with Figs. 14.1 and 14.2. (From Weichert.)

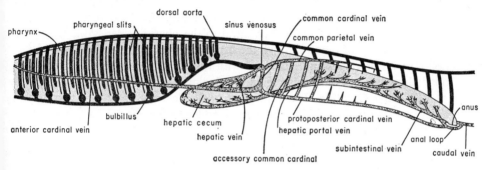

The Blood Vascular System

One of the most remarkable similarities of amphioxus to the vertebrates is seen in its circulatory system. The arrangement almost perfectly matches an imaginary prototype from which the vertebrate type may well have evolved. Of course the exact nature of the early vertebrate circulatory system will never be known, but a highly reliable approximation to the prototype can be made by extrapolation from the types known in primitive living vertebrates (cyclostomes), in primitive fishes (elasmobranchs, dipnoans, etc.), and in the cephalochordates. The modifications of this prototype in different lines of evolution have been, for the most part, in the nature of deletion and fusion of various sections. Relatively few new vessels of importance in the basic evolutionary picture have been added.

Thus the evolutionary story of the blood vascular system in vertebrates begins with a hypothetical prototype (Figs. 14.1, 14.2) closely resembling that of amphioxus (Fig. 14.3). The most obvious differences are the intact subintestinal vein, the subcardinal veins, absence of contractile bulbilli on the bases of the aortic arches, absence of accessory ducts of Cuvier, and absence of common parietal veins. These are, to the vertebrate line of evolution, inconsequential specializations that for our purpose need not be emphasized.

Hypothetical Prevertebrate System

Ventral Aorta. Extending forward along the midventral line below the pharynx is the unpaired ventral aorta. Blood flows anteriorly in this vessel.

Heart. The heart is not present as a compact organ in the hypothetical prevertebrate. All living vertebrates do have a well-formed heart, but embryological as well as protochordate (especially amphioxus) evidence reveals that a tubular structure, merely the base of the ventral aorta, was the forerunner of the vertebrate heart. Thus a *cardiac region,* not a true heart, is recognized in the prevertebrate prototype. It consists of muscular tissue concentrated along a short length of the base of the ventral aorta immediately in front of the liver, ventral to the pharynx. Peristaltic waves effect movement of blood through the cardiac region. In subsequent evolution a series of valves and chambers with thickened muscular walls developed along the length of this region, producing the familiar cardiac organ.

External Carotids. The ventral aorta divides anteriorly into two arteries, the external carotids, that carry blood into the ventral head region.

Aortic Arches. A series of paired arteries connect the ventral aorta with a pair of dorsal vessels extending lengthwise near the dorsolateral wall of the pharynx. The number of arches consistent with the prevertebrate stage is not precisely limitable; a maximum of ten is inferred for vertebrates (ostracoderms), but almost certainly a still greater number existed in ancestral prevertebrates. Arbitrarily the number may here be assumed to vary between twelve and sixteen.

The function of the aortic arches is purely mechanical—transporting blood from the ventral aorta to the dorsal vessels. There is *no special adaptation for a respiratory function* as in primitive vertebrates, for the pharynx itself is primarily a food-capturing device.

Dorsal Aorta. This is the most important vessel in distribution of blood to various parts of the body. It receives blood solely from the aortic arches in the pharyngeal region, where the vessel is paired. The paired vessels, or *radices of the aorta,* carry blood posteriorly to approximately the level of the liver, where they unite to form the unpaired aorta that extends into the tail as the *caudal artery.*

Internal Carotids. The continuations of the radices of the aorta anterior to the first aortic arch are the internal carotid arteries, which carry blood forward into the head region. Thus two pairs of arteries supply the cephalic area. Although both persist throughout vertebrates, their composition changes greatly by the addition of parts of the aorta and aortic arches. Nevertheless, the internal carotids are invariably regarded as primarily the anterior extensions of the dorsal aorta and the external carotids as primarily the anterior extensions of the ventral aorta.

The apparent anomaly of a two-directional flow of blood in the dorsal aorta and its anterior extensions is simply a matter, in effect, of the internal carotids functioning as branches receiving blood from the aorta in **much** the same fashion as any other branch, division, or fork of the aorta or other artery. The angle of diversion is unusually great, but the situation is not otherwise atypical.

Unpaired Visceral Aortic Branches. Typically in vertebrates three large, unpaired arteries supply the postpharyngeal gut. They are the *celiac,* supplying the stomach and part of intestine; the *anterior mesenteric,* supplying most of the small intestine; and the *posterior mesenteric,* supplying chiefly the large intestine. There is little fundamental significance in the rather considerable variation occurring in different vertebrates. Lesser unpaired branches supply other parts, particularly anteriorly, in various vertebrates.

Paired Somatic Aortic Branches. The vessels supplying the body wall and paired abdominal organs (gonads, kidneys) are paired. Most prominent are the *parietals,* supplying the body wall; *genitals* (*ovarian* or *spermatic*) supplying the gonads; and the *renals* (supplying the kidneys). These arteries, reduced to as few as a single pair in some cases, are constant in occurrence in vertebrates. Branches of lesser constancy occur in limited vertebrate groups.

Caudal Vein. The numerous capillary systems supplied by the dorsal and ventral aortae are drained by a system of veins somewhat more complex than the arterial system. Actually the primitive vertebrate possesses many enlarged, thinly walled spaces (sinuses) to collect the blood drained in turn by the true veins that are provided with their own distinctive walls. There is a general trend in the evolution toward mammals for reduction of the number of sinuses, most becoming thick-walled and narrower, and thus assuming the form of veins.

The caudal vein, unpaired, lies ventral to the caudal artery, draining the tail. It terminates at the level of the anus, where it divides into two.

Subintestinal. A single vessel, collecting blood from the intestine, extends forward from the anal loop along the intestine and onto the liver, thence to the ventral aorta, with which the subintestinal is continuous. The line of demarcation between the two vessels corresponds with the common cardinals (see below).

Protoposterior Cardinals. The paired vessels into which the caudal vein passes are commonly called "posterior cardinals," but they are far different from the posterior cardinals found in adult fishes and modified as a postcava in tetrapods. The so-called "posterior cardinals" of the prevertebrate (also cyclostomes, amphioxus) become the renal portals and contribute to only a fraction of the posterior cardinals of subsequent vertebrates. This ambiguity of application of "posterior cardinal" is highly confusing and unnecessary, as the name must always be explained when used. To avoid this, a simple expedient is limitation of the name *neoposterior* cardinal to the composite vessel of most fishes, and application of "protoposterior cardinal" to the unmodified vessels of protochordates, agnathans, and the prevertebrate prototype.

The protoposterior cardinals lie in the lateral body wall and extend forward from the caudal vein. They drain (1) the body wall by means of *parietal veins* paralleling the parietal arteries; (2) the gonads by means of *genital (ovarian, spermatic) veins;* and (3) kidneys by means of *renal* veins.

Anterior Cardinals. These are paired veins draining the cephalic capillary systems, carrying blood posteriorly along either side of the body to a point of union, opposite the rear heart region, with the protoposterior cardinals.

Common Cardinals. The two blood streams carried by the anterior cardinal and protoposterior cardinal unite and pass as one, on either side, through a *common cardinal* vein (or duct of Cuvier) into the base of the heart region.

Subcardinals. Lying to either side of the dorsal aorta are two veins beginning in the middle abdominal region and carrying blood posteriorly into the base of the protoposterior cardinals. They drain the body wall by means of segmental *parietal veins.*

It is to be assumed that the subcardinal veins originally came into being simply as a device for draining the lateral body wall. Evolution of the kidney between the areas drained by the protoposterior cardinals and the subcardinals resulted in drainage of the kidneys by both sets of veins. Subsequent evolution resulted in a most important division of labor between these two sets of vessels.

Actually no adult vertebrate possesses subcardinals in the relationships described here for the hypothetical prototype, although most gnathostomes possess them embryonically. Amphioxus has a somewhat comparable pair of vessels draining forward into the heart region, however. These and other data indicate the probable existence at one time of adults possessing subcardinals functioning as described above despite the lack of definite knowledge of such forms. Cyclostomes do not have them either as embryos or adults, but that they secondarily lost them, making other ad-

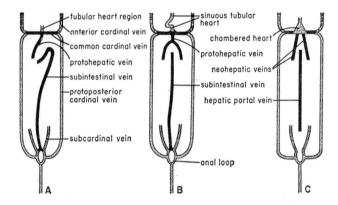

FIG. 14.4 Inferred phylogeny of the hepatic portal system, in successive stages A-C.

justments for kidney function, is possible. It is possible, of course, that the subcardinals appeared on the scene subsequent to the time of common ancestry of gnathostomes and cyclostomes. In either case the inclusion of the vessels in the prototype discussed here is fully justified, for the cyclostomes clearly are a group of very ancient divergence from the line of evolution of gnathostomes.

With this basic structure in mind, we may now examine this system piecemeal and trace the evolution of each part separately.

Evolution of the Subintestinal Vein

Formation of the Protohepatic Vein. It is presumed that in certain protochordates ancestral to the vertebrates the hepatic cecum became well developed and acquired functions that required the blood from the intestine and stomach—that is, in the subintestinal vein—to pass through its capillary network. What was a continuous vessel from the anal loop to the union of the common cardinals became differentiated into two parts: (1) an anterior *protohepatic vein* serving solely to drain blood from the capillary network of the hepatic cecum into the ventral aorta, and (2) a more posterior part still retaining the name of subintestinal, draining blood from the anal loop, intestine, and stomach and emptying it into the capillary network of the hepatic cecum (Fig. 14.4). At this stage the subintestinal vein actually functions as a portal vessel, carrying blood from one set of capillaries directly to another, without passing through the heart.

No living chordate possesses exactly the arrangement of vessels described for this stage, although the Amphioxus closely approaches it.

Formation of the Hepatic Portal Vein. The embryogeny of most vertebrates provides a clue to the next step in evolution: the subintestinal vein became detached from the anal loop, draining only the gut. Thus modified, the vein is the *hepatic portal vein,* which persists with only minor changes throughout vertebrates.

At perhaps about the same time that the hepatic portal vein evolved, the liver became enlarged and bilobed. To accommodate to this bilobed condition the single, unpaired protohepatic vein also became divided, ultimately assuming the form of paired *neohepatic* veins. The hepatic veins persist as paired vessels throughout all gnathostome fishes except the Choanichthyes.

As defined here, hepatic veins are the vessels draining the liver, regardless of their evolutionary status. The early, unpaired hepatic vein may be distinguished as the protohepatic vein, whereas the later, paired hepatic veins may be regarded as neohepatic vessels. The latter are modified to a certain degree in tetrapods, one assuming a new function while the other persists with the ancient function of liver drainage. Thus although tetrapods are provided basically with an unpaired hepatic vessel, in adults, that vessel represents only one neohepatic vein, not the original protohepatic vein.

Further explanation of these changes is given in the discussion of evolution of the postcava.

Embryonic Origin of the Hepatic Portal Vein. Since species of chordates now living fail to exemplify the adult stages intermediate between protochordates and fishes, the facts of evolution of the hepatic portal vein may be regarded as inaccessible. The possible phylogeny may be inferred but embryology contributes relatively little to the picture and actually tends to obscure it, because of the caenogenetic specializations imposed by the necessities of embryonic function.

The story of embryogeny (Fig. 14.5) begins with the *vitelline veins,* the earliest to appear in embryogeny of vertebrates. They are of immediate importance for carrying inert food materials from the yolk to the growing embryo. The two veins, one from either side, converge in the liver region near the ventral surface of the body and growing forward as paired vessels promptly fuse to form a single vessel, the ventral aorta. The heart forms in the posterior part of the ventral aorta.

From near the point of union of the vitelline veins a *subintestinal vein* grows posteriorly along the ventral surface of the alimentary tract and into the tail (caudal vein), skirting the anus by means of a continuous anal loop. The protoposterior cardinals subsequently unite with the anal loop, whereupon the subintestinal becomes detached from the loop and at the same time becomes of portal function by losing its direct connections with the vitelline veins. The remnant of the subintestinal has thus become the hepatic portal vein, draining blood from all postesophageal parts of the alimentary tract and conducting it to the liver where it is filtered for many purposes. The functional importance of this circuit is proved by its invariable occurrence and remarkably constant form in all adult vertebrate animals.

The vitelline veins likewise break down into a loose network of vessels in the liver, leaving two stubs intact near the former union of the vitellines; these two stubs are the *hepatic veins.* The rest of the vitelline veins disappear at birth or hatching.

Nature of Portal Systems. Two portal systems are commonly recognized among vertebrates: the hepatic portal system and the renal portal system. An adrenal portal system is limited to certain reptiles (for example, snakes).

Portal systems have in common one or more large *portal veins* receiving blood from various capillary systems by way of a variety of lesser venous tributaries; and a *capillary network* (of a *portal organ,* paired or single), which receives the blood supplied by the portal vessels. A portal system may be defined as a *venous* (not arterial) network connecting one system of capillaries directly with another. Somewhat similar (but not to be confused) is the system of arterial vessels (dorsal aorta and associated arteries) directly connecting the capillary system of piscine (fish) gills with the various somatic capillary systems; or the comparable system of arterial vessels (efferent glomerular arteriole) in the mammalian kidney connect-

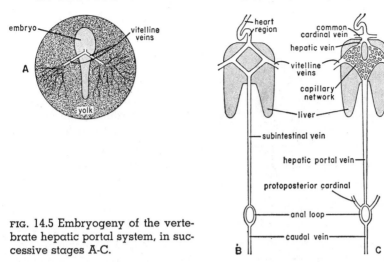

FIG. 14.5 Embryogeny of the verte-brate hepatic portal system, in successive stages A-C.

ing the glomerular capillaries with the tubule capillaries; in both cases the connecting vessels are arteries not veins. The connection of liver or somatic capillary systems and lung capillary systems is also somewhat similar, but in these cases the heart is intercalated between the opposing terminal systems; the connection between is not "direct."

The value of portal systems in general is to provide the opportunity for extraction or filtering from the blood of certain waste or food materials, some of which are to be processed for storage, immediate use, or excretion.

In a way portal systems are inefficient, as the venous blood received by portal organs is deficient in oxygen, and the organ thus must be supplied with arterial blood as well as with portal blood. An essentially double circulation in the portal organ is the result. Of great interest is the fact that one of the portal systems (renal) of primitive vertebrates has been eliminated in higher vertebrates, being replaced by a more efficient single circulation in the kidneys, which receive only arterial blood. The hepatic portal system has persisted throughout vertebrates, however, with no diminution whatsoever. The very narrow limits of tolerance of body cells to certain materials, such as sugar absorbed into the blood through the intestinal walls, assure a permanent place for the hepatic portal system. The fluctuations in blood contents, were the system to be eliminated, would require a wholesale physiological reorganization presumably impossible to effect at this advanced stage of evolution.

Evolution of the Mammalian Postcava

The mammalian postcava has had a long and involved ancestry. All details are not known, but embryological and comparative anatomical evidence agree on the major features.

A postcava first appeared in choanichthyan fishes, and is absent in all other fishes. All tetrapods possess a postcava, but that of mammals is markedly different from the postcava of other vertebrates. The latter we here distinguish as the *protopostcava,* whereas the mammalian vessel is a *neopostcava.*

Four important stages in evolution of the mammalian postcava seem clearly indicated: (1) formation of the renal portal system; (2) formation of the protopostcava; (3) formation of the supracardinals; and (4) loss of the renal portal system. The major changes associated with each of these stages are discussed in the following sections.

Formation of the Renal Portal System. It is thought that prevertebrate ancestors possessed a pair of subcardinal veins, the chief purpose of which was to drain the paravertebral body walls, supplementing the protoposterior cardinals which drained the lateral and ventral body walls. Such an arrangement is compatible with the flattened body form known to have existed in many primitive Agnatha (ostracoderms). Amphioxus retains some of this paravertebral drainage system in the form of "common parietal" veins; these differ from the subcardinals only in that they drain anteriorly into the common cardinals rather than posteriorly into the protoposterior cardinals.

Be this as it may, the fact remains that living Agnatha (cyclostomes) lack subcardinals. It is thought that the absence is due to loss of an ancestral trait, not to complete absence in their ancestors. The loss may be attributed to (a) assumption of a more compact, cylindrical body form readily drained by the protoposterior cardinals alone, and (b) failure to develop an efficient coordination of circulatory and excretory system by the cyclostome kidney. It was chiefly because of the later-adopted excretory role of the subcardinals that these vessels were retained (with modified connections) in other primitive vertebrates.

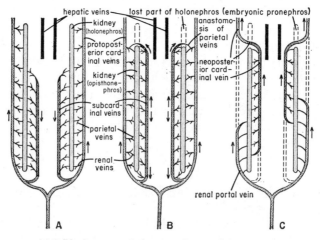

FIG. 14.6 Phylogeny of the renal portal system, in successive stages A-C.

In the main line of evolution, the subcardinals were to play the key role in formation of the renal portal veins. They originally drained the body wall by means of segmental *parietal veins,* but as the kidneys assumed a more important excretory role the subcardinals apparently picked up connections with the renal capillary system, eventually developing essentially segmental *renal* veins to drain the kidneys. The protoposterior cardinals in the meantime developed a series of similar vessels from the more lateral body parts: *parietals* draining the body wall, *renals* the kidneys (Fig. 14.6A).

A propensity for development of anastomoses (fusions of parallel or divergent vessels) is one of the most universal characteristics of the circulatory system. Presumably this propensity was responsible at this stage for development of at least a few connections of the parietals of the subcardinal and of the protoposterior cardinal. Of these an extreme anterior one (which we may call the *parietal anastomosis*) became of the utmost importance (Fig. 14.6B), permitting a flow of blood forward through the subcardinals, whereas previously only a posterior flow was possible. This anastomosis opened up a whole new world not only for kidney function but for ways of life; probably few alterations in the vertebrate body have been more dramatically significant than this, even if inauspicious at the beginning.

As the kidney gradually utilized more completely these new filtering possibilities, the posterior unions of the subcardinals and protoposterior cardinals were lost, as were the connections between the middle and anterior parts of the protoposterior cardinals (Fig. 14.6C). The renal portal system was thus born, with blood drained by the rear parts of the protoposterior cardinals being forced to pass through renal capillaries, drained in turn by the old subcardinals. The isolated posterior part of each protoposterior cardinal is the *renal portal vein* (paired); the subcardinal veins and anterior parts of the protoposterior cardinals, fused by way of the anastomosed parietals, are now called the *neoposterior cardinal veins*. This basic condition occurs throughout adult gnathostome fishes except the Choanichthyes, in which the veins are rearranged to form a protopostcava.

The significance of the formation of a renal portal system merits a more careful exposition. Before it appeared, chordates utilized a primitive kidney system (essentially a holonephric kidney) which functioned chiefly by drainage of the celomic fluids that picked up body wastes by diffusion and interstitial drainage. This system is admirably adapted to the marine life the ancestral protochordates are thought to have led, for the animals would have little problem in replacing inorganic materials lost by kidney action. They would have a problem in maintenance of an adequate water level, however, living in a medium hypertonic to that of body fluids.

Subsequent penetration of the fresh-water habitat by vertebrates may be regarded as an adjustment to the lack of control of water loss, but in turn that move introduced the new problem of maintenance of the proper hypertonic level of body fluids, whose tonicity tended to be lowered by excess intake of water from the surrounding, hypotonic fresh-water medium. Obviously a mechanism to dispose of metabolic wastes without loss of so much of the essential constituents of body fluids was imperative if survival was to be possible in the fresh-water habitat. The answer to the problem involved development of an impervious bony integument to cut down water intake, and use of the renal portal system as a device to extract useful inclusions from the kidney filtrate obtained from the blood supplied by the renal arteries and drained by the neoposterior cardinal veins. The filtrate was, as in higher holonephric types, received from minute capillary networks (glomeruli) at the ends of the renal arteries, and was carried away into the kidney by long uriniferous tubules that in turn connected with the excretory duct leading to the exterior. The renal portal capillaries formed a network about these uriniferous tubules and extracted useful materials (including water) from them. Thus a *double circulation,* characteristic of all portal organs, was formed in the kidney. It is only to be expected that the initial stages in evolution of so complex a structure as the advanced kidney should be of simple construction, and that integration of structure and function should have been relatively crude. As a matter of fact, not until reptiles appeared was much progress made toward streamlining the system and reducing it to a single cycle of circulation. The kidney possessed by vertebrates through this long period of dominance of the renal portal system was the opisthonephros. The structure of this and other types of kidneys and the solutions various vertebrates adopted to the problems of such different demands on the kidney as are imposed by reinvasion of marine habitats, invasion of terrestrial habitats, and semiarid modes of life are discussed with the urinogenital system.

Formation of the Protopostcava. The protopostcava, existing in choanichthyan fishes and in all living tetrapods except mammals, is a composite of the right hepatic vein and the fused subcardinal portions of the neoposterior cardinal veins (Fig. 14.7A). No living or fossil intermediates are known between this condition and that of paired neoposterior cardinals devoid of hepatic connections, although they of course existed at one time. Nevertheless it is likely that the transition was rather abrupt, being effected by retention and elaboration in adults of some embryonic connections of previously transitory nature. The sole advantage that served to preserve the connection was apparently substitution of a single direct channel to the heart in place of the more devious bilateral channels. Simplification of structure has been a strong tendency throughout vertebrate evolution, and this is an important example of that principle.

The paired, divergent anterior parts of the posterior cardinal vein at first retained their union with the protopostcava, as in modern Urodeles, but subsequently (as in all "higher" vertebrates) their connections with the protopostcava were lost (Fig. 14.7B). Their vestiges remain, however, as highly important drainage channels for the thoracic body wall in some reptiles and especially in mammals, emptying into the common cardinal veins or their derivatives.

Formation of the Supracardinals. In one group of advanced reptiles the renal portal veins developed direct connections with the forked posterior ends (representing the subcardinals) of the protopostcava. Thus no portal circulation through the kidney actually exists in that group, despite use of the name "renal portal" for the veins. The same advanced condition is preserved in birds (Fig. 14.8A).

In primitive reptiles, including those ancestral to mammals, a different sort of renal bypass was in the making. A pair of dorsolateral vessels developed between the anterior ends of the neoposterior cardinals and the renal portal veins. These vessels, the *supracardinal veins,* served to drain the body wall by collecting blood from segmental parietal veins, and to provide a more direct passageway for the blood going from posterior quarters to the heart than the renal portal system permitted. In the embryos of mammals, and therefore perhaps in adults of their immediate reptilian ancestors, an anastomosis, the *renal collar,* developed on each side between the supracardinal and the renal vein, enabling blood from the posterior parts of the body to flow still more directly into the heart *via* the protopostcava (Fig. 14.8B).

Loss of the Renal Portal Veins. In mammals all parts of the supracardinals disappeared except for the anterior end of each and the section of the right vessel between the right renal collar and the right renal portal. The renal portal veins, as such, likewise completely disappeared, but the small segment between the posterior end of the right supracardinal and the caudal vein did persist as a component of another functional system of veins (the postcaval system). Thus the true mammalian postcava came into a being: a single vessel of highly complex origin, extending from the caudal vein to the heart (Fig. 14.8B, C). It includes six sections recognizably distinct in evolution (although not in appearance). From anterior to posterior these six parts are as follows: (1) the right hepatic vein; (2) parts of the right and left neoposterior cardinals fused together (subcardinal parts only); (3) a small part of the right neoposterior cardinal, continuous laterally into the right renal vein (the left subcardinal diverges farther anterior, at the end of the fused section, as the left renal vein);

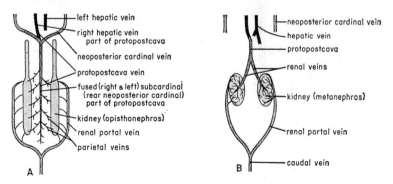

FIG. 14.7 Phylogeny of the protopostcava, in successive stages A-B.

(4) the right renal collar; (5) the posterior part of the right supracardinal vein; and (6) the posterior end of the right renal portal vein. The terminal tributary is the caudal vein.

The details of composition of the neopostcava just reviewed are not characteristic of all mammals. Each order thus far studied by anatomists exhibits certain peculiarities, and furthermore considerable individual variation exists. Mammals are uniformly unique, however, at least so far as is now known, in having a postcava consisting not only of parts of the hepatic and subcardinal veins but also of parts of the supracardinals, renal portals, and usually the renal collars. It is the exact part of each of the additional systems of vessels from which the neopostcava is formed in different mammals that varies.

Evolution of the Precavas and Their Tributaries

The veins involved in evolution of the precava from the prototypic pre-vertebrate are the anterior cardinals and common cardinals. These vessels persist through the fishes with relatively minor changes (Fig. 14.9A). In the amphibians, however, with development of a neck and the shift poste-riorly of the heart, the common cardinals tend to shift forward to become nearly longitudinal rather than transverse in position (Fig. 14.9B). At about the same time the anterior drainage channels develop new pathways. In earlier types (fishes) the anterior cardinals arise chiefly about the eye and brain in a superficial position. Gradually better-protected internal chan-nels develop to drain the same areas, supplanting the more superficial anterior tributaries of the anterior cardinal. These become, in amphibians

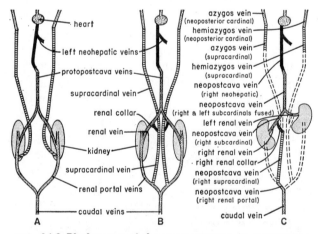

FIG. 14.8 Phylogeny of the neopostcava, in successive stages A-C. A, hypothetical condition in mammallike reptiles; B, embryonic mammalian arrangement; C, a common arrangement in the mammalian adult.

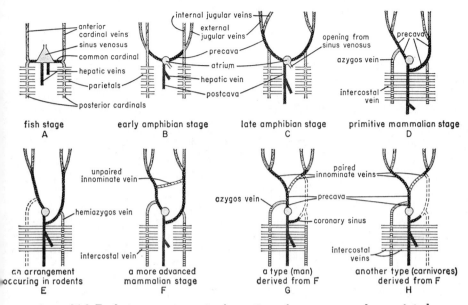

FIG. 14.9 Evolutionary stages in formation of precavas and associated vessels.

and in all classes derived from them, the internal jugulars, which are continuous posteriorly with the anterior cardinal. The latter vessel is thus regarded as constituting, in the tetrapods at least, the basal portion of the internal jugulars.

The external jugulars also appear in amphibians, where they constitute superficial tributaries of the old anterior cardinal, draining the lateral and ventral surfaces of head and neck. They are elaborations of formerly inconspicuous branches and are thus not homologous with any well-known or conspicuous forerunner in fishes. They are, in this sense, "new" acquisitions, but this statement should not be construed as implying sudden formation in tetrapods from nothing whatsoever in their piscine ancestors; on the contrary, like any other structure, whether "new" or altered from some conspicuous forerunner, these vessels have evolved over long periods from ancestral contributions which, in this case, were originally inconspicuous and gave no indication of the long and important history they were to have in tetrapods.

The common cardinals, now (in some amphibians) of longitudinal position, are directly continuous with the jugular veins, which by their junction form the common cardinals. These are called *precavas* or *anterior vena cavas* in tetrapods. They carry blood from the jugulars into the right atrium of the heart. They receive en route to the heart the two subclavians (usually near the junction of the jugulars) and in most tetrapods the posterior cardinal sinuses or homologs thereof. The latter, in conjunction with the shift forward of the old common cardinals, commonly unite with the precavas near the heart rather than in the primitive position at the junction of the jugulars.

In many mammals a curious diagonal anastomosis, the *innominate vein,* develops embryonically between the two precavas (Fig. 14.9F), carrying blood in a short cut from the anterior part of the left precava to the posterior part of the right precava. This has no phylogenetic forerunner, but seems to be a cenomorphic device originating in embryonic development with the simple advantage of effecting a more direct flow of blood from the left side of the head and neck to the heart. Some mammals (Insectivora, Chiroptera, some ungulates, and Rodentia) retain the embryonic innominate in the adult, without conspicuous alteration of the precavas, but in others (for example, primates, Carnivora, Figs. 14.9E, 14.9H) the left precava disappears between the innominate vein and vicinity of the heart. Thus in these mammals a Y-shaped conformation results, only one branch of the Y (the left) being the true (*unpaired*) innominate vein. Yet the symmetry of structure in adults is such that to name the two branches differently would be highly confusing. Accordingly both branches are, in postembryonic stages, called *paired* innominate (or brachiocephalic) veins.

The primitive left precava thus persists in such animals as the cat and man as a small, anterior part of the left innominate vein. Another vestige is the extreme posterior part against the dorsal heart wall. Into this part the coronary veins characteristically drain in all tetrapods; this function requires retention of this part as the coronary sinus, even in those animals in which the more anterior portion of the left precava is lost.

The primitive right precava in turn is represented in such animals as the cat and man by (a) the right innominate vein, and (b) *the* "precava."

Azygos and Hemiazygos Veins. It will be recalled that the neoposterior cardinals have disappeared almost completely in modern reptiles and birds. Their only intact vestige in adults is a short part at the anterior ends of the supracardinals. In mammals the supracardinals also disappear as such in adults, but a thoracic vestige of each persists, continuous with a short proximal section constituting the posterior cardinal, as the azygos vein on the right side, the hemiazygos on the left.

These veins persist with a special function of body wall drainage, being supplied by a series of parietals known specifically as *intercostals* for obvious reasons. The intercostals of the two vessels tend to anastomose with each other middorsally, thus rendering either vessel actually capable of draining both sides of the thoracic wall. In mammals possessing both precavas, some have only the azygos vein, some only the hemiazygos. Mammals possessing only a single precava (always the right, if but one) perforce retain the azygos, and in most of this type (for example, carnivores) the hemiazygos is completely absent. Man represents an intermediate condition in this respect (less advanced than the cat), having but one precava and a well-developed azygos, but also a thin, functionless, variable, hemiazygos vein blind at both ends.

Evolution of the Pulmonary Veins

The most primitive vertebrates known to possess pulmonary veins are the Dipnoi. It is believed, on reliable grounds, that crossopterygians also possessed such vessels, as lungs are thought to have occurred in them. There is even a possibility that they may have occurred in some placoderms, inasmuch as they possessed an apparently lunglike structure.

The phylogenetic origin of the pulmonary veins is nevertheless shrouded in complete obscurity, even to a greater degree than the lungs, with which of course the veins must have arisen. The veins are in essentially the same relation to heart and lungs in all vertebrates in which they are known, and no living vertebrates without lungs are known to possess vessels that could convincingly be called homologs of pulmonary veins. The embryogeny of the vessels likewise appears to offer no suggestion of ancestral origin. It is entirely possible, even probable, that the basic pulmonary architecture was established *before* or concomitantly with the elaboration of pharyngeal pouches as gill structures. In such case even the heart may not yet have been differentiated from the ventral aorta. The puzzling pulmonary vein may thus simply have been modified from an aortic arch attached in the position where the atrial chamber of the heart eventually differentiated. Failure by most Osteichthyes and all Chondrichthyes to utilize the lunglike placoderm structures as respiratory organs would have rendered the cardiac connection a liability instead of an asset, with resultant loss and failure to exhibit a homolog of the pulmonary veins.

In all vertebrates in which the pulmonary veins occur, they have the same function—that of transporting oxygenated blood from the lungs to the left atrium of the heart. Often the lungs lie close enough to the heart for several branches to empty independently into the left atrium. In others, a single trunk for each lung unites with a common trunk in turn uniting with the heart.

Evolution of the Heart

The evolutionary changes of the heart lead from a primitive, simple straight tube in the protochordates, through the sinuous multichambered organ seen in fishes, and the partially subdivided but otherwise simple structure of early tetrapods, to the compact, highly efficient structure of mammals and birds. There is little gross similarity between the extremes save in function. Yet the amazing transition was made in a logical series of steps, the important ones or groups of which we may summarize as follows: (a) the protochordate stage with the alimentary pharynx; (b) the piscine stage with the branchial pharynx; (c) the early tetrapod stage with primitive lungs; (d) the later tetrapod stage of higher ectotherms; and (e) the stage of endothermic tetrapods. As implied by the names designating these stages, the heart reflects changes in other structures, particularly respiratory organs.

The Protochordate Heart. The protochordates ancestral to vertebrates presumably possessed a simple, tubular heart beating simply by peristaltic waves. It was little more than a slightly specialized region at the base of the ventral aorta. Arteries in general may be envisioned as preadapted to formation of this primitive sort of heart, since their walls are more highly muscularized than those of veins. This extensive muscularization of arteries has its functional significance in forcing blood into the smaller vessels (capillaries or the like) from which the blood may return without special means of propulsion since it is passing from smaller into larger vessels. Thus the stage was set for the evolution of the heart in the far distant past of prechordate ancestors in which blood vessels themselves were being organized as arteries and veins.

The hypothetically ancestral protochordate heart is paralleled closely by that seen in living cephalochordates. There is little similarity in existing representatives of either the urochordates or hemichordates.

Lack of need in the protochordate stage for a more specialized heart can be explained on the basis of lack of respiratory function, at this stage, of the pharyngeal clefts. These are alimentary in function, aiding in capture of food by serving much as a sieve. Thus the blood does not pass through a capillary network in the pharyngeal walls, but merely uses the aortic arches as the most convenient channels through which to reach the dorsal aorta.

The Piscine Heart. As the descendants of ancestral protochordates developed an integumentary armor preventing continued use of the skin as a respiratory organ, the pharyngeal filtering device became diverted from an exclusively alimentary function to at least in part a respiratory function. We see evidence of this shift in fossil ostracoderms. Much of our own structure has been built upon the early heritage of a pharyngeal food-filtering device; how vastly different vertebrate structure would now be had a different pharyngeal structure existed in preostracoderm ancestors!

In any event, the capillary network necessarily evolving in the pharyngeal pouches in order to facilitate gaseous exchanges required a more efficient, specialized pump to force blood through to the dorsal aorta. Thus it

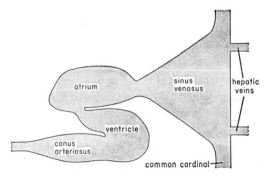

FIG. 14.10 Piscine heart, ventral view with parts drawn to side instead of superimposed as in life.

is in the fishes that a true heart is seen for the first time—a heart consisting of a series of specialized chambers to which the function of forcible propulsion of blood in arterial channels is restricted.

Actually two operations must be performed to carry out efficiently the cardiac function in a gill-respiring vertebrate. The blood must be collected, as well as pushed along. Collecting chambers thus appear at the rear and propulsive chambers at the front. There is a rather remarkable uniformity in structure of these chambers in fishes, with a *sinus venosus* posteriorly, preceded by an *atrium,* then a *ventricle,* and finally a *conus arteriosus* (Fig. 14.10). There is a flaplike enlargement, the *auricle,* on each side of the atrium in many if not all fishes. As would be expected in view of the tubular ancestry of these chambers, the sequence of beat is the peristaltic sequence: from the rear toward the front. Despite all shifts in relative positions of the chambers in later vertebrates, this sequence of beat is maintained unchanged throughout: we still see that each heart beat in mammals and birds is initiated at the phylogenetic posterior part of the heart (atrium), despite the fact that this part has shifted into an anterior position.

The shift of relative antero-posterior position of certain heart chambers is presaged in fishes themselves by assumption of a sinuous form of the heart. The atrium extends forward dorsally, overlying the ventricle which extends caudad ventrally. The advantages accruing from the sinuous form are presumably dual: (a) the collected blood can reach the propulsive chambers (ventricle and conus arteriosus) with the aid of gravity as well as by the force applied by the weakly contractile atrium; and (b) the walls of the collecting chambers (atrium, sinus venosus) must remain thin in order to receive the blood with the minimum resistance and thus permit the chambers to bulge more easily forward than in any other direction. The sinuous form is thus chiefly an adaptation to the aquatic environment. Although certainly not essential for the terrestrial mode of life, the relationships of heart chambers inherited from piscine ancestors are retained in tetrapods. The atrium lies dorsal and anterior to the ventricle throughout all tetrapods, a direct result of the form developed by fishes for their aquatic environment. Had tetrapods evolved directly on land, without an aquatic history, the heart probably would not have evolved this peculiarity of a basically sinuous structure. The heart could have been just as that now existing in tetrapods, but modified directly from a straight tube, with the atrial chamber at the rear and the ventricle, anterior. If any shift occurred to adjust for a more erect posture, it would likely have been simply to a more dorso-ventral position.

The sinus venosus is little more than an expansion of the junction of the primary somatic (common cardinal) and visceral (hepatic) veins. The walls are very thin and apparently are virtually incapable of contraction. A slight negative pressure actually exists in this chamber, resulting from the integration of atrial contraction and action of the sinauricular valve. Through a *sinauricular valve* the blood passes with minimum cardiac assistance into the atrium. From there it is forced by gravity and atrial contraction through the *atrioventricular* valve into the ventricle. The thickened walls of the ventricle provide certain resistance to incoming blood, and thus the atrium must be more active in pumping than the sinus venosus. The relatively powerful ventricular walls then provide the energy to move the blood into the gills. The gradual pressure advancement of the blood in three stages to the climactic ventricular chamber is an ingenious and efficient mechanism.

Once received in the ventricle, the blood passes one or more series of *semilunar valves* in reaching the conus arteriosus, which adds still further push to the blood and smooths its flow (makes it less strongly pulsating) on its way to the ventral aorta. The entrance into the latter is guarded by several rows of other semilunar valves.

The Early Tetrapod Heart. The stage was set by development of air bladders in pretetrapod ancestors for the perfection of the aerial respiratory function in tetrapods, as one of the very many alterations associated with shift from the aquatic to the terrestrial mode of life. A variety of substitutes for gills was tried out, obviously, as amphibians experimented with the various possibilities that would enable them to survive in this new terrestrial habitat. The air bladder, gradually perfected to serve the chief or indeed eventually the sole role in external respiration, was the most successful of all experimental "models." Increase in its perfection meant, however, not only modifications of the lungs themselves but also improvement of the mechanism of supplying the body with aerated blood. This required, chiefly, changes in the heart. The aerated blood received by the atrium through the pulmonary vein was, in ectothermic tetrapod stages, mixed in the ventricle with the nonaerated blood received by the atrium from the sinus venosus. Such a complete mixture rendered the pulmonary system much less efficient in supplying aerated blood to body tissues than the gill system; small wonder that amphibians were, and are, such sluggish creatures compared with most fish. In this and other respects tetrapods probably were actually not safe from their piscine ancestors; even today aquatic amphibians are conspicuously unsuccessful competitors with fish. One must remember that the gill respiratory system of most fishes is a most highly efficient one second only to the pulmonary system of birds and mammals (certainly not to the pulmonary or other respiratory systems of amphibians and reptiles). For only one major reason have fish failed to attain ecto-thermically the metabolic perfection of endothermic mammals: lack of a pumping mechanism to force *aerated* blood from the gills to the other body structures. This has been an insuperable obstacle for fish, but their respiratory system is nevertheless superior to that of all tetrapods save birds and mammals because it supplies body structures with *only* aerated blood.

Although perfection of the cardiac portion of the pulmonary cycle required 100 million years or more, until appearance of birds and mammals, early tetrapods were not long in taking at least a few steps to remedy the existing imperfections (Fig. 14.11).

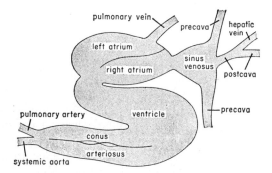

FIG. 14.11 The early tetrapod heart, ventral view with parts drawn to side instead of superimposed as in life.

First and most important, the atrium was subdivided into two chambers: a *systemic chamber* (right), receiving nonaerated blood from the sinus venosus; and a *pulmonary chamber* (left), receiving aerated blood from the pulmonary vein. At least the initial phase of establishment of a double circulatory cycle in the heart was thus accomplished. Modern salamanders and lungfish have the atrium only partly divided; it is completely divided in modern anurans and in all living reptiles, birds, and mammals. This alteration was specifically and incontrovertibly associated with the development of an air-breathing mechanism (lungs) instead of an aquatic device.

It would seem that all the effort to separate pulmonary and systemic chambers in the atrium went for naught because of the absence of a separation in the next chamber (ventricle) the blood entered, but this appears not to be wholly true. A second, related alteration involved a partial separation of two chambers in the conus arteriosus, serving apparently to direct the aerated blood (from the left side) chiefly into the anterior vessels of the ventral aorta, whereas the nonaerated blood (from the right side) was directed chiefly into the posterior pair of vessels bearing the pulmonary arteries. The dividing ridges were slightly spiraled, inasmuch as they had to direct blood from right and left sources into channels essentially dorsoventral in relation to each other (the pulmonary arches dorsal, systemic arches ventral). Thus we can recognize a pulmonary and a systemic chamber in the conus arteriosus, but it is important to realize that the content of each was just the reverse of the atrial chambers of the same names: the pulmonary conus chamber contains chiefly *nonaerated* blood, the systemic chamber chiefly *aerated* blood. In the case of the conus arteriosus we think of where the blood is going, whereas with regard to the atrium we think of where the blood came from.

A third alteration was union of the bases of the sixth aortic arches and separation of them from the ventral aorta as far back as the conus arteriosus. This meant two virtually separate exits from the conus arteriosus.

A fourth alteration consisted of reduction of the sinus venosus both in size and importance as a blood-gathering chamber. The functional advantage bestowed by this change is not immediately apparent, but was very likely involved with adjustment to the lesser pressures of the aerial environment as compared with the relatively great pressures of the aquatic environment. Venous flow in fishes unquestionably is accomplished under difficulties, since it must counterbalance the greater pressures exerted by the surrounding water. A large, thin-walled heart chamber (sinus venosus) into which the blood can flow against an absolute minimum of resistance is essential for fishes. In land-dwelling vertebrates, subjected to the markedly lesser atmospheric pressures, such an elaborate collecting device is not essential; in later stages it is discarded completely. Air-breathing vertebrates that have reinvaded the aquatic habitat to an extreme degree (as seals, whales, etc.) have thus been forced to evolve a compensatory safety valve system, not found in fishes, of *retia mirabilia* enabling arterial blood to pass more or less directly into venous channels for brief periods when the body is subjected to extreme pressures (as when diving to great depths). These retia are networks of fine anastomoses directly connecting the large arteries and veins with each other.

The early tetrapods are thus advanced to a stage in which the heart has six completely or partially separated chambers, two main entrances (right and left), and two main exits (ventral and dorsal). Although it is convenient to regard the piscine heart (as described here) as a stage from which the tetrapod heart is derived, this is unlikely, at least so far as venous connections with the atrium are concerned; otherwise the generalization is true. Actually the heart of most living fishes, lacking a pulmonary vein or homolog thereof, is an evolutionary side line not involved at all with the tetrapod line in which *at all stages* a pulmonary vein (or homolog thereof) was present.

The Later Ectotherm Stage. Living reptiles, varied in cardiac structure though they are, exhibit uniformly a number of improvements over the early tetrapod heart. Presumably these alterations were effected in ancient reptiles as well as in modern survivors; for they are essential steps in the chain of events that led to the remarkable organization of the avian and mammalian heart.

First (Fig. 14.12), the sinus venosus continued its reduction in size and in advanced types ancestral to mammals it no doubt disappeared com-

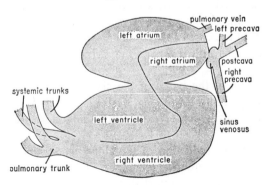

FIG. 14.12 Late ectothermic heart, ventral view with parts drawn to side instead of superimposed as in actual structure.

pletely as a chamber, although it is present in all living reptiles. From the very first vertebrates, however, the sinus served a function not only as a collecting chamber but as a site of origin of the heartbeat. Although its identity as a chamber may have been lost in at least some reptiles and certainly was in birds and mammals, the function it formerly possessed for initiation of heartbeat could not be discarded. The excitatory tissue remained imbedded in the wall of the right atrium, near the point of entry of the veins that now, with the loss of the sinus as a chamber, empty directly into the atrium. This myogenic center is the *sinatrial* (or *sinauricular*) *node,* which serves in all amniotes lacking the sinus venosus as the originator of each heartbeat.

Second, the conus arteriosus also disappeared, but not simply by reduction in size. It was subdivided to form the bases (*trunks*) of the large arteries leaving the heart, and which thus became connected directly with the ventricle. The spiral ridges seen in early tetrapods united so that the dorsal pulmonary trunk connected directly with the right side of the ventricle, whereas the more ventral systemic trunk united with the left (chiefly) side of the ventricle. Actually, the systemic trunk is paired in many reptiles (Squamata and Crocodilia), the right trunk connecting with the left side of the heart, the left with the right side. The left systemic trunk would receive nonaerated blood if a complex valvular arrangement had not been developed so that most of its blood is received from the left ventricle and is therefore aerated. In those types in which such an arrangement is not effected, the left arch is reduced in size and has no important branches; the right arch supplies blood to the head and pectoral limbs.

Just what functional loss is involved in the structural loss of the conus arteriosus is uncertain. It is to be assumed that in fishes the conus serves some purpose in connection with the gills, perhaps effecting a more clearly *continuous* flow than the ventricle alone could provide; this is not essential in nongill-breathing vertebrates since the arterial flow becomes essentially continuous by the time it has traversed the long vascular systems separating the heart from most capillary networks. The close proximity of heart and gills in fishes could scarcely have failed to result in a highly spasmodic, discontinuous branchial flow had it not been prevented by development of a specialized structure such as the conus to absorb the initial pressure and thus to even the flow. Accordingly the conus is not essential to the air-breathing vertebrates and is eventually lost by subdivision in the late ectothermic stage.

Despite the loss of the role of the conus arteriosus as a cardiac chamber in reptiles, the semilunar valves that the conus formerly possessed remained of the utmost importance. These persist at the bases of the pulmonary and systemic trunks in all amniotes, but are reduced in number to three valves in each vessel.

A third alteration was a partial subdivision of the ventricle, resulting in a rather effective separation of venous and arterial blood. A complete partition is found in living crocodilians, which have a left aortic arch as well as a pulmonary trunk attached to the right ventricle. Curiously, the left arch does not receive blood directly from its own (right) ventricle, since the semilunar valves there are enlarged so as actually to prevent flow from ventricle to aorta except under unusual stress situations. The virtually functionless left arch does receive blood, however, through a *foramen of Panizzi* connecting the right and left arches where they cross a short distance from the heart.

Thus in the late ectothermic stage only three cardiac chambers remain of the six occurring in the preceding stage, but one of those three (the ventricle) is still further subdivided so that in this stage there are four cardiac chambers at least partly separated from each other.

The Endotherm Stage. Only a few, relatively slight alterations have occurred in endotherms to effect the maximum efficiency of the heart. Most important is the complete closure of the ventricular wall, rendering absolutely impossible any mixture of aerated and nonaerated blood (Fig. 14.13). The trend toward double circulation in the heart, initiated perhaps as early as placoderms, and certainly in choanichthyans, thus attains final perfection in endotherms. Closure of the ventricles along with simplification of the systemic aorta is the last step in reaching the greatest possible perfection in the cardiac link of the "forced-draft" respiratory mechanism unique to birds and mammals and chiefly responsible for their endothermic condition.

A second alteration, in birds only, is reduction of the ventricular exits from three to two, with loss of the left aortic trunk. Mammals evolved from a group of reptiles having but a single aortic trunk.

In mammals and birds we thus see a heart whose four chambers were evolved from only two chambers of the four-chambered fish heart. It possesses only two of the three sets of valves present in piscine ancestors: the semilunar valves and the atrioventricular valves. The latter set is now divided into two (as are the chambers they separate) to which the names *tricuspid valve* (the right atrioventricular valve) and *bicuspid* or *mitral valve* (the left atrioventricular valve) are applied in mammals. The endothermic heart is truly a masterpiece of evolutionary sculpture. That from a one-cycle heart pump serving a single vascular system a single organ could have evolved to serve as a double pump operating two wholly separate vascular systems at once is not a whit less marvelous that we understand at least a few of the stages through which it has passed in achieving its ultimate perfection. As we look disdainfully upon our lowly relatives in other vertebrate classes we could well pause occasionally to consider that these are the descendants of the animals but for whose long and very often fatal experiments we should not have attained the presumed advantages we now hold.

Adaptive Trends in Cardiac Evolution. Most of the changes of the heart in vertebrate evolution can be associated with one of the following

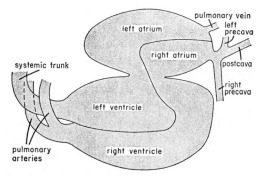

FIG. 14.13 Endothermic heart, ventral view with parts drawn to side.

adaptive areas: (1) air breathing instead of "water breathing"; (2) aerial pressures instead of aquatic pressures; and (3) a largely intrinsic control of temperature and metabolic rates, instead of a largely extrinsic (environmental) control. All the adaptive trends have evolved in such a manner as to preserve or attain the utmost simplicity consistent with the maximum possible efficiency.

Evolution of the Aortic Arches

Vertebrate, or at least gnathostome, evolution of the aortic arches has been confined for the most part to only six pairs of the undoubtedly greater number present in earlier types. Even some Chondrichthyes possess derivatives of more than this number, and the cyclostomes, of course, possess a larger number (as many as eight in lampreys, fifteen in hagfishes). Nevertheless, only six figure in the structures persisting in all tetrapods and in virtually all fishes. We shall accordingly restrict our attention to these six, knowing that still others were present in primitive gnathostomes but have left no important traces. The condition of six complete aortic arches may be referred to as the "prototypic" condition (Fig. 14.14).

Even thus confined, the many variations from the prototype found in living vertebrates of different groups may seem a little frightening in complexity upon first examination. Yet there has been a very reasonable, logical sequence of events leading up to each combination now in existence. The more commonly encountered conditions of living fishes, amphibians, and reptiles, respectively, do, as a matter of fact, appear to correspond very closely with the presumed course of phylogeny of the arches in the birds and mammals, the most advanced groups in arch modification.

The Prototypic Condition. The dorsal aorta (Fig. 14.14) was undoubtedly paired throughout the length of the pharynx in early vertebrates, and may be regarded as similarly paired in the prototypic six-arch condition.

The *ventral aorta* was likewise probably paired in prevertebrate ancestors, but there is little evidence of a paired vessel in living vertebrates, and even in amphioxus it is single. Thus the vessel is represented as paired only anterior to the fourth aortic arches in the prototype, since the external carotid arteries (paired, of course) originate in most vertebrates at the level of the fourth arches.

The anterior extensions forward of the *paired aorta* (or *radices of the aorta*) are termed the *internal carotid arteries*. They carry blood forward into the head (especially about the brain and sense organs), whereas the aorta posterior to the origin of these carotids carries blood posteriorly.

The ventral extensions forward of the ventral aorta are termed the *external carotid arteries*. They carry blood forward into the head (especially about the jaws and external surface), whereas the blood flow in the aorta posterior to the origin of these carotids is dorsad into the aortic arches.

The existence of a blood flow into the head from the *ventral aorta* via the external carotids corroborates the thought that in early vertebrates or their ancestors the aortic arches were not carrying "venous" blood destined for prompt oxygenation in the pharynx walls. Venous blood, as here defined and as generally understood, means carbonated, deoxygenated blood with low sugar and high waste content, as characteristic of blood leaving somatic capillary systems. Either arteries (as the pulmonaries) or veins (most veins from nonrespiratory organs) may carry venous blood. Arterial blood may likewise flow in either veins or arteries. In these earlier animals, as in living protochordates, the aortic arches are merely mechanical devices for getting the blood from the ventral trunk to the dorsal trunk; the respiratory function is of integumentary execution. Subsequent loss by the integument and adoption by the pharynx walls of the respiratory function were a prime factor in evolution of the divided aortic arches characteristic of all fishes. This splitting of the arches goes hand in hand with forcing the blood to pass through a series of branchial capillary systems, making the gills efficient respiratory organs.

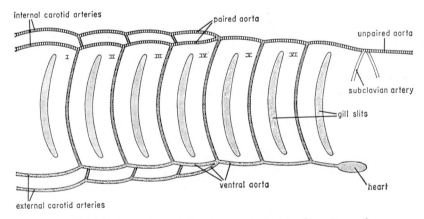

FIG. 14.14 Prototypic vertebrate arrangement of aortic arches.

In the prototype, of course, the visceral arches and clefts are regarded as unmodified for any cranial function. They presumably functioned in prevertebrates as food-trapping structures (as in all living protochordates), and are regarded as having the same function in the six-arched prototype.

Formation of Afferent and Efferent Branchials. The integument of most protochordates and presumably of prevertebrates was composed of a single layer of cells and could thus readily serve as a respiratory membrane. The integument of all living vertebrates is composed of several or many layers and is even covered by a more or less impervious cellular or non-cellular layer. Evolution of such an integument, no longer capable of serving as a respiratory organ, must have required elaboration of a compensatory respiratory organ. The walls of the pharyngeal gill slits, covered by a single layer of epithelium and lying in close proximity to the abundant circulatory channels of the aortic arches, were admirably preadapted for the new function of respiration that became imposed upon them by natural pressures.

Precisely what steps were followed in evolution of the early branchial (gill) slits probably will never be known. Gill or branchial slits, with a respiratory function as their defining characteristic, are to be carefully distinguished from *visceral* or pharyngeal clefts or slits, which may have any function whatsoever. Whatever the means, eventually the walls of the slits were enlarged by development of relatively diagonally placed, antero-posteriorly compressed *gill pouches*. The anterior and posterior walls of these pouches were of greatest significance in elaboration of respiratory membranes. The adjacent pouch walls were locked more or less firmly together by connective tissue supported inwardly by skeletal *visceral arches*. The two walls of adjacent pouches thus bound together formed a single *gill* or *holobranch*. The vascularized and often folded pouch wall on either side of a *holobranch* is termed a *demibranch*. Each holobranch thus includes two demibranchs connected with each other by an *intrabranchial septum* in which lies the visceral arches and the various divisions of the aortic arches involved in supplying blood to and draining blood from the respiratory capillary network on the gill surfaces.

In order to make it necessary for blood to pass through this capillary network, a simple division of each aortic arch into ventral and dorsal halves was required. The ventral half of each arch is termed the *afferent branchial artery* (carrying blood *to* the gills), the dorsal half the *efferent branchial artery* or *epibranchial* artery (carrying blood *away* from the gills). The single afferent branchial artery suffices for supplying blood to an entire holobranch, but even at a very early stage efficient drainage required a separate branch of the efferent branchial for each demibranch of each holobranch.

Thus in what may be regarded as the second stage in arch evolution (Fig. 14.15), six afferent and six efferent branchial arteries, derived from the six originally continuous aortic arches, are seen. Furthermore, each efferent branchial arises from two vessels, one for each of the two demibranchs drained by each epibranchial. The anterior branch is the *prebranchial artery,* the posterior one the *postbranchial artery.*

At perhaps nearly the same time as these changes were effected the dorsal aortic radices became fused forward to approximately the level of the fourth aortic arches. This condition is more or less constant throughout living gnathostomes.

Formation of Collector Loops. Utilization of the entire inner surface of the gill pouches was probably the important factor in bringing about a union of the postbranchial of one epibranchial with the prebranchial of the succeeding epibranchial, thus establishing a complete circuit about each gill pouch. These secondarily established unions, or anastomoses, became functionally more efficient than the former unions of each epibranchial with two branchial branches; obviously a circuit about the gill pouch is of greater functional value than a circuit about a holobranch.

Thus with formation of the *collector loops* (Fig. 14.16) about the gill pouches, each epibranchial is now supplied by its own former prebranchial (now called the *postrematic,* in reference to its position on the posterior edge of the gill *pouch*) and by the former postbranchial (now called *pretrematic*) of the preceding epibranchial.

The *intertrematics* that probably were present in the earlier stage of branchial (as opposed to trematic) tributaries of the epibranchials persist with formation of the collector loops. These make possible an adoption by any one epibranchial of the duties of either adjacent vessel should localized pressures (as when swallowing large food objects) interfere with normal blood flow. The most posterior set, of course, serves an additionally important function since only through it can the pretrematic vessel of the seventh visceral pouch be drained. This vessel became isolated as the collector loops were formed through separation of each postbranchial from its own epibranchial and fusion with the next following prebranchial.

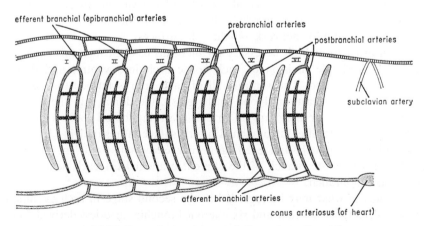

FIG. 14.15 Second stage in evolution of aortic arches.

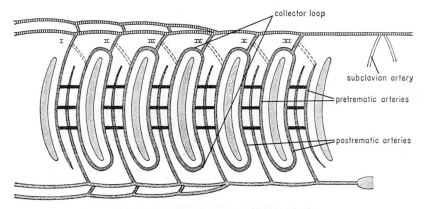

FIG. 14.16 Formation of collector loops.

Since no branchials occur posterior to the last holobranch, the last post-branchial remains as an isolated pretrematic drained only by cross trunks emptying into the postrematic of the sixth epibranchial.

Loss of Mandibular Gill Circulation. Positional approximation of the branchial apparatus to the jawless mouth resulted in fusion of the first (mandibular) gill pouch with the mouth and, of course, a concomitant loss in gill (respiratory) function of the pouch. The visceral arch supporting the first pouch likewise became considerably altered, adopting the totally new function of jaws. It is to be remembered that the visceral arches in vertebrates always lie *posterior* to their corresponding visceral pouches.

With loss of branchial function of the mandibular pouch, the epibranchial for that pouch (Fig. 14.17) became virtually useless as a drainage system for the first gill pouch, but it nevertheless remained with a modified function as a secondary channel for blood flow through the internal carotids to the head.

Although positive evidence is lacking, it is likely that the placoderms possessed an aortic arch organization essentially like the hypothetical stage just described, for they (the placoderms) possess well-developed visceral arch (mandibular) jaws, but the visceral arches (and presumably the gill pouches) posterior to the jaws were unmodified and presumably still possessed unaltered a respiratory (gill) function. This may thus be regarded as the *placoderm stage.*

Because of its (to some) controversial nature, discussion of one other feature included here as part of the placoderm stage has been deferred for the last. It was long thought that the lungs and pulmonary arteries characteristic of tetrapods first appeared in their crossopterygian ancestors. Actually, however, lunglike structures (air bladders) were known even in placoderms, and thus they presumably were already present in the earliest osteichthyans. Of further support to this hypothesis is the fairly well-established supposition that the lungs were formed from a pair of gill pouches posterior to the set of seven so regularly in evidence in all gnathostome

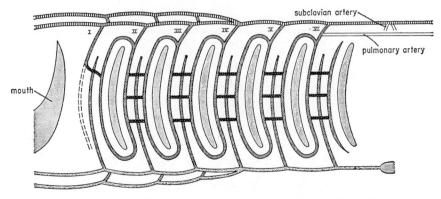

FIG. 14.17 Placoderm stage of aortic arch evolution.

evolution. A pulmonary artery must have been present when the forerunner of lungs evolved. Its absence in most fishes may be attributed to complete loss of the pleural (lung) forerunner; or to modification into other structures homologous with lungs but of widely different function (as swim bladders); or to origin from a different placoderm group (as has often been thought may have been the case in the Chondrichthyes) from that which give rise to the Osteichthyes. Of considerable interest is the fact that the pleural (lung) homolog is supplied by typical pulmonary arteries in at least two primitive actinopterans, Polypterus and Amia, as well as in dipnoans (the only living choanichthyans for which information is available). In other living osteichthyans the swim bladder has either obtained a more direct blood supply from the aorta or has been secondarily lost.

These data make it an entirely reasonable postulate that, even as early as the placoderm stage, a *pulmonary artery* was present. It may be regarded to have existed at that stage as a branch from the sixth epibranchial, as it indeed is in all vertebrates possessing such a vessel.

The origin of the pulmonary artery prior to the placoderms is, of course, unknown. It may be a posterior epibranchial which shifted in attachment to a more anterior vessel, or it may be a persistent nutrient vessel comparable to the *esophageal* artery of the dogfish, which not only supplies aerated blood to the esophagus but also to several posterior holobranchs.

Despite fairly clear evidence that the pulmonary organ and circulation were branchial in origin, the conclusion remains inescapable that the pattern of evolution of these structures is completely unknown and provides one of the most entrancing—but apparently insoluble—problems in vertebrate phylogeny.

EARLY ICHTHYAN STAGE. In all living gnathostomes not only is the mandibular pharyngeal pouch and visceral arch devoted to a new function, but so also is the second pouch, with its skeletal arch. In the fishes (Osteichthyes and Chondrichthyes) usually only the second arch and pouch are modified, in addition to the mandibular; in tetrapods all are modified.

In the two living classes of jawed fishes the second gill arch is modified chiefly as a hinge mechanism connecting the jaws with the brain case or skull; thus altered it is termed the hyoid arch. The lower parts of the hyoid arch serve other functions, none of which are branchial. Thus the hyoid gill pouch perforce has become reduced in size, persisting as a *spiracular cavity* in primitive pretetrapod fishes, in a variety of chondrichthyan fishes (including most sharks, skates, and rays), and in a few living osteichthyan fishes (most Chondrostei).

With loss in function of the hyoid pouch, the first afferent branchial, which formerly supplied the rear half of the first pouch and the front half of the second pouch, lost all its functional value and accordingly disappeared (Fig. 14.18). It was presumably retained in the placoderm stage to supply only the front half of the second pouch, even as the second afferent branchial in the ichthyan stage supplies only the front half of the third pouch. Thus in the early ichthyan stage five pairs of afferent branchials are typically present.

The second epibranchial likewise lost its branchial function with reduction of the second pouch to a spiracle. Exactly as occurred in the case of the mandibular efferent artery in the placoderm stage, the hyoidean efferent remained attached to the third collector loop by means of retention of the uppermost intertrematic. The hyoidean efferent thus served as another subsidiary channel for blood flowing forward through the internal carotid arteries into the head. As a matter of fact, the hyoidean adopted the bulk of the duty of carrying blood to the internal carotids, thus relieving the bases of the aortic radices of their function. These, the "paired aortae" or "aortic radices" observed in the dogfish (Squalus) became vestigial and eventually disappeared.

It would seem that with formation of a good blood source for the internal carotids (*via* the hyoidean efferent arteries), the need for the mandibular efferent (which served much the same purpose in the placoderm stage) would have been eliminated. On the contrary, the vessel seems to have been required in many fishes for supplying aerated blood to the spiracular region. This remained possible, despite loss of parts of the hyoidean collector loop, by retention of (a) a lower intertrematic originating from the pretrematic branch of the third collector loop; (b) the lower end of the second collector loop; and (c) the pretrematic branch of the hyoidean collector loop as far upward as its union with the mandibular epibranchial. The parts of this continuous vessel between the third collector loop and spiracle comprise the *afferent pseudobranchial* artery, and those between the spiracle and internal carotid comprise the *efferent pseudobranchial* artery.

A final alteration in the early ichthyan stage was connection of the external carotid arteries with the third collector loop. Since the external carotids are to be regarded as the anterior extensions of the ventral aorta, their sudden appearance as branches of the efferent branchial system seems totally inexplicable. Actually the shift is an embryological aberration and is readily understood by following the embryogeny of these vessels (Fig. 14.19).

In phylogeny it must be assumed that the ventral aortic radices (external carotids) shifted outward and upward on the anterior (then the second) afferent branchial arteries on each side. This shift progressed to such a point that, as the embryonically complete aortic arches split to form epibranchials and afferent branchials, the external carotids were left attached to the *upper* division (epibranchial) rather than the *lower* division of the second aortic arch. The prebranchial then grew forward as a branch of the second postbranchial. With the formation of the third collector loop, the second postbranchial became the pretrematic of the third efferent loop, where the vessel is seen in the dogfish and many other fishes. The functional advantage of shift of the external carotids from the afferent system carrying nonaerated blood to the efferent system, which carries aerated blood, is obvious.

The most prominent alterations required of the placoderm aortic arrangement to produce the early ichthyan conformation may be summarized as follows: (a) loss of first afferent branchial leaving five afferent branchials; (b) formation of a nonbranchial hyoidean epibranchial; (c) loss or reduction to a nonfunctional vestige of the dorsal aortic radices between the second and third arches; (d) formation of an afferent spiracular; (e) formation of an efferent spiracular; and (f) shift of the external carotids from the ventral aorta to the third efferent collector loop. Most of these alterations accompanied the loss of branchial function of the hyoid gill pouch.

The Dogfish Aortic Circulation. The dogfish circulation in the branchial region (Fig. 14.20) matches almost completely the hypothetical ichthyan stage in evolution of the tetrapod aortic circulation. The only conspicuous difference is the lack of a pulmonary artery, presumably be-

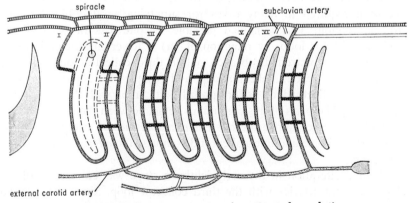

FIG. 14.18 Early piscine stage of aortic arch evolution.

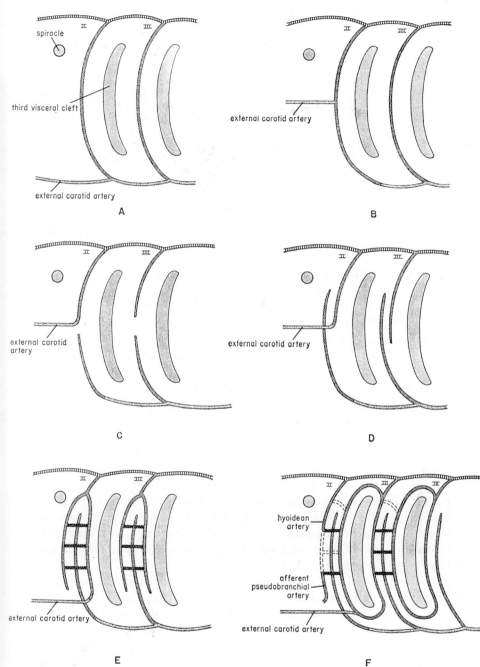

FIG. 14.19 Transposition of the external carotid arteries from the afferent to the efferent branchial circulation. A-E, embryonic sequence; F, adult condition.

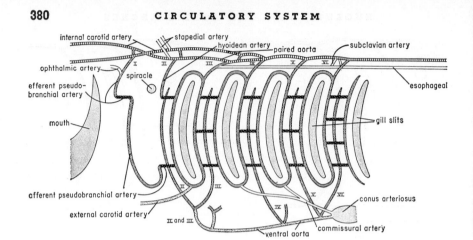

FIG. 14.20 Dogfish branchial circulation, lateral view, drawn to emphasize derivation of vessels.

cause of origin from a group of placoderms different from that giving rise to osteichthyan groups. The prechondrichthyan placoderms presumably did not possess pulmonary structures, or lost them very early in evolution, contrary to the preosteichthyan placoderms which definitely did have pleural structures. It is possible that the nutrient *esophageal* artery of the dogfish may be homologous with the pulmonary artery of pretetrapod fishes.

Early Amphibian Modifications. Certain steps outlined in the preceding discussion may actually not have occurred in the preamphibian line of evolution. In particular, the collector loops may not have been present, although they do occur in some living Dipnoi. The variety of connections and omissions of the various branchial vessels occurring in different living fishes is bewildering in complexity; there is little evidence on which a reliable conjecture can be based as to what the arrangement may have been in the piscine ancestors of tetrapods. For the sake of convenience, since the dogfish is such a commonly utilized example, we may assume that the evolutionary sequences thus far described may, with reasonable plausibility, closely correspond with the true course of events. They do not, in any event, disagree with known facts.

The tetrapod internal carotid arteries are commonly considered—on clear embryonic evidence—to be represented, anterior to the third aortic arch, by simply the aortic radices and extensions thereof (Fig. 14.21). A careful consideration of the relative importance of various possible channels in living fishes makes it highly likely, on the contrary, that in the piscine ancestors of tetrapods the internal carotid received its blood, as in the dogfish, from the hyoidean efferent or its homolog; and, therefore, that a part of the internal carotid in all amniotes has been derived in evolution, even if not in embryogeny, from the second aortic arch.

In support of this view, it should be emphasized that long-impressed organizational patterns are not likely to be modified except as the alternative may offer a functional superiority—and in the present case no functional superiority is evident in the alternative of craniad blood flow through the aortic radices rather than through the long-established channel of the hyoidean epibranchial.

The hyoidean epibranchial offers a direct channel for the blood to reach the head after passing through the gills; so long as the third gill pouch (and third epibranchial) retain a branchial function (as they certainly must have for a long period in early amphibian phylogeny), a reversion to use of the less direct channel through the aortic radices would have been highly unlikely. Even after loss of branchial function the channels forward from the third arch would probably not have been improved by a shift to the radices. Direct evidence is lacking, but the implication that a homolog of the hyoidean epibranchial has been retained as a part of the internal carotid artery of all tetrapods seems clearly acceptable. It should be emphasized, however, that there is no *embryonic* evidence of participation of the second aortic arch in the composition of the internal carotid artery; the evidence is entirely from comparative adult anatomy. Obviously neither embryology nor comparative anatomy furnishes evidence that may be regarded as conclusive.

The most important early amphibian alterations in branchial circulation from the early ichthyan stage involve (1) disappearance of the spiracular arteries as the spiracle is modified as an auditory structure; and (2) loss of branchial function of the entire third visceral pouch, resulting in elimination of the second afferent branchial, loss of most of the pretrematic vessel of the third epibranchial, and in formation of a common carotid artery chiefly from the base of the third epibranchial artery.

The spiracular cavity, retained in most tetrapods as the narrow Eustachian tube and middle ear cavity, lost the spiracular artery, which in ancestral types supplemented the blood supply to the internal carotid arteries as well as supplying the vestigial spiracular pseudobranch. The

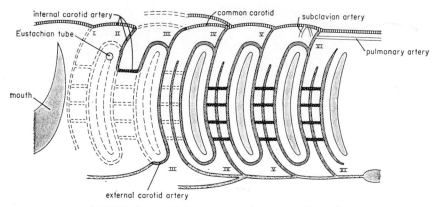

FIG. 14.21 Early amphibian stage of aortic arch evolution.

shift of the spiracle to auditory function was accompanied by a shift of its blood supply from the spiracular arteries to the internal carotid arteries. The latter, in turn, received blood only from the hyoidean epibranchials, losing the former additional source from the spiracular arteries.

A common carotid artery probably developed early in amphibian evolution through continued progressive degeneration, at least for branchial purposes, of the anterior gill pouches. Loss of the third pouch, involving the posterior face of the hyoid holobranch (now completely nonbranchial in function) and the anterior face of the third holobranch, resulted in blood for the two carotid arteries on each side coming from the third epibranchial, the flow in which was then craniad instead of caudad. Thus the third epibranchial serves as a *common carotid* artery, the first to appear in vertebrate phylogeny. This is not, however, homologous with the common carotid arteries of later amphibians and of amniotes, for in them the vessel consists of the base of the third *afferent* branchial.

The second afferent branchial artery, deprived of any demibranchs to feed on either side of the hyoid holobranch, likewise disappeared at this time. Thus four afferent branchials (third through the sixth) and three efferent branchials (fourth, fifth, sixth) remained at this stage.

Later Amphibian Stage. In later amphibians a further amount of freedom from the aquatic respiratory device of gills was effected, with loss of at least pouches six and seven, only four and five (if any) remaining in living species. The fifth arch was dropped completely (Fig. 14.22), but the third, fourth, and sixth arches remained. These differed considerably from earlier types, however, because of a reversion to the ancient continuous arch. This change presumably was made possible by retention in adult stages of an embryonic recapitulation of the primitive continuity possessed by these vessels. The common carotid developed in early amphibians was thus lost in later amphibians in which the two carotids on either side sprang from a continuous third aortic arch.

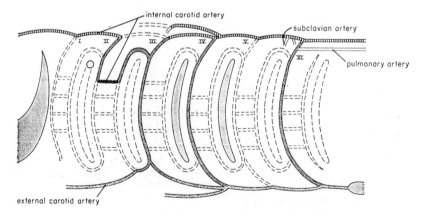

FIG. 14.22 Later amphibian stage of aortic arch evolution.

Reptilian Alterations. Reptiles, in which the larval aquatic stages characteristic of amphibians were eliminated, completely lost in post-embryonic stages all vestiges of the remaining gill pouch cavities (4 and 5). Second, the dorsal part of the third aortic arch (dorsal to the origin of the internal carotid) was lost (Figs. 14.23, 14.24), making a common carotid artery composed of the ventral part of that arch. The two common carotid arteries were united together in some kinds as a single trunk in turn united with one or both *subclavian* arteries which in many species (as of turtles) have shifted forward from their primitive position as branches from the dorsal aorta. When united with each other as well as either or both subclavians, the common vessel is called the *brachiocephalic*.

A third reptilian modification was a division of the ventral aorta into two or three vessels. Always one of these constituted a common trunk (*pulmonary trunk*) of the sixth aortic arches (now primarily the pulmonary arteries) connected with the right ventricle of the heart. The remainder of the ventral aorta was in some reptiles (including those ancestral to mammals) retained intact, forming a common trunk (*ventral aortic trunk*) for the two aortic arches. It was attached to the chamber of the left ventricle only, but received at least some blood from the right ventricle because of the absence of a complete interventricular septum. In other reptiles (including those ancestral to birds) the nonpulmonary part of the original ventral aorta split into two vessels; one was continuous with the *right* fourth aortic arch, connected with the *left* ventricle, and the other was continuous with the *left* fourth aortic arch, connected with the *right* ventricle. By remarkable devices, too complex to be discussed here, the blood even in the left aortic trunk was derived (at least primarily) from the left ventricle.

A fourth reptilian modification was a transformation of the dorsal part of the sixth aortic arch in adults to a ligament (*arterial ligament* or *ligament of Botallus*), which connected the remainder of the arch now

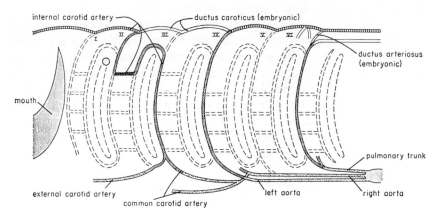

FIG. 14.23 Reptilian stage (preavian) of aortic arch evolution.

serving only as the pulmonary artery, with the dorsal aorta. Each ligament represented a connective tissue vestige of an embryonically functional vessel (*ductus arteriosus* or *ductus Botalli*) which permitted most blood to bypass the embryonically functionless lungs.

It is not to be assumed that none of the reptilian alterations described do not occur in some amphibians, or that all mentioned have occurred in all reptiles. All changes except the third are true of anurans, and even the ventral aorta is split, but in a different way (into right and left common trunks for the fourth and sixth arches). This is simply a partial parallelism of anuran and reptilian lines of evolution. It is a result of the common (even though independent) parallel invasions of and adaptation to a more and more completely terrestrial way of life. The variations from the characteristic reptilian arrangement are numerous and need not be treated here; most are in one way or another less advanced.

The Mammalian Modifications. Mammals have evolved from that group of reptiles (Fig. 14.24A) in which the ventral aorta had subdivided into but two vessels: the aortic trunk and the pulmonary trunk. One major change from this reptilian condition was the loss of most of the right fourth aortic arch (Fig. 14.25). Since the right subclavian was attached to this arch, the ventral base of the right fourth aortic arch remained, the dorsal part formerly connecting with the dorsal aorta disappearing. The ventral base of the right fourth aortic arch then became in effect but a part of the right subclavian, as it is recognized in the adult. The left aortic arch remained intact, but carried all blood leaving the heart for organs other than the lungs.

A second alteration in mammals hinged upon the interruption of the right fourth aortic arch. Since the right radix of the dorsal aorta received blood formerly from that arch, the right radix itself disappeared with the arch.

Thirdly, with loss of the right dorsal aortic radix the right arterial duct and ligament of the right sixth aortic arch disappeared, for there was then nothing with which it could connect dorsally.

Primitively in mammals a common vessel (brachiocephalic artery) connected both carotids and the left subclavian arteries with the aorta; this constituted the main ventral aorta between aortic arches three and four. Both the primitive tripartite brachiocephalic and the right subclavian arteries are subject to considerable variation, however, with nearly every conceivable combination occurring in different groups. In some mammals the brachiocephalic does not exist, its usual components being connected separately with the aortic arch; in others the brachiocephalic incorporates all four carotid and subclavian arteries.

The phylogenetic composition of the mammalian aortic derivatives, as compared with the primitive piscine condition, may be recapitulated as follows:

EXTERNAL CAROTID ARTERY: (1) the paired ventral aorta forward

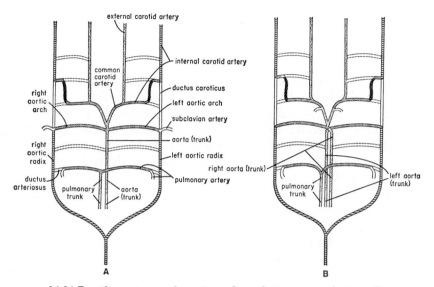

FIG. 14.24 Reptilian stages of aortic arch evolution, ventral view. A, pre-mammalian reptiles; B, preavian reptiles, as shown in Fig. 14.23.

from the third or fourth arch; (2) at least the proximal part of the extension forward from the ventral aorta (the primitive external carotid); and (3) more anterior parts of complex and rather obscure origin.

INTERNAL CAROTID ARTERY: (1) all of the third aortic arch except the dorsal and ventral ends; (2) a cross trunk between arches two and three; (3) the hyoidean epibranchial (that is, the dorsal part of arch two); (4) the paired dorsal aorta anterior to arch two; and (5) the anterior extensions of the paired dorsal aorta (the primitive internal carotids).

COMMON CAROTID ARTERY: ventral end of arch three.

INNOMINATE ARTERY: parts or all of the paired or unpaired ventral aorta between arches three and four.

SYSTEMIC AORTA (or *"aorta"*): (1) the unpaired dorsal aorta poste-rior to arch four; (2) the left fourth aortic arch; (3) the entire ventral aorta between arches four and six; (4) part of the ventral aorta between arch six and the level of the former conus arteriosus; and (5) part of the conus arteriosus.

PULMONARY TRUNK: (1) part of the ventral aorta between arch six and the level of the former conus arteriosus; and (2) part of the conus arteriosus.

PULMONARY ARTERIES: (1) ventral and middle parts of the right and left sixth aortic arches; and (2) a branch extending to the lungs from near the upper end of arch six.

LIGAMENTUM ARTERIOSUM: extreme dorsal part of *left* (only) sixth aortic arch.

RIGHT SUBCLAVIAN ARTERY: (1) ventral part of right fourth aortic arch; and (2) a branch to arm from near dorsal end of fourth aortic arch.

The Avian Modifications. Birds, unlike mammals, evolved from the group of reptiles (Fig. 14.24B) in which the ventral aorta was split into three parts between the sixth arch and heart. One part was continuous with the right and one with the left fourth aortic arch, the other with the pulmonary arteries. In reptiles the left systemic aorta, as mentioned previously, received both aerated and nonaerated blood, whereas the right systemic aorta tended to receive more nearly an exclusively aerated flow. Accordingly the carotid and subclavian arteries already in reptiles had become attached to the right fourth aortic arch, setting the stage for further alterations in birds.

In birds (Fig. 14.26) the already useless (1) right aortic trunk and (2) left fourth aortic arch, as well as the (3) left dorsal aortic radix, completely disappeared. Also the (4) left arterial duct and ligament of the left sixth aortic arch were lost. Except for these four alterations, the derivatives of the aortae and arches are essentially the same in birds as in mammals.

Mammalian Derivatives of the Hypothetical Prevertebrate System

VENTRAL AORTA: (1) External carotids, (2) brachiocephalic arteries.

CARDIAC REGION: (1) Sinauricular node, (2) 2 ventricles, (3) 2 atria, (4) part of pulmonary trunk, (5) part of aortic trunk.

AORTIC ARCHES: I—lost; II—part of internal carotid; III—(1) common carotids, (2) part of internal carotid; IV—(1) right, base of right sub-

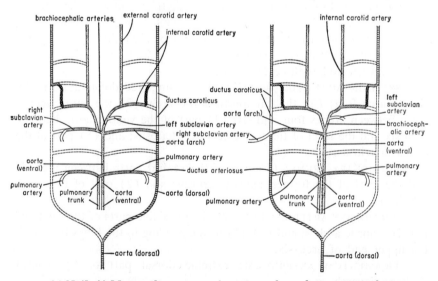

FIG. 14.25 (Left) Mammalian stage of aortic arch evolution, ventral view.
FIG. 14.26 (Right) Avian stage of aortic arch evolution, ventral view.

clavian, (2) left, aortic arch; V—lost; VI—(1) base of pulmonary arteries, (2) left, ligamentum arteriosum.

DORSAL AORTA: (1) Part of internal carotids, (2) dorsal aorta, posterior to fourth aortic arch.

EXTERNAL CAROTIDS: Part of same.

CELIAC: Same.

ANTERIOR MESENTERIC ARTERY: Same.

POSTERIOR MESENTERIC ARTERY: Same.

PARIETALS: (1) Intercostals, (2) lumbars, (3) cervicals.

GENITALS: Same.

RENAL ARTERIES: Same.

CAUDALS: Same.

SUBINTESTINAL: (1) Anterior part of postcava, (2) hepatic veins, (3) hepatic portal vein.

PROTOPOSTERIOR CARDINAL: (1) Base of hemiazygos vein, (2) base of azygos vein, (3) posterior part of postcava.

ANTERIOR CARDINALS: Internal jugulars.

SUBCARDINALS: (1) Part of postcava between right hepatic vein and left renal vein, (2) right, part of postcava between right and left renals, (3) right, right renal, (4) left, left renal.

COMMON CARDINALS: (1) right and left precavas, and when only one (right) precava present, (2) right, right brachiocephalic, (3) left, anterior tip of left brachiocephalic, (4) left, coronary sinus.

It is notable that forerunners of all the major vessels of mammals are present as conspicuous vessels in the hypothetical prevertebrate stage, except for (a) derivatives of the reptilian supracardinals [posterior parts of the (1) azygos and (2) hemiazygos; and (3) part of the postcava between renal collar and former renal portal vein], the (b) external jugulars, the (c) renal collar derivatives (part of postcava between right renal vein and former right supracardinal), and the (d) pulmonary veins.

The Lymphatic System

The early vertebrate lymphatic system was no more than a system of intercellular spaces in which the capillary filtrate (lymph) from the blood vascular system collected and eventually was conducted back into the veins by no particularly specialized method at all. This quite generalized mode of operation of the lymphatic system was scarcely adequate for the needs of later, highly competitive vertebrates, which eventually did evolve a very efficient and complex lymphatic vascular system. The problems involved in the long history of lymphatic evolution are simple, necessitating the return of as much fluid volume to the blood vascular system as is received in spite of the difficulties posed by (1) an increasing blood pressure (in endotherms as opposed to ectotherms) and (2) a progressively more completely closed venous system. Although the transition between extremes was very gradual, as is the case of all structural evolution, an understanding of the changes that occurred is facilitated by recognition of some six stages corresponding more or less with the conformation in living examples of a succession of vertebrate classes.

Venolymphatic Stage. No morphologically separate lymphatic system whatsoever occurs in the most primitive of living vertebrates, the cyclostomes and Chondrichthyes. This condition is, therefore, presumably primitive for vertebrates in general. It is a corollary of the fact that most veins in these animals are in reality sinuses, and that these can pick up interstitial fluid (lymph) as well as could special lymphatic channels.

Pretetrapod Stage. In all fishes cardiac pressure is effective solely in transporting blood through the branchial capillaries. Capillary pressure elsewhere is presumably produced by voluntary muscular activity and as a result may be assumed generally to be relatively low as compared with that in tetrapods or with that of the ventral aorta (Mott, 1957). Low arterial capillary pressure causes relatively small amounts of lymph filtration through arterial capillary walls and a larger proportion of return through venous capillary walls. If indeed, as seems likely, arterial capillary pressure was very low in ancient fishes, there was a minimum need for a distinct lymphatic system.

In osteichthyan fishes, which represent the pretetrapod stage, a recognizable lymphatic system first appeared in vertebrate phylogeny as a response to more complete elimination of venous sinuses. The lymphatic vessels included a pair of *subvertebral ducts* (sometimes fused) emptying into the anterior cardinal veins, and a pair of vessels emptying into the iliac veins (Fig. 14.27). These four openings, and sets of lymphatic vessels, are retained in all tetrapods, at least embryonically. There are no specialized devices in most fishes to move the fluid within the lymphatic vessels chiefly because most of the lymph can and does return by way of the venous capillaries. Considerable variation exists in arrangement of lymphatic vessels in living fishes, but the described pattern appears to be primitive.

Early Tetrapod Stage. It is in the amphibians that the first serious problem in lymph return is introduced. The branchial capillary system was lost in favor of the pulmonary respiratory system, thereby permitting cardiac pressure to reach all arterial capillaries of the aortic branches. Since the amount of capillary filtrate is proportional chiefly to blood pressure, the increase of pressure at the arterial capillaries meant a greater amount of interstitial fluid than was formed in fishes (other factors remaining the same). The venous capillaries, even with a slightly increased osmotic pressure as compared with fishes, could not reabsorb all of the increased volume of filtrate, and thus the burden of taking up the slack was necessarily left to the lymphatic system. Improvement of details to accomplish this task

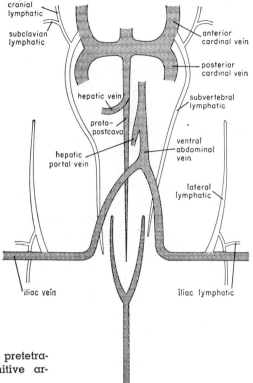

cranial lymphatic

subclavian lymphatic

anterior cardinal vein

posterior cardinal vein

hepatic vein

subvertebral lymphatic

proto- postcava

hepatic portal vein

ventral abdominal vein

lateral lymphatic

iliac vein

iliac lymphatic

FIG. 14.27 Lymphatic vessels in pretetrapod fishes, hypothetical primitive arrangement.

was made continuously through several successive classes of vertebrates.

Two avenues of modification to meet the new tetrapod needs were possible and both were tried. The lymph could simply be allowed to collect in interstitial spaces (lymph sinuses), failing to elaborate the few vessels inherited from fishes. This was the anuran solution. In the Caudata and Apoda, however, the vessels were increased in number, and there were fewer and smaller lymphatic sinuses. All amphibians were faced with the necessity of speeding the flow in the vessels and spaces in order to assure maintenance of low pressures in the collecting areas. Even a slight increase in pressure meant failure to drain the excess lymph. Lymph hearts appeared on the scene in amphibians as an adaptation to this need. It is thought that primitively one pair of lymph hearts was present for each body segment. Salamanders and caecilians have retained much of this primitive segmental distribution (Fig. 14.28B); as many as about 200 occur in certain species. In anurans, however, with the reduction in number of segments, hypertrophy of lymphatic sinuses, and concomitant reduction in lymphatic vessels, the hearts were also reduced in number; advanced species possess but four, one at each of the points of union of lymphatic and venous systems (Fig. 14.28A). Some primitive anurans have as many as ten hearts. These hearts are provided with a single opening (*efferent ostium*) into the vein (or lymphatic vessel, if it is placed along its length), and one or more *afferent ostia* receiving lymph from tributary vessels or adjacent spaces. The former is commonly guarded by valves to prevent backflow of venous blood into the lymphatic vessels or spaces.

Higher Ectotherm Stage. In reptiles the extensive system of lymphatic vessels was retained, but the number of entrances into the veins was stabilized at the primary four found in fishes. The number of hearts was also reduced, only the posterior pair being retained. The loss of the anterior hearts is not readily explicable, but at any rate it is clear that the lymph hearts are still essential to maintain adequate flow.

Avian Stage. Birds certainly are not on the line of mammalian evolution but they do possess a lymphatic system intermediate in structure between those of reptiles and of mammals: a conformation which mammals undoubtedly duplicated somewhere in their ancestry, either in early representatives of the mammals or in the mammallike reptiles.

The most important changes in birds are (1) loss of all lymph hearts, and (2) development of valves in lymphatic vessels. One hinges on the other, for the valves perform the function served by the hearts, causing the lymph to flow fairly rapidly toward the venous ostia. General bodily activity causes the lymph to move, and because of the valves it moves in but one direction. This is apparently a more efficient mechanism than the hearts.

Mammalian Stage. In mammals, for some reason not clearly evident, the posterior (iliac) venous ostia are closed (open only in embryos), and the vessels formerly associated with them are drained either exclusively by way of the left subvertebral duct, here (as in birds) called the thoracic duct, or by both thoracic ducts. Since anastomoses normally exist in all vertebrates between the vessels (or spaces) drained by the various venous ostia, obviously any one (or even as many as three) ostium could close, the remaining openings carrying the load. Only in mammals, however, is there actually a loss of ostia. The only obvious advantage conferred by this modification is the orientation in the same direction of all valves in posterior lymphatic vessels. This would be a real advantage subsequent to enlargement of the anastomoses mentioned previously. Compensating anastomoses do occur in some mammals, however, with the postcava near the renal veins.

The second mammalian modification is loss of the right thoracic duct. This is present in a rudimentary form embryonically, but through an early anastomosis of its tributaries with those of the left duct the right one fails to continue development. Only efficiency seems to be the advantage in this case. Not all mammals, however, lose one thoracic duct; some lose most of both (those with postcaval lymphatic connections) and others lose neither (some primates).

In most mammals, however, the right venous ostium drains vessels from the right side of the head and neck and the right foreleg; the left venous ostium drains all the rest of the body, with the thoracic duct (left)

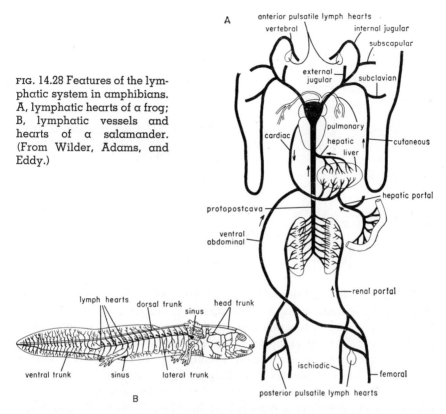

A

anterior pulsatile lymph hearts
vertebral
internal jugular
subscapular
external jugular
subclavian
cardiac
pulmonary
hepatic
cutaneous
liver
hepatic portal
protopostcava
ventral abdominal
renal portal
lymph hearts
dorsal trunk
head trunk
sinus
ventral trunk
sinus
lateral trunk
ischiadic
femoral
posterior pulsatile lymph hearts
B

FIG. 14.28 Features of the lymphatic system in amphibians. A, lymphatic hearts of a frog; B, lymphatic vessels and hearts of a salamander. (From Wilder, Adams, and Eddy.)

being the main tributary draining the trunk and hind quarters (Fig. 14.29).

Related Structures. Commonly lymph nodes are treated as part of the lymphatic system, but it appears that actually their association with lymph vessels is purely secondary; they are primarily hemopoietic (blood-forming) organs, taking other forms in other vertebrates. We shall discuss them in the following paragraphs.

The Hemopoietic Organs

No set of vertebrate organs is more confusing to analyze phylogenetically than the hemopoietic organs—those that form the blood cells.

Vertebrates differ from all other animals in the possession of a variety of blood cells, chief among them the red blood cells (*erythrocytes*) and several kinds of white blood cells (*leucocytes*). These are formed by the so-called reticulo-endothelial tissues, formed embryonically from mesenchyme cells. Oddly enough, this hemopoietic tissue is not constant in its location in vertebrates; in fact its position differs most perplexingly in different classes. Furthermore the location of hemopoietic tissues in the embryo may differ completely from the location in the adult. Tissues hemopoietic in function in embryos may become completely different in function

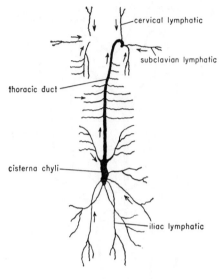

FIG. 14.29 An arrangement of lymphatic vessels common in mammals. (From Quiring.)

postembryonically, and tissues having no hemopoietic function in embryos subsequently become of major importance in this respect. To be certain, the tissues do not vary in function and position from individual to individual, but the variation from group to group (classes, subclasses, even orders) seems completely fortuitous. Finally, even the type of blood cells produced by any one locus of hemopoietic tissue varies from group to group.

Unorganized Tissues. There are only a very few grossly recognizable organs serving primarily a hemopoietic function. Cyclostomes and lung-fishes have none whatsoever. All hemopoietic tissues in these and most of it in other vertebrates are scattered at various points in the body. The kidneys (teleost adults, embryos of all save mammals), gonads (sharks, lung-fishes), liver (embryos of most vertebrates, adults of teleosts, amphibians, turtles), and red bone marrow (amphibians to a slight degree, more in reptiles, very important in birds and mammals) are organs containing certain types of hemopoietic tissue. As examples of occurrence of reticulo-endothelial tissue completely independent of other organs, we may cite the aggregation about the heart in Chondrostei; in the intestinal wall in most vertebrates; in the esophagus or pharynx wall or in both, and around the gut in cyclostomes and lungfishes. There appears to be no marked phylogenetic trend in these variations, except perhaps the increase in importance of the bone marrow in the amphibian-endotherm line of evolution.

Organized Tissues. Discrete hemopoietic organs are few in vertebrates. Most conspicuous is the spleen, but also of importance are the tonsils, lymph nodes (including the pancreas Aselli), hemal nodes, and possibly the thymus and ultimobranchial bodies.

The spleen is a single organ found in all living vertebrates save cyclostomes and lungfish, in both of which it presumably is represented by unorganized tissue about the stomach and intestine. Oddly enough in no vertebrate does it have any lymphatic connections; it has only blood vessel connections. Despite gross association with the digestive system it has no digestive function whatsoever and has no direct connection with the alimentary tract. For an organ of such constancy of occurrence and large size the variations in function are surprising. All types of blood cells are formed there embryonically in all vertebrates, and likewise in adults of all save most mammals in which the spleen forms only lymphocytes. The red bone marrow in mammals assumes the chief adult hemopoietic role. Important also, however, is the function of the spleen in storage of blood and erythrocytes and destruction of old blood cells. These would seem to be the chief functions in mammals.

Supplemental "spleens" occur in some mammals (for example, the hoofed mammals) near the origins of the large abdominal branches of the aorta. These are *hemal nodes*. They appear to be "graveyards" for red blood cells, like the spleen, and may also manufacture erythrocytes.

QUESTIONS

1. Diagram, label, and indicate direction of blood flow in the blood vessels of the hypothetical prevertebrate. State what has become of each vessel in mammals.

2. What veins of adult tetrapods are derived directly from the vitelline veins? From the embryonic subintestinal vein? What supposedly was the phylogenetic origin of these derivatives?

3. What functional advantage was bestowed by formation of the hepatic portal system? The renal portal system? What shift in habitat was apparently correlated with formation of the renal portal system?

4. Diagram the arrangement of vessels involved in evolution of the renal portal system at (a) an early, primitive stage, and (b) at a definitive stage, labeling completely. Explain how the transition occurred between the two extremes.

5. In what vertebrates does a protopostcava occur, and what is its phylogenetic composition?

6. What functional advantage accrues to the owner by formation of the protopostcava? Supracardinals?

7. In what class along the line of evolution toward mammals was the renal portal function first lost? In what class were the renal portal veins, as such, first completely lost?

8. Name in proper sequence from front to rear all the phylogenetic components of the mammalian postcava. Diagram the changes involved in each of the four main stages of evolution of the mammalian postcava.

9. What has become in mammals of the anterior ends of the posterior cardinals and supracardinals of earlier ancestors? Briefly describe variations that occur.

10. Briefly describe the changes involved in transformation of the piscine anterior and common cardinals into the derived vessels of primitive mammals.

11. Briefly describe how the left precava of primitive mammals is altered in mammals such as carnivores and primates; the right precava. What is the phylogenetic composition of the feline left innominate vein? Right innominate vein?

12. Where does the mammalian external jugular first appear phylogenetically, and what is its source?

13. Diagram the dogfish aortic circulation in lateral view in such a way as to show evolutionary composition of each vessel.

14. Account for the differences between birds and mammals in their aortic arch patterns.

15. State the phylogenetic composition of each of the following mammalian vessels: external carotid artery; internal carotid artery; common carotid artery; aorta; ligamentum arteriosum; pulmonary trunk; pulmonary arteries; innominate artery; right subclavian artery.

16. Be able to state and diagram what has become in mammals or birds of each aortic arch.

17. How does the conformation of the ancestral ventral aorta differ in reptiles from that of birds or mammals?

18. Diagram the early amphibian aortic circulation in lateral view in such a way as to show the evolutionary composition of each vessel. Label.

19. Name the most important early amphibian alterations in aortic circulation.

20. Diagram the late amphibian aortic circulation in lateral view, in such a way as to show the evolutionary composition of each vessel. Label.

21. Name the most important late amphibian alterations in aortic circulation.

22. Diagram the reptilian aortic circulation in lateral view and in ventral view in such a way as to show the evolutionary composition of each vessel. Label. Do the same for birds, ventral view only.

23. Name the most important reptilian alterations in aortic circulation. How did preavian and premammalian reptiles differ in aortic construction?

24. Diagram the mammalian aortic circulation in ventral view in such a way as to show the evolutionary composition of each vessel. Label.

25. Name the most important mammalian alterations in aortic circulation.

26. The evolution of chambers in the heart in fishes may be interpreted as an adaptation to what change in mode of life from that of protochordates?

27. Fishes, ectothermic tetrapods, and endotherms represent three levels of metabolic efficiency. Account for their relative position (on the basis of supply of aerated blood to body tissues).

28. What is the specific function of the piscine sinus venosus and how is it performed? Of the atrium? The ventricle? The conus arteriosus?

29. How does the structure of the atrium in the early tetrapods reflect a change in function of this chamber from that of fishes?

30. Name the changes occurring in the early tetrapod heart as compared with the fish heart.

31. What structural alterations in other parts of the body made it possible for reptiles to dispose of the conus arteriosus? What becomes of it?

32. Name the adaptive trends in cardiac evolution.

33. Trace a droplet of blood through the mammalian heart, listing in proper order the chambers, vessels, valves, and capillary beds through which it passes.

34. (a) How can the absence of a lymphatic system in the Agnatha and Chondrichthyes be explained? (b) What effect did loss of the gills have upon lymphatic mechanics?

35. (a) Describe of what the lymphatic system consists in different amphibian groups. (b) How did endotherms compensate for loss in them of the lymphatic hearts present in all their tetrapod ancestors?

36. (a) Describe the stages through which mammals passed in evolution of their lymphatic system, beginning with early tetrapods. (b) What is the role of the lymphatic system in the mechanics of circulation in the body? (c) Name the endotherm advancements in construction of the lymphatic system.

37. Specify the location of some of the hemopoietic tissues of vertebrates that are not organized into specific organs.

38. Name specific hemopoietic organs and the vertebrate groups in which each occurs, and the known or suspected function and location of each.

39. In what respects, relative to the circulatory system, do the Dipnoi resemble the amphibians and differ from most other fishes?

40. Define the following words, and where possible state occurrence or give an example:

afferent branchial
   artery
afferent lymphatic
   ostium
afferent
   pseudobranchial
   artery
anterior cardinals
aortic arch
aortic trunk
arterial blood
arterial capillary
atrioventricular valve
atrium
auricle
azygos vein
bicuspid valve
brachiocephalic
branchial cleft
capillary
celiac
collector loop
common cardinal
common carotid
conus arteriosus
coronary sinus
demibranch
dorsal aorta
double circulation in
   heart
double circulation in
   kidney

ductus arteriosus
ductus Botalli
efferent branchial
   artery
efferent lymphatic
   ostium
efferent pseudobran-
   chial artery
epibranchial artery
erythrocyte
external carotid
external jugular
foramen of Panizzi
hemal node
hemiazygos vein
hemopoiesis
hemopoietic tissue
hepatic vein
holobranch
hyoidean epibranchial
innominate vein
internal carotid
internal jugular
intertrematic
leucocyte
ligamentum arteriosum
ligamentum Botalli
lymphatic system
lymph heart
lymph node
mitral valve
neohepatic vein

neopostcava
neoposterior cardinal
   vein
pancreas Aselli
parietal anastomosis
parietal vessels
portal organ
portal system
portal vein
postbranchial artery
postcava
posterior cardinal
postrematic artery
prebranchial artery
precava
pretrematic
protohepatic vein
protopostcava
protoposterior cardinal
pseudobranchial artery
pulmonary artery
pulmonary trunk
pulmonary vein
radices of aorta
renal collar
renal portal vein
retia mirabilia
semilunar valve
sinatrial node
sinauricular node
sinus
sinus venosus

subcardinal
subclavian
subintestinal vein
supracardinal
systemic aorta

tricuspid valve
venolymphatic
  circulation
venous blood
venous capillary

ventral aorta
ventricle
vitelline vein

15

SENSORY SYSTEM

A SENSE ORGAN is a structure adapted for generation of nervous impulses in response to fluctuations within a given range of a specific environmental variable to which the organ is selectively hypersensitive.

Functional Limitation. Selectivity of sense organs is, of course, a mechanical necessity. The human eye is sensitive to light waves varying in length from .0004 to .0008 millimeters, but fails to register longer infrared rays or the shorter ultraviolet rays. The optic range of the dog eye is even less. The human ear detects frequencies from 30 to 20,000 per second, but does not register either higher sound frequencies (to which some mammals such as dogs, bats, and whales are known to be sensitive) or lower sound frequencies. Chemical sensitivity similarly is limited within a narrow range; taste, for example, is at best limited to detection of sourness, saltiness, sweetness, and bitterness. Vast chemical and physical worlds (for example, electric waves, ultraviolet rays, x-rays) exist to which we are largely or totally insensitive (Fig. 15.1), although the limits of sensitivity clearly vary from species to species, and perhaps from individual to individual, to a degree that actually is not reliably authenticated.

In general, sensitivity in all vertebrates is thought to vary chiefly in range and but little in kind. A known exception is the piscine lateral line system serving to detect minute variations in pressure. Unfortunately it is difficult accurately to assay sensitivity (a) in animals other than ourselves, and (b) to environmental variables with which we are not familiar. "Extrasensory perception," in the sense of "response to an external event not presented to any known sense," does occur without question. The uncanny flight of bats in total darkness, wherein the animals almost invariably avoid obstacles, involves what would at one time, before the mechanism was understood, have been called "extrasensory" perception. The mechanism is now well known (the bats constantly emit high-frequency sounds that by their echo reveal presence and location of obstacles), and the perception can scarcely be called "extrasensory" because the sense and sense organ is well established. In like manner it is probable that other little-understood responses now called "extrasensory," will eventually be explicable in terms all can accept. Nevertheless, ESP as well as the even less reputable related phenomena of "psychokinesis" (direct physical influence of the mind *alone* upon matter) are not widely accepted by scientists because they are so bizarre and unconventional in concept and because by definition *no* perception can exist without some sort of sensory receptor; thus ESP by *literal* definition is impossible. The very term ESP has met with such resistance that students of "psi phenomena" (ESP and psychokinesis) confess guardedly to research in "parapsychology" or "psychological physics": the psychologist is sure it is not psychology, the physicist is sure it is not physics, and the unbiased onlooker correctly assumes it is both. The recent acceptance (1958) by the American Medical Association of hypnosis as a valid surgical adjunct marks the beginning of a new era in recognition of the existence of little-understood mental phenomena. The open-minded student must recognize that only by distorted definition can "extrasensory perception" be flatly rejected at the present time, and that far from all is known either about receptors or limits of perception.

Kinds of Sensation. Far from the "five senses" we are often said to possess, actually some fifteen to twenty-five or more exist. Warmth, cold, pain, sight, hearing, position, balance, touch, pressure, hunger, thirst, nausea, taste, smell, muscle tension are among those commonly recognized. Some of these and still others sometimes recognized are thought possibly to be the product not of completely different organs or nervous divisions, but of some sensation that, arising elsewhere, would have different significance. For example, joint sensitivity is often regarded as a distinct sense but may also be regarded as the product solely of pressure sense organs such as are widely distributed elsewhere in the body; as a matter of course those at a joint reveal position of the bones entering that joint. Inasmuch as there are fewer distinct forms of receptors than of sensations produced by them, unfortunately the senses cannot be defined on the basis of receptor form. Definition of the separate senses thus becomes a highly subjective matter. Many or few could be recognized.

Morphological Types of Sense Organs. Sense organs may be recognized as having some four levels of organization. At one extreme is the terminal branching of nerve cells—the bare fibers serving as the receptors (Fig. 15.2). At this extreme an "organ" scarcely exists, although the term is generally used. Pain, the circulatory system's chemoreceptors (carotid and aortic bodies), touch, heat, cold, and most sensations of the gut are thought to be wholly or in part the product of such free nerve endings.

TABLE OF PHYSICAL VIBRATIONS

PHYSICAL PROCESS	WAVE-LENGTH	NUMBER OF VIBRATIONS PER SECOND	RECEP-TOR	SENSA-TION
MECHANICAL CONTACT	....	from very slow to 1552 per second	skin	touch and pressure
WAVES IN MATERIAL MEDIA	above 12,280 mm	below 30 per second	none	none
	12,280 mm to 13 mm	30 per second to 30,000 per second	internal ear	tone
	below 13 mm	above 30,000 per second	none	none
ETHER WAVES	∞ to .2 mm (electric waves)	0 to 1500 billion (1.5×10^{12})	none	none
	.1 mm to .0004 mm	3000 billion (3×10^{12}) to 800,000 billion (8×10^{14})	skin	radiant heat
	.0008 mm to .0004 mm	400,000 billion (4×10^{14}) to 800,000 billion (8×10^{14})	retina	light and color
	.0004 mm to .000008 mm (ultra violet rays)	800,000 billion (8×10^{14}) to 40,000,000 billion (4×10^{16})	none	none
	.00002 mm to .0000001 mm (x-rays)	15,000,000 billion (1.5×10^{16}) to 30,000,000,000 billion (30×10^{18})	none	none
	.00000014 mm to .0000000005 mm (γ-rays)	2 billion billion (2×10^{18}) to 600 billion billion (6×10^{20})	none	none
	.00000000005 mm to .000000000008 mm (cosmic rays)	6,000 billion billion (6×10^{21}) to 40,000 billion billion (4×10^{22})	none	none

FIG. 15.1 Table of physical vibration. (From Herrick.)

True "organs" in their simplest form exist for most tactile and pressure sensations; corpuscles of Merkel, Meissner, Krause, and Pacini are examples (Fig. 15.3). In these the actual receptors are, as for pain, the terminal fibers of nerve cells, but the unique feature of these organs is that the terminal fibers are housed in structures composed of *supportive* cells (of connective tissue) specialized for reception of particular stimuli.

A third type of receptor exists in the eye, ear, and taste buds (Fig. 15.4), in all of which exist not only (a) accessory cells adapted to aid in reception of the particular stimuli involved, and (b) terminal fibers of nerve cells carrying impulses to the central nervous system (as in the preceding type), but also (c) specially adapted sensory cells quite separate from the former two. Impulses generated in the sensory cells are transmitted to the nerve cells that lead to the brain. In this type the concept of actual *receptors* (for example, the rods and cones of the eye) and of the organ itself should be carefully distinguished.

A fourth type of organization, actually the most primitive although superficially appearing fairly complex, is exemplified by the olfactory organ (Fig. 15.5). In this type the receptors are neither the terminal branches of nerve cells (as in the first and second types), nor separate sensory cells as in the third type, but they serve not only as receptors but also as the nerve cells, having fibers carrying impulses to the central nervous system. The organ thus consists of (a) the *neuroreceptors* and (b) supportive cells.

Evolutionary Levels of Sensory Cells and Sense Organs. These four morphological types represent three different levels of evolution of sensory cells and also of sense organs (Fig. 15.6). In chordate ancestors certain epithelial cells (neuroreceptors) undoubtedly served simultaneously as receptors or sensory cells, and as sensory nerve cells, transmitting impulses to the central nervous system. The receptors of the olfactory organ still exemplify this early condition. Because of the addition of supportive

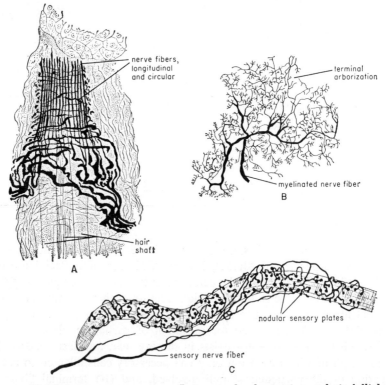

FIG. 15.2 Primary sense organs. A, terminal arborization at hair follicle; B, free nerve endings in mucous membrane of cat esophagus; C, free terminals on a single muscle fiber. (From Herrick, Maximow, and Bloom.)

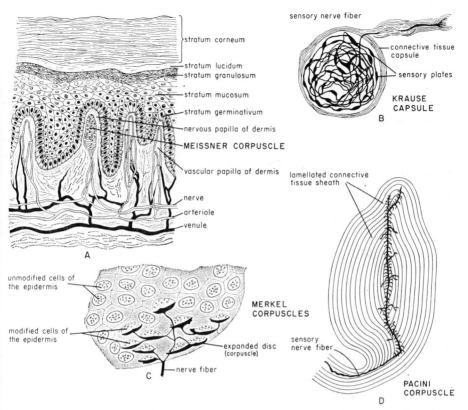

FIG. 15.3 Secondary sense organs. A, Meissner corpuscle, in position in skin; B, Krause capsule from conjunctiva of man; C, Merkel corpuscles from skin of pig snout; P, Pacini corpuscle from cat peritoneum. (From Herrick.)

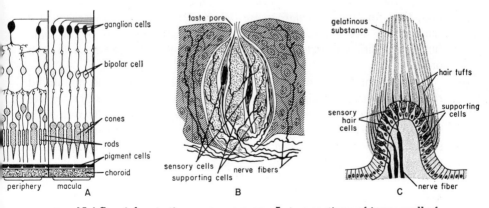

FIG. 15.4 Special or tertiary sense organs. A, two sections of inner wall of eye (the section at "macula" is near the fovea); B, a taste bud; C, a crista from ampulla of a semicircular canal of inner ear. (From Herrick and Netter.)

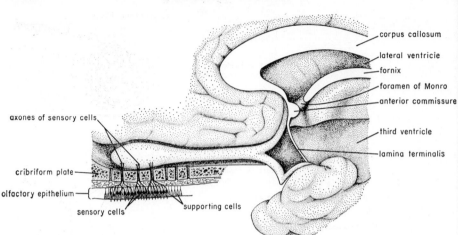

corpus callosum

lateral ventricie

fornix

foramen of Monro

anterior commissure

axones of sensory cells

third ventricle

lamina terminalis

cribriform plate

olfactory epithelium

sensory cells

supporting cells

FIG. 15.5 Section of a tertiary or special sense organ, the olfactory organ, in man. (From Netter.)

cells among the numerous receptors, however, the olfactory organ itself is an advanced and specialized organ belonging to the group of other complex sense organs, such as the eye and ear, known as the *special sense organs*. It is, obviously, the most *primitive* in structure of all special sense organs.

In the second stage of evolution of sensory cells, the primary receptors withdrew into the subcutaneous tissues and became modified as essentially conductive structures, the sensory nerve cells. For reception of the stimuli to which they were sensitive no supplementary epithelial sensory cells were necessary. Naked nerve endings thus in these cases served as *primary sense organs,* perfected by entwinement about effector organs such as muscle fibers, and by terminal arborization as at hair roots. Further advancement involved formation of special terminal capsules about the nerve endings, thus forming *secondary sense organs*. Both primary and secondary sense organs are *general sense organs* since there are many of the same function in different parts of the body. Only one receptor cell exists in each organ.

In the third stage of sensory evolution, reception of some stimuli did require numerous specialized epithelial sensory cells in addition to the deeper, conductive nerve cells. These *secondary sensory cells* with their supportive cells and sensory neuron connections may be regarded as constituting the *tertiary* or *special sense organs* of a more *advanced* type than the olfactory organ.

Sense Organs as a System. All sense organs function only to initiate nervous impulses in response to selected stimuli. The sensation itself is a product of the brain. Sense organs are an essential part of the integrating systems. The integument shuts out the environment to a large degree, yet adjustment to that environment is essential to survival. The more acutely aware an animal becomes of its environment the more successful it may be, and thus enormous selective pressure favors any improvement of the sensory system. Sense organs are the advance guards of the nervous and endocrine systems, which can perform their roles of integration solely through the "awareness" conveyed by the sense organs. Thus, although the sense organs are isolated from each other and of widely varying form, they are linked by a common function and role in animal life. They may be regarded as constituting a system in the same manner as the endocrine organs.

Subdivisions of the Sensory System. Sense organs can be conceived as consisting of integrated groups, actually subdivisions of the sensory system, only on the basis of relation to environment. Neither function nor structure is a basis of integration. In relation to environment, however, three groups are readily apparent. One group is receptive exclusively of external environmental stimuli. The organs included are located exclusively in the integument or at apertures therein and represent all morphological types. They are collectively referred to as *exteroceptors,* of the *exteroceptor division* of the sensory system. All special sense organs except the taste buds (and even some taste buds in fishes and amphibians) belong in this group.

Other sense organs are receptive only of internal environmental stimuli, within the walls of the gut or derivatives thereof. These are located in the viscera and represent all morphological types, and are collectively referred to as *interoceptors,* of the *interoceptor division* of the sensory system. Both taste buds and olfactory organs are, if their whole vertebrate

FIG. 15.6 Evolution of sensory cells and neurons, in three stages A-C. Stage A exists in the olfactory organs, B in the primary and secondary sense organs, and C in all special sense organs except the olfactory organs.

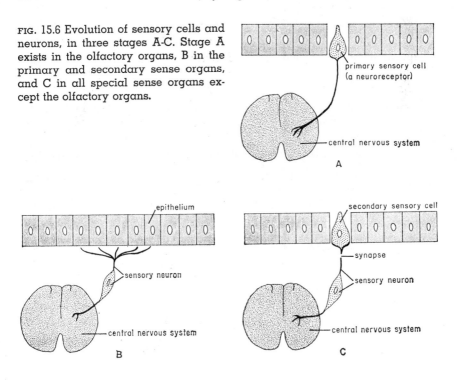

history is considered, both exteroceptive and interoceptive. All other complex (special) sense organs are exteroceptive exclusively.

Still a third group of sense organs detect truly internal body conditions in the zone between the ectodermal and endodermal epithelia; these are *proprioceptors,* of the *proprioceptor division* of the nervous system. They make one aware of the degree of tension of a given muscle, the position of the components of a joint, etc. Lack of proprioceptors ("muscle sense") renders it necessary to follow all actions with the eye; simple semi-automatic movements such as walking require a degree of mental concentration almost incomprehensible to those who possess the proprioceptor system unimpaired. All proprioceptors are primary and secondary sense organs unless, as some authors suggest, the vestibular functions (direction of movement, position) of the inner ear are regarded as proprioceptive. The vestibular functions actually are exteroceptive, since they concern the relation of the animal to its environment and are in no sense concerned with intrinsic body conditions.

Functional Types of Sense Organs. Two sorts of functions may be considered in grouping sense organs: (a) the kind of stimulus received, and (b) the kind of innervation.

On the basis of nature of stimulus, three main groups of sense organs may be recognized: *mechanoreceptors,* sensitive to mechanical stimuli such as pressure of varying degrees, injury, and low frequency vibrations (up to perhaps 30,000 cycles per second); *radioreceptors,* sensitive to high-frequency vibrations (temperature and light); and *chemoreceptors,* sensitive to chemical stimuli.

On the basis of location, four groups are recognized. Generally distributed sense organs of the alimentary tract and other viscera, not limited to specific areas, are *general visceral sensory* organs. Sense organs of limited distribution in the alimentary tract, such as taste buds, are *special visceral sensory* organs. The generally distributed sense organs of the integument and voluntary muscles are *general somatic sensory* in function, whereas those of limited distribution (for example, eyes, olfactory organs, inner ears) are *special somatic sensory.*

Evolutionary History. The evolutionary history of the gross morphology of the proprioceptors and the less complex interoceptors and exteroceptors is simple and has been outlined previously. Only the special sense organs have undergone extensive gross morphological changes in the course of vertebrate evolution, and it is to these our further attention is directed.

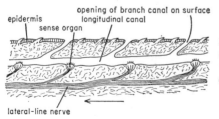

FIG. 15.7 Lateral line organs and associated structures of a fish, as seen in vertical section of the skin. (From Goodrich.)

They include a series of three chemoreceptors (taste buds, olfactory organs, vomeronasal organ), several mechanoreceptors (acusticolateralis system and its derivatives) and two or more radioreceptors (most importantly, the eyes and pit organs).

Origin of Special Sense Organs. All special sense organs of the vertebrate body are widely regarded as having probably evolved at least in part from clumps (*neuromasts*) of sensory cells profusely distributed over the entire integument and into the mouth of primitive fishes. A neuromast is a small group of sensory cells among a few supportive cells, all primitively situated in a small depression in the skin. Each sensory cell possesses a short slender, apical projection.

In fishes the neuromasts became differentiated as diverse organs: the taste buds, the lens of the eye, the sensory loci of the inner ear and of various lesser organs like the ampullae of Lorenzini, pit organs, and the lateral line system. Thus all the special radioreceptors (except for nonlenticular parts of the eye), mechanoreceptors and the chemoreceptors appear to have evolved from the primitive neuromast system of early chordates.

Special Mechanoreceptors. Mechanoreceptors that evolved from the neuromast system retain much of the primitive neuromast form. Those of modern fishes are frequently collectively referred to as the *acusticolateralis system,* since the ear and lateral line organs are the most conspicuous components.

The lateral line system (Fig. 15.7) is developed through alignment of neuromasts in a more or less regular pattern including (1) a series (the *lateral line*) down each side of the body from head onto the tail (all innervated by the lateral branch of the vagus cranial nerve); and (2) a number of cranial series (Fig. 15.8), including a *supratemporal, supraorbital, infraorbital, mandibular,* and *hyomandibular* series (all innervated by the facial and trigeminus cranial nerves). Primitively the organs were in disconnected pits, but they early became protected by formation of a continuous deep groove, as in modern holocephalans. Later, as in all other living gnathostomes, the grooves closed except for scattered pores opposite the neuromasts, forming a system of canals virtually invisible from the exterior and evidenced externally solely by the tiny scattered pores for the ducts connecting the longitudinal canals with the exterior.

The primary function of the lateral line system is to register differences in water pressure. The owner is aware of its depth in the water, and is furthermore advised by pressure waves either of the approach of a large object or of its own approach to a large object. In lampreys the lateral line organs are strongly light sensitive. The system is, however, wholly adapted for aquatic use. Completely terrestrial animals lack all trace of it, including the branches of the cranial nerves formerly supplying the sense organs. Amphibians, in their intermediate state, retain the system in aquatic stages and lose it in terrestrial stages. Turtles, as the most primitive living reptiles, retain nonfunctional vestiges of the system in adults, but other living reptiles, birds, and mammals have no remnants whatever of the system. Complete loss was unquestionably a handicap to those reptiles and mammals returning in their evolution to an aquatic mode of life, but although a partially effective substitute sensory system may have been devised in some, and in time perhaps even a better system may evolve, the highly efficient system of their ancestors is gone beyond recall.

The inner ear was clearly a very early derivative of the neuromast system. Evidence of a neuromast origin of the ear is supplied by the fact that the ear (1) originates embryonically in vertebrates as an epithelial placode similar to a neuromast, and (2) retains in its adult structure throughout vertebrates the same neuromastlike form of receptor cells, each with a papillary projection directed into a fluid-filled area. No derivative of the neuromast system has become so thoroughly modified as the ear, however, the ultimate form revealing little evidence of its humble origin. Its complex history is deferred for later discussion.

Special Radioceptors. Other neuromast derivatives, differentiating concurrently with the lateral line system, include the cranial *ampullae of Lorenzini* of elasmobranchs (Fig. 15.9) and the *pit organs* of the head and anterior part of the trunk of fishes generally. Both appear to be thermoreceptors, and as such are astonishingly similar to the *labial pits* of pythons and *facial pits* of pit vipers (Fig. 15.9), both known to be delicately sensitive thermoreceptors. The phylogeny of the ophidian pit organs is unknown, but a reasonable probability is that they have evolved from embryonic vestiges of the pit organs of their piscine ancestors.

The eye, another radioreceptor found in all vertebrates, is thought to be derived in part from the neuromast system. The lens forms embryonically as a thickened placode opposite the optic evagination of the brain, appearing much as a neuromast (Fig. 15.10). The remainder of the eye is of independent origin. Its evolution is deferred for later discussion.

Special Chemoreceptors. Two sets are important in vertebrates: the olfactory organs and the taste buds. Evolution of the olfactory organs has been relatively complex and is discussed in a separate following section.

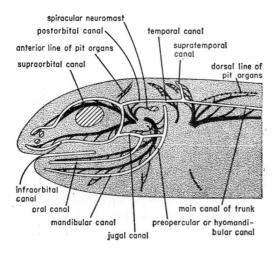

spiracular neuromast
postorbital canal
anterior line of pit organs
supraorbital canal
temporal canal
supratemporal canal
dorsal line of pit organs
infraorbital canal
oral canal
mandibular canal
jugal canal
main canal of trunk
preopercular or hyomandibular canal

FIG. 15.8 Generalized lateral line system (white) in craniopharyngeal region, showing innervation. (From Goodrich.)

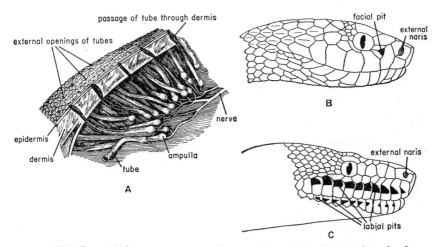

FIG. 15.9 Cranial thermoreceptors. A, ampullae of Lorenzini of a shark; B, facial pit of a pit viper; C, labial pits of a boa. (From Blanchard, Goodrich, Jan, and Sordelli.)

Taste bud evolution has been relatively simple. Taste buds arose as neuromasts on the anterior part of the body and in the mouth, becoming somewhat modified as ovoid or barrel-shaped bodies in early fishes. Even in some modern fishes taste buds are scattered over the surface of the head or even the trunk as well as in the mouth. In amphibians they are of general occurrence within the mouth and pharynx. In one group, the caecilians, a most extraordinary taste organ, the *gustatory tentacle* (often said erroneously to be olfactory) is evertible at will from its housing on the side of the snout between the nostril and eye. Reptiles and birds retain chiefly the taste buds of the pharynx, whereas in mammals primarily those of the tongue persist. Thus four stages, two of them concurrent rather than successive, can be recognized in the evolution of the taste buds.

Taste and smell differ in many ways, and there is every reason to believe that all the valid distinctions have existed throughout virtually the entire phylogeny of vertebrates. Taste is, of course, first of all a function of taste buds, whereas smell is a function solely of the olfactory organs. Second, the nerves involved in taste are the facial and glossopharyngeal cranial nerves, whereas only the olfactory nerve is involved in olfaction. Third, taste buds are capable of giving rise basically to but four sensations: sourness, sweetness, bitterness, and saltiness. On the contrary the olfactory organs have largely different and a much wider range of sensitivity. Fourth, the olfactory organs are fantastically sensitive—as much as 50 thousand times as sensitive as the taste organs.

Olfactory organs must have been in existence long before taste organs evolved, and throughout the long history of fishes each type of organ maintained its separate identity despite the fact that both functioned by sampling fluid-borne chemicals. Yet taste and olfaction as practiced in primitive vertebrates are easily confused because one conspicuous and

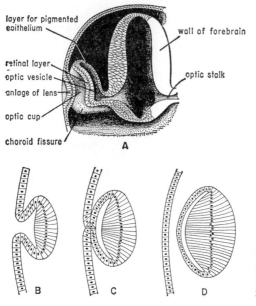

layer for pigmented epithelium

wall of forebrain

retinal layer

optic vesicle

optic stalk

anlage of lens

optic cup

choroid fissure

A

B

C

D

FIG. 15.10 Embryonic formation of the lens of the eye, in successive stages A-D. Only the lens and epidermis are shown in stages B-D. (From Kingsley.)

superficially valid (but actually invalid) distinction between the functions in tetrapods does not exist in fishes: taste in tetrapods involves sampling of fluid-borne chemicals, whereas olfaction (it is commonly but erroneously accepted) involves sampling only air-borne chemicals. Actually, as discussed in the following paragraphs, one important part of the olfactory organ in all tetrapods save a few mammals is adapted specifically for olfaction of fluid-borne chemicals. Furthermore *all* air-borne substances must enter into solution, even on the nasal epithelium, in order to be detected. Thus the medium of transport (air or water) of chemicals is a totally false distinction between olfaction and taste.

Olfactory Organs

Origin. Early though the neuromast system is thought to have appeared in chordate evolution, olfactory organs presumably were still earlier to appear. The primitive structure of the olfactory receptors and the existence in correlation with them of one of the extremely primitive lobes of the brain seemingly justify this belief.

Piscine Stage. The olfactory organs have evolved through some six major stages, four of which lie in the mammalian line of evolution (Fig. 15.11 and Fig. 11.16). One other distinctive stage occurs in a nonmammalian line of vertebrate evolution. In the earliest stage, still exemplified by all fishes except most Choanichthyes and cyclostomes, the organs are simple, blind, paired sacs, one on each side just preceding the mouth, opening only to the exterior, and with an augmentation of surface area accomplished only by lamellar folds of the epithelial lining. A simple, smooth-walled cranial capsule houses the sensory sacs. In many fishes a flap bisecting the formerly single opening, the *external naris,* has evolved. The flap primitively is loose at one end, as in sharks, but in many teleosts is fused at both ends and the two external openings may be rather widely separated. This feature renders the nasal passage tubelike in form and obviously provides improved water circulation and, therefore, improved olfaction.

Agnathan Stage. In cyclostomes, and as was true presumably in many ostracoderms, the olfactory sacs are secondarily fused as a single organ; the nerves remain paired. This condition is clearly secondary and not on the tetrapod line of evolution.

Choanichthyan Stage. In the second (premammalian) stage, exemplified by living choanichthyans, the posterior opening of the tubular nasal passage opened into the mouth instead of the exterior. This was at first no distinct mechanical advantage. It did preadapt these vertebrates for air breathing, but it was at the outset simply a relatively insignificant variant evolved in the persistent trial for improvement of olfaction.

Early Tetrapod Stage. In the third premammalian stage, exemplified by all ectotherm tetrapods, the tubular olfactory sacs were promptly forced through a trial run as a detector of airborne odors. Actually they proved inadequate for the job, and were supplemented by an ingenious and long-adequate mechanism. The olfactory sac developed two sensory areas, one preferably termed the *nasal organ,* and the other called a *vomeronasal*

FIG. 15.11 Successive stages in evolution of the olfactory organs. Parasagittal sections at left and cross sections (at levels indicated by dashed lines) at right in A-D. A, nonchoanate fish; B, choanate fish; C, amphibian; D, primitive reptile; E, ungulate, cross section; F, man, cross section. (In part from Neal and Rand.)

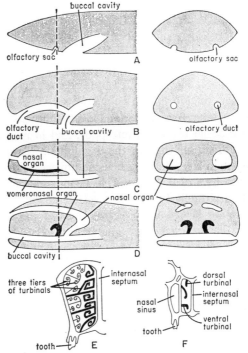

organ (or *Jacobson's organ*). The latter, usually wholly separate from the nasal organs in adults, is present (as a paired structure) in all tetrapods save mammals. Its long existence through so many vertebrate groups demands recognition of its functional indispensability at least up to the mammalian level.

The vomeronasal organs are blind cavities opening in adults into the anterior tip of the roof of the mouth. They sample fluids of the buccal cavity. In the squamate reptiles the organs reach their greatest efficiency, sampling fluids brought to them by the tongue. The latter, protruded from the mouth, picks up airborne particles which go into solution in the fluid covering of the tongue, in turn placed against Jacobson's organs. By this circumvention the olfactory organs (and the vomeronasal organ is, despite its distinctive name, to be regarded as an olfactory organ) can efficiently although indirectly sample airborne odors. In the long process of perfection of aerial olfaction, the vomeronasal organs (and tongue) served an important stop-gap role. Without them the olfactory function could well have been lost.

Sauropsidan Stage. Most reptiles and birds have particularly well-developed Jacobson's organs and lean heavily upon them for olfaction, to an important degree because of the absence of taste organs on the tongue. Apparently buccal tasting is in these groups replaced almost entirely by olfactory processes. Reduction of vomeronasal organs in turtles and crocodilians may be regarded not as a parallel of the mammalian condition, but as an adaptive correlative of reversion to aquatic habits, since the nasal organ itself can function under water and no buccal substitute is essential. Three lateral ridges (*conchae*) project into the nasal chamber in crocodilians, increasing the area on which the olfactory epithelium is distributed and presumably thereby increasing olfactory acuity. Birds, having evolved from the same gross reptilian stock as crocodilians, likewise possess three nasal conchae, although the vomeronasal organs, degenerated in the crocodilian line, have also been retained.

Mammalian Stage. The nasal organs continued slowly to be perfected for aerial use in all tetrapods, and in mammals they finally attained such an efficiency that for the first time in tetrapod history the vomeronasal organs in a whole class became unnecessary irrespective of habits of various members of the class. This stage is characterized by (1) loss or reduction to a virtually functionless vestige of the vomeronasal organs, and (2) formation of extensive convolutions of the nasal epithelium, overlying parts of the *turbinated* capsular bones. It is apparently the extreme increase in epithelial area contingent upon evolution of the turbinate bones that was chiefly responsible for increase in nasal acuity and resultant loss of the vomeronasal organs as superfluous accessories. The appearance of turbinals is presaged by the conchae of advanced reptiles. Curiously, the chief remnants of the turbinates in those mammals, like man, with a degenerate olfactory apparatus, are three conchae essentially the same as those of crocodilians and birds. The human condition seemingly involves retention of a formerly embryonic condition in the adult, therefore neoteny.

Visual Organs

Kinds of Visual Organs in Vertebrates. The visual organs of most vertebrates are exclusively the paired eyes located between olfactory and otic organs. Aside from the photoreceptor abilities of the lateral line system in cyclostomes, actually at least two other visual organs appear to have existed in the dim past of vertebrate phylogeny. They are the closely placed median dorsal *parietal* (anterior) and *pineal* organs, both formed as evaginations from the brain in much the same manner as the paired eyes (Fig. 15.12). Either of these is properly termed an *epiphysis,* although that name is used by some authors for the pineal evagination only. The more anterior *paraphysis* also possibly represents a vestige of a visual organ. Rods and cones as well as a rudimentary sort of integumentary lens and a cornea are present in the pineal or parietal organs of primitive vertebrates. A median foramen near either the front or the rear of the skull is correlated with presence of either organ. The foramen was present in primitive vertebrates (ostracoderms, placoderms); is retained in a variety of later living groups (Chondrichthyes, some reptiles); was present at least in primitive fossils of all classes save mammals and birds; but has been lost in most living vertebrates.

Origin and Evolution of the Unpaired Visual Organs. Apparently well developed in the earliest known vertebrates (ostracoderms), the pineal and parietal eyes presumably evolved much earlier and perhaps at about the same time as the paired eyes. These collectively provided a series of visual structures in which functional superiority of any one over another could readily be demonstrated by natural selective processes.

That several visual organs should have evolved in early chordates is reasonable in view of the general distribution of light-sensitive cells along the entire length of the inner wall of the central nervous system (for example, as in amphioxus). Elaboration of them at the cranial end was likewise implicit in the active mode of life of early chordates. Subsequent protrusion of parts of the brain possessing visual cells toward the integument where light could more readily be detected was not a difficult accomplishment, although a very important one. Perhaps even more visual evaginations existed in early chordates than is now supposed but, at any rate, at least four (paired eyes, pineal and parietal eyes) are clearly evident in vertebrate phylogeny, all formed from the second lobe (diencephalon) of the brain.

The way of life of early chordates eventually placed a greater degree of favor (selective pressure) upon improvements of the paired eyes than upon those of the unpaired eyes, with the result that the paired eyes rapidly came to assume the entire visual function, the parietal and pineal eyes degenerating. The pineal organ shows some vestige of visual structure in cyclostomes but in all other living vertebrates has degenerated into a small, glandlike protuberance. Its regular presence throughout vertebrates strongly suggests some essential value, for useless structures seldom, if ever, persist over such a long period. The present function, if any, remains nevertheless uncertain, although a *homeostatic* role helping to prevent metabolic excesses and to reestablish homeostasis following periods of activity has become increasingly plausible in recent years.

The parietal organ also possesses a visual structure in cyclostomes, as well as in some lizards and in Sphenodon, but in none of these is a visual function present. Instead it now appears to be homeostatic in function, although undoubtedly the ancestral function was visual. In most vertebrates the parietal organ is present only embryonically, serving as an "extraventricular choroid organ"—a vascular structure of nutritive function.

The paraphysis, of unknown function in adults of living vertebrates although possibly of visual function in ancestral types, serves embryonically in all living vertebrates as an extraventricular choroid organ, and is absent in amniote adults. It has no visual structure at any stage of development in any living vertebrate, but is similar in position and general form to the epiphyses.

Since none of these unpaired structures actually are functional as visual organs in any known living vertebrate, however primitive, doubt has been expressed that they ever were of visual function at any time in their phylogeny. However, it seems very unlikely that these organs in their earliest, preostracoderm evolution were anything but visual, as indeed are the pigmented spots in amphioxus. The homeostatic function is mediated by light reception in vertebrates that have a foramen in the skull over these organs; the brain connections are visceral, not somatic. It seems highly likely that the homeostatic function was a minor one in early evolution, and that with perfection of the paired eyes for vision the unpaired eyes became solely of homeostatic function. In advanced vertebrates of all classes the homeostatic function has become independent of light reception. Except as one or the other organ became degenerate and essentially nonfunctional, we can thus recognize four stages in functional evolution of the epiphyses, all paralleled by appropriate morphological changes: (a) visual function only in some prevertebrate stage; (b) both visual and homeostatic functions, the latter mediated by light reception presumably in primitive extinct vertebrates; (c) solely a homeostatic function, mediated by light, as in many primitive vertebrates, all with a parietal or pineal foramen; and (d) a homeostatic function independent of light reception, as in mammals and all other more advanced vertebrates lacking means of direct exposure of the organs to light.

Origin of the Paired Eyes. Apparently the earliest complex sense organs of chordates were the olfactory and optic organs, each reflected in

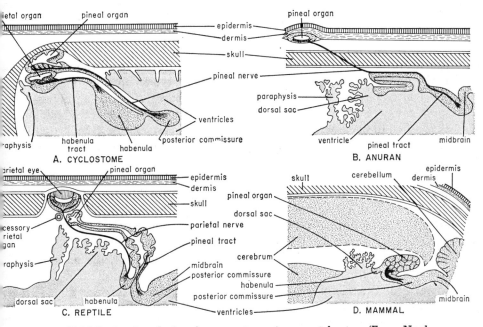

FIG. 15.12 Parietal and pineal organs in various vertebrates. (From Neal and Rand.)

brain structure by the presence of a separate vesicle. The third or otic vesicle appeared at a later time, in correlation with its differentiation from a relatively complex neuromast system that probably came into existence subsequent to the olfactory and optic organs.

The eye is a strictly vertebrate organ of basically the same complex structure from cyclostomes to mammals. It is not presaged by any structure of similar nature in known protochordates. The phylogeny of the basic eye structure is thus unknown. Unfortunately embryogeny provides few clues; for in the process of embryonic development, functional integration is only a final achievement, whereas in phylogeny a functional integration occurred of necessity throughout all evolutionary stages. The more rudimentary parietal and pineal organs suggest how the eye might have evolved as a unit from a simple juxtaposition of a light-sensitive brain region and a light-pervious section of the integument (Fig. 15.13). There is no reason to suspect that the evolutionary processes that followed, bringing about the crowning achievement of the vertebrate eye, were any different from those evident in any other evolutionary series, despite our lack of knowledge of the exact steps.

Already in earliest vertebrates an organ of virtually maximal efficiency, so far as intrinsic structure is concerned, the eye itself was subject to relatively little basic improvement in vertebrate evolution. In relatively minor ways it became adapted to different ways of life adopted by different vertebrate groups, but it was already adequate in most respects. Accessory structures do, however, go through marked evolutionary change in vertebrates.

Basic Eye Structure and Embryogeny. The vertebrate eye is a hollow sphere whose wall is composed of three layers of tissue, and whose inner cavity houses a lens situated opposite and internal to an aperture in a partition incompletely separating a small anterior cavity from a larger posterior cavity (Fig. 15.14). An optic "nerve" (in reality a part of the brain) is attached to the inner border of the eye wall, away from the lens.

The outer layer of the eye wall, the *scleroid* coat (or *sclera*), surrounds the entire eyeball, is opaque over most of its area, but in an oval or round area at the exposed surface of the eyeball is transparent. The transparent scleroid area is usually fused with a very thin area of the skin (*conjunctiva*) covering the orbit (eye socket). The conjunctiva, like the scleroid coat, is opaque over most of its area, even on parts of the eyeball as well as on the walls of the invaginated pocket about the exposed surface of the eyeball; but where the scleroid coat is transparent, the conjunctiva is also transparent. The two transparent layers, fused together, form the *cornea*. The scleroid coat varies in thickness more or less according to size of eye, disproportionately increasing as the eye diameter increases; thus the scleroid coat of the large whales is tremendously thickened. In all vertebrates, except cyclostomes, salamanders, snakes, and eutherian mammals, the scleroid coat is strengthened by cartilage.

The *choroid* coat (or *choroidea*) lies immediately internal to the scleroid coat. Both the scleroid and choroid coats are of mesodermal origin.

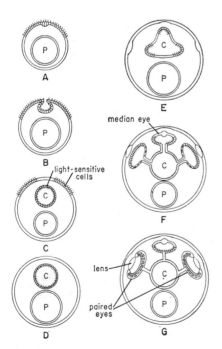

FIG. 15.13 Diagrams illustrating presumed origin of certain parts of the vertebrate eye. Symbols: c, central nervous system; p, pharynx. The closely placed cross hatching represents light-sensitive cells throughout, and their direction of facing is indicated by the short line protruding from each schematized cell.

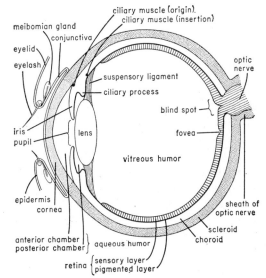

ciliary muscle (origin).
ciliary muscle (insertion)
meibomian gland
conjunctiva
eyelid
eyelash
optic nerve
suspensory ligament
ciliary process
blind spot
iris
pupil
lens
fovea
vitreous humor
epidermis
cornea
sheath of optic nerve
scleroid
choroid
anterior chamber
posterior chamber
aqueous humor
retina {sensory layer, pigmented layer}

FIG. 15.14 Basic features of the vertebrate eye, diagrammatic.

The former is chiefly protective and supportive in function and has a stiff, rigid structure. The choroid coat is nutritive and soft; it contains most ramifications of optic blood vessels.

Internal to the choroid coat lies the sensory *retina,* of ectodermal origin. The retina is a double coat, being formed essentially as a hollow evagination (Fig. 15.10A) (*optic vesicle*) from the diencephalon of the brain. The cavity of the optic vesicle is collapsed in embryonic development by progressive increase in size of an invagination of the distal part of its wall. The distal and proximal walls come to lie in complete contact, obliterating the vesicular cavity and producing a somewhat saucer-shaped retinal structure. This enlarges and forms a hollow spherical capsule open only by an aperture opposite the optic stalk. This capsule, upon approximation to the embryonic epidermis, initiates formation of the lens. After separation of the lens from the ectoderm, choroid and scleroid coats close about the retina to form the completed eye.

The sensory cells of the retina lie on the inner face of the distal wall, directed away from the source of light and buried in the nonvisual cells of the proximal retinal wall. The mechanical disadvantage of facing away from the light source is slight, since the light need penetrate so little material to reach the sensory cells. The seemingly odd orientation is an inevitable result of the location of epidermal sense organs on the outer surface of the epithelium. With formation of the central nervous system, the former outer surface is seen to face into the neurocele. As the optic evagination forms, the former outer surface lines the interior of the optic vesicle, and it is on the distal wall, nearest the light, that the sensory cells remain. The proximal wall forms a black, light-absorptive, nonrefractive layer.

The sensory cells of the retina are of two sorts: *rods* and *cones,* named on the basis of shape in man, although the shapes are different in many other vertebrates. The two types can be distinguished in all vertebrates, despite variation in shape, by a number of other features: (1) in general, each cone transmits its impulses to the brain through a pathway that remains separate from all others, whereas several rods form synaptic junctions with a single intermediary cell (Fig. 15.15); (2) thus sharpness of vision is considerably greater in the parts of the retina where cones are abundant than where the rods predominate; (3) cones are much less sensitive than rods; and (4) cones are sensitive to different wavelengths and thus register color, whereas rods do not discriminate wavelengths and register only grays, black, and white. Distribution of rods and cones on the retina varies greatly among vertebrates, some having rods only, others cones only, and still others having mixtures of all proportions. Nocturnal types tend to have more rods, diurnal types more cones. The two types may be uniformly distributed over the retina, or there may be one or two areas (*area centralis, area temporalis*) where cones are more abundant. The eyes normally are so directed as to throw the visual center of interest directly onto one or the other area. Often a central depression marking a *fovea* is present in the cone area; this is the area of sharpest vision.

Color perception occurs in teleosts, turtles, lizards, birds, and primates, but the degree of perception differs very markedly. Humans are exceptionally discriminating, and amphibians seem to be perhaps the least. To most vertebrates the world appears a monotonous study in gray, with colors for the most part feebly distinguishable if at all.

Sensory cells are absent from the retina where the optic nerve emerges from the eyeball. Due to their absence there is a *blind spot* (Fig. 15.14) in each visual field. It is medial to the fovea, and is not evident in normal sight unless one eye is closed, and even then can be detected only by use of special techniques.

The choroid and retinal layers do not encompass the entire orbit. They are closely united with the scleroid layer except anteriorly, where they turn inward to form a curtain, the *iris*. The iris is incomplete in the center, leaving a gap of varying shape called the *pupil*. The lens is hung opposite and just within the pupil, attached by a membrane, the *suspensory ligament,* to a ringlike thickening, the *ciliary body,* near the attachment of the iris to the orbital wall. The ciliary body, containing a mesodermal *ciliary muscle,* controls focusing. Although the iris curtain is more conspicuous, the only complete inner partition of the eyeball is furnished by the lens and its attachment to the iris. The small anterior cavity, in front of the lens, is the cavity of the more fluid *aqueous humor;* that behind the lens is the cavity of the more gelatinous *vitreous humor.* The iris, dangling into the cavity of the aqueous humor, partially separates an *anterior chamber* (external) from a *posterior chamber* (internal) of that cavity.

Evolution of Intrinsic Structure. Four especially noteworthy intrinsic structures of the eye are subject to variation in vertebrate evolution. They are, or are related to, the focusing mechanism, scleroid bones, vitreous intrusions, and diel (nocturnal and diurnal) adaptations.

ACCOMMODATION. Visual accommodation (focusing) is either (a) *lenticular,* or (b) a combination of lenticular and *corneal.* Lenticular accommodation involves only the lens of the eye, whereas corneal focusing involves only the cornea. No vertebrate normally focuses with the cornea alone (man does, to an astonishingly efficient degree, when the lens is removed), but fishes use the lens alone. Tetrapods tend to utilize both the lens and cornea, with the general trend being toward increase in importance of the corneal role. Primitive tetrapods utilize the cornea relatively little in accommodation. Fishes cannot do so since the refractive index of the cornea is virtually the same as that of water. The cornea aids in accommodation by change in degree of its curvature. Contraction of the ring-shaped ciliary muscle invariably exerts a force upon the outer edges of the cornea. Unless some provision exists to prevent it, that force thus shortens the diameter of the cornea slightly and increases its anterior curvature. The greater the curvature, the shorter the distance of focus.

Lenticular accommodation is effected in two grossly different ways in vertebrates: by change in *position* of the lens, which moves either forward or backward (*extrinsic lenticular accommodation*); or by change in *shape* of the lens, its position remaining approximately fixed (*intrinsic lenticular accommodation*). In all amniotes (except ophidians) only intrinsic lenticular accommodation occurs, whereas the primitive vertebrate

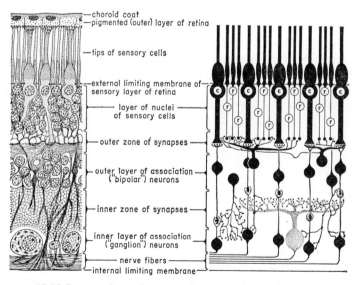

FIG. 15.15 Section through retina showing relationship of receptors and pathways extending from them. (From Romer.)

mode is *via* extrinsic lenticular movements (in all anamniotes and, secondarily, in snakes). The adaptive value of intrinsic lenticular accommodation, as opposed to the anamniote type, is that it makes possible the great range of focus that aerial vision permits. Because of the highly variable refractivity of water, clear aquatic vision is ordinarily possible only at relatively short distances. The extrinsic movements of the lens required for such near vision are relatively slight and can readily be accommodated within the confines of the eye. The greater extrinsic movements that would be required for focus over the much wider range of aerial vision presumably cannot readily be accommodated within the eye.

The explanation of the peculiar reversion of snakes to the more primitive extrinsic lenticular accommodation is to be found in the fact that snakes evolved from blind lizardlike ancestors in which optic degeneration extended to loss of the ciliary body. The newly evolved ciliary body of snakes is of different embryonic origin from the ciliary body of other amniotes, and it is of significance that the accommodation that was redeveloped in snakes was of the most primitive type known in vertebrates, rather than the more highly evolved type of the immediate ancestors of snakes.

There is a marked distinction within anamniotes between the tetrapods (amphibians) and most fishes in the normal position of the lens. Fishes in general (not elasmobranchs) possess a presumably primitive relation of lens and retina, with the lens in a near-sighted, forward position as would be expected in an aquatic environment. Focusing for far vision occurs by contraction of ciliary muscles (except in cyclostomes), moving the lens backward (Fig. 15.16A). In cyclostomes a unique extrinsic corneal muscle flattens the cornea and pushes the lens closer to the retina.

In elasmobranchs and in amphibians, the latter initiating an adaptation to terrestrial life, the lens is situated normally in a far-sighted rear position, and focusing for near vision occurs by contraction of ciliary muscles moving the lens forward (Fig. 15.16B). Nearer than normal vision in most fishes, or more distant vision in amphibians, is made possible by complete relaxation of the muscles which by their normal tonus maintain the lens in a position between the two possible extremes.

Just as in anamniotes, under normal tensions (the ciliary muscle in tonus) the eye in amniotes is adjusted in some (reptiles, birds) for far vision and in others (mammals) for near vision. The difference is due to shape of the relaxed lens; intrinsic pressures and tensions cause the lens to assume a more flattened shape in reptiles and birds, and a more convex and rounded shape in mammals, when no extrinsic forces are in effect.

In mammals, the lens is held to the ciliary body by ligaments that in the relaxed state of the ciliary muscle are under constant tension from the corneal pull, in turn a product of the turgidity of the eye. The ciliary muscles, contracting to produce nearer vision, pull the ciliary body nearer the lens, releasing the tension on the latter and at the same time bowing the cornea. The lens of its own resiliency then resumes its relaxed round form;

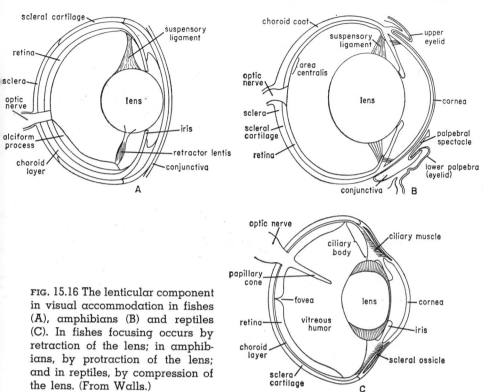

FIG. 15.16 The lenticular component in visual accommodation in fishes (A), amphibians (B) and reptiles (C). In fishes focusing occurs by retraction of the lens; in amphibians, by protraction of the lens; and in reptiles, by compression of the lens. (From Walls.)

no muscles actually force it into a rounded form. With increased age the resiliency of the lens often is reduced, with the result that the lens no longer can resume as rounded a form (and thus as close a focus) at least as quickly as before, nor can it be flattened as much for far vision by any given tension. The most distant vision is provided by complete relaxation of the ciliary muscle, which allows the maximum pull of the cornea on the lens, flattening it as indeed the cornea is flattened. Tonal contraction of the ciliary muscle produces a focus in man but 2½ feet or so from the eyes.

In reptiles and birds the ciliary body is in direct contact with the periphery of the lens. Contraction of the ciliary muscle forces the lens into the rounded shape necessary for near vision (Fig. 15.16C). The astonishingly soft lens of primitive reptiles facilitates manipulation by the ciliary body.

In both mammals and sauropsids a contraction of the ciliary muscle produces a closer focus, by two mechanisms: it bows the cornea, and it produces a more convex lens. In both groups a relaxation of the muscle produces a more distant focus. The actual corneal effect of the ciliary muscle is limited extensively by the rigidity of the scleroid coat, an aspect that is discussed in connection with the scleroid bones.

The evolutionary pattern is thus a succession of four stages:

(1) Extrinsic lenticular focusing from near vision adjustment;
(2) extrinsic lenticular focusing from far visual adjustment;
(3) corneal and intrinsic lenticular focusing from far lenticular adjustment;
(4) corneal and intrinsic lenticular focusing from a near lenticular adjustment.

The functional value of the evolutionary pattern in accommodation is at least in part apparent. The shift from extrinsic to intrinsic lenticular focusing, from anamniotes to amniotes, is understandable as an adaptation to aerial vision, not coming fully into effect in amphibians because of their dual ways of life. The shift from near vision to far vision from fishes to amphibians is likewise intelligible, on precisely the same basis. Even the shift of mammals from the far lenticular adjustment of their ancestors to near vision may be accepted as an adaptation to preoccupation with what is near at hand instead of far away. In fact the mental development (neopallium) so conspicuous in mammals probably could not have occurred without this alteration in visual adjustment.

SCLEROID BONES. In many early and primitive vertebrates, including some members of all major groups save living amphibians, snakes, chondrichthyans, and mammals, the scleroid coat was strengthened by the formation within it of a series of usually quadrangular, overlapping bones forming a ring around the cornea about as wide as the distance from the edge of the cornea to the edge of the orbit (Fig. 15.17). They thus usually covered only the lateral part of the eyeball unprotected by the orbit wall; in a few extremes the bones curved into the deep orbital parts of the cornea. In some ostracoderms the whole noncorneal scleroid coat was ossified.

Some authors have held that two sorts of scleroid bones have evolved

A

FIG. 15.17 Scleroid bones in a bird. A, the bony ring of scleroid bones, seen separately; B, the scleroid ring in place in a dry skull; C, orientation of the bony ring on eyeball. (From Walls.)

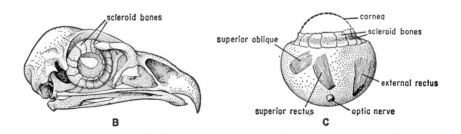

B   C

in vertebrates, one type from the sclera itself, the other from a circumorbital ring of dermal bones. It is now thought that dermal bones have never contributed to the scleral ring.

The function of scleroid bones has generally been accepted as provision of resistance to deformation of the eyeball. They thus are presumed to be of special value in offsetting extraocular pressures from wind or water in types that fly and swim extensively. They also offset changes in intraocular pressures, and in this connection it is especially plausible that scleroid bones have served most importantly of all as an adjunct in the process of accommodation. The bones would tend to (1) offset the constrictive action of the ciliary muscles upon the cornea (reducing the bowing effect); (2) resist the pushing effect of the naturally flat lens upon the wall of the eye (as in sauropsids); and (3) provide a firm, nonyielding origin for the ciliary muscles in pulling the lens forward or backward (as in anamniotes). With certain exceptions, animals with well-developed scleroid bones rely extensively (if not entirely) upon lenticular accommodation (as opposed to corneal accommodation), whereas those without such bones may or may not have exclusively lenticular accommodation. Many birds, especially the birds of prey, have been able to retain the scleroid bones without loss of corneal accommodation by differentiation of the ciliary muscle into two parts. One part (*Brucke's muscle*) forces the lens into a rounded shape in the usual sauropsid manner, whereas the other part (*Crampton's muscle*) bows the cornea. No mammals, on the other hand, either fossil or recent, possess scleroid bones; they clearly would have been a handicap to the corneal mechanism of accommodation so important in mammals, and they are not necessary to offset intrinsic lenticular pressures since the lens is suspended by ligaments.

VITREOUS INTRUSIONS. One of the most puzzling structures of the eye is the series of vitreous intrusions occurring in scattered vertebrate groups. Unfortunately their history in extinct groups is unknown. The most primitive living vertebrates possessing them are the teleosts. Here the choroid coat projects into the vitreous chamber through a slit in the optic cup, the *choroid fissure* (Fig. 15.10A), in the form of a ridgelike *falciform process* serving as the point of attachment for the origin of the lens retractors (Fig. 15.16A).

In reptiles a *papillary cone* (Fig. 15.16C) of presumably nutritive function replaces (and possibly evolved from) the piscine falciform process. In birds the papillary cone becomes ridgelike, forming the *pecten* (Fig. 15.18), which is unique in possessing many vertical grooves down each side of the structure. Presumably the pecten is yet of nutritive function, but its primary function has become the augmentation of visual acuity. No vitreous intrusions of any sort have persisted in modern mammals; presumably the vascularization of the choroidea has been sufficiently improved in mammals to render a nutritive vitreous intrusion unnecessary.

NOCTURNAL AND DIURNAL ADAPTATIONS. Four sorts of diel adaptations are especially noteworthy: they involve pupil shape, color of the aqueous humor, refractivity of the choroid coat, and relative abundance of rods and cones. The latter was discussed previously.

The shape of the pupil, the central aperture in the iris, varies greatly from species to species as well as from time to time (Fig. 15.19). Species whose eyes are adapted to a given narrow range of light intensity, but which are active at times within a much wider range of light intensity, have a pupil varying considerably in diameter. The aperture is broad under conditions of minimal light, narrow under conditions of maximal light. Accordingly, four adaptive situations are prominently evident among vertebrates. First, species which are active solely in daylight, but under conditions wherein the light is never excessive (many fishes), exhibit little variation in the breadth of the large pupillary opening. Under aerial conditions, however, diurnal animals are exposed to much greater extremes and have mobile irises capable of forming either large or small pupils. The constricted pupil is of highly variable shape, but characteristically is round, less frequently is rhomboidal, and in some is of a quite irregular outline (Fig. 15.19). Third, a slitlike pupil is found in normally nocturnal tetrapods (for example, cats, rattlesnakes, geckos) which are active also at times during the day. In such animals, however, the eyes are so light sensitive that the pupil becomes a vertical or horizontal slit in the contracted state, although it is round when expanded. Narrow constriction or closure is mechanically simpler for a slit than for a round aperture. The slit pupil is not to be construed as an adaptation to nocturnality, but rather an adaptation of nocturnal animals to diurnal conditions. Finally, those species which are exclusively nocturnal and do not voluntarily seek diurnal exposure (for example, coral snakes) have a round pupil in both the contracted and expanded state.

The aqueous humor is characteristically without color, of nearly perfect transparency. In some animals, especially diurnal snakes, the fluid has evolved a yellowish color known to be of value in increasing diurnal visual acuity.

In nocturnal animals efficient utilization of light is an end toward which optic modifications are directed. Diurnal animals need not be so

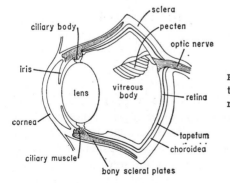

FIG. 15.18 The avian eye in cross section, showing the pecten and scleral ring. (From Walters.)

FIG. 15.19 Variation in pupil shape in vertebrates. (From Walls.)

chary of available light; they take special pains to suppress excess light in various ways, among them by the black retinal and choroid layers absorptive of all rays not directly impinging upon the sensory cells. In nocturnal animals the retina is less pigmented and the choroid layer bordering it often develops a reflective surface, the *tapetum,* serving to reflect unused light back into the sensory layer where it may be utilized. The eyes of such animals shine in the dark when a strong light is directed at them. Considerable individual variation, as well as interspecific variation, seems to occur in this respect. Some humans have eyes reflecting direct light at night, others do not.

Extrinsic Adjustments. Three extrinsic adjustments of the eye have undergone noteworthy evolution in vertebrates: bathyopsis, stereopsis, and protection *via* eyelids and orbital glands.

BATHYOPSIS. Visual distance—or depth—perception, more properly known as *bathyopsis,* has evolved slowly among vertebrates, reaching its greatest refinement in birds and mammals. Two mechanisms provide for bathyopsis: *stereopsis* and *accommodation.* Distance perception is present wherever accommodation occurs, but it is highly inefficient by accommodation alone as compared with the combination of stereopsis and accommodation. Five stages of perfection may be recognized: (1) monocular-field vision without fixation; (2) binocular-field vision without fixation; (3) binocular-field vision with monocular-field fixation; (4) binocular-field vision with binocular-field independent fixation; and (5) binocular-field vision with binocular-field conjugate fixation.

1. *Monocular-field Vision without Fixation.* In presumably all of the early vertebrates the visual fields of the two eyes were wholly separate. Relatively few species now living, however, possess wholly separate visual fields. Cyclostomes, and a certain few sharks, salamanders, penguins, and whales constitute these exceptions to the general rule.

Fixation involves two actions: (a) turning of the eye so that the most sensitive part of the retina is directed toward the object of interest; and (b) focus of the eye upon that object. Primitively eyes were incapable of fixation, *because the primary function in vertebrates was to detect motion,* and motion is detectable just as readily in one part of the retina as another. Not until discrimination became an important aspect of survival did fixation become a common phenomenon. Even in early stages of binocular-field vision, fixation did not occur.

2. *Binocular-field Vision without Fixation.* All vertebrates whose two monocular fields overlap have binocular-field vision within that area of

overlap. Almost all living vertebrates possess some binocularity, the maximum occurring in certain mammals such as man with 140 degrees of binocular-field vision and 30 degrees on each side of monocular-field vision at the horizontal level. Certain birds have as much as 70 degrees of binocularity, reptiles as much as 46 degrees, amphibians relatively little, fishes as much as 40 degrees. Within the region of overlap there is singleness of vision, or *stereopsis,* resulting from overlap of images. The chief advantage of stereopsis is that it does give an idea of depth—it is one means of bathyopsis. The bathyscopic value diminishes, of course, with distance, as the angle of convergence diminishes. There is in this early stage of binocularity little perception of *relative* depth, as this is possible only with development of a specialized center of discrimination (fovea). There is no fovea and, therefore, no fixation. Living vertebrates exemplifying this stage are most fishes, all amphibians save those in stage one or with degenerate eyes, crocodilians, most turtles, and most snakes.

3. *Binocular-field Vision with Monocular-field Fixation.* The next step in ocular improvement was the development of a special retinal area of sensitivity. A relatively broad *area centralis* first developed, and this ultimately became perfected with a *fovea* in the form of a conical pit of varying depth. The image of the object of visual interest is in areate or foveate eyes projected upon the region of greatest sensitivity. With development of foveae, for the first time fixation becomes a physiological necessity, so that the eye may be turned voluntarily into the most favorable position. Prior to attainment of the foveate stage, no voluntary fixation occurred simply because the image was transmitted as well from one part of the retina as another. Extrinsic eye muscles are present in all vertebrates save those with degenerate eyes, but in prefoveate types the only movements they caused were reflexive gyroscopic movements essential to detection of movement in components of the environment even while the head is being turned. *Gyroscopic compensation* remains reflexive in the more advanced vertebrates, but voluntary fixative movements came into being only when the foveae appeared.

Fixation in its earliest stage seemingly was exclusively monocular, the eyes moving and fixating independently. The voluntary movements of the eyes in all vertebrates except mammals are independent. It is true that in none is this independence so clearly evident as in the true (Afro-Asiatic) chameleons with their conical lids and highly mobile eyes, but the phenomenon of independent ocular fixation is not by any means unique to them. (Actually chameleons represent the fourth stage, since they can fixate within the binocular field.)

Vertebrates representing the present stage, in which fixation is limited to the monocular fields, include only some few fishes and most lizards.

4. *Binocular-field Vision with Binocular Independent Fixation.* A capacity to fixate within the binocular as well as the monocular field was the next sequel, enabling animals attaining this stage to see much more efficiently in the binocular field.

Vertebrates exemplifying this stage include a few fishes, lizards, and snakes, and all birds. All have either (1) a highly mobile eye or (2) a relatively immobile eye. It is somewhat surprising that ocular mobility has not been developed more commonly among vertebrates; actually it is quite limited outside of the mammals. The eye fits very tightly in the orbit in most birds and cannot be moved except to a very limited degree. Species with mobile eyes (notably chameleons) possess central foveae, which by convergent movements of the eye can fixate binocularly. Species with fixed eyes must, and do, if the eyes are laterally situated, have the foveae in a posterior ("temporal") position where the images would necessarily fall in binocular fixation. A few snakes possess horizontal (even keyhole-shaped) pupils permitting vision through the pupil directly forward thus achieving binocular fixation without convergence in species with laterally directed eyes.

In most birds both a temporal and central fovea occurs, the former permitting binocular-field fixation, the central foveae permitting monocular-field fixation (Fig. 15.20). Birds exhibiting extreme *frontality* (both eyes directed forward)—for example, owls—possess but one set of foveae.

A seemingly necessary compensation for slight ocular mobility in binocularly fixating species is extreme cranial mobility; birds have an exceptionally mobile neck, and so do snakes.

Whether relatively mobile or immobile, the two eyes in all vertebrates save mammals fixate independently, even though the fixation may be binocular. The rapidity of fixation is greatly facilitated by ocular immobility, but it still remains a separate process for each eye.

5. *Binocular-field Vision with Binocular-field Conjugate Fixation.* In all mammals, and in mammals alone, one further step has been taken in bathyscopic improvement: fixation by the two eyes has become *conjugate,* in the sense that movement by one eye must necessarily (except under abnormal conditions) be accompanied by identical movements of the other eye. Binocular fixation in other vertebrates is coordinated, but still independent for each eye; in mammals it is mechanically impossible for the eyes to move independently in normal situations. The advantage for

FIG. 15.20 Visual fields and areas of fixation in birds. Relative resolving powers are proportional to closeness of hatching. Symbols: x, blind region; c, area of fixation from central foveae in monocular fields; T, area of fixation from temporal foveae in binocular fields.

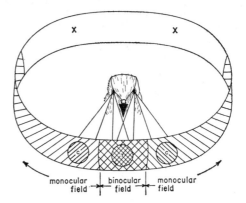

bathyopsis is the speed it permits in binocular fixation. Clearly certain birds, with immobile eyes requiring only movement of the head for fixation, and mammals have the most efficient bathyscopic devices evolved in vertebrates.

The peculiarity of mammals that has effected conjugation of vision is the *partial* rather than complete decussation of optic fibers at the optic chiasma. In all vertebrates except mammals *all* fibers decussate (cross from one side to the other) at the chiasma. The number of fibers failing to decussate in mammals varies considerably, an approximate 50 to 50 ratio being attained in the most frontal-eyed species (as man), the least in the lateral-eyed forms as lagomorphs with a ratio of about 1 or 2 nondecussating to 20 decussating fibers. All mammals have some binocularity, therefore some nondecussating fibers, and accordingly conjugate vision.

STEREOPSIS. Stereopsis is the coincidence of overlapping images. Binocular fields may exist, in the sense of a certain area being visible at the same time with both eyes, without there being a coincidence of images. Where the images coincide there is stereopsis. A stereoscopic effect of three dimensions occurs in the binocular field of all vertebrates whose monocular fields can be made to coincide in any part. The basic mode of stereopsis is the same for all species except mammals. That of mammals may be designated half-field stereopsis, whereas that of other vertebrates is full-field stereopsis.

In full-field stereopsis the entire image of the binocular field is transmitted to the opposite side of the brain, and "fusion" of the images in the brain necessarily involves all of both fields (Fig. 15.21A).

In half-field stereopsis only one half of the entire image *of the binocular field* is transmitted to the opposite side of the brain (Fig. 15.21B). The other half is transmitted to the same side. The right half-image from both eyes goes to the right half of the brain, both left halves to the left. Thus each side of the brain receives two half-images (one from each eye) of the binocular field. "Fusion" of the images is accomplished in each side independently, and only a matching of stereoscopic half-images is necessary to produce a complete image.

The ratio of decussating to nondecussating fibers at the chiasma may readily be seen to be directly and fairly closely correlated with the size ratio of the monocular to the binocular fields. The greater the proportionate size of the binocular field, the greater the proportion of nondecussating fibers, with a 50 to 50 ratio the maximum between decussating and nondecussating fibers in an eye with complete binocular vision. As stated previously, no vertebrates possess complete binocular vision, but mammals approach most closely to that "ideal."

Thus the partial decussation occurring in mammals has produced two effects unique to that class: conjugate fixation and half-field stereopsis. The survival value of conjugate fixation is tremendous and has been dis-

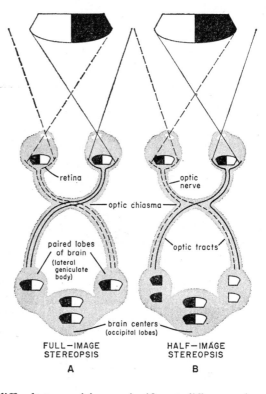

FIG. 15.21 Contrast of mechanisms of stereopsis in non-mammalian vertebrates (A) and mammals (B).

retina

optic nerve

optic chiasma

paired lobes of brain (lateral geniculate body)

optic tracts

brain centers (occipital lobes)

FULL—IMAGE STEREOPSIS

HALF—IMAGE STEREOPSIS

A   B

cussed previously, but it is difficult to envision a significant difference in adaptive value of half-image and full-image stereopsis. Presumably half-image stereopsis was a necessary adjunct of partial decussation (which was essential to conjugate fixation) and was of no significance in itself.

Eye Coverings. Four types of eye coverings are evident in vertebrates: (1) the *spectacle,* consisting of a translucent or transparent area of skin under which the eye is freely mobile; (2) the *conjunctiva,* a transparent area of skin fused to the sclera to form a part of the cornea (only primitively are the two layers distinguishable in the cornea); (3) *eyelids,* mobile flaps of skin over the eye; and (4) *opaque skin* (and sometimes bone as well) in those types having degenerate eyes.

EYELIDS. Vertebrates began their evolution without eyelids. Flaps or ridges above and below the eyes in fishes may be regarded as rudimentary eyelids, but in no fish do these structures develop to the extent of deserving recognition as true eyelids.

In a second stage of eyelid evolution, exemplified by amphibians generally, *upper* and *lower eyelids* appear, together completely covering the eye. The upper lid is large, but generally simply covers the eye above and is immobile except as the eyeball itself is protruded or retracted in the orbit. The lower lid covers most of the surface of the eyeball, and is mobile. The eye is "opened" by movement of the lower lid and, in some types like anurans, by protrusion of the eyeball. Both upper and lower lids persist throughout later classes, although their relative mobility is reversed in the ultimate (mammalian) stage.

In a third stage, exemplified generally by modern sauropsids, a third or *nictitating eyelid* is added. It is characteristically a thin, translucent structure attached to the anterior (medial) corner of the orbit. It thus covers the eye in a direction at right angles to that of the two other lids, which overlie the nictitating membrane. Unable to blink quickly, and generally so opaque that vision was impossible when closed, the eyelids were incapable of keeping the corneal surface moist without visual interference until the nictitating eyelid was evolved. The function of the latter eyelid was thus to prevent desiccation of the cornea without interference with vision, or with as little interference as possible. Birds are said to keep the nictitating membrane closed in flight. In this stage the lower eyelid, where functional, has remained mobile and the upper eyelid essentially immobile, except as the eyeball pushes it up in protrusion, or pulls it down in retraction, as in crocodilians. In most types the eyeball is not extensively mobile, and thus the upper eyelid moves little or not at all.

In a fourth stage, exemplified by mammals, two major changes were effected: (1) the nictitating eyelid became degenerate, and (2) the upper eyelid became mobile as the lower eyelid degenerated and lost its mobility. The two changes were reciprocal, one dependent upon the other. Both were made possible by the invasion of the facial region in mammals by the platysma. The presence of this integumentary muscle led to the muscularization of the formerly immobile upper eyelid. The new musculature apparently proved much more efficient than the earlier musculature of the lower eyelid, permitting an almost instantaneous closure and opening of the optic aperture. This interfered less with vision than the often cumbersome nictitating membrane, and was equally efficient in maintaining a moist surface over the cornea. Thus the nictitating eyelid is of rather rare and scattered occurrence in mammals. It may be considered on its evolutionary way out.

In chameleons and a few other lizards, the eyelids have become partially fused in such a way as to form a conelike covering with a small apical perforation. The perforation can be directed forward or backward, downward or upward, with a nearly 180-degree range in any one plane.

SPECTACLES. A noncorneal, semitransparent covering of the eye is a spectacle. *True* spectacles are fixed in position. *Palpebral spectacles* form part of a mobile eyelid and can, therefore, be in operation when the eyelids are closed, but not when the eyelids are open.

Three types of true spectacles are recognized. The *primary spectacle* (Fig. 15.22A), occurring in lampreys and wholly aquatic amphibians (including tadpoles), represents the most primitive relationship between skin and sclera (that is, wholly separate) in vertebrates, and the most primitive cornea (lacking a conjunctiva), the *primary cornea*. In later types a *partial* fusion of skin (now conjunctiva) and sclera produced the *second-*

ary cornea, characteristic of most fishes (Fig. 15.22B). In a few fishes (amphibious teleosts) and amphibians (some cave salamanders), however, the ancestral conjunctiva became thickened and less transparent, and a space redeveloped between skin and sclera. They thus possess *secondary spectacles,* indistinguishable morphologically from primary spectacles.

In tetrapods the conjunctiva and sclera became indistinguishably fused as the *tertiary* or *definitive cornea,* and the eyelids became well developed (Fig. 15.22C). From this morphotype evolved the *tertiary spectacle* or *brille* (Fig. 15.22D) occurring in a very few teleost fishes, some lizards, and all except the blind or near-blind snakes. In these the ancestral eyelids or, in the fish, opaque skin flaps about the eye, became transparent and fused over the eye, leaving a lymph-filled space between the spectacle and the conjunctiva of the cornea. In gross appearance eyelids seem to be absent and the brille looks like the eyeball itself; histological preparations are necessary to demonstrate the existence of an extra outer covering.

Intermediate stages in the evolution of the lizard brille are exemplified by certain lizards in which the movable lower lid has a transparent central disc (the *palpebral spectacle,* Fig. 15.23), serving much the same function as the brille, enabling the animal to see even with the lids closed. In others the lower lid is actually fused with the upper, and the central disc is smaller than the fully evolved brille. Snakes and other animals with a tertiary spectacle are not accurately described as lidless; their eyelids are simply fixedly closed and transparent. In many anurans the palpebral spectacle (Fig. 15.16C) takes the form of a translucent border on the lower eyelid, permitting some vision even as the eyelids are closed. This structure often has been called a nictitating membrane, but it definitely is not, nor is it homologous.

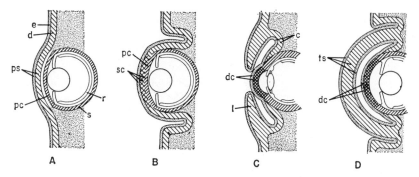

FIG. 15.22 Evolution of true spectacles (as opposed to palpebral spectacles) in vertebrates. A, stage represented by cyclostomes, larval amphibians, and a few adult anurans; B, stage represented by most gnathostome fishes; C, stage represented by most tetrapods; D, stage represented by certain squamate reptiles (snakes, some lizards) and a few teleost fishes. Symbols: c, conjunctiva; d, dermis; dc, definitive cornea; e, epidermis; l, lower eyelid; pc, primary cornea; ps, primary spectacle; sc, secondary cornea. (From Walls.)

The brille and palpebral spectacles occur in types of tetrapods lacking a nictitating membrane, with which they may be regarded analogous, although there is no homology. There seems to be a definite survival value in many vertebrates for a transparent protective covering over the cornea, although this does not seem to be true for many mammals, perhaps in correlation with the mobility of the upper eyelid.

ORBITAL GLANDS. The eyelids function to keep the eyeball free from extraneous matter, but more importantly, if less dramatically, to keep the exposed corneal surface moist. Moisture is supplied by a set of orbital glands arising simultaneously with eyelids in amphibians. Two sets are of general occurrence: (1) *lacrimal glands,* which secrete a relatively thin fluid and are located in a posterodorsal position in the orbit, in relatively close association with the upper eyelid; and (2) *Harderian glands,* which secrete a more viscous fluid and are located in an anteroventral position in the orbit, in relatively close association with the lower eyelid and nictitating membrane. A *nasolacrimal* duct piercing a foramen of the same name in the external anteroventral border of the orbit drains the excess fluid from the orbit into the nasal cavity and thence into the buccal cavity or pharynx. More or less linked with specific eyelids, the glands vary in occurrence as much as the lids. The Harderian glands are found in few mammals, in harmony with the degeneration of both the lower and nictitating eyelids. On the other hand, the lacrimal glands, like the upper eyelids, are hypertrophied in mammals. When the eyes are irritated, or in certain species (for example, man, bears) under certain emotional conditions, the lacrimal glands are capable of producing copious quantities of its secretion (in *weeping,* not crying), which cannot be drained off in the usual fashion but escape between the eyelids as *lacrimae* (tears). This reversal in development of the orbital glands is another unique attribute of mammals, hinging upon a whole linked succession of unique modifications beginning with platysmal hypertrophy in mammalian ancestors.

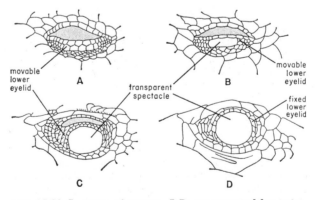

FIG. 15.23 A series of stages, A-D, represented by existing species of lizards, illustrating evolution of the tertiary spectacle in advanced lizards. (From Malcolm Smith.)

Some turtles somewhat simulate the tearful capacity of mammals, but they do so chiefly because they lack a nasolacrimal duct.

Ear

Complex though the eye may be, the ear is unquestionably, in its most advanced form, the most complex of mammalian sense organs. Fortunately, unlike the eye, most of its evolution occurred within the history of vertebrates and is fairly well documented.

The definitive ear may be regarded as consisting of three parts: an inner, a middle, and an outer "ear." The most ancient of these is the inner ear, originally serving to detect position, and subsequently direction of movement as well; detection of sound and pressure is superimposed still later. The middle ear was added in amphibians, and throughout subsequent evolution served the single primary function to aid in hearing; it was and is an adaptation to a life in an aerial medium. The outer ear was a final addition of reptiles (further elaborated in mammals) involving hearing accessories only. Most of the truly marvelous changes occurring in the ear in vertebrates concern, oddly enough, the auditory function, itself a secondary function of the ear.

Outer Ear. As it first appeared in reptiles, the outer ear consisted only of a short tube, the *external auditory meatus* extending from the tympanum to the exterior (Fig. 15.24A). No outer ear existed in amphibians, the tympanum if present lying flush with the body surface. Even in reptiles relatively few groups (some lizards, crocodilians) possess an external auditory meatus. In some reptiles a flap, more or less movable at will, closes the external opening of the duct (as in crocodilians); in others (for example, certain lizards) the flap became fused permanently, completely concealing the tympanum; in still others (for example, certain other lizards) the external orifice has become narrowly constricted.

All birds and mammals (Fig. 15.24B, C) possess an external auditory meatus, however, usually elongate. In all mammals and a few birds, a group of *wax (ceruminous) glands* open into the canal, serving presumably to maintain a proper condition for the tympanum.

In mammals a cartilaginous *pinna* is usually present about the external orifice of the auditory canal, serving to catch sound waves that otherwise would not reach the ear. Aquatic and burrowing mammals have lost the pinna, as an adjustment to their peculiar ways of life. On the other hand the hypertrophy of the pinna seen in some mammals is of questionable utility in hearing.

Evolution of the outer ear can thus be regarded as representing three stages, as exemplified by (1) reptiles, with (a) a short meatus in some groups, (b) no ceruminous glands, and (c) no pinna; (2) birds, with (a) a longer meatus regularly present, (b) ceruminous glands in some groups, and (c) no pinna; and (3) mammals, with (a) a still longer meatus regularly present, (b) ceruminous glands regularly present, and (c) a pinna except where degenerate. Mammals of course were not derived from birds but the latter do exemplify a stage in this phase of ear evolution through which mammals probably passed.

Middle Ear. The middle ear consists essentially of three parts: a tympanum, a middle ear cavity, and one to three bones (ear ossicles) connecting the tympanum with the inner ear.

TYMPANUM. The tympanum is a thin but strong membrane on the surface of the body or at the inner end of the external auditory meatus, serving to receive sound vibrations and to transmit them to the middle ear ossicles. It is a double membrane, the outer part representing a very thin area of the skin, the inner wall consisting of endoderm and representing the wall of the second gill pouch. Among tetrapods three variations are noteworthy: (1) the tympanum is subject to sexual dimorphism in size in some anurans, being larger in males than in females; (2) the outer wall of the tympanum is thickened like the rest of the skin, and thus indistinguishable in position, in some anurans and some lizards; and (3) the tympanum as well as the middle ear cavity are absent in all salamanders, caecilians, and snakes, and in some anurans and lizards. Varying degrees of reversion to the original skin condition occur.

MIDDLE EAR CAVITY. The middle ear cavity is a part of the former second gill pouch. The remainder of that pouch is a narrow Eustachian tube—short in amphibians, most reptiles, and birds, relatively long in crocodilians and mammals—connecting the middle ear cavity with the pharyngeal cavity (Figs. 15.24; 15.25). The Eustachian tube is regularly present in vertebrates with a middle ear cavity and is an indispensable accessory maintaining the same pressure in the middle ear cavity as in the surrounding air. Lacking such a device, the tympanum could well be damaged by the pressure differential. The two tubes (right and left) are secondarily united in some anurans and in crocodilians and birds to open into the pharynx by a single aperture.

The middle ear cavity, wider than the Eustachian tube and limited to the area adjacent to the otic capsule, is bordered extensively by the quadrate bone in those amniotes, exclusive of mammals, with a tympanum. As a matter of fact, in these groups most of the border of the tympanum is attached to the edge of the quadrate bone, which thus serves an auditory as well as an articular function. In mammals the tympanum is bordered by an *ectotympanic* bone, formerly the angular of the lower jaw. In amphibians a variety of bones borders the tympanum, and in these the quadrate has no auditory function. Thus three evolutionary stages in bony support of the tympanum may be recognized (amphibians, a series of bones not including the quadrate; sauropsids, the quadrate; mammals, the ectotympanic), and three comparable stages in functional evolution of the quadrate (amphibians, articular but no auditory function; sauropsids, both articular and auditory function; mammals, auditory function only).

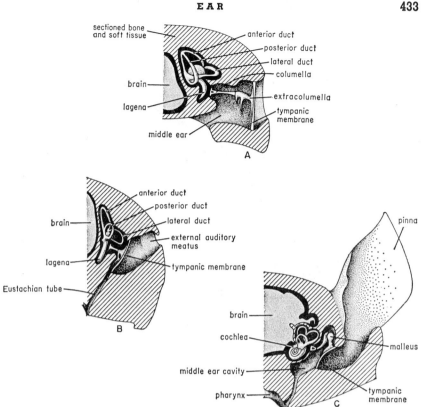

FIG. 15.24 The ear of reptiles (A), birds (B), and mammals (C), as seen in cross section, showing certain aspects of evolution of outer ear. (From Adams and Eddy.)

In all salamanders and caecilians, a few anurans and lizards, and in all snakes, the middle ear cavity has been lost, along with the Eustachian tube and tympanum. The entire middle ear, except for the columella, is thus missing. The cranial musculature intrudes into the area formerly occupied by the middle ear, surrounding the columella. As a result these animals are deaf to airborne sounds, although sound waves carried through the ground or water and thence through the body can be registered by the inner ear. Possibly the inhabitants of water of this group are more sensitive to sound waves than are the terrestrial representatives. Curiously enough, in some salamanders the sound transmission is by way of the arm, shoulder girdle, and a special musculature to the middle ear ossicle and thence to the inner ear; in others transmission occurs by way of the lower jaw to the middle ear ossicle.

MIDDLE EAR OSSICLES. The middle ear ossicles first appeared in amphibians (Fig. 15.25B) with the *columella,* a small bone representing the transformed hyomandibula of their piscine ancestors, in which it served a quite different primary function in jaw suspension (articulation). Three important factors predisposed the hyomandibula to serve an even-

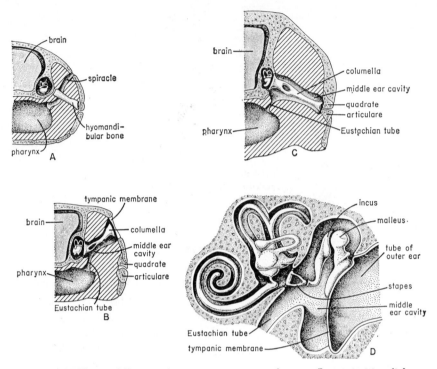

FIG. 15.25 The middle ear of representative vertebrates. A, a primitive fish, showing relation of hyomandibula to spiracular cavity (no middle ear present); B, a primitive amphibian, showing shift of columella into former spiracular cavity, and formation of a tympanum distant from the quadrate; C, a reptile, showing shift of columella to vicinity of quadrate (tympanum just to rear of level of section); D, a mammal, showing shift of former quadrate and articular into middle ear. (From Romer.)

tual auditory function. First, with shift of jaw articulation forward and release of the hyomandibula from any important function, it was conveniently present and available for the purpose of sound conduction in the new aerial medium into which tetrapods emerged. Second, lying in fishes immediately posterior to the second gill pouch (Fig. 15.25A), the hyomandibular needed but little shift to come to lie within that pouch and to spread upon the surface of the skin in order to transmit vibrations efficiently to the inner ear. Third, in fishes it already possessed an attachment to the otic capsule. In fact, it is highly probable that in fishes themselves the hyomandibula developed some auditory function and that loss of the articular need simply released it for adaptation solely to auditory needs.

Stapedial Evolution. The stapes has evolved through some three prominent stages in tetrapod history. In the earliest (amphibian) stage, a small, oval or round part of the otic capsule is separated from the rest as the *operculum* and is fused onto the *columella* (forerunner of the *stapes*). The aperture into which the operculum fits is the *fenestra ovalis.* Thus vibrations carried by the columella can be transmitted with little loss of energy to the fluid of the inner ear. Actually the operculum, as an element embryonically derived from the otic capsule, is evident only in salamanders; in other vertebrates the part of the stapes or columella fitting into the fenestra ovalis is not distinguishable embryonically from the rest of the bone, and thus the presence of a strict homolog of the operculum is questioned. There is no direct phylogenetic evidence, of course, but as the phylogenetic origins of minor structures are often masked by embryonic alterations, it may be regarded as quite possible that the stapes-columella of all tetrapods includes a homolog of the capsular wall.

In the second (sauropsidan) stage of stapedial evolution, a cartilaginous distal tip (*extracolumella,* apparently a fragment from the end of the hyoid arch) of the columella spreads fingerlike in different directions upon the inner surface of the tympanum, perhaps as a more delicate receptor of lesser vibrations than a direct membrane-bone articulation might be (Fig. 15.26). Processes of the extracolumella also reach the quadrate bone.

In the final (mammalian) stage (Fig. 16.25D), the extracolumella is either fused with the bony part, now called the stapes, or lost; and for the first time the columella or its derivative is not in contact with the tympanum (when present), but instead the articulation is retained with the quadrate which now is in the form of another ear ossicle, the incus.

Whether other middle ear accessories are present or not, the stapes-columella persists throughout all tetrapods, be they deaf or of acute hearing.

Incus. The other middle ear ossicles are restricted to mammals. The *incus* (Fig. 15.25D) represents the quadrate which because of release from articular function, coincident with shift forward of the jaw articulation, is free for adaptation solely to auditory needs. As previously described, the quadrate already played an auditory role, even though minor, in sauropsids. The columella lies, in sauropsidans, in close association or contact with the quadrate; thus, not surprisingly, the incus, as the mammalian representative of the quadrate, remains articulated with the stapes as the middle bone of the ossicle series.

Malleus. The outer bone of the middle ear ossicles is the *malleus* (Fig. 15.25D), representing the articular and prearticular (fused) of non-mammalian vertebrates. This is the only bone of the ossicle series not

FIG. 15.26 The parts of the columella in a bird. (From Adams and Eddy.)

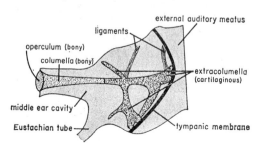

known to have had a long history of auditory function to an important degree before it became exclusively of auditory function. As it is, seemingly the only cause for dragging the articular and prearticular into the auditory act was the fact of their close association with the quadrate and the origin of two (quadrate, articular) from the same embryonic source (mandibular arch). Some auditory function of the articular and prearticular must be assumed to have existed in all tetrapods possessing these bones, simply because they were in contact with the quadrate, which in turn was in contact with the columella. In the relatively brief period of evolution of the two outer ear ossicles in premammalian reptiles, the articular and prearticular presumably did, of course, shift gradually and rapidly from an articular to an auditory function. The structure of certain fossils representing this intermediate period bears out this supposition.

Piscine Analogs of Tetrapod Middle Ear Ossicles. A piscine analog of the middle ear involves a series of *Weberian ossicles* of totally different origin (as vertebral derivatives) from the middle ear ossicles, connecting the swim bladder with the inner ear. The system is of value as an aid in registering pressure as well as sound waves.

Inner Ear. The complex parts of the inner ear may be considered as comprising three groups: (a) the skeletal labyrinth, (b) the membranous labyrinth, and (c) the perilymphatic structures.

SKELETAL LABYRINTH. A capsule of bone or cartilage, or both, the *otic capsule* is a hollow structure whose inner contours closely reproduce those of the membranous structures of the ear. When ossified, it consists chiefly of the prootic and, less importantly, the opisthotic bones, respectively the petrous and mastoid bones of mammals.

As a primary stage in evolution, the skeletal labyrinth forms a completely imperforate covering of the inner ear in fishes, except for openings for nerves and for membranous protrusions of little evolutionary significance. As a second stage, in amphibians the wall is perforated by an opening of great significance, the *fenestra ovalis,* through which sound waves reach the membranous labyrinth. Sound waves entering the labyrinth must be permitted an easy way out, else they would tend to confound themselves and become a meaningless jumble. This release is effected by the provision of a simple device of a second opening in the capsular wall. Pressure waves received at the fenestra ovalis are released at the second opening. Modern amphibians use a perforation of the otic capsule into the brain cavity as a release for sound pressure waves, but this was fortunately not the device adopted by reptiles and their derivatives or, presumably, remote amphibian ancestors. In these, representing a third stage, the second opening, the *fenestra rotunda,* perforates the capsular wall and opens into the middle ear cavity. Vibrations received via the fenestra ovalis are thus emitted via the fenestra rotunda. The outgoing vibrations do not interfere with the incoming ones because of the ingenious device of having different pathways: the incoming vibrations are carried exclusively by the middle ear *ossicles* and thus are immune to the outgoing vibrations released into the *air* of the middle ear cavity.

MEMBRANOUS LABYRINTH. The actual receptors of the ear are all concentrated within the membranous labyrinth, a fluid-filled sac whose walls possess at specific locations clumps of sensory cells, *cristae* and *maculae,* located at the ends of the branches of the auditory nerve. The entire labyrinth is filled with a fluid called *endolymph.* In most vertebrates this is a rather viscous fluid apparently produced by the cells of the labyrinth wall, but in elasmobranchs the labyrinth is connected with the exterior and is filled with sea water. The major divisions of the primitive membranous labyrinth include (a) the *utriculus,* a central baglike structure to which are attached (b) one or more *semicircular canals* and (c) another baglike structure, the *sacculus* (Figs. 15.27, 15.28). These particular parts constitute the *vestibule,* which excludes only the auditory part of the sacculus that evolved in endotherms—the cochlea.

Utriculus. The utriculus, not evident in the hagfish as a recognizably separate part, is divided into two quite separate lobes in elasmobranchs, but is typically single in vertebrates. It typically contains a single sensory *utricular macula* registering position, but in fishes and amphibians it possesses also a single or paired *macula neglecta* (on the sacculus in amphibians) apparently of transitory auditory function. The utriculus usually lies dorsal to the sacculus with which it is broadly in contact except in mammals, in which only a narrow connection exists (Fig. 15.28).

Semicircular Canals. The semicircular canals are three in number in all gnathostomes and are so arranged as to permit movement of the fluid in response to any movement of the body. There is thus a horizontal

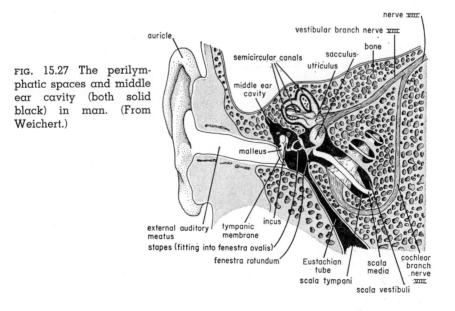

FIG. 15.27 The perilymphatic spaces and middle ear cavity (both solid black) in man. (From Weichert.)

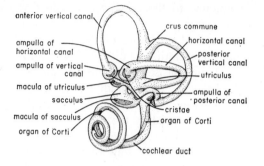

anterior vertical canal

crus commune

ampulla of horizontal canal

horizontal canal

ampulla of vertical canal

posterior vertical canal

macula of utriculus

utriculus

sacculus

ampulla of posterior canal

macula of sacculus

cristae

organ of Corti

organ of Corti

cochlear duct

FIG. 15.28 The membranous labyrinth of a guinea pig, showing sensory areas. (From Romer.)

canal, an oblique posterior vertical, and an oblique anterior vertical canal. Each canal possesses at one end a small vesicular enlargement, an *ampulla,* in which is located a *crista* containing sensory cells (Fig. 15.28). All cristae are restricted in occurrence to the ampullae. Like the maculae, the cristae are composed of columnar cells whose free surfaces are provided with minute projections any movement of which generates a nervous impulse (Fig. 15.31A). Movement of the body, unless it is very slow, results in movement of the sensory projections of the cristae because the endolymphatic fluid of the cavity into which they project tends to be somewhat delayed by inertia following bodily movement.

Relatively little evolutionary change is evident in the semicircular canals in gnathostomes. They are in a rudimentary (some think vestigial) state in cyclostomes, however, as the horizontal canal is absent and the vertical canals are incompletely differentiated, especially in the hagfish (Fig. 15.29). The simple state of the inner ear of the hagfish bears an obvious similarity to the simple invagination of a neuromast organ.

Sacculus. The sacculus is invariably unpaired and is presumably the most primitive part of the ear. It is connected embryonically with the ex-

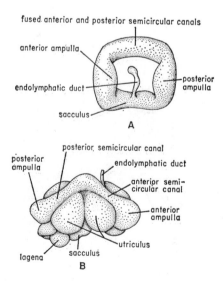

fused anterior and posterior semicircular canals

anterior ampulla

posterior ampulla

endolymphatic duct

sacculus

A

posterior ampulla

posterior semicircular canal

endolymphatic duct

anterior semicircular canal

anterior ampulla

utriculus

lagena

sacculus

B

FIG. 15.29 Membranous labyrinths of cyclostomes. A, hagfish; B, lamprey. (From Weichert.)

terior by way of an *endolymphatic duct* and *invagination canal*. The
latter closes in the adult except in elasmobranchs. An *endolymphatic sac*
occurs primitively as an outpouching along the length of the common endolymphatic and invagination ducts, marking the point of distinction between them. The outpouching characteristically becomes very elongate,
much longer than the invagination canal, forming a long tube terminating
blindly in the endolymphatic sac (Fig. 15.30B). The latter tube, the *secondary endolymphatic duct,* is primitively indistinguishable from the
primary endolymphatic duct in adults, in which the invagination canal
disappears. In higher vertebrates the "true" endolymphatic duct is absent,
and thus the invagination canal and secondary endolymphatic duct are attached separately to the sacculus.

Lagena. A second major adjunct of the sacculus is the lagena, of
major importance since it becomes the fundamental component of the
cochlea in later vertebrates. In gnathostome fishes this is a shallow,
rounded pit in the rear floor of the sacculus. It is provided with a (1) *lagenar macula* persistent throughout vertebrates except in viviparous mammals, and a (2) *basilar macula* or homolog thereof, in all tetrapods. The
lagenar macula, like the single *saccular macula* and the *utricular macula,*
apparently registers static position only. All of these maculae perform this
function through the tactile effect of relatively heavy structures in the form

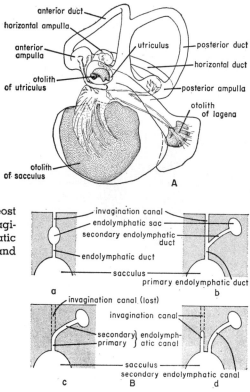

FIG. 15.30 Otoliths (A) in a teleost
fish, and evolution (B) of the invagination canal and endolymphatic
duct. (In part from Adams and
Eddy.)

of one or more solid *otoliths,* or finely particulate *otoconia* or *otarena.* These impinge upon the hairlike projections of the sensory cells composing the maculae. Differences in direction of pressure resulting from differences in body position relative to the direction of gravitational pull push the macular sensory processes in different directions and thus reveal the position of the body. Otarena, fine particles of sand, occur only in elasmobranchs, with an opening of the sacculus to the exterior persisting in adults. Otoconia, present in all vertebrates lacking otarena or otoliths, are crystals of calcium carbonate, not dispersed generally over the labyrinth walls or in the endolymph, but held in a gelatinous material covering the maculae (Fig. 15.31B). In most bony fishes the calcium carbonate, instead of being present in tiny crystals, is fused to form one or more solid masses, the otoliths (Fig. 15.30A), varying in shape according to species. Separate otoliths may occur in each macular area (utriculus, sacculus, lagena), or only one may be distinct, the others represented by otoconia. The saccular otolith is of most regular occurrence. Otoliths seem to have been primitive in tetrapods, being present in amphibians and fossil reptiles. Few modern reptiles possess them, and no birds or mammals. In primitive aquatic vertebrates, the otoliths were so well developed it appears possible they may have been the most efficient of the three weight devices of the maculae in determination of position in a medium otherwise defying orientation. Reduction of the otoliths to otoconia is perhaps to be regarded as another adaptation to terrestrial life, in which orientation was simplified by tactile senses and ready vision. If position perception in man is a reliable exam-

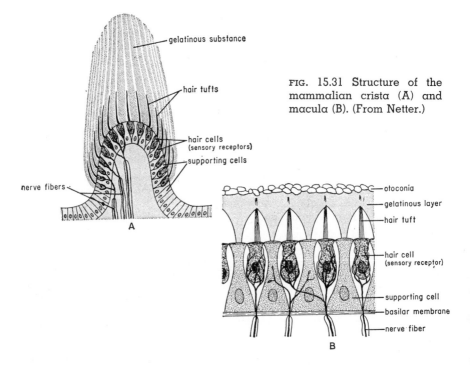

FIG. 15.31 Structure of the mammalian crista (A) and macula (B). (From Netter.)

ple of amniote perception, the otic role in this function must indeed have
degenerated markedly, for man deprived of sight and other extraneous
means of position determination cannot reliably judge position.

Basilar Macula. The basilar macula may have had some auditory
function in amphibians, supplementing the macula neglecta, but its auditory role must have been slight. In reptiles, however, it took over the entire auditory function (Fig. 15.32A) and in the crocodilians (Fig. 15.32B)
it became very elongate (*organ of Corti*) although straight, as is the lagena
(now termed the *cochlear duct* or *scala media*) which houses it. Birds retained a crocodilian form of both structures. In mammals the cochlear duct
became so tremendously elongate that it is coiled, as many as five complete
turns occurring (Fig. 15.32C). The organ of Corti likewise became elongate, extending the full length of the cochlear duct. Its elongation permitted specialization of certain parts to register certain tones, the lower
notes being detected at one end (at the blind tip of the cochlear duct), the
higher notes at the opposite end. Sound perception clearly was far more
crude in primitive vertebrates than in those with an organ of Corti.

PERILYMPHATIC SPACE. The membranous labyrinth is not directly in
contact with the skeletal labyrinth. The two are separated from each other
by a *perilymphatic space* filled with lymph (specifically termed *perilymph,*
but actually continuous with the fluid of other lymphatic spaces). A blind
evagination of the perilymphatic space, often terminating at a saclike enlargement, the *perilymphatic sac,* pierces the capsular wall in many vertebrates but does not open to the exterior. In elasmobranchs it extends
dorsad, piercing the skull near the invagination duct of the membranous
labyrinth. In primitive amphibians it opens into the brain case, and in more
advanced amphibians and amniotes it terminates at the fenestra rotunda.

In fishes the perilymphatic space serves little function other than protection for the membranous labyrinth, cushioning it in the bony labyrinth.

In all tetrapods the perilymphatic space serves the function of transmitting sound vibrations, since the stapes impinges not upon the membranous labyrinth but upon the perilymphatic walls, consisting of the
periosteum or perichondrium. The sound vibrations are directed through an
expanded, channellike perilymphatic area that curves about the auditory
macula (basilar macula or, in modern amphibians, the macula neglecta)
on its way to the compensatory perforation in the capsular wall. Retention
of this relationship of *perilymphatic duct* and macula leads, in crocodilians
and birds, to the formation by the duct of a loop about the cochlear duct.
An afferent part of the loop (*vestibular duct* or *scala vestibuli*) leads from
near the fenestra ovalis to the tip of the cochlea, and an efferent part
(*tympanic duct* or *scala tympani*) lies against the organ of Corti as it returns from the tip of the cochlear duct to the fenestra rotunda. Precisely
the same relationships are retained in mammals (Fig. 15.33), the sole
gross difference being the development of a coiled instead of a straight
cochlear structure.

The *cochlea* thus consists of three ducts, or scalae, only one of which,

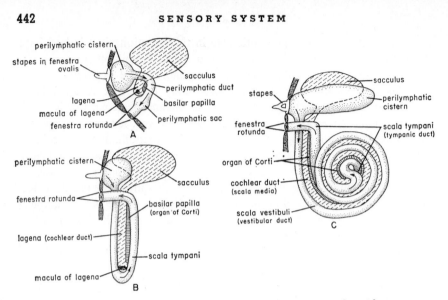

FIG. 15.32 Evolution of the organ of Corti. A, primitive reptile with an unmodified basilar papilla; B, stage represented by modern crocodilians
and birds, with an elongate basilar papilla (or rudimentary organ of
Corti); C, mammalian stage, with a fully developed organ of Corti. (From
Romer.)

the medial cochlear duct, is a part of the membranous labyrinth. Sound
vibrations received at the fenestra ovalis from the stapes, in traveling the
longest possible route, are conducted directly into the vestibular duct,
thence into the tympanic duct where sensory impulses are induced in the
bordering organ of Corti, and finally to the middle ear cavity through the
fenestra rotunda, closed by the membranous end of the tympanic duct.
Actually the sound waves do not travel this "long" route, but permeate the
entire cochlea at once.

    RECAPITULATION. In review of the mammalian evolution of the inner
ear, five stages seem conspicuous. In the *initial* stage there are but one or

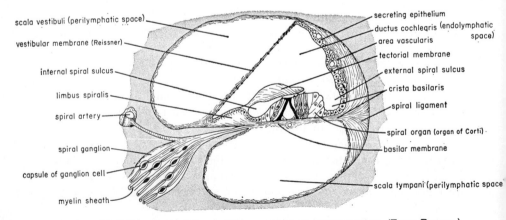

FIG. 15.33 Structure of the cochlea, as seen in cross section. (From Romer.)

two semicircular canals and a poorly differentiated sacculus. In the second, *piscine* stage the third semicircular canal, two utriculi (still broadly attached to the sacculus from which they evolved), conspicuous ampullae, and a lagena are important additions. In the third, *amphibian* stage a perilymphatic duct, fenestra ovalis, fenestra rotunda, basilar macula, and a series of essential accessories of the middle ear (middle ear cavity, Eustachian tube, middle ear ossicle) are added. *Crocodilians* and *birds* represent the fourth stage, in which the cochlear duct (from the lagena), perilymphatic ducts (now split into tympanic and vestibular ducts), and organ of Corti (from the basilar macula) are evolved. Finally, in the *mammalian* stage, a spiral cochlea, a near-complete separation of functional components (utriculus and semicircular canals, movement; sacculus, position; cochlear duct, hearing), and two middle ear accessories (malleus, incus) are innovated.

QUESTIONS

1. Name, characterize, and give examples of the four morphological grades of sense organs. Differentiate and give examples of evolutionary levels of sensory cells and of sense organs.

2. Name and differentiate the subdivisions of the sensory system, stating which morphological types of sense organs occur in each.

3. Name and give examples of the functional types of sense organs, from the standpoint of nature of stimulus and from that of location.

4. Name the evolutionary derivatives of the neuromast system.

5. Describe the function of the lateral line system.

6. What unique function does the lateral line system possess in lampreys?

7. Name the thermoreceptors of vertebrates and describe their possible phylogeny.

8. How do taste and olfaction differ (four ways)? Explain.

9. Characterize four stages in evolution of the taste buds and state the occurrence of each. What is the unique feature of caecilians with respect to taste?

10. Briefly describe the origin, evolution, and functional role of Jacobson's organ.

11. Characterize the five levels of olfactory evolution in vertebrates, and state of which vertebrate group each stage is characteristic.

12. Name the three unpaired organs of presumed visual function in ancient vertebrates and describe their origin. What is their function in embryonic and adult mammals? Describe the hypothetical four stages in functional evolution of the pineal organ.

13. Diagram and label a cross section of the vertebrate eye.

14. Account for the peculiar position of the vertebrate visual sensory cells on the basis of embryogeny and phylogeny.

15. Distinguish rods and cones five ways.

16. What is the adaptive significance of variation in relative proportion of rods and cones in different vertebrates?

17. What is the anatomical basis for the difference between nocturnal and diurnal animals in visual acuity for color? Explain.

18. Accommodation is effected in vertebrates by manipulation of what two structures? Describe the variation that exists among vertebrates in relative importance of these two structures in accommodation, and specify which groups exemplify each condition.

19. By what four mechanisms does the lens effect accommodation? State the groups characterized by and the survival value of each mechanism.

20. Exactly how are the lens and cornea made to produce parallel accommodatory effects in (a) reptiles and (b) mammals?

21. What sort of accommodation generally exists in vertebrates with scleroid bones, and why? Explain how birds constitute an exception to this generality. What are other supposed functions of scleroid bones?

22. Trace the evolution of the vitreous intrusions in vertebrates. What functions do they serve?

23. Name four diel adaptions of the eye.

24. Describe the four adaptive situations evident among vertebrates with reference to variability of the pupil.

25. What is the value of the tapetum?

26. In what way and in what animals has color of the aqueous humor been altered to increase visual acuity?

27. Name three extrinsic adjustments of the eye that have undergone evolutionary change in vertebrates.

28. State and explain the five successive stages in perfection of visual bathymetry in vertebrates.

29. Contrast the mechanisms of stereopsis in mammals and nonmammals.

30. What were the two results of partial decussation in mammals and the survival value of each?

31. Name the four types of vertebrate eye coverings and distinguish them.

32. Characterize the four stages in the main course of evolution of eyelids in vertebrates. Specify the groups exemplifying each stage and explain the functional significance of each shift from one stage to another.

33. Name and locate the orbital glands and briefly review their evolution. With what eyelids is each associated? How is the unique arrangement of eyelids in mammals reflected in development of the orbital glands? How is this different from the condition in other tetrapods?

34. Name the three major anatomical divisions of the ear and briefly summarize their evolution. What are the functions of each division?

35. Characterize the stages in evolution of the outer ear.

36. In what manner is transmission of sound waves to the inner ear different in snakes and salamanders from most other tetrapods?

37. Describe the structure of the tympanum and three of its variations.

38. What is the value of the Eustachian tube?

39. Name the mammalian ear ossicles in their proper order from the inner to the outer ends of the series, and give the identity and function of each in earlier stages of evolution in vertebrates.

40. What analogs of the tetrapod middle ear ossicles occur in fishes? How do they differ in origin, position, and function?

41. How do the cristae and maculae differ in function and location?

42. How does the endolymph of elasmobranchs differ from that of other vertebrates?

43. How does the utriculus differ in various vertebrates in occurrence, in function, in extent of subdivision, and in size of connection with the sacculus?

44. Describe the position, arrangement, and manner of function of the semicircular canals.

45. How do the semicircular canals of gnathostomes and cyclostomes differ?

46. Name, distinguish, and state the occurrence of the various kinds of solids aiding in stimulating the maculae registering position.

47. Trace the evolutionary history of the lagena; of the basilar macula.

48. Trace a set of sound vibrations by the longest possible route from the tympanum to the pharynx in a mammal, naming the structures or cavities through which they pass; name the ducts comprising the cochlea and the fluid contained in each; sketch their position as seen in cross section; name and describe the location of the organ of sound perception.

49. How does the cochlea of sauropsidans differ from that of mammals?

50. Describe the five stages of evolution of the mammalian inner ear.

51. Define the following words and where appropriate state an example or give the occurrence:

accommodation (lenticular and corneal)
acusticolateralis system
ampulla
ampulla of Lorenzini
anterior chamber
aqueous humor
area centralis
area temporalis
auditory
basilar macula
bathyopsis
binocular fixation (conjugate and independent)
binocular-field vision
binocular vision
blind spot
brille
Brucke's muscle
chemoreceptor
choroid coat and fissure
choroidea
ciliary body and muscle
cochlea
cochlear duct
conchae
cones
conjunctiva
cornea (primary, secondary, tertiary)

Corti (organ of)
Crampton's muscle
crista
decussation
diel
discrimination
diurnal
ear (middle, inner, outer)
endolymph
endolymphatic duct (primary, secondary)
epiphysis
external naris
extrinsic lenticular accommodation
exteroceptors
extracolumella
extrasensory perception
facial pit
falciform process
fenestra ovalis
fenestra rotunda
fixation (conjugate, independent)
fovea
frontality
general sense organ
gustatory
gustatory tentacle

gyroscopic compensation
Harderian glands
homeostasis
incus
internal naris
interoceptor
intrinsic lenticular accommodation
invagination canal
iris
Jacobson's organ
Krause corpuscle
labial pit
labyrinth (skeletal, membranous)
lacrimae
lacrimal duct
lacrimal glands
lagena
lagenar macula
lateral line system
macula neglecta
maculae
malleus
meatus (external auditory)
mechanoreceptor
Meissner corpuscle
Merkel corpuscle
monocular-field vision
monocular vision

nasal organ
nasolacrimal duct
neuroreceptor
neuromast
nictitating eyelid
olfaction
olfactory organ
operculum
optic vesicle
orbital glands
otarena
otic nerve
otic organ
otoconia
otolith
nocturnal
Pacini corpuscle
papillary cone
paraphysis
parapsychology
parietal organ
partial decussation

pecten
perilymph
perilymphatic (duct, sac, space)
pineal organ
pinna
pit organs
posterior chamber
primary sense organ
proprioceptor
psi phenomena
psychokinesis
pupil
radioreceptor
receptor cells (3 types)
retina
rods
saccular macula
sacculus
scala media
scala tympani
scala vestibuli

sclera
scleroid bones
secondary sense organ
semicircular canals and ampullae
sense organ (4 morphotypes)
sensory cell
sensory nerve cell
smell
somatic sensory (general and special)
special sense organ (primitive, advanced)
spectacle (palpebral, primary, secondary, tertiary, true)
stapes
stereopsis (half- and full-field)
suspensory ligament

16

NERVOUS SYSTEM

THE NERVOUS SYSTEM is anatomically the most complex system of the body. It would require a volume to treat it relatively as well as we have other systems, even granting that the coverage of the other systems has been superficial. That this should be true may be understood by reflection upon the necessity of maintaining a connection of every voluntary muscle fiber and every sensory cell with the central nervous system; of integrating all sensory impulses with all possible effectors, including glands as well as muscles; and of maintaining to a greater or lesser degree an ability to select the response to an infinite number of sets of stimuli. Thus for the present our chief objective is narrowed primarily to an understanding of basic construction; only a few of the most conspicuous evolutionary trends are to be discussed.

Components of the Nervous System

Cellular Components. Two types of cells are included in the nervous system: the neural "connective" tissue, or *neuroglial* cells, wholly supportive in function and not conductive, and the wholly conductive cells, or *neurons*.

NEUROGLIA. The only type of neuroglial cells commonly observed is the neurilemma cells sheathing certain nerve fibers. Some four other types of neuroglia, chiefly asteroid in form, occur abundantly elsewhere in the nervous system (Fig. 16.1). One type is mesodermal in origin, all the others neurectodermal.

NEURONS. Virtually all of the nervous system consists of uniquely designed neurons, which are characterized by having a large *cell body* housing the nucleus and other vital inclusions (Fig. 16.2), and two or more *fibers* projecting from the cell body and serving to conduct impulses to (*afferent*) or from (*efferent*) the cell body. The fibers are equivalent to excessively slender pseudopods containing cytoplasm within an outer cell membrane. The main trunk, if any, of any fiber is the *axis cylinder*.

Many afferent fibers (*dendrites*) may be attached to a cell body, thus coming in from various directions, or there may be but one; there is always but one efferent fiber (*axon*), however. The two types of fibers differ also in number of branches, angle of branching, length, and sheathing. Dendrites usually have many branches, all or most connected at an angle like branches on a bush or tree; axons have very few branches, and those emerge more or less at right angles to the main axis. If there is any significant difference in length, the axon is usually the longer, except in some

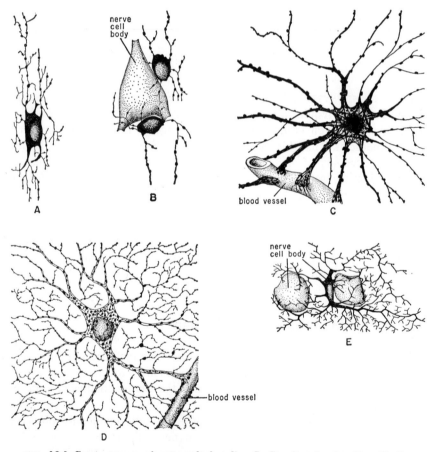

FIG. 16.1 Some types of neuroglial cells. A, B, oligodendroglia; C, D, astrocytes (fibrous and nonfibrous, respectively); E, microglia. (From Bailey.)

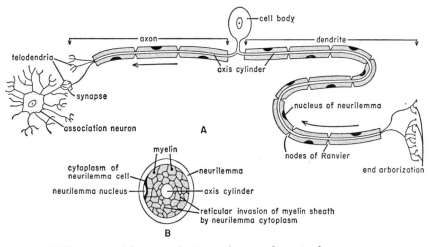

FIG. 16.2 Diagram of the gross features of a unipolar spinal sensory neuron. A, entire neuron; B, cross section of axon.

sensory neurons. Dendrites of sensory neurons are sheathed (Fig. 16.2), others generally (or virtually) bare (Fig. 16.3); axons of most sensory and motor neurons are sheathed.

The sheaths are of two sorts: a nonliving *myelin* or *medullary* sheath secreted by neuroglial cells, and a *neurilemma* or *sheath of Schwann* composed of separate, nonconductive, supporting cells and the sheath secreted by them. The myelin sheath is innermost, if both are present, and is composed of a fatty substance which, in quantity, appears white, thus giving rise to the term "white matter" used in reference to the parts of the nervous system that consist chiefly of myelinated fibers. The thickness and continuity of the myelin sheath varies greatly in different parts of the nervous system. The neurilemma sheath consists of a series of cells, each encircling the fiber; adjacent cells meet at the site of constrictions through the myelin sheath, reaching the axis cylinder. The constrictions are *nodes of Ranvier*.

Both the myelin and neurilemma sheaths are typically present on dendrites of the sensory neurons (fibers from free nerve endings sensitive to pain, heat, and cold are unmyelinated) and on all axons of the neurons of the peripheral nervous system. No other dendrites are sheathed. The medullary sheath only is present on axons within the white matter of the central nervous system, the neurilemma only on some autonomic axons, and no sheaths whatsoever on the fibers in the gray matter of the central nervous system and on some autonomic axons. The cell bodies are not sheathed except for those in the cranial and spinal ganglia, where *satellite cells* (specialized parts of the neurilemma sheath) form a capsule about the neuron cell body.

The critical distinction between axons and dendrites is the direction of conduction of impulses under normal conditions. Curiously enough the orientation is not intrinsic: if experimentally an axon or dendrite is stimulated anywhere along its length, an impulse travels in *both* directions from that point. Orientation is effected at the *synapse,* the minute hiatus between successive neurons in any nervous pathway. The stimulus can jump the gap only from the axon to the dendrite; even under experimental conditions the gap cannot be bridged from the opposite direction with normal impulses.

Neurons vary greatly in shape and can be recognized rather readily with respect to function and location simply by their gross appearance. Some types are shown in Fig. 16.4.

Gross Components. The nervous system consists of (1) a central nervous system, (2) a peripheral nervous system, and (3) an autonomic nervous system.

CENTRAL NERVOUS SYSTEM. The central nervous system consists of the brain and spinal cord. It typically forms in early embryonic development (Fig. 16.5) from two neural ridges that sweep medially from the two sides of the dorsal surface of the embryo. The ridge crests lean progressively farther mediad as the two ridges roll toward the midline, like the crests of waves approaching a beach. The two approaching ridges fuse to form a tube entirely composed of ectoderm, concealed below the median dorsal surface. A cavity (*neurocele*) extends the length of the tube and

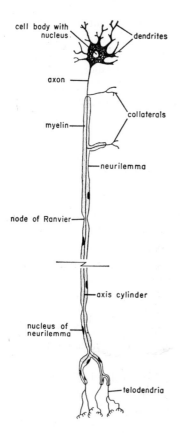

cell body with nucleus

dendrites

axon

collaterals

myelin

neurilemma

node of Ranvier

axis cylinder

nucleus of neurilemma

telodendria

FIG. 16.3 Diagram of a peripheral motor neuron. Compare with Fig. 16.2, noting absence of an elongate, myelinated dendrite. If the axon were shown with its full length in proportion to the size of the cell body, it would be as much as 750 times as long as here indicated (some 250 feet). (From Maximow and Bloom.)

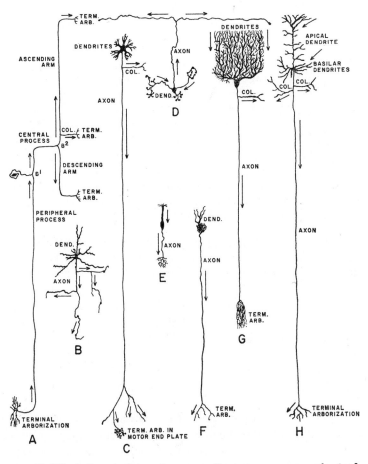

FIG. 16.4 Variations in form of neurons. A, sensory neuron, of spinal cord; B, association neuron of cerebral cortex; C, motor neuron of spinal cord; D, association neuron of cerebellum; E, olfactory sensory neuron; F, sympathetic postganglionic motor neuron; G, association neuron of cerebral cortex; H, association neuron of afferent function extending from cerebral cortex to motor level of spinal cord. (From Bailey.)

persists in all vertebrates. In the brain the neurocele is enlarged in some lobes as *ventricles,* elsewhere it is narrow; in the spinal cord it persists as a tiny central duct called the *canalis centralis.*

In the cephalochordates the neurocele of the spinal cord is a narrow vertical slit with an extremely thin dorsal wall. This is a primitive condition; in all vertebrates the neurocele is more nearly circular in cross section.

The brain or *encephalon* is wider than the spinal cord even embryonically. In vertebrates it possesses three embryonic, primordial divisions, in order from front to rear the *prosencephalon, mesencephalon,* and *rhombencephalon* (Fig. 16.7). These are associated with, respectively, the olfactory, optic, and otic sense organs, integrating bodily activity with the

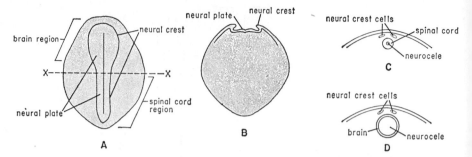

FIG. 16.5 Early stages of formation of central nervous system in amphibian embryos. A, dorsal view; B, cross section at level of line X in A; C, cross section of dorsal wall of embryo after closure of neural tube, in region of spinal cord; D, same as C except in region of brain.

information supplied by these organs. The fact that the most complex integrating sector of the brain in the "brainiest" of all animals (mammals) is a part of a division formerly of olfactory function only is perhaps of some significance.

By the end of the embryonic period (Fig. 16.6) the prosencephalon subdivides into two parts, the anterior *telencephalon* (identified by the *cerebral hemispheres*) and the low, dorsally thin-walled *diencephalon*. The mesencephalon (identified by the *optic lobes*) possesses no comparable division, but the rhombencephalon subdivides into an anterior *metencephalon* (with its dorsal *cerebellum*) and posterior *myelencephalon* (the *medulla oblongata*).

PERIPHERAL NERVOUS SYSTEM. The neurons attached to any *voluntary* (that is, subject to direct control at will) effector organ and those attached to all sense organs are collectively referred to as the *peripheral nervous system*. The name refers to the fact that all such neurons connect the central nervous system with other parts of the body or vice versa. Many nerves carry only peripheral fibers, but a large number of others also carry autonomic fibers.

AUTONOMIC NERVOUS SYSTEM. The autonomic nervous system consists of those neurons extending from the central nervous system to any in-

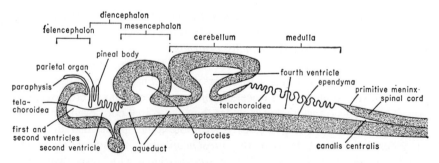

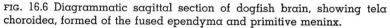

FIG. 16.6 Diagrammatic sagittal section of dogfish brain, showing tela choroidea, formed of the fused ependyma and primitive meninx.

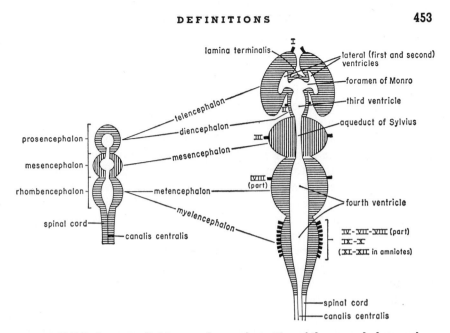

FIG. 16.7 Embryonic divisions and neural cavities of the encephalon, and the derived divisions and chambers of adults. Attachments of nerves to brain divisions shown in solid black, and indicated by Roman numerals I–XII.

voluntary effector. Only motor fibers, it is important to note, are involved in this system.

Definitions

A few basic terms require early definition.

WHITE MATTER. Those portions of the nervous system composed chiefly or wholly of medullated fibers comprise the white matter.

GRAY MATTER. Those portions of the nervous system composed chiefly or wholly of nonmedullated neurons, or parts thereof, constitute the gray matter.

GANGLION. The cell bodies of neurons are not haphazardly distributed. They occur in clumps. The clumps occurring outside the central nervous system are regarded as *ganglia*.

NUCLEUS. The clumps of cell bodies occurring within the central nervous system are regarded as *nuclei*.

NERVE. Nerve fibers, like cell bodies, are not haphazardly distributed. They are grouped into long strands or cords. Cords outside the central nervous system are *nerves*.

TRACT. Cords of nerve fibers in the central nervous system are *tracts*.

COMMISSURE. Tracts extending transversely in the central nervous system rather than directly longitudinally are called *commissures*. A *chiasma* is a crossing of tracts passing from one side to the other, connecting different levels. Those fibers within the chiasmatic tracts that actually cross from one side to the other are said to *decussate*.

Reflex Arc. The reflex arc is the basic functional unit of the nervous system, connecting cause with effect—the sense organ with the effector. It consists of (a) a single *sensory neuron,* never more; (b) a single *motor neuron,* never more, except in the autonomic nervous system, with two; and (c) usually one or more (usually more) *association neurons* connecting the sensory and motor neurons (Fig. 16.8). The arc may be limited to the level of the central nervous system at which the stimuli are received and the adjustment takes place, or it may extend to the brain and thence to some other part of the central nervous system. Instincts may be regarded as complex reflex patterns.

The transition between cogitation (often taken as a unique human trait) and reflex action—between thoughtful response and instinct—appears to be as gradual and imperceptible as any anatomical transition in the history of the vertebrate body. The number of association neurons involved in thoughtful and instinctive responses may be regarded as usually greater than in the simple reflex arc. In turn the association neurons involved with thoughtful responses presumably tend to be more numerous than those concerned with instinct, but surely are often fewer. The most useful functional distinction involves the extent of fixation of the nervous pathway. Instincts and reflexes are channelized: the exact association neurons and ultimate motor neurons the nervous impulses will pass along are fixed; the synapses of that pathway offer so much less resistance than others that the impulses cannot travel elsewhere. To be sure, thoughtful responses can, by repeated occurrence, establish pathways into which impulses are channelized in a near-instinctive (reflexive) manner. The basic distinction between true instincts and set patterns of thoughtful responses is that one (the former) is inheritable, the other not.

An evolutionary trend exists in vertebrates, and in other animal groups

FIG. 16.8 Simple reflex arcs. A, a two-neuron reflex arc; B, a 3-neuron reflex arc. (From Bailey.)

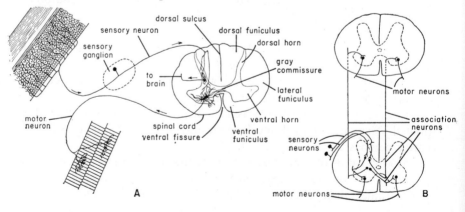

as well, toward increase in the number of association neurons involved in responding to an increasing number of environmental situations. Behavior has become more complex. It was primitively largely stereotyped and so remains in primitive living forms, but an evolutionary trend seems to exist for it to have a progressively greater degree of latitude of expression, reaching a peak of latitude in man. Even in man, however, behavior is strictly limited by inherited capacity and experience; the range of actual choice, given a certain genetic makeup and experience, is nil. All animals are thus limited; man's distinctiveness from other animals lies not in possession of any unique freedom of choice but simply in an ability to store more experience (both direct and vicarious) and thus to correlate complexly.

Freedom of choice of action in any given situation, at any plane of intellectuality, and in any organism, in reality does not exist. Worry or debate over ultimate action gives an erroneous illusion of exercise of choice. Improvement of appropriateness of action can come, obviously, only from either (a) an increase in amount of experience (which means, for man, education in the experience of others as well as by direct experience), or (b) betterment of genetic makeup. Genetic improvement is at best a very slow process, is available only for phylogenetic (racial) but not for ontogenetic (individual) improvement, and is impractical for exercise at present upon man. Improvement of man's place in nature must necessarily come from an increase in the amount of experience—the education —back of each individual.

Conductive Functions of Neurons

Neurons are regarded as either sensory, motor, or association. Sensory neurons, or fibers, are those carrying impulses from sense organs to a nucleus of association in the central nervous system; motor neurons, or fibers, extend from a nucleus or ganglion into the peripheral or autonomic nerves. Sensory neurons are, therefore, *afferent;* motor neurons, *efferent.*

Visceral and somatic divisions are recognized in each of the motor and sensory divisions. Visceral fibers are those associated with structures derived from the endoderm, mesomere, hypomere, and dermatome; these are parts involved originally (not exclusively) in adjustment to the internal environment—the intrinsic body conditions (Fig. 16.9). Somatic fibers are associated with structures derived from the ectoderm, sclerotome, and myotome; these are parts involved in adjustment to the external environment.

General and special divisions are recognized for most of the visceral and somatic components. The general visceral sensory fibers are those of general distribution associated with the organs innervated by the autonomic system; special visceral sensory fibers are those associated with the taste buds and olfactory organs.

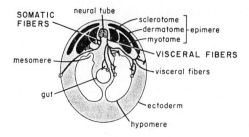

FIG. 16.9 Anatomical correlation with neuron functions. Note difference in distribution of somatic and visceral fibers. Motor fibers are indicated by a short line at right angles to fibers; sensory fibers are indicated by a small terminal circle.

General somatic sensory fibers are concerned with generally distributed, relatively unspecialized sense organs on the external body surface; special somatic sensory fibers are associated with specialized sense organs on or derived from the external body surface (eye, ear, lateral line system).

General visceral motor fibers are those of the autonomic system; special visceral motor fibers supply the branchiomeric muscles which, although derived from the hypomere, are of voluntary function. No differentiation of general and special functions is recognized for somatic motor neurons; the function is, in effect, exclusively special.

Topographic Arrangement of Neurons

The different functional types of neurons are not heterogeneously mixed in the central nervous system, but are sorted out in a pattern recognizable upon gross inspection. The arrangement is primitively the same in the brain and spinal cord, but there is a progressive trend toward reversal of arrangement in parts of the brain.

In certain areas of the brain, especially the cerebrum and cerebellum, the association neurons (and thus the gray matter) tend to be peripheral in position, whereas the afferent and efferent tracts are central, radiating or branching out to the association centers. The mammalian cerebellum with its "arbor vitae" (tree of life) pattern of white tracts radiating out to the gray periphery is an excellent example. This reversed arrangement is true of the cerebellum of all vertebrates, but in the cerebrum it is a progressive trend beginning with amniotes and becoming complete only in mammals.

In other parts of the brain and in the spinal cord the gray matter, consisting chiefly of association neurons, is centrally located, and the tracts (sensory and motor) are peripheral in position. In the spinal cord and medulla the functional components are consistently arranged with somatic sensory, visceral sensory, visceral motor, and somatic motor components in order from the dorsal to the ventral surface.

The gray matter of the spinal cord is, in most vertebrates, arranged in a somewhat H-shaped pattern, as seen in cross section, partially dividing the peripheral white matter into sections (Fig. 16.10). The dorsal arms or

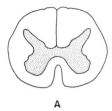
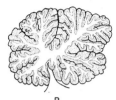

A   B

FIG. 16.10 Relative position of white and gray (stippled) matter in various parts of the mammalian central nervous system. A, spinal cord, cross section;
B, cerebellum, sagittal section; C, cerebrum, cross
section. (From Papez, Gray, Kimber, and Stackpole.)

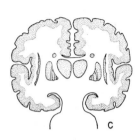

C

horns represent somatic sensory (medial) and visceral sensory (lateral)
columns, whereas the ventral horns represent visceral motor (lateral) and
somatic motor (medial) columns. A *gray commissure* (Fig. 16.8), around
the *canalis centralis,* connects the bilaterally symmetrical columns. The white
matter progressively decreases in size relative to the gray matter from
anterior to posterior end of the spinal cord. The white matter consists of
tracts grouped in much the same manner as are the neurons of the gray
matter. The horns of the gray matter provide topographic markers delimiting in the white matter a *dorsal funiculus* (somatic sensory), a *lateral
funiculus* (visceral sensory and visceral motor) and a *ventral funiculus*
(somatic motor).

Spinal Cord

The internal structure of the spinal cord has already been described.
In superficial appearance it is an elongate structure extending in anamniotes into the tail, giving rise at each segment to a pair of spinal nerves
(Fig. 16.11). The nerves vary in size according to the amount of tissue
they innervate, and nerve size in turn is correlated with the diameter of
the spinal cord (Fig. 16.12). In fishes the difference in thickness at different levels is slight, but in tetrapods with their complex limbs distinct
brachial and pelvic enlargements are evident. Indeed the pelvic enlargement rivaled or even exceeded the size of the brain in some reptiles, as, for
example, dinosaurs like Tyrannosaurus. One whimsical observer suggested that such a beast had two brains, one fore and one aft, and "thus
could he reason *a priori* as well as *a posteriori*. No problem bothered
him a bit, he made both head and tail of it. If something slipped his forward mind, 'twas rescued by the one behind."

In tetrapods there is a progressive tendency for the spinal cord to become greatly shortened, the nuclei of the rear segmental nerves shifting farther forward. The nerves thus emerge from the spinal cord anterior to the parts innervated, and extend backwards within the neural canal, beside the spinal cord as far as it goes, to the appropriate points in the vertebral column where they turn peripherally. The functionless posterior part of the spinal cord becomes extremely slender, and is called the *filum terminale*. The functional part of the spinal cord extends in man only to the level of the first lumbar vertebra. Beyond this point the many nerves running in the neural canal resemble the tail of a horse—thus the name, *cauda equina*.

Lateral to the vertebral column, in the vicinity of the limbs, the spinal nerves lie relatively close together in a *brachial plexus* (pectoral) and a *lumbosacral plexus* (pelvic). Almost invariably a certain degree of anastomosis occurs between the nerves of each plexus, becoming more complex in higher vertebrates.

A deep dorsal and a similar ventral groove (*sulcus* or *fissure*), pro-

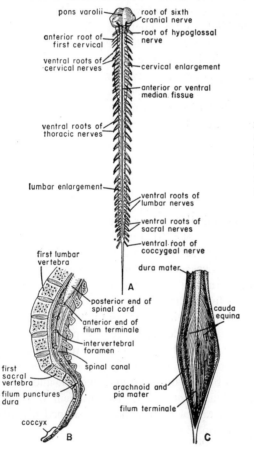

FIG. 16.11 Gross form of spinal cord in man. A, dorsal view; B, sagittal section of posterior end; C, dorsal view of posterior end. (From Gray, Kimber, and Stackpole.)

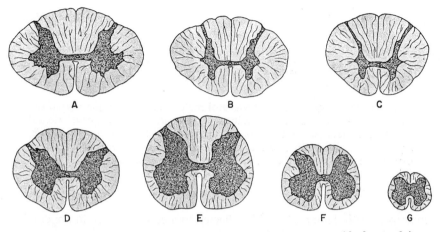

FIG. 16.12 Variation in relative proportions of gray matter (dark stipple) and white matter in the spinal cord at successive anterior-posterior levels in man. A, at fifth cervical nerve; B, second thoracic; C, eighth thoracic; D, first lumbar; E, third lumbar; F, first sacral; G, third sacral. (From Netter.)

viding ready access of blood vessels to the interior of the cord, extend the length of the spinal cord.

Spinal Nerve Pathways

Were the vertebrate body of simple construction, one might expect every segment to be provided with nerves representing each of the four major functional divisions (somatic sensory, visceral sensory, visceral motor, somatic motor) of the nervous system. Probably this was actually the case primitively, but in the cranial region a vast divergence from this arrangement has evolved, resulting in a diverse functional composition and segmental association of the cranial nerves. In the spinal region the hypothetically primitive condition is approximated, although some variations do occur, as, for example, the absence in some nerves of the visceral motor component. Each segment otherwise retains its own complement of functional divisions in its own segmental nerve.

The spinal nerves primitively were paired on each side. One nerve on each side, ventral in position, passed to the voluntary muscles of that segment, therefore being exclusively somatic motor in function. The other nerve, innervating structures beyond the myotomes and associated with the integument or gut, was attached dorsally to the spinal cord at a level corresponding with the position of the myoseptum. Thus dorsal and ventral nerves alternated along each side of the spinal cord, one at middle of the segment, the other at the margin. The dorsal nerves contained all sensory and visceral motor components of the segment. Such an arrange-

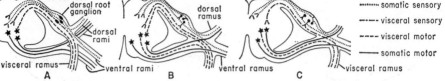

somatic sensory
visceral sensory
visceral motor
somatic motor

FIG. 16.13 Evolutionary shift of visceral motor pathways in the vertebrate spinal nerves. A, primitive condition (cyclostomes) with separate dorsal and ventral nerves, and only somatic motor fibers in the ventral nerve; B, intermediate condition (gnathostome ectotherms), the two formerly separated nerves fused and the ventral root with some visceral motor fibers; C, mammalian condition, with complete shift of visceral motor fibers into ventral root. (From Romer.)

ment persists in lampreys, and is reflected to a certain degree in the cranial nerves of all vertebrates (Fig. 16.13).

In successive levels of vertebrate evolution there is a trend toward fusion close to the spinal cord of the two anatomical components of each spinal nerve. The fusion is no doubt a product of the division of the myotomes into epaxial and hypaxial components, each requiring both sensory and motor nerve fibers. Whatever the procedure may have been, in all vertebrates save lampreys the two segmental nerves on each side remain separate at their attachment to the spinal cord, but are fused at a *chiasma* a short distance from the cord. The parts of the nerves proximal to the chiasma are the *roots* and those distal to the chiasma are *rami,* which carry both motor and sensory fibers (Fig. 16.15).

Fusion of the spinal nerves of each segment led also to a shift of the visceral motor fibers to the ventral root, thus leaving the two roots exclusively either motor (ventral) or sensory (dorsal). In at least a few primitive members of every class, however, some visceral motor fibers continue to pass through the dorsal rather than the ventral root. The visceral sensory fibers (both axons and dendrites) are nonmyelinated; most others are myelinated.

The rami are three in number: (a) a *dorsal ramus,* extending to the somatic epaxial region; (b) a *ventral ramus,* extending to the somatic hypaxial region; and (c) a *visceral ramus,* through which all visceral fibers pass (Fig. 16.14). Visceral rami vary greatly in composition; the other rami vary little in basic composition.

Autonomic System

Functional Characteristics. As previously stated, the autonomic system is exclusively general visceral motor. It is utilized in all totally involuntary nervous actions, and only in them. It is true that indirectly a limited control can be developed over some normally involuntary actions, but only with exceptional effort or under unusual circumstances. The

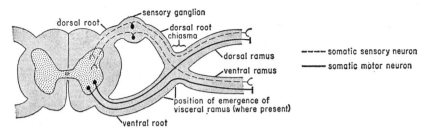

FIG. 16.14 Cross section of a thoracic spinal nerve, showing somatic pathways.

autonomic system does not concern normally *reflexive* actions that actually are under conscious control at will, such as eyelid movement, breathing, etc.

Anatomical Characteristics. A number of unique anatomical characteristics differentiate the autonomic system from other parts of the nervous system. (1) Two sets of fibers with opposing functions, with few exceptions, innervate every organ involved. These two sets belong to the parasympathetic and sympathetic systems, as diametrically opposed in their action as are the members of an antagonistic pair of skeletal muscles. (2) The fibers of the proximal neuron (that is, the one whose cell body is in the brain or spinal cord) never (with rare exception—those to the adrenal gland) reach the end organ, for (3) two motor neurons rather than one are present between brain or spinal cord and effector. Therefore (4) one cell body, that of the second neuron, is present along the nervous pathway between the brain or spinal cord and effector. The cell bodies of these neurons are, as is characteristic generally of nerves, grouped together in ganglia, but these ganglia are the only motor ganglia anywhere in the nervous system. The neuron leading up to an autonomic ganglion is termed a *preganglionic neuron;* the succeeding one with which it forms a synapse in the autonomic ganglion is called, somewhat misleadingly, the *postganglionic neuron.* The postganglionic neurons are the only neurons wholly outside the central nervous system. Finally (5) the postganglionic fibers are largely non-medullated. The axon may be naked or possess a neurilemma, but there is no, or at the most, a very thin medullary sheath. The autonomic nerves are the only ones of which this is true. Preganglionic axons do, of course, possess both sheaths, although the myelin is moderately thin.

Distinctions between Sympathetic and Parasympathetic Systems. One of the strangest features of the vertebrate body is the double innervation of most involuntary organs. It is a device perforce evolved to cope with the more or less self-perpetuating operation of most involuntary organs, which tend to continue to function as though generating their own nervous stimulation until positively blocked. A double innervation can and does efficiently accomplish the necessary antagonistic action. A control system of antagonistic hormone stimulation, operated by way of the circulatory system, is an adjunct of the antagonistic innervation. The balance between these two is subject to considerable individual variation and is an important factor in personality. Hypersympathetic activity is evident in the behavior of some individuals, hyperparasympathetic in that of others. Control of adjustment of these two systems, or of closely correlated mechanisms, is of great significance in the correction of human maladjustment in the world man has built for himself but to which he is not always temperamentally or physically adapted.

The fully binary autonomic system (as it exists in mammals) reached its present perfection only in higher vertebrates (endotherms). In lower vertebrates no morphological distinction of two sets of fibers is evident and the functional distinctions are incomplete.

Differences between the sympathetic and parasympathetic systems, in mammals, are conspicuously evident in at least eight features: (1) role in general bodily function, (2) organs innervated, (3) neurohumors, (4) sheathing, (5) ganglia, (6) locus of origin from the central nervous system, (7) relation to sympathetic chains, and (8) composition of visceral ramus. Each is discussed in the following paragraphs.

The sympathetic system as a whole alerts the body for somatic activity; it is a *somatic stimulator,* preparing the body to meet the challenge of a shifting external environment at the same time that it *depresses* digestive and other "vegetative" processes. The parasympathetic system has precisely the reverse action. Neither system is wholly excitatory or wholly depressive in action.

The sympathetic system alone innervates the involuntary organs of the skin (the integumentary glands, hair muscles, skin capillaries) and the smooth muscle of blood vessels in general; the parasympathetic system alone innervates the ciliary muscle of the eye (adjusting focus). The other involuntary organs have dual innervations.

The sympathetic system is *adrenergic,* the organs it innervates being stimulated or depressed by epinephrin and related compounds carried to them by the blood, exactly as sympathetic fibers themselves would affect them. On the contrary, the parasympathetic system is *cholinergic,* the organs it innervates being stimulated or depressed by acetylcholine or related drugs in exactly the same way as stimulation of the parasympathetic fibers would affect them. Ganglionic synapses, however, are cholinergic in both the sympathetic and parasympathetic systems. *It is at the neuroeffector junctions only that a difference is evident,* and it is the sympathetic system that is unique. In fact at the end arborization of sympathetic fibers an epinephrinlike *"neurohumor" (sympathin)* is produced and causes the actual motor action (glandular secretion or muscular contraction); an acetylcholinelike neurohumor (*parasympathin*) plays a similar role in the parasympathetic system. Quantities of epinephrin can be produced almost instantaneously by the adrenal glands, with an obvious value in situations calling for speedy reaction; no similar glandular source of acetylcholine has been generally recognized, again for the apparent reason that there is little selective value in speedy return to a "vegetative" condition. That there should be a great positive survival value in genetic variations favoring hypertrophy of epinephrin-secreting glands is obvious. On the other hand, it is possible that some glands augment the parasympathetic function in much the same way that the adrenals are known to support the sympathetic functions. Recent studies indicate that the pineal and parietal organs, long of unknown function, may play a homeostatic role, in support of the parasympathetic system (see the discussion on sense organs and the references for Chap. 15, Sensory System).

The postganglionic fibers of the sympathetic system possess a neurilemma sheath; those of the parasympathetic system are naked.

The segmental sympathetic nerves possess a unique intersegmental connection, via a sympathetic chain on either side of the spinal cord. The parasympathetic system has no peripheral intersegmental integration.

The ganglia of the sympathetic system are generally situated at some distance from the organs innervated, in a *paravertebral* position in the sympathetic chain, or in a *collateral* position intermediate between the chain and the innervated organs. Those of the parasympathetic system are *terminal* in position, lying on or near the very organs innervated.

The sympathetic fibers emerge from the central nervous system exclusively via the thoracic and anterior lumbar spinal nerves ("thoracolumbar outflow," Fig. 16.16), whereas the parasympathetic fibers emerge exclusively via the cranial nerves (the "cranial outflow") and the sacral spinal nerves (the "sacral outflow").

All sympathetic pathways pass through the sympathetic chain, arising from the thoracic and lumbar spinal nerves; none of the parasympathetic fibers pass through the sympathetic chain.

The visceral ramus of the spinal nerves carrying preganglionic sympathetic fibers has two components, the *white ramus* and the *gray ramus*. The white ramus carries preganglionic fibers into the ganglia of the sympathetic chain running parallel with the spinal cord on either side, whereas the gray ramus carries postganglionic fibers running from the ganglion of

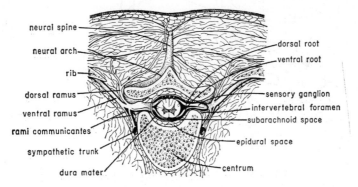

neural spine

neural arch

rib

dorsal ramus

ventral ramus

rami communicantes

sympathetic trunk

dura mater

dorsal root

ventral root

sensory ganglion

intervertebral foramen

subarachnoid space

epidural space

centrum

FIG. 16.15 Relation of a thoracic spinal nerve to neural canal and vertebra, as seen in cross section in thoracic region in man. (From Netter.)

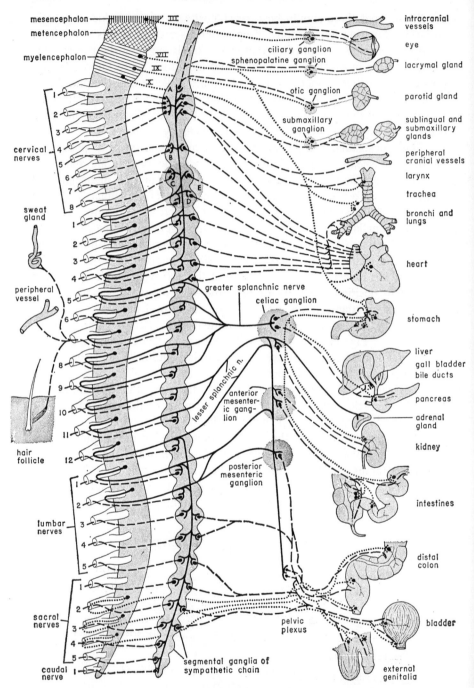

FIG. 16.16 Diagram of the autonomic nervous system in man. Preganglionic sympathetic fibers, continuous lines; postganglionic sympathetic fibers, dashed lines; preganglionic parasympathetic fibers, large-dotted lines; postganglionic parasympathetic fibers, small-dotted lines. A, anterior cervical ganglion; B, middle cervical ganglion; C, posterior cervical ganglion; D, first thoracic chain ganglion; E, stellate ganglion (C and D fused, as in cat). (From Netter.)

that visceral ramus back to the dorsal and ventral rami, thence to integumentary organs of epaxial and hypaxial areas, respectively (Fig. 16.15). All other spinal nerves carry only a gray ramus (or equivalent) for the postganglionic sympathetic fibers. The parasympathetic components of both spinal (sacral) and cranial nerves are exclusively white. Some sacral nerves have both sympathetic (gray) and parasympathetic (white) rami (Fig. 16.18C).

Structural Pattern of the Sympathetic System. All fibers of the sympathetic system emerge through the ventral roots of the thoracic and anterior lumbar spinal nerves and thence pass through the white ramus of the visceral ramus (Fig. 16.16). There a parting of the ways sees a small group of fibers forming synapses at the ganglion of that visceral ramus with postganglionic neurons, whereas the others pass to other levels of the chain (anterior or posterior) or extend directly away from the chain to collateral ganglia. The postganglionic neurons arising from (and whose cell bodies are solely responsible for) the *chain ganglia* either pass directly to nearby involuntary organs or pass through the gray ramus back to the

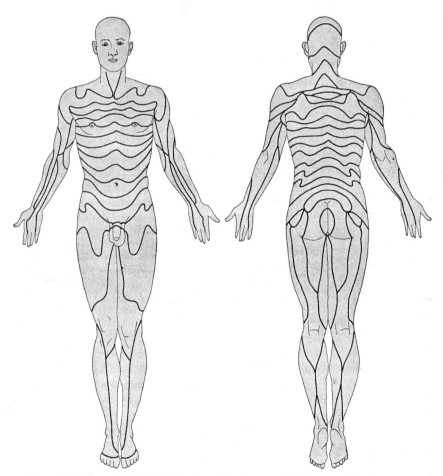

FIG. 16.17 Segmental distribution of integumental innervation in man. (From Netter.)

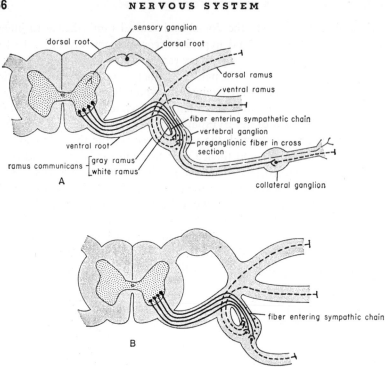

FIG. 16.18 (*Above and facing page*) Diagrammatic cross sections of spinal nerves at different levels showing variation in visceral pathways (somatic pathways omitted; see Fig. 16.14). A, anterior lumbar and rear thoracic; B, anterior thoracic; C, middle sacral; D, cervical, posterior lumbar, and anterior sacral; E, posterior sacral and caudal spinal nerves. All fibers are sympathetic except those labeled otherwise.

ventral and dorsal rami, thence to the integument; they do not travel along the chain. The integumental fibers are restricted more or less to segmental areas corresponding to their respective spinal nerves (Fig. 16.17).

The most conspicuous anatomical feature of the sympathetic system is the *sympathetic chain* which parallels most or all of the spinal cord. The chain itself is made up of medullated fibers that bypass the segmental ganglia on their way to other levels of the chain. Some of the thoracic, lumbar, and sacral ganglia of the sympathetic chain are formed exclusively of the cell bodies of postganglionic neurons directed to the skin by way of the gray rami.

The cervical part of the sympathetic chain lacks preganglionic connections with spinal nerves (Fig. 16.18D). Postganglionic fibers do, however, pass out to the skin by way of gray rami. The cervical ganglia have lost their segmental arrangement. Only three remain—the *posterior* (inferior), *middle,* and *anterior* (superior) cervical ganglia. The posterior is often fused with the first thoracic ganglion, forming the *stellate* ganglion; the posterior as well as the middle ganglion are concerned exclusively with thoracic organs. The anterior cervical ganglion is chiefly concerned

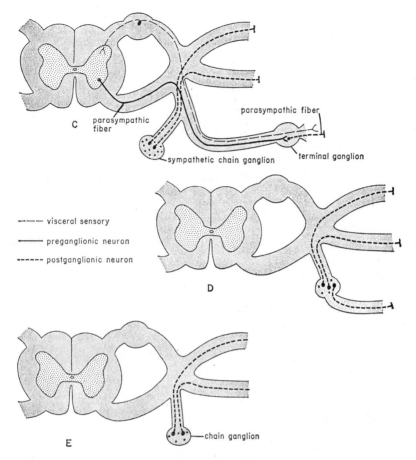

with cranial functions, with some fibers directed to thoracic organs.

Those fibers not destined at their point of emergence from the spinal cord for the skin or other organs innervated directly via the chain, pass up or down the chain to other levels, where they synapse or pass directly to *collateral* ganglia. The latter include three distinct pairs: *celiac, anterior* (superior) *mesenteric* (sometimes fused), and *posterior* (inferior) *mesenteric ganglia.*

By way of several *splanchnic* (*greater* and *lesser*) nerves preganglionic fibers emerge from the sympathetic chain, having gained access to the chain at various levels, and may either (1) pass to and synapse at the *celiac ganglion,* governing the stomach, liver, pancreas, duodenum, kidney, and esophagus, or (2) pass through the celiac ganglion without synapsing to reach the *anterior mesenteric ganglion;* from here some fibers pass directly (without synapsing) to the adrenal glands, whereas others synapse and pass to the small intestine, kidneys, ascending colon, and gonads. Some fibers pierce both of these ganglia and extend on to the *posterior mesenteric* ganglion, where they synapse with postganglionic neurons whose fibers extend to most of the large intestine and the rectum.

No preganglionic fibers pass through the posterior mesenteric ganglion, as a general rule. Other preganglionic fibers reach the mesenteric ganglia via separate branches from the more posterior parts of the lumbar sympathetic chain. Subdivision or fusion of these three pairs of ganglia occurs in various mammals.

The bladder and the posterior parts of the reproductive tracts, in at least man, contrary to general rule, are said to be innervated by preganglionic fibers that bypass the inferior mesenteric ganglion and reach terminal ganglia on or near the organs innervated.

Of great evolutionary interest is the preganglionic innervation of the adrenal glands. The postganglionic cells of the adrenal pathway are represented by part of the glands themselves, the medulla of which is derived from neural crest cells as are indeed the postganglionic cells elsewhere in the sympathetic system.

Structural Pattern of the Parasympathetic System. The cranial outflow of the parasympathetic system utilizes cranial nerves, innervating "prerenal" organs. Preganglionic, medullated fibers extend to the very organs innervated, and there synapse with short postganglionic neurons at terminal ganglia that are usually hidden on, or just within, the surface of the organs. All ganglia of the cranial outflow are terminal.

Four cranial nerves carry parasympathetic fibers: the oculomotor, facial, glossopharyngeal, and vagus nerves. Those on the oculomotor synapse at a *ciliary ganglion* with fibers innervating the iris and ciliary muscles of the eye. Those on the facial nerve synapse at a *sphenopalatine ganglion* to innervate the orbital glands and part of the salivary glands; and at the *submaxillary ganglion,* to innervate the submaxillary and sublingual salivary glands. Those on the glossopharyngeal nerve synapse at the *otic ganglion,* innervating the parotid salivary gland. Those on the vagus nerve synapse at numerous ganglia bearing the names of the organs innervated.

The sacral outflow utilizes a few of the median sacral spinal nerves (three in man). All of its preganglionic fibers synapse at terminal ganglia, the postganglionic fibers innervating all the "postrenal" viscera, for example the large intestine, bladder, and reproductive tracts.

Cranial Nerves

The cranial nerves as they now exist in vertebrates have evolved so far from the primitive condition, by splitting and secondary fusion, that their relation to the original segmentation is almost hopelessly obscured. Part of the picture is evident, but a much larger part remains to be detected.

Nomenclature. So firmly fixed is the statement that vertebrates possess ten (most anamniotes) or twelve (a few anamniotes, all amniotes) cranial nerves, even though the omission of one other has long been realized, that there is possibly little point in attempting to correct it. Actually eleven occur generally in anamniotes, thirteen in amniotes. The most anterior, the *terminal nerve,* is commonly counted as number 0 in order not to disrupt the time-honored sequence beginning with the olfactory nerve as number 1, the most anterior.

Another example of inconsistency—of little real difficulty—is seen in the second so-called "cranial" (optic) nerve. This is in reality a brain tract, but it has been counted as a nerve for so long that the appellation is immutable.

The remaining nerves, numbered in sequence from front to rear of the brain, are the (3) oculomotor, (4) trochlear, (5) trigeminus, (6) abducens, (7) facial, (8) otic, (9) glossopharyngeal, (10) vagus, (11) spinal accessory, and (12) hypoglossal.

A "mnemonic crutch" guiltily adopted in its exact or equivalent form by virtually all unsophistic zoology students to aid in mastery of the sequence of the cranial nerves is "On Old Olympus's Towering Top A Finn Or German Viewed A Hop." The first letter of each capitalized word is the same as that of the name of the corresponding nerve by number.

Some of the cranial nerves possess branches whose names are of importance in the present summary. The trigeminus is so named because it possesses three branches in man, as in all other amniotes: the *ophthalmic, maxillary,* and *mandibular* branches. In anamniotes, however, four branches are present: the (a) *superficial ophthalmic,* (b) *deep ophthalmic,* (c) *maxillary,* and (d) *mandibular.* The second, being associated solely with the lateral-line system of sense organs, is lost in amniotes, and the first becomes known simply as the "ophthalmic." The vagus possesses a *lateral* branch (likewise lost in amniotes, for the same reason as the deep ophthalmic) and a *visceral* branch, the latter as well as the glossopharyngeal possessing *branchial* branches in gilled vertebrates, one for each gill cleft. Primitively all the nerves serving the pharyngeal pouches were provided with *pretrematic, postrematic,* and *pharyngeal* branches, but in gnathostomes the actual branches, or their identity, tend to be lost. The trigeminus nerve is the nerve of the mandibular arch and cleft; the maxillary and mandibular branches represent the pre- and postrematic branches, respectively, whereas the deep ophthalmic is thought to represent an entirely different premandibular branchial segment. The facial nerve is the nerve of the hyoid arch and cleft; its buccal, hyomandibular, and palatine branches represent the pre- and postrematic and the pharyngeal branches, respectively. The identity of the comparable branches of the glossopharyngeal and vagus nerves in amniotes is lost.

Curiously enough most of the nerves are attached to the medulla. The terminal and olfactory are attached to the telencephalon, of course; the optic, to the diencephalon; the oculomotor and trochlear to the mesencephalon; the otic to the metencephalon and myelencephalon; and all others to the myelencephalon only.

Tetrapod Adaptations. The shift from the aquatic to the terrestrial mode of life is profoundly reflected in the cranial nerves. The various branches from the lateralis system of sense organs, itself completely lost, likewise disappear: gone are the deep ophthalmic of the trigeminus, the superficial ophthalmic of the facial nerve, the lateral branch of the vagus, and the somatic sensory component of the glossopharyngeal nerve.

Another series of changes, involving loss of identity of pre- and postrematic branches, is related chiefly to the loss of the gill system.

Of lesser importance is the separation from the vagus (in crossopterygians and in all tetrapods save modern amphibians) of the spinal accessory, bearing special visceral motor components to branchiomeric muscles that become hypertrophied in adaptation to land life, acting as levators of the foreleg and manipulators of the head.

The final major contrast is addition of a former spinal nerve, the hypoglossal, to the cranial nerves (in crossopterygians and in all tetrapods save modern amphibians). This modification seems to be an example of the inherent tendency of cell bodies of neurons to move toward the source of stimulus, thus shortening the dendrites and lengthening the axons (*neurobiotaxis*). This phenomenon results in a trend evident not only in telescoping of nerves into the cranial area but also in shift of brain nuclei forward into the cerebrum and in the remarkable shortening of the spinal cord with formation of the cauda equina and filum terminale. This tendency to draw forward is an aspect of cephalization.

Ten cranial nerves may be recognized as a primitive condition occurring in all fishes except crossopterygians, and as a secondary condition in modern amphibians. Twelve cranial nerves first appeared in the crossopterygians and were retained by all tetrapods save the groups of living amphibians, which secondarily reverted to the primitive condition. All early (fossil) amphibians possessed twelve cranial nerves.

Functions. Varied as are the functions of the cranial nerves, the nerves readily fall into three functional groups: (a) those of purely sensory function, (b) those of somatic motor function, and (c) those of mixed function, or exclusively of visceral motor function, but lacking somatic motor components (Fig. 16.19).

The olfactory, optic, and otic nerves are of special sensory function only. The olfactory nerve is regarded as of visceral function, the others somatic. Also the terminal nerve appears to be somatic sensory, presumably general. Its function is poorly known, although the nerve is evident in all vertebrates save cyclostomes, crocodilia, squamata, and birds.

The somatic motor group is virtually pure. The trochlear supplies the superior oblique muscle; the abducens, the external rectus muscle and nictitating membrane muscle (where present); and the hypoglossal innervates all the hypobranchial muscles (geniohyoid of segment 6; lingualis, genioglossus, hyoglossus, and styloglossus of segment 7; sternohyoid, sternothyroid, and thyrohyoid of segment 8). The oculomotor supplies the four remaining eye muscles (superior rectus, inferior rectus, internal rectus, inferior oblique), but also carries general visceral motor (autonomic: parasympathetic) fibers to the intrinsic eye muscles.

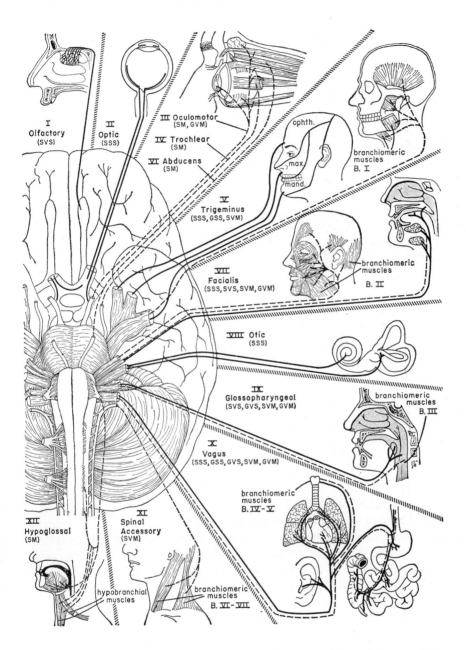

FIG. 16.19 Diagram of distribution of the cranial nerves, adapted to man. Sensory fibers shown by continuous lines, motor fibers by dashed lines. Symbols: B. I–VII, branchiomeres I–VII; GSS, general somatic sensory; GVM, general visceral motor; GVS, general visceral sensory; SM, somatic motor; SSS, special somatic sensory (in aquatic ichthyopsids only on cranial nerves VII, IX and X); SVM, special visceral motor; SVS, special visceral sensory. (From Netter.)

The remaining cranial nerves all possess visceral motor functions. The spinal accessory is pure visceral motor (special), supplying the trapezius, cleidomastoid, and sternomastoid, all at least in part derived from the levators of the sixth and seventh branchiomeres (since these muscles also are said to have cervical innervation they may be in part of myotomic origin). The others are mixed.

The trigeminus carries special visceral motor fibers to the branchiomeric muscles of the mandibular arch (masseter, temporal, anterior belly of the digastric, mylohyoid, pterygoid, tensor tympani), and general somatic sensory fibers from the skin of the head, teeth, and anterior two thirds of the tongue.

The facial carries special visceral motor fibers to the branchiomeric muscles of the hyoid arch (stapedius, posterior belly of the digastric, platysma, stylohyoid); general visceral motor (parasympathetic) fibers to the salivary glands (except parotid) and to the tear glands; special visceral sensory fibers from part of the taste buds; and, in anamniotes, special somatic sensory fibers from cranial derivatives of the lateralis system.

The glossopharyngeal carries special visceral motor fibers to the derivatives of the third branchiomere (stylopharyngeus); general visceral motor (parasympathetic) fibers to the parotid salivary gland; special as well as general visceral sensory fibers from the taste buds and pharyngeal sense organs, respectively; and in anamniotes special somatic sensory fibers from the lateral line system.

The vagus carries special visceral motor fibers to derivatives of the fourth and fifth branchiomeres (cricoarytenoid, thyroarytenoids, cricothyroid); general visceral motor (parasympathetic) fibers to postcranial prerenal organs of involuntary action; general visceral sensory fibers from the same organs; general somatic sensory fibers from the skin about the ear; and special somatic sensory fibers in anamniotes from the lateral line system.

Ganglia. As previously stated, in vertebrates all nerves carrying sensory fibers possess ganglia along their length shortly before entrance to the central nervous system; for no sensory neuron (with certain exceptions we may here disregard) possesses its cell body within the central nervous system. Furthermore all autonomic nerves possess ganglia housing the cell bodies of the distal neurons. Cranial nerves are no exception to these rules. Thus several ganglia, some sensory and some motor, are present on the cranial nerves. Every nerve carrying either sensory or autonomic fibers would be expected, accordingly, to have at least one ganglion for the cell bodies of each of the two types of fibers.

The terminal nerve possesses a *terminalis* ganglion of general somatic sensory function. The oculomotor nerve possesses a *ciliary* ganglion for its autonomic fibers extending to the eye. The trigeminus possesses a sensory *Gasserian* or *semilunar* ganglion; the facial possesses a sensory *geniculate* ganglion, a motor *submaxillary* and a motor *sphenopalatine* ganglion; the glossopharyngeal, a *petrosal* ganglion for special visceral sensory fibers, a *superior* ganglion for general visceral sensory function, and an *otic* ganglion for the parotid glands; the otic possesses somatic sensory *cochlear* and *vestibular* ganglia; and the vagus has a general somatic sensory *jugular* ganglion for fibers coming from the skin about the ear region, a general visceral sensory *nodosal* ganglion for fibers coming from the prerenal viscera, and a series of parasympathetic terminal ganglia.

Two cranial nerves seem to be exceptions to the rule that ganglia are to be found on all nerves with sensory fibers; for the olfactory and optic nerves do not possess ganglia. There are good reasons for the apparent discrepancy, for neither nerve is typical in other respects. The optic nerve is not actually a nerve at all, as explained previously, but is a tract of the brain. The olfactory sensory cells are actually the cell bodies of the olfactory sensory neurons, and thus the olfactory ganglion or equivalent thereof is spread over a considerable area as a part of the olfactory epithelium.

Meninges

One or more specialized, protective membranes of connective tissue, the *meninges,* surround the central nervous system. The number of membranes has tended to increase in the mammalian line of evolution (Fig. 16.20). Fishes have but a single membrane, a thin *primitive meninx,* but in amphibians as in reptiles and birds the single membrane is represented by a thick, outer *dura mater* and a thin inner *secondary meninx.* In mammals the dura mater persists, but the secondary meninx has split into a superficial weblike *arachnoid* membrane and an inner *pia mater* (Fig. 16.21).

The primitive meninx is a thin membrane lying close to the brain or spinal cord. The later development of a thick outer meninx as well as a thin inner membrane, the latter still closely applied to the neural tube, is not readily explicable. It occurs with adoption of terrestrial life and may have been brought about through selective advantages of more efficient movement of lymphatic fluid (*cerebrospinal fluid*) around the neural tube or of more adequate protection from shock. Both factors undoubtedly were involved, but the former was probably of greater importance. The higher

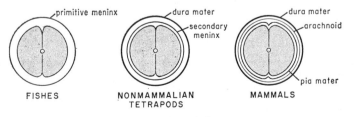

FIG. 16.20 Evolution of the meninges.

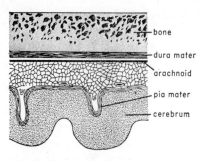

bone

dura mater

arachnoid

pia mater

cerebrum

FIG. 16.21 Diagram of the mammalian meninges, as seen in cross section of part of the brain and skull. (From Walter.)

blood pressure of tetrapods, resulting from elimination of the gill circulation between heart and somatic vessels, must have caused greater diffusion of intercellular fluid into spaces about the brain and spinal cord; capture of that fluid by a thick membrane (dura mater) would go far toward solving the problems of having too great a diffusion and of siphoning the fluid off more rapidly.

The division of the secondary meninx of early amniotes into two layers in mammals seems to be simply an improvement of the mechanism for returning the cerebrospinal fluid to the blood (see following). The arachnoid meninx has specific functions of (1) protection (by holding a shock-absorbing fluid about the entire central nervous system), and (2) return of the cerebrospinal fluid to the blood. Thus the arachnoid membrane lies close to the dura mater, with weblike attachment to the pia mater. The latter is the only one of the three membranes to follow closely the superficial brain contours; it carries the smaller blood vessels as they penetrate the brain or spinal cord.

Brain

Cavities. The neurocele, represented in the spinal cord by the tiny canalis centralis, is of larger size in the brain, where it is expanded primitively in each lobe as a *ventricle* (Fig. 16.7). The two halves of the telencephalon contain the *first* and *second,* or *lateral,* ventricles, communicating with a *third* ventricle in the diencephalon by way of one or a pair of *interventricular foramina* (*foramina of Monro*). The third ventricle continues posteriorly into a *mesocele* in the optic lobes of the mesencephalon or, in amniotes, into an *aqueduct of Sylvius* (or *cerebral aqueduct*). This expands posteriorly into a *fourth ventricle* of the metencephalon and medulla. An expansion of the fourth ventricle into the body of the cerebellum in anamniotes is the *cerebellar ventricle,* a fourth ventricle subdivision.

With each of the third and fourth ventricles is associated a *choroid plexus,* consisting of (a) the wall of the brain, there embryonically thin and represented only by the *ependyma,* the inner epithelial lining of the neurocele; (b) the innermost meninx (pia mater, primitive meninx, or secondary meninx), which with the ependyma forms the *tela choroidea;* and

(c) plexi of blood vessels. The entire cerebrospinal fluid in the neurocele is derived from these choroid plexi, through whose walls a capillary filtrate constantly seeps into the ventricles. In mammals a slow current carries the fluid posteriorly from all the ventricles through the various parts of the neurocele into the fourth ventricle, whence it emerges into the subarachnoid space through two or three perforations (foramina of Luschka and Magendie) in the tela choroidea (Fig. 16.22).

The subarachnoid space, continuous about the entire central nervous system, is drained by means of *arachnoid villi* that project into venous sinuses situated in the dura mater (Fig. 16.23) in the area between cerebellum and cerebrum. The subarachnoid space receives cerebrospinal fluid not only from the perforations of the medullary choroid plexus but also from channels about the blood vessels that penetrate the central nervous system. There are no lymph vessels associated with the central nervous system. The fluid escaping from capillaries within the spinal cord and brain flows back alongside the blood vessels until it reaches the periphery of the cord or brain, and is there impounded in the subarachnoid space (Fig. 16.24).

The choroid plexi are of major importance as a means of supplying necessary materials to the cells of the brain interior; blood vessels branching inward from the exterior do not actually penetrate into the neurocele,

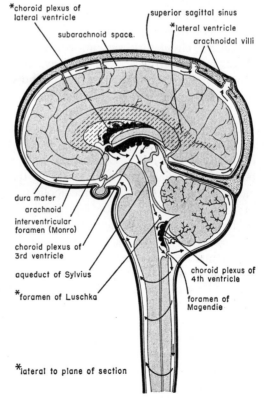

*choroid plexus of lateral ventricle

superior sagittal sinus

subarachnoid space.

*lateral ventricle

arachnoidal villi

dura mater
arachnoid
interventricular foramen (Monro)
choroid plexus of 3rd ventricle
aqueduct of Sylvius
*foramen of Luschka

choroid plexus of 4th ventricle

foramen of Magendie

*lateral to plane of section

FIG. 16.22 Circulation of cerebrospinal fluid in the brain and spinal cord of man. (From Netter.)

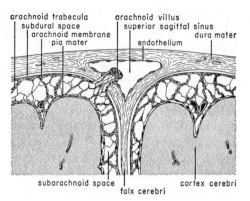

arachnoid trabecula   arachnoid villus
   subdural space   superior sagittal sinus
     arachnoid membrane   dura mater
       pia mater   endothelium

subarachnoid space   cortex cerebri
         falx cerebri

FIG. 16.23 Arachnoid villi, as seen in brain of man. (From Bailey.)

and thus the maintenance of a favorable oxygen tension (and other equilibria as well) about the neurocele depends upon diffusion from a constantly replaced cerebrospinal fluid in the ventricles, originating at the choroid plexi. This choroid mechanism requires, of course, a continuous neurocele for its operation, and in mammals it also requires the arachnoid meninx and villi.

A number of problems are unique to nutrition in the central nervous system: (1) there are no internal vessels supplying the innermost cells of this system—all vessels and branches thereof are superficial; (2) and the tissue is exceptionally dense, with little interstitial space. At least four adjustments to these problems have evolved in vertebrates: (1) a unique independent circulatory system, consisting essentially of (a) a choroid plexus-meningeal cycle, (b) a perivascular-meningeal cycle, (c) direct venous escape of cerebrospinal fluid, and (d) complete circumvention of the vascular lymphatic system; (2) direct supply to the brain of the most highly oxygenated blood the body can deliver; (3) limitation in actual thickness of brain and cord walls, the area actually increasing more by folds and flexures; and (4) direct supply to the CNS of metabolic fuel (glycogen→sugar) by establishment of a storage structure, the glycogen body, in the spinal cord (see following discussion). Despite these rather considerable adjustments, the metabolic margin of safety for many cells of the CNS is extremely narrow—probably narrower than for any other cells of the body. Due to the density of tissue and distance across which diffusion must occur, the gradients between the cerebrospinal blood vascular system and the innermost CNS cells are extremely steep; despite high levels of oxygen and sugar concentration at the cerebrospinal blood vessels, the levels at the innermost cells are relatively low. Brain cells notoriously are among the first to degenerate upon cardiac failure (irreparable damage follows three minutes thereafter), but not because they need more oxygen or sugars than other cells (tissues of, for example, the liver and pancreas have higher requirements); they are simply supplied more inefficiently than most others.

Birds are of particular interest in connection with nutrition of the central nervous system, primarily as a result of the fact that they live more recklessly than any other vertebrates; their rate of metabolism is higher than that of other animals. If they depended extensively upon glycogen as a source of energy they would no doubt experience very marked variation in blood sugar levels, especially in the periods before, during, and after flight. Yet blood sugar levels could not drop very low very long without damaging cells of the central nervous system which can metabolize only sugars. In long flight the physiological problem of brain nutrition would be critical. Two unique adjustments to this problem have evolved. For one, birds possess the ability to metabolize fats and proteins for general body use; a very large part (about 80 percent) of the energy a bird utilizes is of fat or protein origin, whereas in most vertebrates it is normally a very small proportion. Secondly, a source of sugars for the cerebrospinal fluid is made available in all birds through an extraordinary *glycogen body*. This is an egg-shaped mass of glycogen lying imbedded in the dorsal sulcus of the spinal cord at the sacral enlargement (Fig. 16.25, 16.26) separating the two halves of the cord and even extending to the canalis centralis. It is covered by the meninges and is thus in direct contact with the cerebrospinal fluid. The glycogen is available at all times to maintain proper sugar levels within the cerebrospinal fluid, but is unavailable for use elsewhere. Birds can starve to death without significant reduction in size of the glycogen body. Apparently the sugars of the cerebrospinal fluid cannot diffuse across the meninges into the blood spaces and vessels lying adjacent to the central nervous system.

As previously stated, certain dinosaurs are famous for the relatively enormous size of the neural canal at the level of the pelvic spinal enlargement, as evidenced by fossilized bones. It has generally been assumed that only an enlargement of the spinal cord occupied the cavity in the neural canal, but it is an intriguing possibility that a glycogen body was present

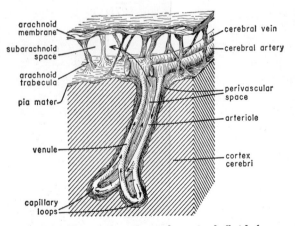

arachnoid membrane
subarachnoid space
arachnoid trabecula
pia mater
venule
capillary loops

cerebral vein
cerebral artery
perivascular space
arteriole
cortex cerebri

FIG. 16.24 Formation of cerebrospinal fluid from peripheral vessels of the central nervous system. (From Bailey.)

in these dinosaurs also, especially since dinosaurs are related to birds, and certain ones gave rise to birds. Whether other animals capable of flight— the pterodactyls and bats—have had the same problem of nutrition of the central nervous system during flight as birds have is not known.

Types of Modification. Five sorts of gross structural modifications account for the variety of form seen in the brain in various vertebrates. They include *evaginations,* such as the epiphyses, infundibulum, and per- haps the cerebral lobes; *folding* of the walls, as in the cerebrum and cere- bellum of mammals, as well as in the choroid plexi; *increase in thickness of walls,* as in the cerebrum, optic lobes, cerebellum; *decrease in thickness of walls* (or retention of embryonic thinness), as in the tela choroidea; and formation of *flexures.* In mammals three flexures are evident (Fig. 16.27): the *apical* flexure at the mesencephalon, the *pontile* flexure at the pons, and the *cervical* flexure at the medulla. The flexures are an adaptation to large size, packing the brain into the least possible space, and to erect posture (where it occurs). The thin-walled zones are a nutritive adaptation, the thick-walled zones a proliferation of association centers. Foldings and

FIG. 16.25 (*Left*) Dorsal view of brain and spinal cord of a chick, showing glycogen body in pelvic enlargement. (From Watterson.)

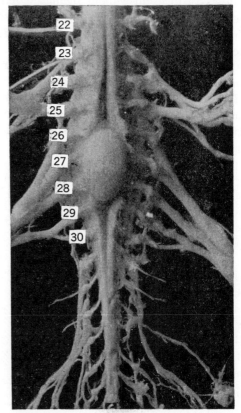

FIG. 16.26 (*Right*) Glycogen body of a chick, dorsal view. Spinal nerves of seg- ments 22–30 indicated by numerals. (From Watter- son.)

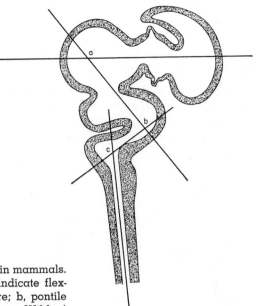

FIG. 16.27 Flexures of the brain in mammals. The intersections of the lines indicate flexures. Symbols: a, apical flexure; b, pontile flexure; c, cervical flexure. (From Wilder.)

evagination increase the surface area or wall space for either nutrition (where the wall is thin) or for associations (where the wall is thick).

Brain Functions. Primitively chordates probably possessed only three lobes in the brain, one corresponding with each of the three major sense organs—olfactory, optic, and otic. Most cranial nerves were attached to what originally was the spinal cord immediately behind the third sensory lobe, and thus a fourth lobe evolved. The narrow diencephalon, now regarded as one of the five main divisions of the brain, undoubtedly evolved simply as a connection between the two adjacent anterior lobes—a function still important throughout vertebrates.

The medulla has thus evolved with the functions of (a) serving as a housing for the primary nuclei for the cranial nerves, (b) as a medium of metabolic exchange *via* its choroid plexus, and (c) as a locus for topographical sorting of nerve fibers in reference to various parts of the peripheral nervous system, both afferent and efferent.

Afferent pathways pass through the cerebellum, which by virtue of its primary otic association governs locomotion, effecting its control by way of the mesencephalon where efferent pathways are reached. The development of the cerebellum is correlated closely with locomotor ability; in amphibians and cyclostomes it is relatively small.

Most afferent pathways then lead through the mesencephalon to the diencephalon, which (a) diverts sensory impulses to the proper part of the brain, and (b) returns efferent impulses to the autonomic system. Up to this level reflexive proprioceptive and autonomic adjustments are made with relatively little influence from other sources.

In anamniotes the sensory impulses sorted by the diencephalon are shifted to the mesencephalon, the seat of the highest level of association in these animals. The optic influence was undoubtedly responsible for the development of a mesencephalic domination. In amniotes, however, the sensory impulses are shifted to the cerebral hemispheres, which replace the optic lobes as the dominant part of the brain. The mesencephalon serves throughout as a primary or (as in mammals especially) a secondary relay center for motor impulses.

The cerebrum originally served as an olfactory center, and subsequently, in amniotes, as a progressively more important association center, eventually the mammalian seat of consciousness.

The brain may be visualized grossly as having incoming and outgoing (sensory and motor) pathways more or less restricted to its floor, and with association centers communicating dorsally with those pathways in three areas: the cerebellum, mesencephalic roof, and cerebrum. The diencephalon plays a major role in connecting the cerebellum and mesencephalic roof, and itself serves as a center of association for autonomic adjustments.

Telencephalon. The telencephalon was primitively of olfactory function alone, serving as a center for relay of olfactory impulses to more posterior areas where associations were made with other sensory impulses and with motor fibers. In reptiles and presumably ancestral amphibians the olfactory function acquired a position of dominance, behavior being influenced more prominently by olfactory than by the other senses. Because of this domination, and perhaps to a lesser degree because of the more advantageous location of association centers toward the anterior terminus of the brain, the association centers formerly concentrated more posteriorly shifted into the telencephalon for closer contact with the olfactory centers. From such inauspicious beginnings evolved the unique machine for complex thought and manipulation that certain mammals possess. This may be regarded as one of the five major evolutionary trends evident in the telencephalon: progressive shift of association centers into the olfactory lobe area of the brain.

A second trend was toward differentiation of olfactory regions. In even the most primitive vertebrates an evagination of the telencephalon, the *olfactory bulb,* projects on each side from the single olfactory lobe to effect contact with the olfactory sac. Beyond the cyclostome stage, the olfactory bulbs tended to withdraw from the lobe, forming a slender *olfactory tract* between the bulb and lobe on each side. A deep median, vertical cleft simultaneously created paired *olfactory lobes* or *cerebral hemispheres* instead of a single median lobe. The two terms are not synonymous, olfactory lobes applying only to that part of the telencephalon, proximal to the tract, of wholly olfactory function. In most vertebrates the cerebral hemispheres include parts other than olfactory centers, but primitively the hemispheres were entirely olfactory. With differentiation of the lobes into other parts (as described in the following) the olfactory centers (lobes)

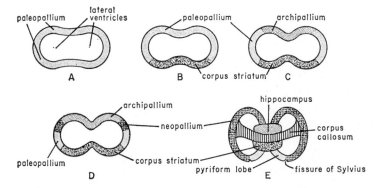

FIG. 16.28 Diagrammatic representation of the groups of association centers in the telencephalon. A, cyclostome stage; B, teleost stage; C, most tetrapods except mammals; D, advanced reptiles; E, mammals.

became restricted to a ventral position while the derivative sections were enlarged so as completely to cover the lobes and tracts from above.

A third trend was toward shift of relative positions of white and gray matter. In anamniotes the gray matter is internal, the white matter external, as in the spinal cord. The mechanical advantage of having the associations occur peripherally where there is little limitation to increase in thickness of the layer is obvious. The shift was gradually accomplished, and culminated in mammals with complete transfer of the gray matter to the periphery of the telencephalon.

A fourth trend was toward increase in number of association centers, or groups of centers, in the cerebral hemispheres (Fig. 16.28). Some four stages are evident. In the most primitive one, as in cyclostomes, a single set of centers existed, comprising all the gray matter of the cerebrum (*paleopallium*) and being solely of olfactory function. In a second stage illustrated to a certain degree by teleosts, two sets of centers existed, with differentiation of a *corpus striatum* from the ventral part of the paleopallium, which name is still retained in reference to parts other than the corpus striatum. The differentiation of corpus striatum represented the first step toward shift of more posterior association centers into the telencephalon. It persists in all tetrapods and seems to be concerned with the most fundamental, largely instinctive, behaviorisms. It has become greatly enlarged in teleosts and birds, especially the latter, in conjunction with the complex instinctive behavior patterns characteristic of each group. In teleosts a marked divergence from the tetrapod course of evolution exists: the olfactory paleopallium is limited to a greatly thickened area lateral to and continuous with the corpus striatum, whereas the roof and much of the sides of the cerebral hemispheres remain extremely thin and nonfunctional. The roof is moderately thin in birds also, but the thickened central area is almost exclusively corpus striatum.

In a third stage of increase in complexity of telencephalic centers, exemplified by amphibians, most reptiles, and all birds, the olfactory paleopallium has become further differentiated with the appearance in its dorsal extremity of an *archipallium,* concerned like the corpus striatum with association with other sensory impulses but unlike the corpus striatum lacking direct motor connections. In most tetrapods the archipallium and corpus striatum account for all cerebral associations. At this stage three major sets of centers (paleopallium, archipallium, corpus striatum) exist in the telencephalon.

In a fourth and final stage, exemplified by some reptiles and all mammals, a *neopallium* differentiated lateral to the archipallium. It is an association center which, more efficiently than any other, permits accumulation and utilization of experience. Other centers permit the same but to a much more limited degree. The neopallium is poorly developed in reptiles and primitive mammals, in which there is little evidence of its unique potentiality. In other mammals it has been greatly enlarged, culminating with the extraordinary hypertrophy seen in man. It seems to have been the seat of the superior cunning and intelligence demonstrated by mammals in general, and by man in particular. The capacity for intelligence provided by this new region—the neopallium—is apparently inexhaustible. The maximum latent potential is thought never to have been closely approximated by even the most brilliant and industrious human. In man approximately 100 billion cortical cells are available, in a continuous blanket measuring about ½ inch in thickness. Its cells are grouped into some six layers commonly recognized, 50 to 100 cells thick (Fig. 16.29). The cells are roughly arranged in vertical columns. The number of correlations these may permit is incomprehensible. It would require several books of this size to write it out in a string of zeros following the numeral 1. Furthermore these cells are grouped according to function, and thus functional areas can be mapped with some accuracy (Fig. 16.30). Curiously enough destruction of an area may eventually be followed by compensatory adaptation by other parts of the brain, performing the same functions equally as well as before, or nearly so.

The variation in ease of cultivation of this enormously complex structure is largely responsible for variation in latent ability—as indeed between forested land on the one hand and bare, fertile prairie on the other. Both can produce, but more labor is required with one than with the other. Industry often makes more of a poor heritage than casual efforts do with good soil. The variations in actual mental potential undoubtedly stem from variations in ease with which synapses are crossed to create and maintain new functional associations.

A fifth evolutionary trend of major importance concerning the telencephalon was the increase in neopallial surface. But a small rudimentary area in reptiles, it became greatly enlarged in primitive mammals, shoving the archipallium (now the *hippocampus*) medially and the paleopallium (olfactory or *pyriform lobe*) ventrally. In more advanced types convoluted

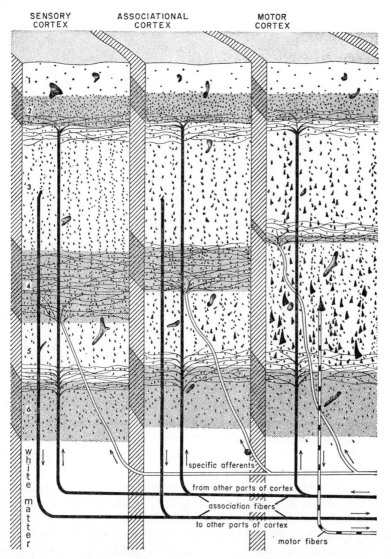

SENSORY   ASSOCIATIONAL   MOTOR
CORTEX   CORTEX   CORTEX

specific afferents

from other parts of cortex

association fibers

to other parts of cortex

motor fibers

FIG. 16.29 Lamination and columnization of cortical cells in the human cerebrum. Afferent pathways from the thalamus (hollow lines) end about in the
center of the cortex (in Zone 4). Association fibers (solid black lines) make associations with other parts of the cortex and with different levels in the same
part (only a few pathways shown); pathways to other cortical parts originate
(as axons) in Zones 3 and 5, and descend to the white matter, whereas those
received by the cortical zones arise from the white matter and are visibly
distributed to Zones 2–3 and 5–6. Motor fibers (dashed lines) originate in a
subcentral layer (Zone 5) and are directed straight out the floor of the brain.
(From Netter.)

ridges (*gyri*) appeared, as a device for increasing the area for association neurons. This trend culminated in man with numerous, closely spaced involutions (*sulci*) between the gyri. In eutherian mammals a special and very large commissure, the *corpus callosum,* developed to connect the enlarged neopallia of the two sides. Throughout the course of increase in neopallial area there was an increase in correlative ability. Man's ability to think, though it be on a level far beyond that realized by any other animal, is not unique.

The rear boundary of the telencephalon coincides dorsally with a deep groove, the *velum transversum,* in front of which is a thin-walled, small evagination, the *paraphysis.* The latter is an extraventricular choroid organ present in the embryonic stage of all vertebrates but in adults only of anamniotes.

The anterior end of the brain in the median plane lies in most vertebrates at a level near the rear part of the cerebral hemispheres. The latter have, in effect, grown forward on either side of the primitive median anterior end. The narrow wall at this point between the two hemispheres is the *lamina terminalis.* It, and a small anterior part of the third ventricle, actually belong to the telencephalon despite a more prominent morphological continuity with the diencephalon.

Diencephalon. This is a narrowed portion of the brain, often overgrown by other parts, housing a rather large third ventricle. Its dorsal wall is the *epithalamus,* the lateral walls the *thalamus,* and the ventral wall the *hypothalamus.* Each part possesses specialized topographic features.

The epithalamus consists chiefly of a thin-walled membrane contributing to a *choroid plexus.* Parts of the roof are evaginated as the *pineal* and *parietal* organs, discussed in the preceding chapter. At the rear, near the mesencephalon, a *habenula* serving as an olfactory nucleus, and a *posterior commissure,* are present.

The thalamus consists of a more ventral somatic motor relay division and a more dorsal somatic sensory division. The motor division serves as a pathway for huge pyramidal or corticospinal tracts between cerebral centers and the spinal cord and cranial nerves. The sensory division in anamniotes handles some somatic sensory impulses, relaying them to the cerebral hemispheres, and in amniotes assumes an important role in this regard in correlation with the development of pallial (cortical) association centers. In mammals, with their complex neopallium, the thalamus is of still greater importance in this respect. Optic centers form protrusions, the *pulvinar* and *lateral geniculate body,* as does the auditory center (*medial geniculate body*), and the two lateral walls fuse across the third ventricle in a cylindrical mass (not a commissure) called the *middle commissure* or *intermediate mass.* The *optic tracts* enter the thalamus in all vertebrates, but in lower vertebrates their relays are chiefly to more posterior levels of the brain.

The hypothalamus includes the optic chiasma, the pituitary gland, and a number of other different features in different vertebrates. The floor, that comprises most of its area, is an association center—the highest in the

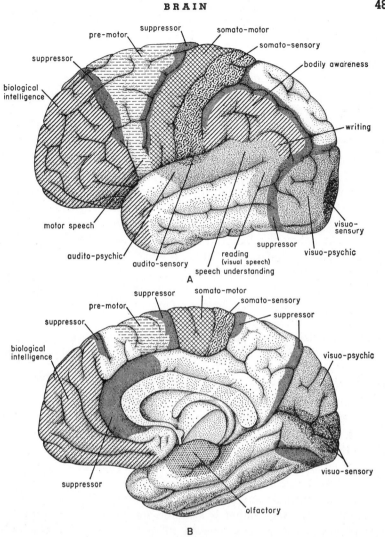

FIG. 16.30 Location of certain motor and sensory areas (centers) on the cerebral cortex, as seen in lateral (A) and midsagittal (B) views of the human cerebrum. (From Netter.)

brain for coordination of general visceral motor functions. All truly involuntary actions, for example temperature control, rate of breathing, sexual impulses, the emotions, and sleep are under hypothalamic control. All visceral sensory impulses including olfaction and taste are integrated here with each other and with involuntary motor control. The *tuber cinereum,* and in mammals the *mammillary* bodies, are centers of olfactory function; their hypertrophy in mammals is a reflection of the increased efficiency of the nasal organs.

Mesencephalon. Even as the initial specialization of the telencephalon in the role of the dominant association area in mammals may be traced to the groveling habits of their amphibian and reptilian ancestors, requiring reliance upon olfactory organs, so also can the earlier parallel role of the mesencephalon be traced to the domination of the optic sense organs. Proprioceptive and autonomic adjustments have been suggested or even carried out by the cerebellum and diencephalon, respectively, before impulses reach the nuclei of the mesencephalon. There an awareness of the situation, and readjustment to fit incoming information from all sources, takes place in fishes, amphibians, and primitive reptiles (Fig. 16.31). In later amniotes the mesencephalon has become progressively less dominant, its activities restricted to important sensory and motor relay (Fig. 16.32).

The walls of the mesencephalon are all thickened, with a few prominences marking the position of certain nuclei and tracts. The dorsal wall, or *tectum,* is expanded into two conspicuous lobes, the *optic lobes* (*corpora bigemina*) in nonmammalian vertebrates. In mammals a second pair of lobes, the *posterior* (inferior) *colliculi,* is added to accommodate the auditory function which reaches a peak of development in that class. The actual nuclei of the posterior colliculi appear in amphibians with the elaboration of a hearing function for the inner ear (previously of vestibular functions only), but only in the mammals do they gain sufficient size to be recognizable superficially. The optic lobes are in mammals termed the *anterior* (superior) *colliculi,* the four colliculi collectively forming the *corpora quadrigemina.*

The corpora bigemina appear to serve in fishes and amphibians as the seat of consciousness. They are largely or wholly supplanted by the cerebrum in amniotes, leaving the tectum with only reflexive optic and auditory functions. Most of the conscious optic function, formerly restricted to it, shifts to the cerebrum.

The mesencephalic floor and side walls, or *tegmentum,* are marked by a pair of large motor tracts on the ventral surface, the *cerebral peduncles,* directed to the medulla and spinal cord. The rest is unmarked by superficial features. The tegmentum is a motor area of major importance, all motor pathways either being relayed there in its substance or passing through to lower levels. One or more nuclei tend to form in it in higher

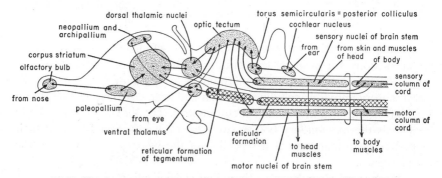

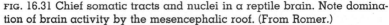

FIG. 16.31 Chief somatic tracts and nuclei in a reptile brain. Note domination of brain activity by the mesencephalic roof. (From Romer.)

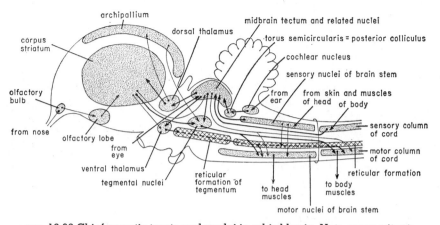

FIG. 16.32 Chief somatic tracts and nuclei in a bird brain. Note concomitant domination of brain activity by the mesencephalic roof and corpus striatum. (From Romer.)

vertebrates; among mammals the *red nucleus* is especially important (Fig. 16.33).

Metencephalon. Originally the brain lobe associated with the otic capsule, the cerebellum has maintained throughout vertebrates a role in integration of muscular activity. The otic organ itself was primitively of proprioceptive function only, revealing position and movement. To the sensory impulses of this nature supplied by the ear are added others from the lateral line system and from muscle sense organs, providing a complete picture of the situation relative to bodily orientation and revealing the adjustment necessary for it.

Proprioceptive adjustment is initiated by the cerebellum whose impulses are relayed to the tegmentum. In most vertebrates they are then relayed to the motor tracts of the medulla and spinal cord, but in mammals they are diverted to the thalamus and thence to the cerebrum, returning via direct pathways to the medulla and spinal cord.

With the integration of cerebral and cerebellar cortex in mammals, a large tract, the pons, conducting impulses from the cerebrum to the cerebellum, appears for the first time. To handle this new source of information a *cerebellar hemisphere* develops on each side, exceeding in size the more primitive proprioceptive *vermis* between. Purely vestibular otic functions (not auditory) are restricted in anamniotes to the *auricles,* one on each side of the *body* of the cerebellum. In amniotes the auricles become somewhat modified as *flocculi,* losing their internal cavity (continuous with the fourth ventricle), but retaining the same function. In mammals the hemispheres form between the flocculus and body on each side, the body itself becoming the vermis. The area for association neurons has in mammals become greatly augmented by formation of many ridgelike folds (*folia*) separated from each other by grooves (sulci).

Despite the differentiation and enlargement of parts of the cerebel-

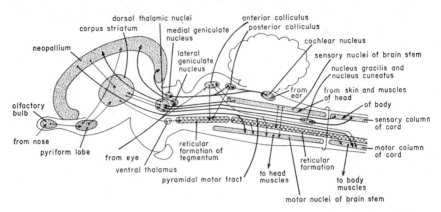

FIG. 16.33 Chief somatic tracts and nuclei in a mammal brain. Note shift of domination of brain activity to the cerebral cortex (neopallium). (From Romer.)

lum and mesencephalon in mammals, the impression remains that, were it possible to circumvent recapitulation of ancient patterns of association in the brain and retain only the essential cerebral, diencephalic, and medullary connections, the mammalian brain could be greatly reduced in size and complexity without interference with efficiency.

Medulla. The medulla receives, or emits, most of the cranial nerves. It also invariably possesses a thin dorsal wall serving as a choroid plexus. These are the two most prominent gross features of the medulla. It is arranged basically like the spinal cord, with a thick outer covering of white matter around the central gray matter and with the typical spinal arrangement of columns and tracts in a dorsoventral sequence of sensory and motor components.

QUESTIONS

1. What are the two types of cells composing the nervous system? Give an example of each.

2. How many types of neuroglial cells are there? Name one. What is their gross embryonic origin?

3. Distinguish axons and dendrites in six ways.

4. What governs direction of impulse in a neuron? How?

5. Name and distinguish as completely as possible the kind of sheaths occurring on neurons.

6. Exactly what is the distribution of the neuron sheaths?

7. Name and differentiate the gross components of the nervous system.

8. Describe the embryonic stages leading up to formation of a neurocele.

9. What are the components of the reflex arc?

10. How do instincts, reflexes and set patterns of thoughtful responses differ?

11. Name and characterize the seven conductive functions of neurons.

12. How does arrangement of white and gray matter differ in parts of the brain (be specific) and in the spinal cord?

13. Diagram and label a cross section of the spinal cord and somatic rami of a spinal nerve, showing columns, funiculi, and the four functional pathways of the rami.

14. Contrast the primitive spinal nerve (as of cyclostomes) and its functional components with that found in gnathostomes.

15. Name the rami of spinal nerves and delimit the area of innervation of each ramus.

16. Distinguish the autonomic system from other divisions of the nervous system in (a) function (one way) and in (b) anatomy (five ways).

17. Distinguish the sympathetic and parasympathetic systems eight ways; be able to elaborate upon each of the differences.

18. Diagram the structure of the human sympathetic system labeling nerves, ganglia, and organs innervated, and distinguishing pre- and postganglionic fibers.

19. Diagram the structure of the human parasympathetic system labeling nerves, ganglia, and organs innervated, and distinguishing pre- and postganglionic fibers.

20. Distinguish the dorsal, ventral, and gray rami from each other as completely as possible on the basis of the identity and function of the neurites composing them.

21. What is an exception to the rule that two neurons are present in autonomic pathways?

22. Name and locate the ganglia of the parasympathetic system and state the function of each.

23. Distinguish (a) thoracolumbar, (b) midsacral, and (c) all other spinal nerves collectively on the basis of gross morphology and identity and function of neurites contained within the visceral ramus.

24. Differentiate the cranial and the sacral outflow according to area of the body innervated.

25. Name the cranial nerves in order.

26. Name the ganglia of the cranial nerves and state the function as fully as possible.

27. How does each of the first three so-called cranial nerves (0–2) differ from the others?

28. Specify the nerves of each branchial arch, and insofar as possible indicate the pre- and postrematic derivatives.

29. List the differences between amniotes and anamniotes in their cranial nerves and branches thereof.

30. Group the cranial nerves according to function, and specify the functions of each.

31. Name the myotomic muscles of each craniopharyngeal segment and give their innervation. Same, branchiomeric muscles.

32. Specify to what part of the brain each cranial nerve is attached.

33. How can it be explained that the olfactory and optic nerves do not constitute exceptions to the rule that sensory nerves invariably have ganglia?

34. Trace and account for the evolution of the meninges.

35. Name and locate the features of the encephalic neurocele, and trace its evolution.

36. Describe and give examples of the five types of mechanical modification of the brain.

37. Where are the mammalian brain flexures located?

38. What is thought to have been a moving factor in shift to the telencephalon of lower association centers?

39. Name five evolutionary trends relating to the telencephalon.

40. Describe differentiation of olfactory tracts, lobes, and bulbs.

41. Trace the increase in number of groups of centers in the telencephalon through four stages, naming structures involved.

42. What is the paraphysis and its function?

43. The velum transversum has what topographic significance? The lamina terminalis?

44. Name the parts of the epithalamus and the function of each, insofar as possible.

45. Name the parts of the mammalian thalamus and the functions thereof; hypothalamus.

46. How does the tectum of amniotes and anamniotes differ in function?

47. Trace the anatomical evolution of the parts of the tectum, naming pertinent structures.

48. Account for the double innervation existing in the autonomic system. What has been the course of its evolution?

49. Account for the absence of a glandular source of acetylcholine, whereas there is a glandular source of adrenalin. What is a suspected parallel in the parasympathetic system of the sympathetic system's adrenal gland?

50. Describe the three possible choices of general pathways for sympathetic impulses emerging at any level.

51. How does the scope of the terms cerebral hemisphere and olfactory lobe differ?

52. What are the approximate dimensions of the human neopallium, in terms of thickness and number of cells?

53. Define and give the functions of the neopallium.

54. Name the three divisions of the diencephalon.

55. Presumably where was the neopallial function performed in the Ichthyopsida, which lack a neopallium?

56. What is the function of the cerebellum?

57. Name the mammalian meninges in order from exterior to interior, and describe the location and form of each. Cite their functions.

58. Name the components of a choroid plexus. Describe the operation of the mammalian choroid circulatory mechanism.

59. How is extraventricular circulation in the central nervous system accomplished in mammals? What are the two primary sources of cerebrospinal fluid?

60. What is the role of the choroid plexi? Foramina of Luschka and Magendie?

61. Name four adjustments to the problems of nutrition in the CNS and four unique features of the independent circulation thereof.

62. Explain why the brain needs the most highly oxygenated blood available in the body.

63. Name the primordial divisions of the brain and the subdivisions to which each later gives rise.

64. What is the functional importance underlying the differentiation of each of the three primordial divisions of the brain?

65. Define the following words as given in the glossary:

abducens
adrenergic
afferent
anterior cervical
  ganglion
anterior colliculus
anterior mesenteric
  ganglion
aqueduct (of Sylvius,
  or cerebral)
arachnoid meninx
arachnoid villus
arbor vitae
archipallium
association neuron
auditory (nerve)
auricle
autonomic
autonomic nervous
  system
axis cylinder
axon
basal (ganglia, nuclei)
body of cerebellum
brachial plexus
buccal nerve
canalis centralis
cauda equina
celiac ganglion
central nervous system
cerebellum
cerebral hemisphere
cerebrospinal fluid
chiasma
cholinergic
choroid plexus
ciliary ganglion
cochlear ganglion
collateral ganglion
commissure
corpora bigemina
corpora quadrigemina
corpus callosum
corpus striatum
cranial nerve
craniosacral outflow

decussation
deep ophthalmic nerve
dendrite
diencephalon
dura mater
effector
efferent
encephalon
end arborization
ependyma
epithalamus
facial nerve
filum terminale
flexure (brain; 3 types)
flocculus
folia
funiculus
ganglion
Gasserian ganglion
general (visceral or so-
  matic, motor or sen-
  sory)
geniculate ganglion
geniculate body
  (lateral, medial)
glossopharyngeal nerve
gray matter
gyrus
habenula
habit
hippocampus
hyomandibular nerve
hypoglossal nerve
hypothalamus
infundibulum
instinct
intermediate mass
interventricular
  foramina
jugular ganglion
lamina terminalis
lateral nerve
lumbosacral plexus
Luschka, foramen of
mammillary body
mandibular nerve

Magendie, foramen of
maxillary nerve
medulla oblongata
medullary sheath
meninx
mesencephalon
mesocele
metencephalon
middle cervical
  ganglion
middle commissure
Monro, foramina of
motor
myelencephalon
myelin
neopallium
nerve
nervous system
nervus terminalis
neurilemma
neurite
neurobiotaxis
neurocele
neuroeffector junction
neuroglia
neurohumor
neuron
nodosal ganglion
nucleus
oculomotor nerve
olfactory (bulb, lobe,
  nerve, tract)
optic (lobe, nerve,
  tract)
otic (ganglion, nerve)
palatine nerve
paleopallium
paraphysis
parasympathetic
parasympathin
paravertebral ganglion
peduncle, cerebral
peripheral nervous
  system
petrosal ganglion
pharyngeal nerve

pia mater
posterior cervical
    ganglion
posterior colliculus
posterior commissure
posterior mesenteric
    ganglion
postganglionic
postrematic nerve
postrenal
preganglionic
prerenal
pretrematic nerve
primitive meninx
prosencephalon
pulvinar body
pyriform lobe
ramus (dorsal, gray,
    ventral, visceral,
    white)
Ranvier (node of)
red nucleus
reflex
rhombencephalon
root (dorsal, ventral)

satellite cells
Schwann, sheath of
secondary meninx
semilunar ganglion
sensory
somatic (motor,
    sensory)
special (visceral or so-
    matic, motor or sen-
    sory)
sphenopalatine
    ganglion
spinal accessory nerve
spinal nerve
splanchnic nerves
stellate ganglion
submaxillary ganglion
sulcus
superficial ophthalmic
    nerve
superior ganglion
sympathetic
sympathetic chain
sympathin
synapse

tectum
tegmentum
tela choroidea
telencephalon
telodendria
terminal ganglion,
    nerve
thalamus
thoracolumbar outflow
thoughtful response
tract
trigeminus nerve
trochlear nerve
tuber cinereum
vagus nerve
velum transversum
ventricle (cerebellar,
    first, second, third,
    fourth, of the brain)
vermis
vestibular ganglion
visceral (motor,
    ramus, sensory)
white matter

DICTIONARY

of Greek and Latin Terms

SINCE LATIN OR GREEK is the source of most scientific terms, the understanding and recollection of them is greatly facilitated by knowledge of a few combining forms from these primary source languages. The following list includes most of the commonly encountered words and prefixes; most of the terms that have identical meanings in scientific and original usage have been omitted. More complete lists and definitions may be found in any of the following references:

BROWN, ROLAND WILBUR, *Composition of scientific names.* Publ. by author, Washington, D. C.: U. S. National Museum, 1954.

CLEMENTS, F. E., *Greek and Latin in biological nomenclature. Nebraska Univ. Studies,* 1902, 3: 1–85.

GOODELL, T. D., *The Greek in English.* New York: Henry Holt and Company, 1927.

JAEGER, E. C., *A source-book of biological names and terms.* Springfield, Ill.: Charles C. Thomas, 1944.

MILLER, WALTER, *Scientific names of Latin and Greek derivation. Proc. Calif. Acad. Sci.,* 1897, Ser. 2, 1 (3): 115–143.

PEPPER, O. H., *Medical etymology.* Philadelphia: W. B. Saunders Company, 1949.

WOODS, ROBERT S., *A naturalist's lexicon.* Pasadena, Calif.: Abbey Garden Press, 1944.

In using this dictionary, look in the proper alphabetical position for matching letter combinations for as many of the letters of the word—in sequence from its beginning—as possible. If the meaning has no connection, try shorter sequences of letters. If more of the letters remain, attempt to find these also. With some experience the meaningful combinations will become evident. For example, αποδα might be thought to consist of the parts απο-δα (απο = *from*), but it actually is composed of the parts α-ποδα (*without foot*). A scientific word may be composed of as many as three or four combining terms. Letters between the terms, or endings for them, are usually altered for the sake of euphony or to produce a pronounceable word, or in conformity with certain rules of agreement in case or number endings.

Although in many cases the original meanings of the combining terms are very appropriate for the modern scientific usage intended, an exact parallel cannot always be found by the originator of a new scientific name. Usually there is some connection of meaning although it is sometimes fanciful to different degrees. Ordinarily a modern term composed of two or more terms is derived from but one language; deriving a single word from parts originating from two languages (for example, polylineatus, from the Greek poly for *many*, and the Latin lineatus for *lined*) is frowned upon.

Plurals for singular forms of words of Latin derivation are formed as follows:

> words ending in -*a*, plural -*ae*.
> words ending in -*e*, plural -*ia*.
> words ending in *ex*, plural -*ices*.
> words ending in *inx*, plural -*inges*.
> words ending in *is*, plural -*es*.
> words ending in *ix*, plural -*ices*.
> words ending in *men*, plural -*mina*.
> words ending in *u*, plural -*ua*.
> words ending in *um*, plural -*a*.
> words ending in *ur*, plural -*ora*.
> words ending in *us*, plural -*i*.
> words ending in *ut*, plural -*ita*.

Plurals for singular forms of words of Greek origin ending in -*ma* are formed as -*mata,* and those in -*thrix* as -*triches.*

α-. G., L., prefix meaning without, from, away, used preceding consonants

ab-. L., prefix meaning without, from, away; used preceding vowels

acantha. G., thorn

acetabulum. L., vinegar cup

acro-. G., prefix meaning top

actis. G., *aktis,* ray

acusticos. G., pertaining to hearing

ad-. L., prefix changed to ac-, af-, ag-, etc., the final letter being replaced by the same as that which follows it, meaning toward, to, upon

adenos-. G., a gland

adros-. G., thick, swollen, bulky, strong, great

agon. G., struggle

ala. L., wing

alba. L., white

allas. G., sausage

allelon. G., of one another, mutually, each other, in turn

alveolus. L., little cavity

amnion. G., bowl, especially for catching blood of sacrificial victims

amphi-. G., prefix meaning both, double

ampulla. L., flask

an-. G., prefix meaning without; used preceding vowels

ana-. G., up, upon, throughout, back, again, similar to

anastomosis. G., a joining, as of two seas

ancon. G., *ankon,* bend of the arm, the elbow

angulus. L., corner

ankylos-. G., bent

annulus. L., a ring

ansa. L., handle

ant-, anti-. G., prefix meaning against, opposed to

antron. G., cave

aortē. G., to lift

Aphrodite. G., Venus

apo-. G., from

apsis. L., G., arch

aqua. L., water

arachnē. G., spider

arbor. L., tree

archos. G., chief, first

arcualis. L., *arcuatus*, bow-shaped

arcus. L., bow

arena. L., sand

arthron. G., joint

artios. G., even numbered

arytaino. G., pitcher, funnel, jug

ascidion. G., leather bottle

astragalos. G., ankle bone

atavus. L., ancestor

atrium. L., hall, entrance room

audire. L., to hear

auricula. L., little ear

aut-, auto-. G., *autos*, prefix meaning self

axōn. G., axle

baculum. L., a staff

balanos. G., acorn

basis. G., base, bottom, foundation

bathys. G., deep, low, broad

bi-. L., prefix meaning two

bios. G., life

blastos. G., germ, bud, blossom

bovinus. L., pertaining to oxen

brachiōn. G., arm, upper arm

branchion. G., gill

bryo. G., to be full of, to swell, sprout up

bryon. G., seaweed, tree moss

bucca. L., cheek, mouth

bulla. L., round seal or locket

bursa. L., purse

caeno-. G., *kainos*, new

calcaneum. L., heel

callositas, callosum-. L., hard-skinned, thick-skinned

calx. L., heel

calyx. L., husk, cup-shaped covering

campe. G., caterpiller

canis. L., dog

capillus. L., hair

capitulum. L., small head

caput. L., head

cardia. G., *kardia*, heart

caro, carnis. L., flesh

carpes. G., *karpos*, wrist

cauda. L., tail

cavernosus. L., full of cavities, hollow

cavum. L., hollow

cecus. L., *caecus*, blind

celia. G., *koilia*, stomach

celos. G., *koilos*, hollow

ceno. G., *kainos*, new

centrum. G., *kentron*, center

cephale. G., *kephale*, head

ceps. L., head

cera. L., wax

cercus. G., *kerkos*, tail

cerebellum. L., little brain

cerebrum. L., brain

cerno. L., to separate (excretory)

cerumen. L., earwax

cervix, cervical. L., *cervix, cervicis*, neck

ceto-. G., *kētos*, sea monster, whale

chaeta. L., bristle

cheir. G., hand

chelōnē. G., turtle

chiasma. G., cross-mark

chiro-. G., *cheir*, hand

choana. G., *choanē*, funnel

chole. G., bile

chondros. G., cartilage, gristle

chorde. G., string

chorion. G., membrane

choris. G., isolated

chrōma, chrōs. G., color

cid. L., to cut

cilium. L., eyelid, eyelash

cinereus. L., ashy

cipitis. L., of the head

circum. L., prefix meaning around

cirrus. L., a curl

clava. L., branch, club

cleido-, cleid-. G., *kleido-*, locked up, to close; *kleis*, key

cleithr-. G., *kleithron*, bar, gate

clisto-. G., *kleistos*, closed, enclosed

cloaca. L., sewer

cnemis. G., *kneme*, shank

cochlea. L., snail

collus. L., neck

colon. G., kolon, member

columella. L., little column

comma. G., *komma*, that which is cut off, fragment

concha. L., shell
condylus. L., knuckle
conidium, conidia. G., *konis,* dust
conjunctus. L., joining together
copro-. G., *kopros,* dung
cor, cordis. L., heart, of the heart
coraco-. G., *korax,* raven, crow
corneus. L., horny
cornu. L., horn
corona. L., crown
corone. G., *korone,* crow
corpus, corpora. L., body
cortex. L., bark, rind
cosmos. G., *kosmos,* orderly arrangement
costa. L., rib
cotyle. G., *kotyle,* cupshaped
cranio-. G., *kranion,* skull
creat. G., *kreas,* flesh
creta. L., chalk
cribrum. L., sieve
crico-. G., *kricos,* ring
crino. G., *krinos,* to separate, pick out
crista. L., crest
crossoi. G., fringe
crus. (pl. crura), L., leg
crypto-. G., *kryptos,* secret, hidden
cteno-. G., *kteis, ktenos,* comb
cucullaris. L., hoodshaped
cum. L., together
cuneus. L., wedge
cutis. L., skin
cyclo-. G., *kyklos,* circle
cyst. G., *kystis,* bladder
cyto-. G., *kytos,* cell

dactylo-. G., *dactylos,* toe, finger
daeum. G., division
de-. L., prefix meaning off, down, away from, deprived of
decussatus. L., crossed, divided crosswise
defero. L., to carry away
delos. G., evident
delta. G., triangle
demi-. G., part, half
demos. G., people, population
dendron. G., stick, tree
dens, dentis. L., tooth, of teeth
denticulus. L., little tooth
derma. G., leather, skin
desmos. G., ligament, binding
deutero-. G., *deuteros,* secondary
di-. G., two

dia. G., between, throughout, crosswise, across, during, over
diastema. G., interval
dicha. G., in two, asunder
didymos. G., testis
dieileo. G., to unroll
digitus. L., finger, toe
diphyes. G., twofold, double
diplosis. G., a doubling
duco. L., to lead
ductor. L., leader
ductus. L., duct
duodeni. L., twelve; in reference to man's duodenum, 12 fingerbreadths long
dura. L., hard

e-, ef-, ex-. L., out, beyond, away
ecdysis. G., *ekdysis,* act of undressing
echinatus. L., spiny, prickly
eco-, oeco-, oikos-. G., house
ect, ecto. G., *ektos,* G., outer, outside
eidos, oidos. G., form, appearance
elasmo-. G., *elasmos,* plate, septum
embryon. G., fetus
encephalos. G., *enkephalos,* brain
enchyma. G., in a fluid
end-, endo-. G., within
endyma. G., garment
enteron. G., gut
ep-, epi-. G., upon
equinus. L., relating to a horse
ergon. G., work
eso-. G., *oiso,* I carry
esophagos. G., food-carrier
ethmo-. G., sieve
eu-. G., true
eury. G., broad
evolutus. L., unrolled
exo-. G., outside
exuviae. L., that which is stripped off

fabella. L., little bean
facies. L., face
falx, falcis. L., sickle
fascia. L., band, bandage
fasciculus. L., little bundle
fauces. L., throat
femur. L., thigh
fenestra. L., window
fero, ferentis. L., to bear, bearing
fibula. L., clasp, buckle, splint
filum. L., thread

fimbria. L., border, fringe, threads

findo. L., to cleft, split

fissura. L., split, cleft, fissure

flagellum. L., little whip

flocculus. L., a little piece or tuft of wool

folium. L., leaf

folliculus. L., a small bag

fontanelle. F., a little fountain

foramen, foramina. L., an opening

fornix. L., arch, vault

fossa. L., pit, cavity

fovea. L., small pit

frenulum. L., little bridle, bit

frons, frontis. L., brow

fundus. L., bottom

fungus. L., mushroom

funiculus. L., small rope, cord

furcula. L., little fork

gametes. G., spouse

ganglion. G., tumor

ganosis. G., brightening

gaster. G., L., stomach, belly

gastrula. L., little stomach

geminus. L., a twin

geneion. G., chin

geniculatus. L., having a kneelike knot

geno, genesis. G., formation

genos. G., descent, clan, race

genu. L., knee

genys. G., chin

germino. L., to sprout.

gigno. L., to reproduce

glans. L., acorn

glene. G., cavity

glia. G., glue

glomerulus. L., little ball

glomus. L., ball, especially of yarn

glossa, glotta. G., tongue

gluteus. G., *gloutos,* rump

gnathos. G., jaw

gone, gonos. G., seed

gracilis. L., slender

gradior, gressus. L., to step, walk

gradus. L., a step

granulum. L., small grain

gubernaculum. L., rudder

gula. L., throat

gusto. L., to taste

gyne, gynaikos. G., woman

gyros. G., round, turn, circle

habenula. L., little strap

hallux. L., big toe

hamatus. L., hooked

hamulus. L., little hook

hedone. G., pleasure

hemi-. G., half

hemo-. G., *haima,* blood

hepar. G., liver

Hermes. G., Mercury

herpes. G., crawler

hetero-. G., *hekros,* different

hilum. L., trifle

hippos. G., horse

holo-. G., *holos,* whole, entire

homo-. G., *homos,* symmetrical, equal, alike, uniform, same

homologia. G., conformity

hormao. G., to excite

hyaleos. G., glassy, shiny

hyoides. G., Y-shaped

hyp-, hypo-. G., L., *hypo-,* below, less than

hyper. G., over, above

ichthys. G., fish

ileo-. G., *eilein,* to twist, wind, turn

ilium. L., flank

in-. L., prefix meaning in, without

incido. L., to cut into

incisus. L., cut

incus. L., anvil

infra-. L., prefix meaning below

infundibulum. L., funnel

inguen. L., groin

innominatus. L., nameless

insula. L., an island, e. g., the Islands of Langerhans

intego. L., to cover

inter-. L., prefix meaning between

intercalo. L., to put between

intestinus. L., inside

intra-, intro-. L., prefix meaning within

iris, iridos. G., rainbow

ischion. G., hip

iso-, isos. G., equal, alike, uniform

iter. L., passage

jejunus. L., empty, hungry, fasting

jugulum. L., collar bone

jugum. L., yoke

Jurassique. F., pertaining to Jura Mts.

keras. G., horn
kinesis. G., movement

labium. L., lip
lacerta. L., lizard
lacrima. L., tear
lagena. L., flask
lagos. G., hare
lamina, lamella. L., thin sheet
larynx. G., gullet
latissimus. L., broadest
latus. L., broad
lekithos. G., yolk
lemma. G., rind, peel, bark
lepis. G., scale
leptos. G., slender, thin, weak
leukos. G., white
levator. L., lifter
lien. L., spleen
linea. L., line
lingua. L., tongue
lipos. G., fat
lithos. G., stone
lobos. G., lobe
logos. G., due ratio, word, discourse
longissimus. L., longest
longus. L., long
lophos. G., crest
lumbus. L., back, groin, loin
luna. L., moon
luteus. L., yellow
lympha. L., clear water

macro-. G., *makros,* large, long
macula. L., spot
magnus. L., great
major. L., the greater -
mala. L., cheek
malleolus. L., little hammer
malleus. L., hammer
mamma. L., breast
mandibula. L., jaw
manubrium. L., handle
manus. L., hand
margo. L., border
marsupium. L., pouch
marsypos. G., pouch, bag
maseter. G., a chew
mastos. G., a breast
mater. L., mother
maxilla. L., jaw bone
maximus. L., largest
meatus. L., passage

mediastinus. L., being in the middle
medius. L., middle
medulla. L., marrow, pith
meion. G., less, fewer
melas, melanos. G., black, blackness
meninx, meninges. G., membrane
mentum. L., chin
meros. G., part
mes-, meso-. G., middle
met-, meta-. G., prefix meaning between, after, reversely, change
metabole. G., change
micro-. G., *mikros,* small
mictos. G., *miktos,* mixed, blended, thrown together
minimus. L., least
minor. L., lesser
minys. G., small
mirabilis. L., marvelous, miraculous
mitre. F., a peaked cap
mitto. L., to send, to cause to go
mola. L., millstone
monos. G., one, single
morphe. G., shape
motor. L., mover
multus. L., many
mutatus. L., change
myelos. G., marrow
myle. G., mill
myo-, mys. G., muscle
myxa. G., slime, mucus
myzeo. G., to suck in or upon

naris, nares. L., nostril
natalis. L., pertaining to one's birth
navicular. L., little ship
nekton. G., swimming
neos. G., new
neotes. G., youth, rashness
nephros. G., kidney
neuron. G., tendon, nerve
nicto. L., to wink
nodosus. L., knotty
nomen, nominis. L., name
nomos. G., law
notos. G., back
nucha. L., nape of neck
nucleus. L., kernel

oblongus. L., oblong
obturo. L., to close, shut
occiput. L., back of the head
occlusus. L., shut up

oculus. L., eye

odo. G., *hodos,* way, channel

-oid. G., *eidos,* form, appearance

olene. G., ulna

olfacere. L., to smell

oligos. G., few

ology, logy. G., *logos,* word, the study of, discourse

omasum. L., paunch

omentum. L., fat skin

omos. G., shoulder

omphalos. G., navel

oniskos. G., ass; a type of insect

ontos. G., a being, organism

oön. G., egg

operculum. L., lid

ophis. G., serpent

ophthalmos. G., eye

opisthen, opistho-. G., prefix meaning behind

opsis, optikos. G., appearance, sight, or pertaining thereto

orbiculus. L., a little circle

orbita. L., orbit

orchis. G., testis

ornis, ornithes. G., bird

os, oris. L., mouth

os, ossis. L., bone

ossiculum. L., little bone

osteon. G., bone

ostium. L., mouth, entrance

ostrakon. G., shell

oto, oticos, ous. G., ear, pertaining to ear

ovum. L., egg

oxys. G., sharp

paedo-. G., pertaining to a child

pais, paidos. G., child

palatum. L., palate

paleo-. G., *palaios,* ancient

pallium. L., cloak

palpebra. L., eyelid

pan. G., all

panniculus. L., tattered cloth

papilla. L., nipple, pimple

para-. G., prefix meaning beside, near

pareo. L., to beget

paries, parietis. L., wall

parietalis. L., pertaining to a wall

pas. G., all

patella. L., small pan or dish

pecten. L., comb

pectoralis. L., pertaining to the chest

pediculus, pedunculus. L., little foot

pellucidus. L., translucent

pelvis. L., basin

penna. L., feather; wing

peri. G., around

perissos. G., odd

peristaltikos. G., grasping and compressing

perone. G., pin or brooch (referring to fibula)

pes, pedis. L., foot, or pertaining thereto

petra, petros. G., rock, stone

petrosus. L., rocky

phageton. G., food

phagein. G., to eat

phalanx. G., battle line

phallus. L., G., *phallos,* penis

pharynx. G., throat

phenos. G., visible, open, evident

pherein. G., to bear

pholis. G., heavy scale

phoreus. G., bearer

phos, photos. G., light

phragma, phragmos. G., barricade, enclosure

phren. G., diaphragm

phylon. G., race, tribe

phyo, physis. G., to cause to grow or produce, growth

physa. G., bladder, bellows

pilos. G., felt

pinea. L., pine cone

pinna. L., feather

pisces. L., fish

pisum. L., pea

pituita. L., mucus, slime, phlegm

pius. L., tender, delicate, kind

placenta. L., cake (applied in reference to shape of placenta in man)

placos, plax. G., *plakos,* plate

planta. L., sole of foot

plasma. G., anything formed or molded, an image

plastron. F., breastplate

platys. G., flat, broad

platysma. G., flat plate

plektos. G., plaited, twisted

plektron. G., hammer

pleura. G., rib, side

plexus. L., interweaving

pluma. L., feather

plumula. L., little feather

pneuma. G., breath, spirit

pneusticos. G., breathing

pnoe. G., breath
podos. G., foot
pogon. G., beard
poiesis. G., creation
poikilos. G., varied, changeful
polys. G., much, many
pons. L., bridge
populus. L., a great number of people
poros. G., passage, opening
porta. L., gate
post. L., prefix meaning behind, after
posthion. G., phallus, penis
pre. L., prefix meaning before
primus. L., first
pro. L., G., prefix meaning before, in front
proktos. G., anus
prope. L., near
proprius. L., one's own, special
prostates. G., in the front rank
proteros. G., before
protos. G., first
proximus. L., nearest, next
pseudes. G., false
psoa. G., muscles of loins
psyche. G., mind, soul
pteron. G., fin, wing
pterygion. G., little wing or fin or projection
pubes. L., hair, especially about external genitalia
puce, posthion. G., penis
pulmo. L., lung
pulvinus. L., cushion
pyge. G., rump, buttocks
pyloros. G., gatekeeper
pyrum. L., pear

quadratus. L., square
quattuor. L., four

rachis. G., spine
radius. L., spoke, ray
radix, radices. L., root
ramus. L., branch
raphe. G., *rhaphe,* seam
rectus. L., straight
remex, remiges. L., a rower
remus. L., oar
renes. L., kidneys
reptile. L., reptile
repto. L., to creep
respiro. L., to breath back

rete, retia, retina, reticulum. L., net, nets
retro. L., backward, behind, back
rhachis. G., spine
rhamphos. G., hooked beak
rhinos, rhis. G., nose
rhynchos. G., snout
rodens. L., gnawing
rostrum. L., beak
rugae. L., wrinkles

saccos. G., *sakkos,* sac
sacculus. L., little sac
sacer, sacrum. L., sacred
sagitta. L., arrow
saliva. L., spit
salpinx. G., trumpet
sartor. L., tailor
sarx, sarkos. G., flesh
sauros. G., lizard
scala. L., ladder
scalenos. G., *skalenos,* uneven
scaphe. G., *skaphe,* boat
scapulae. L., shoulder blades
schistos. G., divided, cleft
schizo. G., to split, cleave
sciaticus. L., hip
scleros. G., *skleros,* hard
scrotum. L., pouch
scutum. L., shield
sebum. L., grease
sella. L., seat, saddle
semen, seminis. L., seed, or pertaining thereto
semi-. L., half
septum. L., fence, wall, partition
serra. L., saw
sesamon. G., seed of sesame
sessilis. L., sitting, having a broad foot
sinus. L., curve, cavity, bosom
skelo. G., to make dry
sol. L., sun
solen. G., pipe
soleus. L., sole of foot
soma, somatos. G., body, or pertaining thereto
species. L., kind
sperma. L., sperm
sphen. G., wedge
spheniscos. G., small wedge
sphinkter. G., binder
spiraculum. L., air hole

splanchnon. G., one of viscera; viscus, entrail
splenion. G., bandage
spondylos. G., spool
squama. L., scale
squamatus. L., scaly
stapes. L., stirrup
stasis. G., a placing, standing, posture
statos. G., standing, placed
stego. G., to cover
stella. L., star
stereos. G., solid
sternon. G., breastbone
sthenos. G., strength
stoma. G., mouth
stratum. L., a spread, cover
stria. L., streak, furrow, channel
striatus. L., striped
striola. L., little streak
stylos. G., column
sub. L., prefix meaning under
sulcus. L., furrow, groove
super, supra. L., prefix meaning above
supinus. L., lying with face or palm upward
sutura. L., a sewing together
symphysis. G., union, joining
syn. G., prefix meaning together, with
syrinx. G., pipe

tabularis. L., pertaining to boards or a table
talus. L., ankle, heel
tapetum. L., drape
tarsos. G., flat surface
taxo. G., to put in order, arrange
tectum. L., roof
tegmen. L., covering
tego. L., to cover
tel, tele, telo. G., far away, end
tela. L., web
teleos. G., whole, perfect
tempus. L., time
tendo. L., to stretch
teno, teino. G., to extend, stretch
teres. L., round
testa. L., shell
tetra-. G., four
thalamos. G., chamber, inner room
thalia. G., abundant
theca. G., *theke*, sheath
thele. G., nipple
therion. G., beast
therme. G., heat

thrix. G., hair (singular)
thrombos. G., clot, lump
thyreos. G., shield
tibia. L., shin bone
tomos. G., cutting, dividing
tonos. G., stretched, braced, strain, brace
topos. G., place
tornos. G., compass, wheel, circle, something turned
trabecula. L., little beam
trabs, trabis. L., beam, club, or pertaining thereto
tracheia. G., windpipe
trachys. G., rough
trapeza. G., table
trema. G., hole, opening
tres, tri-. L., three
trichinos. G., of hair
trichos. G., hairs
triploos. G., triple
triquetrus. L., triangular
trochanter. G., a runner
trochlea. L., pulley
trochos. G., wheel
trophos. G., one who feeds
tropis. G., keel
tuber. L., a swelling
tuberculum. L., a little swelling
tubus. L., tube
tumidus. L., swollen
tunica. L., garment, undergarment
turbinal. L., *turbinatus,* contorted
turbo. L., whirling
turcica. L., turkish
tympanum. L., drum
typhlos. G., blind

ulna. L., elbow
ultimus. L., farthest, last, extreme
umbilicus. L., navel
uncus. L., hook
unguis. L., claw, nail
ungula. L., hoof
unus. L., one
upsilon. G., Y-shaped character
uro-. G., *ouro,* tail
ure-. G., *ouron;* L., *urina,* urine
uterus. L., womb
utriculus. L., little bag

vagina. L., sheath
vagus. L., wandering

vallo. L., to surround by a wall
vas, vasa. L., a duct
vastus. L., vast
velum. L., veil
vena. L., vein
venter. L., belly
vermis. L., worm
vertebra. L., joint
vesica. L., bladder
vibrissae. L., hairs in nostrils
villus, villi. L., shaggy hair
viscus. L., internal organ
vita. L., life
vitellus. L., yolk
vitreus. L., glassy
vivus. L., alive

voro. L., to devour
vulva. L., covering

xanthos. G., yellow
xiphos. G., sword

-yle. G., *hyle,* a woods (pterylae)
ypsiloid. G., *upsilon,* Y-shaped

zeugos. G., things paired
zoon. G., animal
zygoma. G., bar, bolt
zygon. G., crossbar, yoke

REFERENCES

To a certain degree the following references supply source material for points of view in the text that might be questioned. For the most part, however, they are selected for their potential general value to the average serious reader. Every student should make an early attempt to glance at as many of the main references of general interest as possible, and in connection with each chapter he should check the potential value that the appropriate special references have for him as a student. It is a mark of maturity to be resourceful in learning and not to depend entirely upon any one source.

GENERAL WORKS

Bolk, L., E. Goppert, E. Kallius, and W. Lobosch, *Handbuch der vergleichenden anatomie der Wirbeltiere,* 6 vols. Berlin: Urban and Schwarzenberg, 1931–1938. The "Bible" of comparative anatomy; a superlatively thorough work.

Brown, Margaret E., *The physiology of fishes,* 2 vols. New York: Academic Press, 1958.

Cole, C. A., *Comparative histology.* New York: Blakiston, 1955.

Cole, F. J., A history of comparative anatomy. London: Macmillan, 1944. The book covers the period from Aristotle to the eighteenth century.

Goodrich, E. S., *Studies in the structure and development of vertebrates.* London: Macmillan, 1930. A comprehensive, scholarly review, systematically arranged, but not including all systems.

Grasse, Pierre-P., *Traité de zoologie,* 17 vols., not all published. Paris: Manson, 1948–   . Completed for chordates are: Vol. 11, echinoderms, hemichordates, protochordates, etc.; Vol. 12, vertebrates in general, including comparative anatomy, embryology; Vol. 13 (3 vols.), fishes; Vol. 15, birds; and Vols. 16–17 (3 vols.), mammals. An indispensable compendium, well-illustrated, competently written, exhaustive.

Gregory, W. K., *Evolution emerging,* 2 vols. New York: The Macmillan Company, 1951. A beautifully illustrated account of vertebrate evolution, largely osteological and paleontological.

Hamilton, W. J., J. D. Boyd, and H. W. Mossman, *Human embryology*. Baltimore: Williams and Wilkins, 1952. The final chapter on comparative vertebrate development is excellent and beautifully and profusely illustrated. Good for embryogenic pattern of the several systems as evident in the best studied of all mammals.

Hyman, L. H., *Comparative vertebrate anatomy*. Chicago: University of Chicago Press, 1942. An extremely concise account of the evolution of various systems.

Maximow, A. A., and William Bloom, *A textbook of histology*. Philadelphia: Saunders, 1948. An encyclopedic source, with the emphasis upon man. An outstanding description of histology and histogenesis of the nervous system.

Neal, H. V., and H. W. Rand, *Comparative anatomy*. New York: Blakiston, 1936. An excellent text, with an unusually good review of theories of chordate origin.

Netter, Frank H., *The Ciba collection of medical illustrations*. Summit, N. J.: Ciba Pharmaceutical Products. Introductory vol., 1948, general coverage; Vol. 1, nervous system, 1953; Vol. 2, reproductive system, 1954; Vol. 3, part 3, liver, biliary tract, and pancreas, 1957. Perhaps the most beautifully illustrated anatomical work ever published; all plates are in color. Human anatomy, pathology, physiology, surgical procedure. No zoologist should fail to examine this series.

Pettingill, Olin Sewall, *A laboratory and field manual of ornithology*. Minneapolis: Burgess, 1956.

Portman, Adolf, *Einführung in die vergleichende morphologie der Wirbeltiere*. Basel, Switzerland: B. Schwabe, 1948. In several respects the best recent college textbook in comparative anatomy. The illustrations are new and original, worthy of inspection even if the text is not read. In German.

Prosser, C. L., *Comparative animal physiology*. Philadelphia: Saunders, 1950. An inexhaustible mine of fascinating information tracing, in so far as possible, the physiological evolution of vertebrates and invertebrates.

Rand, H. W., *The chordates*. New York: Blakiston, 1950. Three sections: a systemic account, a systematic account by class, and a historical account. The last is especially valuable.

Romer, A. S., *The vertebrate body*. Philadelphia: Saunders, 1955. An excellent general text.

Scott, G. G., and J. I. Kendall, *The microscopic anatomy of vertebrates*. Philadelphia: Lea and Febiger, 1947. One of the better comparative histologies.

Wallace, George J., *An introduction to ornithology*. New York: The Macmillan Company, 1955.

Walter, H. E., and Leonard P. Sayles, *Biology of the vertebrates*. New York: The Macmillan Company, 1949. One of the better general texts, entertainingly written.

Wilder, H. H., *The history of the human body*. New York: Henry Holt, 1923. One of the most perceptive evolutionary accounts of vertebrate anatomy. Particularly detailed for integumentary system.

Wolfson, Albert, *Recent studies in avian biology*. Urbana: University of Illinois Press, 1955.

Young, J. Z., *The life of vertebrates*. New York: Oxford University Press, 1950. The organization is taxonomic rather than systemic, but the digestive and respiratory systems receive a novel functional treatment under each taxonomic group, and the account of protochordate anatomy, function, and evolution is stimulating.

INTRODUCTION

Aiken, Henry D. "Introduction" in David Hume, *Dialogues concerning natural religion*. New York: Hafner, 1951. A plea for religious tolerance.

Brough, James, "Time and evolution." Chap. 2, pp. 16–38, in T. Stanley Westoll (ed.), *Studies on fossil vertebrates*. London: University of London, 1958. A provocative discussion.

deBeer, G. R., *Embryos and ancestors*. New York: Oxford University Press, 1951. A brief but highly provocative account forcefully presented. Limited to evolution in ontogenetic processes—an aspect often neglected in accounts of evolution.

Dodson, E. O., *A textbook of evolution*. Philadelphia: Saunders, 1952. Chap. 19, "Retrospect and prospect," pp. 389–398. A brief statement of several speculations on the future of man.

Fromm, Eric, *Man for himself*. New York: Rinehart, 1947. A philosopher's approach to humanism. Lucid but not easy reading. Rather completely inclusive of the psychological and philosophical aspects of humanism.

Gregory, W. K., "On interacting causal networks converging toward observed results in evolution." Chap. 4, pp. 59–70, in *Studies on fossil vertebrates. Op. cit.* University. A very brief review of some "laws" of evolution.

Huxley, Julian, *Evolution in action*. New York: Harper, 1953. An almost wholly philosophical approach via evolution to a religion of science—evolutionary humanism. Very easily readable.

Lerner, I. Michael, *The genetic basis of selection*. New York: Wiley, 1958.

Shapley, Harlow, "Cosmography: an approach to orientation." *Amer. Scientist* (1954), 42(3): 471–486. A brief but somewhat breath-taking glimpse through the portals to an infinitely wide perspective.

Simpson, G. G. *The meaning of evolution*. New Haven, Conn.: Yale University Press, 1949. A semipopular account, the initial chapters laying an evolutionary foundation, the final chapters applying that body of principles to the problems of man.

————, *Life of the past*. New Haven, Conn.: Yale University Press, 1953. Chap. 10, "Theories of evolution," pp. 140–150. A brief but lucid review of the history of evolutionary thought, with a statement of the modern or "synthetic" theory of evolution.

————, *The major features of evolution*. New York: Columbia University Press, 1953. A thorough and scholarly account of the mechanics of evolution, without deliberate attention to philosophical matters; synthesizes features revealed by genetics, neontology, and paleontology. For embryonic features, not there dealt with, see deBeer, above.

Young, J. Z. *Doubt and certainty in science*. New York: Oxford University Press, 1951. A neurological approach to an understanding of why we interpret things as we do. Highly readable, almost conversational; strongly recommended as an antidote for scientific complacency.

PREVERTEBRATES

Brian, Paul, *et. al.*, "Les cordes." In Pierre-P. Grasse, *Traité de zoologie*, vol. 11, pp. 533–1040, figs. 1–460. Paris: Manson, 1948. An encyclopedic source on cephalochordates and urochordates, beautifully illustrated. In French.

Dawydoff, Constantin, *et. al.*, "Embranchement des stomocordes." In *Traité de zoologie. Op. cit.*, pp. 365–532, figs. 1–134. An encyclopedic source on anatomy and taxonomy of hemichordates. In French.

deBeer, G. R., *Embryos and ancestors*. New York: Oxford University Press, 1951. Chaps. 8 and 16, pp. 60–62, 107–108. Stimulating and novel suggestions on vertebrate phylogeny.

Harmer, Sidney F., "Hemichordata." In *Cambridge Natural History*. London: Macmillan, 1904. Vol. 7, pp. 3–32, figs. 1–14. An old but thorough anatomical account.

Herdman, W. A., "Ascidians and amphioxus." In *Cambridge Natural History*. London: Macmillan, 1904. Vol. 7, pp. 35–138, figs. 15–90. An old but thorough anatomical account.

Hyman, L. H., *The invertebrates*: *Protozoa through Ctenophora*. New York: McGraw-Hill, 1940. Chap. 5, "Introduction to the Metazoa," pp. 249–282; Chap. 2, "Classification," pp. 22–43. A definitive synthesis of information having a bearing on the phylogeny of the Metazoa, with a phylogenetic tree of animal groups.

———, *The invertebrates*: *Platyhelminthes and Rhynchocoela, the acoelomate Bilateria*. New York: McGraw-Hill, 1951. Chap. 1, "Introduction to the Bilateria," pp. 1–51. A further analysis of the materials for construction of a metazoan classification.

Ivanov, A. V., "New Pogonophora from Far Eastern Seas." *Syst. Zool.* (1954), 3(2): 69–79, figs. 1–8.

———, "Pogonophora." *Syst. Zool.* (1955), 4(4): 170–178, figs. 1–3. The best descriptive accounts in English of this group.

Lohmann, Hans, *et. al.*, "Tunicata." In Kükenthal's *Handbuch der zoologie*. Berlin: W. de Gruyter (1933–1940), 5(2): 1–768, figs. 1–581. A monographic descriptive and taxonomic account of urochordates. In German.

Newman, H. H., *The phylum Chordata*. New York: The Macmillan Company, 1939. Chaps. 3, 4, and 5, pp. 49–104. One of the best summaries of the protochordates in a comparative anatomy text.

Pietschmann, Victor, "Acrania-Cephalochorda." In Kükenthal's *Handbuch der zoologie*. Berlin: W. de Gruyter (1929), 6(1): 1–124, figs. 1–117. A monographic descriptive and taxonomic account of cephalochordates.

EMBRYOLOGY

Barth, L. G., *Embryology*. New York: Holt, 1953. A concise, lucid account of vertebrate embryology.

deBeer, G. R., *Embryos and ancestors*. New York: Oxford University Press, 1951. Chaps. 1, 2, and 3, pp. 1–33. A vigorous critique of the biogenetic law.

deBeer, G. R., "Prophetic fossils." Chap. 1, pp. 1–15, in T. Stanley Westoll (ed.), *Studies on fossil vertebrates*. London: University of London, 1958. Description of numerous cases of paedomorphosis in vertebrate evolution.

Hyman, L. H., *The invertebrates*: *Protozoa through Ctenophora*. New York: McGraw-Hill, 1940. "Introduction to the Metazoa," Chap. 5, pp. 249–282. This chapter includes a highly illuminating discussion of the biogenetic law, summarizing eight aspects pointed out by Sewertzoff.

Nelson, Olin E., *Comparative embryology of the vertebrates*. New York: Blakiston, 1953.

Romer, A. S., "Orgin of the amniote egg." *Sci. Monthly* (1957), 85:57–63, figs. 1–5.

Smith, H. M., "Paleogenesis the modern successor to the biogenetic law." *Turtox News* (1956), 34:178–180, 212–215.

Witschi, Emil, *Development of vertebrates*. Philadelphia: Saunders, 1956.

VERTEBRATE CLASSIFICATION

Berg, Leo S., *Classification of fishes, both recent and fossil*. Ann Arbor, Mich.: Edwards, 1947.

Blair, W. F., *et. al.*, *Vertebrates of the United States*. New York: McGraw-Hill, 1957.

Brattstrom, Bayard H., David L. Jameson, and Grace L. Orton, "Problems in the phylogeny of the Salientia." *Syst. Zool.* (1957), 6(2):70–74.

Darlington, Philip J., *Zoogeography: the geographical distribution of animals*. New York: Wiley, 1957. A thorough analysis of the origin and distribution of vertebrates.

Inger, Robert F., "Ecological aspects of the origins of the tetrapods." *Evolution* (1957), 11(3):373–376.

Mayr, Ernst, and Dean Amadon, "A classification of recent birds." *Amer. Mus. Novitates* (1951), 1496:1–42.

Piveteau, Jean, *Traité de paléontologie*. Paris: Manson, 1955. Vol. 4, fishes; Vol. 5, amphibians, reptiles, birds; Vol. 6, mammals. Voluminous, detailed, well-illustrated descriptive accounts.

Robertson, James P., "The habitat of the early vertebrates." *Biol. Rev.* (1957), 32(2): 156–187. A very thorough review and fresh analysis of the problem.

Simpson, G. G., "The principles of classification and a classification of mammals." *Bull. Amer. Mus. Nat. Hist.* (1945), 85:i–xvi, 1–350.

White, E. I., "Original environment of the craniates." Chap. 11, pp. 212–234, in T. Stanley Westoll (ed.), *Studies on fossil vertebrates*. London: University of London, 1958.

INTEGUMENTARY SYSTEM

Fox, D. L., "The pigments of fishes." Chap. 7, pp. 367–386, in Margaret E. Brown (ed.), *The physiology of fishes*, Vol. 2. New York: Academic Press, 1957.

Harvey, E. Newton, "The luminous organs of fishes." Chap. 6, pp. 345–366, in *The physiology of fishes. Op. cit.*

Odiorne, J. M., "Color changes." Chap. 8, pp. 387–402, in *The physiology of fishes. Op. cit.*

Parker, H. W., "Luminous organs in lizards." *J. Linnean Soc. London, Zool.* (1939), 40:658–660, pl. 22.

Smith, H. M., "The phylogeny of hair and epidermal scales." *Turtox News* (1958), 38:82–84, figs. 1–2.

Taylor, E. H., and A. B. Leonard, "Concerning the relationship of certain neotropical gekkonid lizard genera, with comments on the microscopical structure of their scales." *Univ. Kans. Sci. Bull.* (1956), 38:1019–1029, figs. 1–2.

Van Oosten, John, "The skin and scales." Chap. 7, pp. 207–244, in *The physiology of fishes*, Vol. 1. *Op. cit.*

SKELETAL SYSTEM: GENERAL

deBeer, G. R., *The development of the vertebrate skull.* New York: Oxford University Press, 1937. An almost encyclopedic reference volume.

Jayne, H., *Mammalian anatomy.* Philadelphia: Lippincott, 1898. Part 1, "The skeleton of the cat." A rare volume with an absolutely unexcelled illustrated description of the cat skeleton.

Kingsley, J. S., *The vertebrate skeleton.* Philadelphia: Blakiston, 1925. An excellent general account.

Reynolds, S. H., *The vertebrate skeleton,* 2d ed. Cambridge, Eng.: Cambridge University Press, 1913. One of the most completely representative comparative osteologies in the English language.

Romer, A. S., *Osteology of the reptiles.* Chicago: University of Chicago Press, 1956. An exhaustive and authoritative account.

POSTPHARYNGEAL AXIAL SKELETON

Evans, F. G., "The morphology and functional evolution of the atlas-axis complex from fish to mammals." *Ann. N. Y. Acad. Sci.* (1939), 39:39–104, figs. 1–15. A thorough and stimulating description and analysis.

Gadow, Hans F., *The evolution of the vertebral column.* Cambridge, Eng.: Cambridge University Press, 1933. An exhaustive factual account interspersed with some sound and some invalid conjecture on phylogeny.

MacBride, E. C., Recent work on the development of the vertebral column. *Biol. Rev.* (1932), 7:108–148, figs. 1–48. An excellent comparative account, well written and well illustrated. References are given to further sources.

Sood, Maheshwar S., "The anatomy of the vertebral column in serpents." *Proc. Indian Acad. Sci.* (1948) 28: 1–26, figs. 1–10.

APPENDICULAR SKELETON

Ewer, D. W., "Tetrapod limb." *Science* (1955), 122: 467–8.

Goin, Coleman J., and Olive B. Goin, "Further comments on the origin of the tetrapods." *Evolution* (1956), 10(4):440–1. A brief re-appraisal of various theories of selective values that led to evolution of limbs from fins.

Gregory, W. K., and H. C. Raven, "Studies on the origin and early evolution of paired fins and limbs." *Ann. N. Y. Acad. Sci.* (1941), 42:273–360, figs. 1–34, pls. 1–4. An impressively thorough study and a model of deductive reasoning.

Schaeffer, Bobb, "The morphological and functional evolution of the tarsus in amphibians and reptiles." *Bull. Amer. Mus. Nat. Hist.* (1941), 78:395–472, figs. 1–21.

————, Notes on the origin and function of the artiodactyl tarsus. *Amer. Mus. Novitates* (1947), 1356:1–24, figs. 1–9.

Westoll, T. Stanley, "The lateral fin-fold theory and the pectoral fins of ostracoderms and early fishes." Chap. 10, pp. 180–211, in T. Stanley Westoll (ed.), *Studies on fossil vertebrates.* London: University of London, 1958. An excellent review.

White, Errol I., "Original environment of the craniates." Chap. 11, pp. 212–234, in *Studies on fossil vertebrates. Op. cit.*

CRANIUM

Radovanovic, M. "Osteologie des Schlangenkopfs." *Jenaische Zeitschr. Naturwiss.* (1937), 71: 179–312, figs. 1–7b, pl. 4.

Romer, A. S., *Vertebrate paleontology.* Chicago: University of Chicago Press, 1945.

Tumarkin, A. "On the evolution of the auditory conducting apparatus: a new theory based on functional considerations." *Evolution* (1955), 9(3): 221–243, figs. 1–12.

Vaughn, Peter Paul, "The Permian reptile *Araeoscelis* restudied." *Bull. Mus. Comp. Zool.* (1955), 113(5): 303–467, pls. 1–2.

Watson, D. M. S., "The evolution of the mammalian ear." *Evolution* (1953), 7:159–177. Chiefly involves the bony accessories. A penetrating analysis of the evidence now known.

MUSCULAR SYSTEM

Bryce, T. H., *Quain's elements of anatomy*, Vol. 4, part 2, "Myology." London: Longmans, Green, 1923. "General myology," pp. 1–30. An especially good account of basic information in myology.

Keynes, R. D., "The generation of electricity by fishes." *Endeavor* (1956), 15(60): 215–222, figs. 1–7.

———, "Electric organs." Chap. 5, pp. 323–344, in Margaret E. Brown (ed.), *The physiology of fishes*, vol. 2. New York: Academic Press, 1957.

Quiring, Daniel P. *Functional anatomy of the vertebrates*. New York: McGraw-Hill, 1950. Chap. 5, "The musculature," pp. 155–199. A good functional account.

DIGESTIVE AND RESPIRATORY SYSTEMS

Armitage, Kenneth B., "Respiration; the definition and use of a biological term." *Turtox News* (1957), 35(6):138–140.

Barrington, E. J. W., "The alimentary canal and digestion." Chap. 3, pp. 109-162, in Margaret E. Brown (ed.), *The physiology of fishes*, Vol. 1. New York: Academic Press, 1957.

Bergman, R. A. M., ["A new organ in sea snakes."] *Geneeskundig Tijd-schrift voor Nederlands Indië* (1938), 78.

Carter, G. S., "Air breathing." Chap. 1, pp. 65–80, in *The physiology of fishes. Op. cit.*

Fry, F. E. J., "The aquatic respiration of fishes." Chap. 1, pp. 1-64, in *The physiology of fishes. Op. cit.*

Jones, F. R. Harden, "The swimbladder." Chap. 4, pp. 305–322, in *The physiology of fishes. Op. cit.*

Lynn, W. G., and H. E. Wachowski, "The thyroid gland and its function in cold-blooded vertebrates." *Quart. Rec. Biol.* (1951), 51:123–168.

Smith, Hobart M., and Louis F. James, "The taxonomic significance of cloacal bursae in turtles." *Trans. Kans. Acad. Sci.* (1958), 61(1):86–96.

ENDOCRINE SYSTEM

Hoar, William S., "Endocrine organs." Chap. 6, pp. 245–286, in Margaret E. Brown (ed.), *The physiology of fishes*, vol. 1. New York: Academic Press, 1957.

Hoskins, Roy Graham, *Endocrinology*. New York: Norton, 1950.

Quiring, D. P., *Functional anatomy of the vertebrates*. New York: McGraw-Hill, 1950. Chap. 12, "The endocrine glands," pp. 458–494. A very good, short, functional account of the endocrine system.

Selye, Hans, *Textbook of endocrinology*. Montreal: University of Montreal, 1950.

Turner, C. D., *General endocrinology*. Philadelphia: Saunders, 1948.

Weichert, C. K., *Anatomy of the chordates*. New York: McGraw-Hill, 1951. Chap. 9, "Endocrine system," pp. 370–411. An excellent comparative and functional account.

Williams, Robert Hardin, *Textbook of endocrinology*. Philadelphia: Saunders, 1955.

UROGENITAL SYSTEM

Black, Virginia S., "Excretion and osmoregulation." Chap. 7, pp. 163–206, in Margaret E. Brown (ed.), *The physiology of fishes*, Vol. 1. New York: Academic Press, 1957.

Fraser, E. A., "The development of the vertebrate excretory system." *Biol. Rev.* (1950), 25:159–187.

Hoar, William S., "The gonads and reproduction." Chap. 7, pp. 287–322, in *The physiology of fishes. Op. cit.*

Kerr, J. Graham, *Textbook of embryology*, Vol. 2, pp. 221–282. London: Macmillan, 1919. A most stimulating account of the phylogeny of the kidney and its ducts, and of the reproductive ducts.

Ruibal, Rodolfo, "The evolution of the scrotum." *Evolution* (1957), 11(3):376–378.

Schmidt-Nielson, Bodil, "Urea excretion in mammals." *Physio. Rev.* (1958), 38(2): 139–168. A review of the countercurrent multiplier principle in urea excretion in different groups of mammals and in mammals in general.

Smith, Homer W., *From fish to philosopher*. Boston: Little, Brown, 1954. A popularized but highly informative, stimulating story of the evolution of the physiology of the vertebrate kidney.

Wirz, H., "Production of hypertonic urine by the mammalian kidney." *The kidney, Ciba Foundation Symposium* (1954), p. 38. A description of the physiological mechanism.

CIRCULATORY SYSTEM

Mott, J. C., The cardiovascular system. Chap. 2, pp. 81–108, in Margaret E. Brown (ed.), *The physiology of fishes*, Vol. 1. New York: Academic Press, 1957.

Huntington, G. E., and C. F. McClure, "The development of the veins in the domestic cat." *Anat. Rec.* (1920), 20:1–21, figs. 1–12 (in color). The formation of the postcava; a brief, clear, beautifully illustrated account gives the complete story.

White, F. N., "Circulation in the reptilian heart." *Gamma Alpha Rec.* (1956), 46(1):3–8. A brief but clear review.

————, "Circulation in the reptilian heart (*Caiman sclerops*)." *Anat. Rec.* (1956), 125:417–431. A detailed and the only accurate account of blood circulation in the crocodilian heart.

SENSORY SYSTEM

Allison, A. C., "The morphology of the olfactory system in vertebrates." *Biol. Rev.* (1953), 28:195–244.

Brett, J. R., "The eye." Chap. 2, pp. 121–154, in Margaret E. Brown (ed.), *The physiology of fishes*, Vol. 2. New York: Academic Press, 1957.

Hasler, Arthur D., "Olfactory and gustatory senses of fishes." Chap. 2, pp. 187–210, in *The physiology of fishes. Op. cit.*

Lowenstein, O., "The acoustico-lateralis system." Chap. 2, pp. 155–186, in *The physiology of fishes. Op. cit.*

Stebbins, Robert C., "An experimental study of the 'third eye' of the tuatara." *Copeia* (1958), 3:183–190, figs. 1–4.

Stebbins, Robert, and Richard M. Eakin, "The role of the 'third eye' in reptilian behavior." *Amer. Mus. Novitates* (1958), 1870:1–40, figs. 1–14.

Walls, Gordon L., "The vertebrate eye." *Bull. Cranbrook Inst. Sci.* (1942), 19. An inexhaustible, beautifully written and illustrated account. Emphasis upon evolution and function as well as anatomy.

Wright, M. E., "The lateral line system of sense organs." *Quart. Rev. Biol.* (1951), 26:264–280.

NERVOUS SYSTEM

Dow, R. S., "The evolution and anatomy of the cerebellum." *Biol. Rev.* (1942), 17:179–220.

Gardner, Ernest, *Fundamentals of neurology*, 3d ed. Philadelphia: Saunders, 1958.

Gray, George W., "The great ravelled knot." *Sci. Amer.* (1948), 179(4): 26–39, illustrated. Reprinted without illustrations in the *Scientific American Reader*. New York: Simon and Schuster, 1953, pp. 493–508. Excellent scientific journalism, chiefly concerned with the human brain.

Healey, E. G., "The nervous system." Chap. 1, pp. 2–120, in Margaret E. Brown (ed.), *The physiology of fishes*, Vol. 2. New York: Academic Press, 1957.

Kappers, C. U. A., *The evolution of the nervous system in invertebrates, vertebrates, and man*. Haarlem, Netherlands: Bohn, 1929.

Morgan, Clifford T., *Introduction to psychology*. New York: McGraw-Hill, 1956. An excellent text; good survey of relation of the nervous system to psychology.

Netter, Frank H., *The Ciba collection of medical illustrations*. Vol. 1, *Nervous system*. Summit, N. J.: Ciba Pharmaceutical Products, 1953. A beautifully illustrated, extremely useful atlas emphasizing functional neuroanatomy of man.

Nicol, J. A. C., Autonomic nervous systems in lower chordates. *Biol. Rev.* (1952), 27:1–49.

Index